The Microscopical Characters
   of
Artificial Inorganic Solid Substances:
Optical Properties of Artificial Minera

The Microscopical Characters
of
Artificial Inorganic Solid Substances:
Optical Properties of Artificial Minerals

Alexander Newton Winchell
Late Professor of Mineralogy and Petrology
University of Wisconsin, Madison, Wisconsin

and

Horace Winchell
Associate Professor of Mineralogy and Crystallography
Yale University, New Haven Connecticut

Academic Press · *New York and London, 1964*

ACADEMIC PRESS INC.
111 Fifth Avenue, New York, New York 10003

United Kingdom Edition published by
ACADEMIC PRESS INC. (LONDON) LTD.
Berkeley Square House, London W.1

LIBRARY OF CONGRESS CATALOG CARD NUMBER: 64-14222

This volume is the third edition of
THE MICROSCOPIC CHARACTERS OF ARTIFICIAL INORGANIC SOLID
SUBSTANCES OR ARTIFICIAL MINERALS.

PRINTED IN THE UNITED STATES OF AMERICA

Preface and Introduction

The first edition of this book was prepared and published in 1927, and the second was published in 1931 as an adjunct to the senior author's "Elements of Optical Mineralogy, Part II, Descriptions of Minerals." The objective here is to emphasize compounds that a chemist might consider relatively "pure"—at least, pure as compared with naturally occurring compounds known as minerals. Such substances have constant compositions and therefore constant physical (including optical) properties. The polarizing microscope is a powerful tool for elucidating these properties quantitatively, and in conjunction with suitable tables, for identifying the substances. The problem of identification in the case of most artificial chemical preparations is likely to be less difficult than it is in the case of minerals because of the widely variable composition, and consequently variable optical properties, of the minerals. A compensating factor, however, is the larger number of artificial compounds. Most minerals can be made artificially, and must therefore be included here; but it is not necessary to treat the effects of chemical variations so thoroughly, and thus there is room to include the many inorganic artificial compounds that do not occur as minerals.

A description of microscopic methods is omitted from this book for two reasons. First, inclusion would make the size of the book unwieldy; and second, there are many good books on crystal optics and the polarizing microscope already. Among these may be listed A. N. Winchell's "Elements of Optical Mineralogy, Part I, Principles and Methods" (John Wiley and Sons, New York); also a useful pair of pocket-sized books, A. F. Hallimond's "Manual of the Polarizing Microscope," and its companion volume, C. E. Marshall's "Introduction to Crystal Optics" (Cooke, Troughton, and Simms, York, England); also N. H. Hartshorne and A. Stuart's "Crystals and the Polarizing Microscope" (Arnold and Co., London); and for a special viewpoint, H. Insley and Van D. Fréchette's "Microscopy of Ceramics and Cements" (Academic Press Inc., New York). A full listing of all of the excellent texts on this subject would be too long for inclusion here.

Descriptions of substances in this book are given in approximately the following order: Chemical formula and name, if any. Crystal symmetry and the dimensions of the unit cell, or the axial ratios if the dimensions are unknown. Brief data on crystal habit, cleavage, twinning, and such. Hardness (H., according to Mohs' scale) and specific gravity (G.), and fusibility (F., according to von Kobell's scale) or melting point in degrees Celsius. Optical properties, including optic orientation; extinction angles to prominent elongation, cleavages, or crystal faces (for which the orientation of the section must always be specified); principal refractive indices

v

(n_X, n_Y, n_Z; n_O, n_E; n; rarely n_1, n_2 for non-principal indices such that $n_X \leqq n_1 \leqq n_Y \leqq n_2 \leqq n_Z$) for light of wavelength corresponding to the Fraunhofer line D of sodium, and if possible for other wavelengths; optic sign, optic axial angle (2V), dispersion, color, pleochroism, and absorption.

The method of synthesis is mentioned briefly if at all, and often refers to the method of preparing crystals suitable for measurement rather than to a method for causing the compound to form. Near the end of each description, the symbol PD stands for "X-ray powder diffraction data" and is followed by the d-spacings of the three strongest lines of the X-ray powder pattern, and then by the serial number of the index card containing the full powder diffraction pattern, as published by the American Society for Testing Materials (1916 Race Street, Philadelphia 3, Pennsylvania), under the auspices of the Joint Committee on Chemical Analysis by Powder Diffraction Methods, in the *X-ray Powder Data File*. In cases where two or more cards are listed in the *Index to the X-ray Powder Data File (1960)*, a star is added to the serial number of the card. The kind permission of Professor J. V. Smith, Editor of the X-ray Powder Data File, to use these card-index references is gratefully acknowledged. His cooperation makes this book considerably more useful to all, and at the same time makes it possible for me to call attention to the existence of X-ray diffraction data that are conveniently available for certain compounds.

A. N. Winchell did considerable preliminary collecting of data for this book while he was Resident Consultant at the Research Laboratories of American Cyanamid Company, Stamford, Connecticut. The stimulating associations and excellent facilities there furthered the project immeasurably. Further collecting and most of the writing were done after he moved to New Haven, Connecticut, and became associated with Yale University as Honorary Fellow in Geology. During this time, and after his death in 1958, the present writer became increasingly responsible for the work, including some collecting, more writing, final checking of data and references, and insertion of X-ray powder data.

It is a pleasure to acknowledge the assistance of Mary E. Mrose, U. S. Geological Survey, Washington, D. C., who performed a herculean task consisting of checking all references and many data throughout the book. The cooperation of the Yale University Library in locating unusual or rare volumes was most important in this research. Editorial and typing assistance by Mrs. Florence S. Winchell, and the assistance of Mrs. Jean H. Winchell in preparing certain tables, are most gratefully acknowledged.

HORACE WINCHELL

Department of Geology
Yale University, New Haven, Connecticut
March, 1964

From the Preface to the First Edition

While preparing the second edition of Part II of the writer's "Optical Mineralogy," it seemed undesirable to attempt to discriminate between natural and artificial minerals since the distinctions between them are so vague and unstable. Therefore the manuscript was prepared so as to include all minerals, both natural and artificial, if their optic properties were sufficiently well known to permit their identification microscopically. More concretely stated, all inorganic substances were included whose indices of refraction had been measured. When the manuscript was completed it was found to be too long for one volume and therefore the part dealing with artificial minerals was eliminated for separate treatment as given in this book. The following account may accordingly be considered as a supplement to Part II[1] of the author's "Optical Mineralogy."

Undoubtedly some artificial substances, whose optic constants are known, have been omitted from this compilation, but the writer has spent many months searching all available literature for data (unfortunately almost never indexed), and trusts that he has achieved a reasonable measure of success.

*   *   *

It is obvious that a work of this kind is largely a compilation of all available data, and in its preparation the writer has made free use of the standard publications on the subject, including especially:

P. Groth: Chemische Krystallographie, Vols. I–II, 1906–1908.

Zeitschrift für Kristallographie, Vols. I–LX, 1877–1924.

H. Dufet: Recueil de Données Numériques, Vols. II and III, 1900.

H. R. Landolt and R. Bornstein: Physikalisch-chemische Tabellen, 1923.

L. J. Spencer, Tables Annuelles Internationelles de Constantes, etc., Vols. I–V for 1910–1922, published 1912–1926.

E. S. Larsen: Microscopic Determination of the Nonopaque Minerals, 1921.

No attempt is made in this work to give the source of all the data which are included. So far as they are derived from the standard reference works already cited it is considered unnecessary to cite these repeatedly. On the other hand, the author has aimed to give references to the source of all data from unusual sources or from current literature.

ALEXANDER N. WINCHELL

Madison, Wisconsin
October, 1927

---

[1] Published by John Wiley and Sons, Inc., New York, 1927.

Contents

PART ONE

Descriptions of Artificial Inorganic Solid Substances Whose Optic Properties Are Known

I. ELEMENTS, CARBIDES, NITRIDES

II. SULFIDES, SELENIDES, TELLURIDES AND SULFOSALTS

III. HALIDES, HYDRIDES, AMIDES, CYANIDES AND CYANATES

IV. OXIDES

V. CARBONATES, NITRATES, AND HALATES

VI. BORATES

VII. SULFATES

X. SILICATES

XI. SILICEOUS GLASSES

PART TWO

Determinative Tables and Charts

Part One

Descriptions of Artificial Inorganic Solid Substances Whose Optic Properties Are Known

I. Elements, Carbides, Nitrides

A. METALLIC ELEMENTS

Fe (Iron) is isometric. Space group $Im3m$. $a = 2.861$ Å. U.C. 2. Distinct cubic cleavage. Malleable. H. 4. G. 7.87. Fuses at 1535° C. Color steel-gray to iron-black. Luster metallic. $n = 2.36$ (Drude); 1.73 (Kundt). Reflection percentages[1]: red 58, orange 59, green 64. Easily forms mix-crystals with nickel up to about 30%. PD 2.03, 1.17, 1.43; 6–0696.

Cu (Copper) is isometric. Space group[2] $Fm3m$. $a = 3.607$ kX. U.C. 4. No cleavage. Malleable. H. 2.5–3. G. 8.95. Fuses at 1083° C. Color copper-red. Luster metallic. Reflection percentages[1]: red 89, orange 83, green 61. PD 2.09, 1.81, 1.28; 4–0836.

Ag (Silver) is isometric. Space group $Fm3m$. $a = 4.07$ Å. U.C. 4. No cleavage. Malleable. H. 2.5–3. G. 19.3. Fuses at 961° C. Color silver-white. Luster metallic. Reflection percentages[1]: red 93, orange 94, green 95.5. Forms a continuous series of mix-crystals with gold. PD 2.36, 2.04, 1.23; 4–0783.

Au (Gold) is isometric. Space group $Fm3m$. $a = 4.078$ Å. U.C. 4. No cleavage. Malleable. H. 2.5–3. G. 19.3. Fuses at 1062° C. Luster metallic. Color gold-yellow. Reflection percentages[1]: red 85.6, orange 82.5, green 47. Opaque except in thinnest films, which transmit some greenish light. Forms continuous series of mix-crystals with silver and with copper. PD 2.36, 2.04, 1.23; 4–0784.

B. SEMI-METALS AND NON-METALS

Se (Selenium) has at least three crystal phases. The α-phase is monoclinic with $a:b:c = 1.635:1:1.610$, $\beta = 104°2'$. Crystals basal plates or nearly equant with $\{001\}$ and $\{111\}$ prominent. G. 4.47. Color orange red. A simpler cell for this has[2a] $a = 8.99$, $b = 8.97$, $c = 11.52$, $\beta = 91°34'$. The β-phase is monoclinic with[2a] $a = 12.74$, $b = 8.04$, $c = 9.25$ kX, $\beta = 93°4'$.

---

[1] Schneiderhöhn and Ramdohr: *Lehrb. Erzmikr.* II, 1931.

[2] Owen and Iball: *Phil. Mag.* XIII, p. 1020 (1932).

[2a] Klug: *Zeit. Krist.* LXXXVIII, p. 128 (1934).

Crystals short prisms or plates. Color dark red. A third phase is trigonal with $a/c = 1.134$. Crystals hexagonal prismatic with[3] $a = 4.36397$ Å., $c = 4.95945$ Å at 20° C. Crystals may show rhombohedral end faces. Good $\{01\bar{1}2\}$ cleavage. H. 2. G. 4.79. Fuses at 220° C. Color gray. Streak red. Luster bright metallic. Transparent only in very thin flakes. Uniaxial positive with[3a] $n_O = 3.00$ Na, $n_E = 4.04$, $n_E - n_O = 1.04$. Liquid selenium has $n = 2.9$. Selenium is recovered from flue deposits in the manufacture of H_2SO_4. Isotropic mixtures of fused selenium and sulfur are useful immersion media for refractive index measurements. Data follow:[4]

% Se	100	90	80	70	60	50	40	30	20	10	0
% S	0	10	20	30	40	50	60	70	80	90	100
n(Li)	2.716	2.53	2.40	2.30	2.22	2.16	2.11	2.08	2.03	2.00	1.978
n(Na)	2.92	2.67	2.49	2.37	2.27	2.20	2.15	2.10	2.06	2.025	1.998
n(Tl)				2.43	2.32	2.25	2.19	2.13	2.09	2.05	2.018

PD 3.01, 3.78, 2.07; 6–0362.

S (Sulfur) has six crystal phases. The low temperature α-phase is orthorhombic dipyramidal with $a:b:c = 0.813:1:1.903$. Crystals pyramidal or varied with poor $\{001\}$, $\{110\}$, and $\{111\}$ cleavages. H. 2.5. G. 2.07. Melts at 112.8° C. after inversion at 98°. Insoluble in acids; soluble in CS_2. The optic plane is $\{010\}$; $Z = c$. $(+)2V = 68°58'$ Na, 68°46′ Tl. $n_X = 1.9398$ Li, 1.9579 Na, 1.9764 Tl, $n_Y = 2.0171$ Li, 2.0377 Na, 2.0586 Tl, $n_Z = 2.2158$ Li, 2.2452 Na, 2.2754 Tl, $n_Z - n_X = 0.2875$ Na. Color yellow. The natural substance is found around some volcanoes and also in some salt and gypsum deposits. β-Sulfur is monoclinic with $a: b:c = 0.996:1:0.9998$, $\beta = 95°46'$. Crystals tabular or elongated; pseudo-isometric. Distinct $\{001\}$ and $\{110\}$ cleavages. H. 1.5. G. 1.958. Melts at 119° C. $Y = b$, $X \wedge c = 52°$ (44° on $\{110\}$). $(-)2V = 58°$. Mean index, $n = 2.058$. $n_Z - n_X =$ weak. Color honey-yellow. Easily crystallized from fusion. γ-Sulfur is also monoclinic[5] with $a:b:c = 1.061:1:0.709$, $\beta = 91°47'$. Crystals thin, tabular. H. soft. G. < 2.075. $Y = b$, $X \wedge c = 1.25°$ ca. $(-)2V = ?$. Refringence and birefringence strong. Colorless to pale yellow. Called *rosickyite*. Three other phases are known; one is probably monoclinic, one is hexagonal (and uniaxial negative) and one (black sulfur) is perhaps hexagonal. PD 3.85, 3.21, 3.44; 8–247 [presumably for α-S].

I (Iodine) is orthorhombic. G. 4.93. M.P. 113.5°C. Color violet black; opaque except in very thin flakes. Metallic luster. Mean index, $n = 3.34$. Volatilizes readily at ordinary temperature, forming a violet vapor. PD 3.10, 3.71, 3.64; 5–0558.

[3] Straumanis: *Zeit. Krist.* CII, p. 432 (1940) [Struc. Rpts. VIII, p. 109].

[3a] Skinner: *Phys. Rev.* IX, p. 148 (1917).

[4] Merwin and Larsen: *Am. Jour. Sci.* CLXXXIV, p. 42 (1912).

[5] Sekanina: *Zeit. Krist.* LXXX, p. 174 (1931).

P (Phosphorus) is polymorphous. One phase is isometric in dodecahedral crystals. G. 1.84. F. 44° C. Isotropic with $n = 2.093$ C, 2.117 D, 2.158 F. Colorless or yellow. Prepared by reduction of phosphate with carbon. Another phase[6] is ditetragonal dipyramidal. Uniaxial positive with $n_O = 2.72$, $n_E = 3.15$, $n_E - n_O = 0.43$. A third phase is hexagonal (trigonal). Uniaxial positive with $n_O = 2.72$, $n_E = 3.20$, $n_E - n_O = 0.48$. A fourth phase is triclinic. $(-)2V = 24°26'$, $n_X = 3.11$, $n_Y = 3.20$, $n_Z = 3.21$, $n_Z - n_X = 0.10$. Phases 2, 3, and 4 are red phosphorus and may be grown from vapor. Amorphous phosphorus has $n = 2.7$ to 3.0. PD 2.64, 2.58, 5.26; 9–20* [which phase?].

C (Carbon) has at least two crystal phases. One is opaque and black and about as soft as a solid can be; the other may be as transparent as the clearest glass and is the hardest substance known.

C (Graphite) is hexagonal with $a = 2.47$, $c = 6.79$ Å. U.C. 4. Crystals usually thin basal lamellæ. Perfect basal cleavage. H. 1–2. G. 2.09–2.23. Infusible. Luster metallic or dull. Color and streak black. Translucent and blue or green only in very thin flakes. Uniaxial negative[7] with n_O between 1.98 and 2.03 Li. In reflected light strongly pleochroic and birefringent. Reflection percentages for O; red 23, orange 23.5, green 22.5; for E: red 5.5, orange 5, green 5. Graphite can be made from coal; also found in some iron melts. PD 3.37, 1.68, 2.04; 8–415.

C (Diamond) is isometric with $a = 3.560$ Å. U.C. 8. Crystals usually equant — cubes, octahedrons, dodecahedrons, etc. Perfect $\{111\}$ cleavage. H. 10. G. 3.51. Infusible. Insoluble. Isotropic in thin plates, but often weakly anisotropic in thick plates, probably due to strain. Very strong refringence and dispersion with $n = 2.4135$ Li, 2.4195 Na, 2.4278 Tl. Colorless, white, yellow, orange, red, green, blue, brown, black. Made at pressures of about 1,500,000 lbs/sq. in. and at temperatures of about 1,000° C.[8] many other attempts to make it have failed or, in a few cases, achieved doubtful results.[8a] PD 2.06, 1.26, 1.08; 6–0675.

C. CARBIDES AND NITRIDES

CaC$_2$ is orthorhombic[9] (?) and pseudocubic with complex multiple twinning on the dodecahedral face; perfect $\{001\}$, $\{010\}$ and $\{100\}$

[6] Roth, DeWitt and Smith: *J. Am. Chem. Soc.* LXIX, p. 2881 (1947).

[7] P. Gaubert: *C. R. Acad. Sci. Paris,* CLXXVII, p. 1123 (1923). Slawson: *Am. Min.* XXXVIII, p. 50 (1953).

[8] Bundy in *Man-made Diamonds,* p. 11 (1955), publ. by Research Information Service of General Electric Co.

[8a] Marshall in *Man-made Diamonds,* (sec. 8), p. 5. (1955).

[9] Warren: *Am. Jour. Sci.* CCII, p. 120 (1921).

cleavages and $\{110\}$ parting. Combines with water freely to form acetylene and calcium hydroxide. Apparently uniaxial to biaxial, with $(+)2V =$
$0°-30°$ and $r < v$; the optic plane is parallel with the twinning lines; extinction parallel with cleavages. Index $n > 1.75$, $n_Z - n_X = 0.050$. Color
purplish red, yellow, greenish; slightly pleochroic in thicker sections; nearly
colorless in very thin flakes. The yellow carbide probably contains other
material in crystal solution; it has extinction at about 10° to 24° to the
cleavages and is probably triclinic. PD 2.74, 2.08, 1.94; 4–0712.

Al_4C_3 is hexagonal[10] in six-sided plates with perfect $\{0001\}$ cleavage.
Uniaxial positive with $n_O = 2.7$ (700 $m\mu$), $n_E = 2.75\pm$, $n_E - n_O = 0.05\pm$.
Color yellow. PD 2.87, 2.80, 1.66; 1–0953.

SiC has many crystal phases, one being isometric, others hexagonal or
rhombohedral. **α-SiC** is hexagonal or rhombohedral; crystals are thin basal
plates with rare twinning on $\{10\bar{1}1\}$ and poor basal cleavage. H. 9.5. G.
3.2. Infusible, but dissociates at about 3400° C. Insoluble even in HF.
Uniaxial positive with extremely high refringence, strong birefringence
and very strong dispersion, as follows[11]:

	$\lambda = 671$(Li)	589(Na)	546(Hg)	486(F)	Dispersion (486–671)
$n_O =$	2.627	2.647–2.649	2.662–2.664	2.692–2.694	0.066
$n_E =$	2.667	2.689–2.693	2.706–2.710	2.741–2.742	0.074
$n_E - n_O =$	0.040	0.042–0.043	0.044–0.046	0.048	0.008

Colorless when perfectly pure, but usually colored green, blue, red, black
by small amounts of iron, aluminum, carbon, etc., present as impurities.
Pleochroic with $E > O$; also, in some cases, $O > E$. Surface films of silica,
often present, produce iridescent colors. Luster brilliant, adamantine.

All hexagonal and rhombohedral polytypes described below have essen-
tially the same optical properties. PD 2.51, 2.63, 1.54; 4–0756*.

β-SiC is isometric with $a = 4.349$ Å and G. 3.216. U.C. 4. Isotropic (but
may have anisotropic lamellæ) with $n = 2.63$ (Li). PD 2.51, 1.54, 1.31;
1–1119.

Polytypes. The crystal structure of SiC may be described as consisting of
$\{0001\}$ layers; in a vertical section along $\{11\bar{2}0\}$, if a C (or Si) atom is at
the origin-point (1) in one layer, the corresponding atom in the next layer
will be at a point either (2), one-third unit to the right, or (3), one-third
unit to the left; in the third layer the next atom may be to the right again

---

[10] Compound prepared by G. W. Morey; properties determined by H. E. Merwin,
pers. comm., Mar. 25, 1931.

[11] Thibault: *Am. Min.* XXIX, p. 327 (1944).

(3) or it may be to the left (1), but in no case may one ever be directly over the one in the preceding layer. In a sequence like (1)–(2)–(1)–(2), the pattern forms a zigzag. If the structure has two to the right, then two to the left, it can be described as 22. If it has three to the right, then three to the left, it is designated 33. But in some cases there may be three to the right, then two to the left; this is repeated three times in the unit cell and it is described as 323232; or it may be abbreviated to 32. These variations of the crystal structure are called "polytypes." This notation is explicit and clear, but it is cumbersome for polytypes with many layers. A simple, but less descriptive system is to write the number of layers in the unit cell followed by the letter C (cubic), R (rhombohedral) or H (hexagonal) to designate the symmetry.

Many polytypes are known; a few examples follow:

Isometric	*Hexagonal*	*Rhombohedral*
β-SiC (3C or 3,–	4H or 22	15R or 323232
no zigzag)	6H or 33	21R or 343434
	19H or 22232323	33R
		51R
		87R
		141R
		etc.

With increasing numbers of layers the length of the vertical axis increases in proportion. For example:

For 19H[12]: $a = 3.073$, $c = 47.75 \; kX = 19 \times 2.512$
For 21R[12]: $a = 3.073$, $c = 52.78 \; kX = 21 \times 2.513$
For 51R[13]: $a = 3.073$, $c = 128.17 \; kX = 51 \times 2.511$
For 87R[14]: $a = 3.073$, $c = 218.66 \; kX = 87 \times 2.511$

SiC was found by Moissan in the Canyon Diablo meteorite and is known as *moissanite*. It is an important product of the electric furnace. It is readily recognized by its extreme hardness, extreme refringence and dispersion.

AgN₃ is orthorhombic dipyramidal[15] with $a:b:c = 1.056:1:1.068$. Crystals acicular along c with $\{110\}$, $\{100\}$, $\{010\}$, and $\{001\}$. Good $\{001\}$ and another cleavage. G. 4.50 (5.02 from X-ray study). The needles have parallel extinction and negative elongation. $(-)2V = ?$, $n_X = 1.80\pm$. n_Y and $n_Z > 2.05$, $n_Z - n_X > 0.25$. PD 2.41, 4.08, 2.04; 3–0906.

[12] Ramsdell and Mitchell: *Am. Min.* XXXVIII, p. 56 (1953).
[13] Thibault: *Am. Min.* XXXIII, p. 588 (1948).
[14] Ramsdell: *Am. Min.* XXXII, p. 64 (1947).
[15] West: *Zeit. Krist.* XCV, p. 421 (1936).

AlN is hexagonal with a = 3.10 and c = 4.965 Å. H. 5. G. 3.25. Crystals long prismatic. Uniaxial positive[16] with n_O = 2.13, n_E = 2.20, $n_E - n_O$ = 0.07. Color pale blue or green. Slowly soluble in molten borax. Made at a temperature of about 2100° C. PD 2.70, 2.37, 2.49; 8–262.

Ba(N₃)₂·H₂O is triclinic; the mean refractive index is 1.7.

Ca(N₃)₂·2N₂H₄ is orthorhombic.[17] Crystals {001} plates with {100}, {110}, {101}, {011}. The optic plane is {100}; Z = c. (+)2V = 80°±, r > v distinct. n_X = 1.583, n_Y = 1.610, n_Z = 1.70, $n_Z - n_X$ = 0.117, all ±0.003.

CaCN₂ is rhombohedral[18] with perfect rhombohedral cleavage at 74° and poor basal parting. Uniaxial positive with n_O = 1.60, n_E > 1.95, $n_E - n_O$ > 0.35. Colorless. Often present in commercial "carbide." PD 2.93, 4.92, 2.42; 3–0656.

PNO₂H₂ is tetragonal[19] with a = 7.57, c = 7.60 kX. Crystals show {100} and {101}. G. 1.775. Uniaxial negative with n_O = 1.522, n_E = 1.479, $n_O - n_E$ = 0.043.

PNO₄H₆ is tetragonal[19]. Crystals show {100} and {101}. Uniaxial negative with n_O = 1.515, n_E = 1.477, $n_O - n_E$ = 0.038 (Senarmont). Again: n_O = 1.5246, n_E = 1.4792, $n_O - n_E$ = 0.0454 (Topsoe and Christiansen).

[16] Kohn, Cotter and Potter: *Am. Min.* XLI, p. 355 (1956).

[17] Dresser, Browne, and Mason: *Jour. Am. Chem. Soc.* LIII, p. 4235 (1931).

[18] Warren: *Am. Jour. Sci.* CCII, p. 120 (1921).

[19] Renaud: *Ann. Chim.* 1935, p. 443.

II. Sulfides, Selenides, Tellurides and Sulfosalts

Few sulfides transmit any light in the visible part of the spectrum, but rather many are transparent to infrared light.

1. Formula Type A_2X

$Na_2S \cdot 9H_2O$ is tetragonal with $a/c = 0.982$. Crystals prismatic. G. 1.45. Uniaxial positive[1] with $n_O = 1.534$, $n_E = 1.550$, $n_E - n_O = 0.016$. Colorless. PD 2.80, 2.98, 3.21; 3–0745.

NH_4SH is ditetragonal[2] dipyramidal with $a = 6.01$, $c = 4.01$ kX. U.C. 2. G. 1.18. Uniaxial negative with $n_O > 1.74$, $n_E < 1.74$, $n_O - n_E =$ moderate.

2. Formula Type AX

MgS is isometric[3] with NaCl space lattice. Perfect cubic cleavage. G. 2.84. Isotropic with $n = 2.254$ C, 2.271 Na, 2.285 Tl. Colorless. Made in an electric oven. PD 2.60, 1.84, 1.50; 8–478.

CaS (Oldhamite) is isometric[3] with $a = 5.686$. U.C. 4. Perfect cubic cleavage. H. 4. G. 2.71. Isotropic with $n = 2.120$ C, 2.137 Na, 2.161 Tl. Colorless. PD 2.85, 2.01, 1.64; 8–464.

SrS is isometric[3] with perfect cubic cleavage. G. 3.913. Isotropic with $n = 2.087$ C, 2.107 Na, 2.122 (540 mμ). Colorless. PD 3.01, 2.13, 3.48; 8–489.

BaS is isometric[3] with perfect cubic cleavage. G. 4.377. Isotropic with $n = 2.140$ C, 2.155 Na, 2.183 Tl. Colorless. PD 3.19, 2.26, 3.69; 8–454.

ZnS has two phases[4]: the α-phase is hexagonal and the β-phase is isometric. PD 2.93, 3.31, 1.91; 10–434.

α-ZnS (Wurtzite) is hexagonal with $a = 3.811$. $c = 6.234$ kX. U.C. 2. Crystals hemimorphic with good prismatic cleavage. H. 3.5–4. G. 4.087. Soluble in HCl. Uniaxial positive with $n_O = 2.330$ Li, 2.365 Na, $n_E = 2.350$ Li, 2.378 Na, $n_E - n_O = 0.022$ Na. PD 3.31, 3.13, 2.93; 5–0492.

---

[1] West: *pers. comm.* 2 Nov. 1936.

[2] West: *Zeit. Krist.* LXXXVIII, p. 97, (1934).

[3] Spangenberg: *Naturwiss.* XV, p. 266 (1927); Haase: *Zeit. Krist.* LXV, p. 509 (1927); LXVI, p. 236 (1928).

[4] Allen, Crenshaw and Merwin: *Am. J. Sci.* XXXV, p. 341 (1912).

Wurtzite, like SiC, has several different polytypes[5] so that the length of the vertical axis varies. The commonest type is 2H, with $c = 6.234\ kX$. Other types are 4H, with $c = 12.44\ kX$; 6H with $c = 18.69\ kX$; and 15R with $c = 46.79\ kX$. The optical properties of the types are the same. All types may contain up to 8 per cent Fe (and less Cd). Pure ZnS is colorless; ordinary wurtzite is colored yellow to brown by iron. With maximum iron $n_O = 2.46\ ca.$ and $n_E = 2.48\ ca.$; weakly pleochroic with O > E. It is stable above 1020° C. (or, with maximum Fe, 880° C.)

β-Zns (Sphalerite) is the stable low temperature phase. It is isometric with perfect dodecahedral cleavage. H. 3.5–4. G. 4.09. Isotropic with $n = 2.34$ Li, 2.368 Na, 2.398 Tl. It may be slightly anisotropic, probably due to strain, since anisotropic areas are easily produced by pressure. Often contains Fe; maximum 8 per cent causes brown to black color and $n = 2.395$ Li, 2.47 Na. Colorless (to yellow?) when pure. PD 3.12, 1.91, 1.63; 5–0566.

CdS has two phases[5a]: the α-phase is hexagonal and the β-phase is isometric. PD 3.16, 3.58, 3.36; 6–0314.

α-CdS (Greenockite) is hexagonal with $a =$[5b] 4.14, $c = 6.72\ kX$. Crystals hemimorphic, short prismatic with distinct prismatic cleavage. H. 3.–3.5. G. 4.82. M.P. 780° C. Soluble in HCl. Uniaxial positive for red to blue-green; negative for blue-green to blue; isotropic for $\lambda = 523$. $n_O = 2.431$ Li, 2.506 Na, $n_E = 2.456$ Li, 2.529 Na, $n_E - n_O = 0.023$ Na. For n_O, $n_F - n_C = 0.23\ ca.$ For $\lambda = 516$. $n_O > 2.6$ and $n_O - n_E = 0.016$. Color yellow with weak pleochroism. Made from solution.

β-CdS (Hawleyite) is isometric[5a] with $a = 5.818$ Å. A fine-grained coating in vugs. G. 4.87 calc. Index not measured but must be near 2.52 since G. of β-CdS is a little above G. of α-CdS. Color bright yellow. Made from solution under reducing conditions from acidic sulfate solutions. PD 3.36, 2.06, 1.75; 10–454.

HgS has three phases,[4] the stable α-phase and two metastable (β- and γ-) phases.

α-HgS (Cinnabar) is hexagonal with $a = 4.160$, $c = 9.540$ Å. U.C. 3. Crystals prismatic or tabular with perfect prismatic cleavage. H. 2–2.5. G. 8.09. Volatile. Uniaxial positive with $n_O = 2.81$ Li, $n_E = 3.14$, $n_E - n_O = 0.33$. Color bright red or scarlet. PD 3.36, 2.86, 1.98; 6–0256.

β-Hgs (Metacinnabar) is isometric with $a = 5.854$ Å. U.C. 4. Black and opaque. G. 7.60. Formed only from acid solutions, and alters to cinnabar rather easily. PD 3.38, 2.07, 1.76; 6–0261.

Another metastable phase is hexagonal and prismatic with G. 7.2.

---

[5] Frondel and Palache: *Am. Min.* XXXV, p. 29 (1950).

[5a] Traill and Boyle: *Am. Min.* XL, p. 555 (1955).

[5b] Bragg: *Phil. Mag.* XXXIX, p. 647 (1920).

Uniaxial positive with $n_O = 2.58$ Li, $n_E = 2.82$, $n_E - n_O = 0.24$. Color bright red.

CuS (Covellite) is hexagonal with $a = 3.802$, $c = 16.43$ Å. U.C. 6. Massive or in basal plates. Perfect basal cleavage. H. 1.5–2. G. 4.67. Opaque except in very thin plates. Uniaxial positive[6] with $n_O = 1.33$ ($\lambda = 610$), 1.45 Na, 1.97 ($\lambda = 505$), $n_E = ?$. Pleochroic with O > E; color blue. PD 2.81, 1.90, 3.05; 6–0464. Reflection percentages: red 10, orange 15, green 18.5.

PbS (Galena) is isometric with $a = 5.95$ Å. U.C. 4. Perfect cubic cleavage. H. = 2.5. G. 7.5. M.P. 1115° C. Opaque. Metallic luster. $n = 3.912$ D. Again:[7] $n = 4.71$. Reflection percentages: red 35, orange 37.5, green 33.5. PD 2.97, 3.43, 2.10; 5–0592.

MnS (Alabandite) is isometric with $a = 5.214$ Å. U.C. 4. Crystals cubic, or octahedral. Perfect cubic cleavage. H. 3.5–4. G. 4.0 $ca.$ (calc. 4.07). Color iron-black. Streak green. Very thin splinters give[8] $n = 2.70$ Li. Reflection percentages: green 24, orange 21, red 20. PD 2.61, 1.85, 1.51; 6–0518.

AsS (Realgar) is monoclinic[9] with $a = 9.27$, $b = 13.50$, $c = 6.56$ Å. $\beta = 106°32'$. U.C. 16. Crystals short prisms with distinct $\{010\}$ cleavage. H. 1.5–2. G. 3.56. M.P. 310° C. Volatile. X $\wedge$ $c = 11°$, Y = b. Strong inclined dispersion with r > v. $(-)2V = 49°34'$ (648), 46°42' (589). For m$\mu = 590$: $n_X = 2.538$, $n_Y = 2.684$, $n_Z = 2.704$, $n_Z - n_X = 0.166$. Color and streak aurora-red to orange yellow; pleochroic with X nearly colorless to orange red, Y and Z pale golden yellow to vermilion red. PD 5.40, 3.19, 2.94; 9–441.

NiS is monoclinic[10] with $a:b:c = 0.888:1:0.848$, $\beta = 90°23'$. Crystals pseudo-cubic with lamellar twinning on $\{\bar{1}01\}$. G. 2.2. Y = b, Z $\wedge$ $c =$ large. $(+)2V$ = large, $n_X = 1.908$, $n_Y = 2.046$, $n_Z = 3.22$ calc. $n_Z - n_X =$ extreme. Color orange red; yellow in powder. PD 2.77, 1.85, 2.50; 3–0760*.

MgSe is isometric[3] with G. 4.268 and $n > 2.42$ Na (2.48 calc.).

CaSe is isometric[3] with G. 3.806 and $n = 2.245$ C, 2.274 Na, 2.292 (555 mμ).

SrSe is isometric[3] with G. 4.544 and $n = 2.190$ C, 2.220 Na, 2.252 (540 mμ). PD 3.11, 2.20, 1.80; 10–182.

BaSe is isometric[3] with G. 4.937 and $n = 2.230$ (675 mμ), 2.268 Na, 2.289 (560 mμ).

[6] Merwin: *J. Wash. Acad. Sci.* V, p. 341 (1915).

[7] Howland and Quigley: *Am. Min.* XXXIII, p. 766 (1948).

[8] Larsen: *U. S. Geol. Surv. Bull.* 679 (1921).

[9] Many sulfides made by Weil *et al.*: *Bull. Soc. Fr. Miner. Crist.* LXXVII, p. 1084 (1954).

[10] Smith: *Min. Mag.* XVI, p. 97 (1911).

ZnSe is isometric[3] with G. 5.42 and $n = 2.89$. PD 3.27, 2.00, 1.71; 5–0522.

CaTe is isometric[3] with G. 4.873 and $n > 2.51$ (2.605 calc.).

SrTe is isometric[3] with G. 5.218 and $n = 2.367$ C, 2.408 Na, 2.460 Tl.

BaTe is isometric[3] with G. 7.593 and $n = 2.379$ C, 2.440 Na, 2.520 Tl. PD 3.50, 2.48, 2.02; 2–0393.

Sb_2S_2O (Kermesite) is monoclinic with $a = 10.97$, $b = 8.19$, $c = 10.36\ kX$, $\beta = 101°45'$. U.C. 8. Crystals lath shaped on {001}, long 11b. H. 1–1.5. G. 4.68. M.P. 516° C. Color cherry-red. Z = b. $(-)2V = ?$, $n_X > 2.72$. Birefringence strong.[8]

3. Formula Type A_2X_3

As_2S_3 (Orpiment) is monoclinic[9] with $a = 11.47$, $b = 9.57$, $c = 4.24\ kX$, $\beta = 90°27'$. U.C. 4. Crystals small with perfect {010} cleavage. Laminæ flexible but not elastic. H. 2. G. 3.48. M.P. 328° C. Volatile. X = b, Y $\wedge$ $c = 1$–3° in acute angle β. $(-)2V = 76°$, r > v strong. $n_X = 2.4\ ca.$ Li, $n_Y = 2.81$, $n_Z = 3.02$, $n_Z - n_X = 0.62\ ca.$ Color yellow with Y yellow, Z greenish yellow. PD 4.82, 2.70, 4.00; 1–0273.

Sb_2S_3 (Stibnite) is orthorhombic[9] with $a = 11.20$, $b = 11.28$, $c = 3.83$ Å. U.C. 4. Crystals long prismatic with perfect {010} cleavage. H. 2. G. 4.59–4.63. M.P. 546–551° C. Soluble in HCl. Y = a; Z = c. $(-)2V = 25°45'$. $n_X = 3.194$, $n_Y = 4.046$, $n_Z = 4.303$, $n_Z - n_X = 1.109$. Very strong dispersion. Color and streak steel-gray, subject to black tarnish. Luster metallic. Nearly opaque to translucent to red and infrared rays. PD 2.76, 3.05, 3.56; 6–0474.

4. Formula Type AX_2

MnS_2 (Hauerite) is isometric with[10a] $a = 6.101$ Å. U.C. 4. H. 4. G. 3.463. Perfect cubic cleavage. $n = 2.69$ Li,[8] 2.58 (910).[10a] Color brown to black; deep red in thin section. PD 3.07, 1.18, 1.84; 10–476.

FeS_2 (Pyrite) is isometric with $a = 5.405$ Å. U.C. 4. H. 6–6.5. G. 5.02 M.P. 642° C. Opaque. Metallic luster. $n^7 = 6.22$. Reflection percentages: red 52.5, orange 53.5, green 54. PD 1.63, 2.71, 2.42; 6–0710.

5. Formula Type $A_mB_nX_p$ with $(m + n){:}p \approx 3{:}2$; also 4:3

$(Ag,Cu)_{16}Sb_2S_{11}$ (Polybasite) is monoclinic with $a = 12.99$, $b = 7.50$, $c = 11.95\ kX$, $\beta = 90°$. U.C. 2. Crystals pseudo-hexagonal basal plates. Perfect {001} cleavage. H. 2–3. G. 6.1. Color iron-black; nearly opaque.[11] X = c, Y = a. $(-)2V = 22°$, $n > 2.72$. Birefringence very strong. Reflec-

---

[10a] Gordon: *Am. Min.* XXXVI, p. 918, (1951).

[11] Larsen and Berman: *U. S. Geol. Surv. Bull.* 848, p. 213 (1934).

tion percentages: red 25.5, orange 25.5, green 29.5. PD 3.00, 3.19, 2.88; 8–123.

Ag_3SbS_3 **(Pyrargyrite)** is hexagonal with $a = 11.04$, $c = 8.72$. U.C.6. Prismatic, scalenohedral, massive. Distinct $\{10\bar{1}1\}$ cleavage. H. 2.5. G. 5.85. M.P. 486° C. Uniaxial negative with $n_O = 3.084$, $n_E = 2.881$, $n_O - n_E = 0.203$. Color deep red. Reflection percentages: red 24.5, orange 27, green 32.5. PD 2.81, 2.57, 3.22; 2–0835.

Ag_3AsS_3 **(Proustite)** is hexagonal[9] with $a = 10.74$, $c = 864$ Å. Space group $R3c$. U.C. 6. Distinct rhombohedral cleavage. H. 2–2.5. G. 5.51. M.P. 490° C. Uniaxial negative with $n_O = 2.9789$ Li, 3.0877 Na, $n_E = 2.7113$ Li, 2.7924 Na, $n_O - n_E = 0.2676$ Li, 0.2953 Na. Color scarlet: deep red by transmitted light and pleochroic with O = blood red and E = cochineal red. Reflection percentages: red 20.5, orange 21.5, green 28. It may contain some Sb in place of As. PD 2.76, 3.28, 3.18; 9–110.

$(Cu,Fe)_{12}Sb_4S_{13}$ **(Tetrahedrite)** is isometric with $a = 10.33$ kX. U.C. 2. Crystals tetrahedral. H. 3. G. 4.97. Color gray to black. Opaque except in very fine splinters which are red.[11a] $n = 3.128$. Reflection percentages: red 20.5, orange 24, green 27. Forms a series with tennantite. PD 2.96, 1.81, 1.54; 3–0639* (obsolete?).

$(Cu,Fe)_{12}As_4S_{13}$ **(Tennantite)** is isometric with $a = 10.19$ kX. U.C. 2. Crystals tetrahedral. H. 4.5. G. 4.62. Color gray to black; opaque except in very thin splinters which are red.[11a] $n = 2.914$ Li. Reflection percentages: red 21.5, orange 24, green 27. PD 2.95, 1.81, 1.54; 2–0715 (obsolete?).

6. Formula Type $A_mB_nX_p$ with $(m + n):p \approx 1:1$; also $<1:1$

$AgSbS_2$ **(Miargyrite)** is monoclinic with $a = 13.17$, $b = 4.39$, $c = 12.83$ kX, $\beta = 98°37.5'$. U.C. 8. Poor $\{010\}$ cleavage. H. 2.5. G. 5.25. Color iron-black to gray. Thin splinters translucent and red.[8] $(-)2V = $ medium. $n_Y > 2.72$ Li. Birefringence very strong. PD 2.89, 3.45, 2.75; 4–0675.

$AgAsS_2$ has two (or three?) crystal phases. The low-temperature phase **(trechmannite)** is rhombohedral with $c/a = 0.653$. Crystals short prismatic with good $\{10\bar{1}1\}$ and distinct $\{0001\}$ cleavages. H. 1.5–2. Uniaxial negative with $n_O = 2.60$; birefringence extreme. Color and streak scarlet. O pale reddish, E nearly colorless. It inverts on moderate heating to a biaxial phase (perhaps smithite) which has $(-)2V = 26°\pm$, r > v strong, $n_X = 2.48$ Li, $n_Y = 2.58$, $n_Z = 2.60$, $n_Z - n_X = 0.12$.

$AgAsS_2$ **(Smithite)** is monoclinic with $a = 17.20$, $b = 7.76$, $c = 15.16$ kX, $\beta = 101°12'$. U.C. 24. Crystals equant with perfect $\{100\}$ cleavage. H. 1.5–2. G. 4.88. Color red.[12] Y = b, Z $\wedge$ c = 6.5°. $(-)2V = 65°\pm$,

[11a] Bailly: *Bull. Soc. Fr. Min. Crist.* LXX, p. 49 (1947).
[12] Smith and Prior: *Min. Mag.* XIV, p. 293 (1907).

$n = 3.27$ Na. Birefringence very strong. Again:[8] $n_{X'} = 3.18$, $n_{Z'} = 3.27$, $n_{Z'} - n_{X'} = 0.18$ [*sic*].

TlAsS$_2$ (Lorandite) is monoclinic with $a = 12.25$, $b = 11.32$, $c = 6.10$, $\beta = 104°12'$. Excellent {100} and good {$\overline{2}$01} and {001} cleavages. H. 2–2.5. G. 5.53. Color red. X nearly $\perp$ 100; Z = b. $(-)2V = $ large, $n_X > 2.72$.[8] Birefringence extreme. Pleochroic with Y purple-red, Z orange-red. PD 3.58, 2.86, 2.96; 2–0367.

Pb$_2$As$_2$S$_5$ (Dufrenoysite) is monoclinic with $a:b:c = 0.651:1:0.613$, $\beta = 90°33.5'$. Perfect {010} cleavage. H. 3. G. 5.53. Color lead-gray. Dark red-brown[8] in splinters. $n > 2.72$ Li. Very strong birefringence. PD 3.74, 3.00, 2.70; 10–453.

(Pb,Tl)$_2$(Cu,Ag)As$_5$S$_{10}$? (Hutchinsonite) is orthorhombic with $a:b:c = 0.612:1:0.462$. Crystals prismatic or acicular. Good {010} cleavage. H. 1.5–2. G. 4.6. Color vermilion to deep cherry-red. X = a, Y = b. $(-)2V = 37°34'$ Na,[12] r < v extreme. $n_X = 3.078$ Na, $n_Y = 3.176$, $n_Z = 3.188$, $n_Z - n_X = 0.118$. PD 2.74, 3.78, 3.05; 8–124.

HgSb$_4$S$_7$ (Livingstonite) is monoclinic with $a = 15.14$, $b = 3.98$, $c = 21.60$ Å, $\beta = 104°$. U.C. 4. Acicular. Perfect {001} and poor {010} and {100} cleavages. H. 2. G. 5.0. Color gray; streak red. Thin splinters translucent red.[8] Z = b. $(-?)2V = ?$ $n \gg 2.72$ Li, $n_Y = 3$. *ca.* Birefringence extreme. Pleochroic with X > Z. PD 3.00, 3.74, 3.48; 4–0654.

Na$_2$SnS$_3$·3H$_2$O is tetragonal;[13] crystals dipyramids. Uniaxial positive with $n_O > 1.8$, $N_E - N_O = $ extreme.

Na$_4$SnS$_4$·18H$_2$O is monoclinic[13] in prisms with positive elongation and $(+)2V = 68°12'$, $n_X = 1.643$, $n_Y = 1.6485$, $n_Z = 1.663$, $n_Z - n_X = 0.020$.

Na$_2$SnS$_3$·8H$_2$O is probably monoclinic[13] in prisms with $(-)2V = 66°\pm$, $n_X = 1.605$, $n_Y = 1.647$ calc., $n_Z = 1.746$, $n_Z - n_X = 0.141$.

Na$_8$Sn$_5$O$_2$S$_{12}$·32H$_2$O is orthorhombic.[13] Crystals acicular with negative elongation. $(-)2V = $ small, $n = 1.79$ (average), $n_Z - n_X = 0.024$.

Na$_4$Sn$_5$O$_2$S$_{10}$·18H$_2$O is probably triclinic.[13] Crystals acicular. $(-)2V = 60°$, with strong dispersion. $n = 1.80$ (average), $n_Z - n_X = 0.0016$.

Na$_4$Sn$_5$O$_2$S$_{10}$·20H$_2$O is orthorhombic.[13] Crystals acicular with negative elongation. $(-)2V = $ small. $n = 1.79$ (average), $n_Z - n_X = 0.019$.

Na$_3$AsS$_4$·8H$_2$O is monoclinic with $a:b:c = 0.668:1:0.528$, $\beta = 103°22'$. Crystals short, prismatic. X $\wedge$ $c = 81°11'$, Y = b. $(-)2V = 87°44'$. $n_Y = 1.6802$, $n_Z - n_X = $ weak. Very weakly pleochroic.

[13] Jelley: *Jour. Chem. Soc.* 1934, p. 1076.

III. Halides, Hydrides, Amides, Cyanides and Cyanates

1. Anhydrous Halides, etc., of Monovalent Bases. Formula Type AX

NaCl (Halite or common salt) is isometric with $a = 5.64$ and a face-centered arrangement of each kind of its atoms as shown in Fig. 3-1. Crystals cubic with perfect cubic cleavage. H. 2.5. G. 2.17. M.P. 750° *ca.* Soluble in water. Isotropic with $n = 1.5407$ C, 1.5443 D, 1.5534 F. Colorless unless stained. PD 2.82, 1.99, 1.63; 5–0628.

KCl (Sylvite) is isometric with $a = 6.29$ and the NaCl space lattice. Crystals cubic with perfect cubic cleavage. H. 2. G. 1.997. F. easy (776°) with violet flame. Soluble in water. Isotropic with $n = 1.4872$ C, 1.4904 D, 1.4984 F. Colorless or stained.

[1] X in this group stands for any halogen or H or CN or CNS or CNO, and A stands for any metal or H or NH₄ (or even I).

NaCl and KCl intercrystallize in all proportions above 400° C., but below that temperature they separate as double salts unless they happen to have the composition of such a salt. Slawson[1a] has shown that these facts can be used to determine the percentages of Na and K in any mixture of these

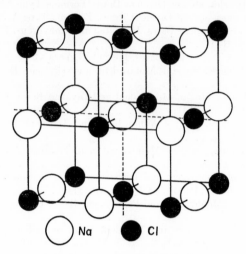

Fig. 3-1. Space lattice of NaCl.

salts as obtained, for example, from a rock analysis, by determining the refractive indices of the chlorides and using the following data:

Salt	n D	Salt	n D
NaCl (100%)	1.544	4NaCl·3KCl	1.518
7NaCl·KCl	1.536	NaCl·KCl	1.514
5NaCl·KCl	1.533	2NaCl·3KCl	1.5085
3NaCl·KCl	1.528	2NaCl·5KCl	1.503
2NaCl·KCl	1.523	2NaCl·7KCl	1.500
3NaCl·2KCl	1.519	KCl (100%)	1.490

PD 3.15, 2.22, 1.82; 4–0587.

NaF (Villiaumite) is isometric with $a = 4.619$. U.C. 4. Perfect cubic cleavage. H. 2.25. G. 2.79. M.P. 980°. Isotropic with $n = 1.3246$ C, 1.3258 D, 1.3285 F. May have weak negative birefringence at room temperature with red to violet color and X golden yellow, Z carmine red. PD 2.32, 1.64, 1.34; 4–0793.

[1a] Slawson: *Am. Min.* XIV, p. 293 (1929). There is probably also 9NaCl·KCl which would have $n = 1.538 \pm$.

The following salts[2] also have the NaCl space lattice with cubic habit and cleavage.

Salt	a^{2a}	G.	n (C)	n (D)	n (F)	$n_F - n_C$	M.P.	PD		
LiCl	5.13	2.07		1.662			613°	2.97	2.57	1.82; 4–0664
LiF[3]	4.02	2.64	1.3909	1.3921	1.3948	0.0039	870°	2.01	2.33	1.42; 4–0857
LiBr	5.49	3.46		1.784			547°	3.18	2.75	1.95; 6–0319
LiI[4]	6.00	4.06		1.955			446°	3.47	3.00	2.12; 1–0592
NaBr	5.96	3.20	1.6355	1.6412	1.6555	0.0200	381°	2.99	3.45	2.11; 5–0591
NaI	6.46	3.66		1.7745			651°	3.24	3.74	2.29; 6–0302
KF[5]	5.34	2.49		1.352				2.67	1.89	3.09; 4–0726
KBr	6.59	2.75	1.5547	1.55945	1.5716	0.0169	730°	3.29	2.33	1.48; 4–0531
KI	7.05	3.13	1.6589	1.6670	1.6876	0.0287	678–705°	3.53	2.50	4.08; 4–0471
RBCl	6.54	2.803	1.4903	1.4936	1.5016	0.0113	715°	3.29	2.33	3.80; 6–0289
RBF[4]	5.64	3.74	1.394	1.396	1.399	0.005	760°			
RbBr	6.85	3.35	1.5483	1.5528	1.5646	0.0163	682°	3.44	2.44	1.99; 8–480
RbI	7.33	3.56	1.6397	1.6474	1.6672	0.0275	642°	3.67	2.60	2.12; 6–0218
NH₄I	7.26	2.50	1.6938	1.7031	1.7269	0.0331	551°	4.19	3.63	2.57; 6–0174

AgCl (Chlorargyrite) is isometric with the NaCl space lattice. Crystals usually octahedral. No cleavage. H. 1–2. G. 5.5. Soluble in NH₄OH. M.P. 452° C. Isotropic with $n = 2.071$ D. Color pearl-gray, greenish gray or white becoming violet in sunlight. Forms a complete series with AgBr which is called *bromargyrite;* an intermediate type is called *embolite* (or, with some I, *iodembolite*), while the whole group is called *cerargyrite.* PD 2.77, 1.96, 3.20; 6–0480.

AgBr (Bromargyrite) is isometric with the NaCl space lattice. Crystals often octahedral. No cleavage. H. 1–2. G. 6.2. M.P. 422° C. Isotropic with $n = 2.252$ (589), 2.263 (546), 2.363 (436). Miscible in all proportions with AgI, with which it forms an isodimorphous series, AgI being hexagonal. The isometric phases[6] are stable from pure AgBr to about 60 per cent AgI and metastable to 90 per cent AgI. With AgBr:AgI = 2:1, isotropic with $n = 2.299$ (589), 2.303 (578), 2.320 (546). With AgBr:AgI = 1:2, isotropic with $n = 2.36\pm$ (589), $2.40\pm$ (546). PD 2.89, 2.04, 1.67; 6–0438. The intermediates are called *iodobromite.*

CsCl has two crystal phases[7]; the room temperature (β-)phase has the simple cubic arrangement of each kind of its atoms shown in Fig. 3-2. Crystals often cubic; no cleavage. G. 3.97. M.P. 646°. Isotropic with $n = 1.6377$ C, 1.6418 D, 1.6523 F. The high temperature (α-)phase has

[2] Spangenberg: *Zeit. Krist* LVII, p. 494 (1923).

[2a] Wyckoff: *Crystal Structures*, Ch. III, Tab. 2 (New York, 1948, 1951, 1958).

[3] Littmann: *Phys. Zeit.* XLI, p. 468 (1940).

[4] Space lattice may be like CsCl.

[5] Measured by H. E. Merwin: *pers. comm.* Mar. 25, 1931. Spangenberg gives $n = 1.361$ D and Wulff and Heigl (*Zeit. Krist.* LXXVII, p. 84, 1931) give $n = 1.3629$ D for KF.

[6] Barth: *Am. Jour. Sci.* XIX, p. 135 (1930).

[7] Wulff: *Zeit. Elektrochem.* XXXIV, p. 611 (1928). For CsCl, $n = 1.6397$ D.

the NaCl space lattice. Crystals often cubic; perfect cubic cleavage. G. 3.56. Isotropic with $n = 1.531$ C, 1.534 D, 1.543 F. PD 2.92, 4.12, 1.68; 5–0607.

CsF has two crystal phases; the room temperature (α-)phase has the

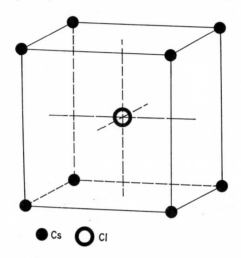

● Cs   ○ Cl

Fig. 3-2. Space lattice of CsCl.

NaCl space lattice. Crystals cubic with perfect cubic cleavage. G. 5.34. M.P. 684° C. Isotropic with $n = 1.575$ C, 1.578 D, 1.583 F. PD 3.00, 2.12, 3.48; 1–0872. The lower temperature (β-)phase has the CsCl space lattice. G. 4.52. Isotropic with $n = 1.476$ C, 1.478 ± 0.005 D,[8] 1.482 F. Crystals from another source have[9] $n = 1.484$ D.

CsBr has two crystal phases; the room temperature (β-)phase has the CsCl space lattice. G. 4.45. Isotropic[7] with $n = 1.6924$ C, 1.6984 D, 1.7126 F. The high temperature (α-)phase has the NaCl space lattice. Crystals cubic with perfect cubic cleavage. G. 3.75. M.P. 636° C. Isotropic with $n = 1.577$ C, 1.582 D, 1.594 F. PD 3.04, 1.75, 1.15; 5–0588.

CsI has two crystal phases; the room temperature (β-)phase has the CsCl space lattice. G. 4.52. Isotropic[7] with $n = 1.7784$ C, 1.7876 D, 1.8115 F. The high temperature (α-)phase has the NaCl space lattice. Crystals cubic with perfect cubic cleavage. G. 3.82. M.P. 621° C. Isotropic with $n = 1.653$ C, 1.661 D, 1.681 F. PD 3.23, 1.87, 2.28; 6–0311.

TlCl is isometric with[6] the CsCl space lattice. G. 7.00. M.P. 430° C. Isotropic with $n = 2.223$ (650), 2.247 (589), 2.400 (436). PD 2.72, 3.84, 1.57; 6–0486.

[8] Merwin: *Jour. Wash. Acad. Sci.* XII, p. 250 (1922).
[9] Merwin: *pers. comm.*, Mar. 25, 1931.

TlBr is isometric with[6] the CsCl space lattice. G. 7.557. M.P. 460° C. Isotropic with $n = 2.384$ (650), 2.418 (589), 2.652 (436). Colorless in thin sheets. PD 2.82, 1.63, 3.98; 8–486.

TlI is isometric with[6] the CsCl space lattice above 175° C; at lower temperatures this phase is metastable and inverts to an orthorhombic phase slowly. Color yellow. The isometric phase has G. 7.0. and M.P. 440° C. It is isotropic with $n = 2.72\pm$ (650), 2.78± (589), 2.85± (546). Color red. PD 3.33, 2.69, 3.23; 6–0279.

TlBr and TlI are miscible in all proportions[6] in the isometric phase. With more than 70 per cent TlI and crystals are metastable at ordinary temperature, but even with as much as 80 per cent TlI the crystals often remain isometric for days. Iodine-rich crystals are opaque for violet and blue rays, but nearly as transparent as glass for yellow and even for green. Mixtures of TlBr and TlI are useful as immersion media for high index of refraction determinations.[10]

Data on refractive indices follow:

TlBr	TlI	$\lambda = 650$	589	578	546
100	0	2.384	2.418	2.424	2.542
89	11				2.482
80	20		2.468		2.511
70	30	2.455			2.541
60	40				2.578
50	50	2.518		2.567	2.616
40	60			2.615	2.660
33	67				2.683
25	75	2.610	2.662	2.673	2.722
0	100	2.72±	2.78±		2.85±

CuCl (Nantokite) is isometric with $a = 5.407\ kX$. U.C. 4. It has the ZnS space lattice. Crystals tetrahedral with {011} cleavage. G. 4.136. M.P. 422° C. Isotropic with[11] $n = 1.955$ C, 1.973 D, 1.996 Tl. Again[12]: $n = 1.930 \pm .005$. PD 3.13, 1.92, 1.63; 6–0344*.

CuBr is isometric with the ZnS space lattice. Crystals tetrahedral with {011} cleavage. G. 5.17. M.P. 504° C. Isotropic[11] with $n = 2.092$ C, 2.116 D, 2.160 Tl. Color white. Dimorphous. PD 3.23, 1.87, 2.29; 6–0310*.

CuI (Marshite) is isometric with the ZnS space lattice. Crystals tetrahedral with perfect {011} cleavage. G. 5.69. Isotropic[11] with $n = 2.313$ C, 2.345 D, 2.385 Tl. Color yellow. Dimorphous. PD 2.17, 1.85, 3.50; 6–0623*.

[10] Barth: *Am. Min.* XIV, p. 358 (1929).
[11] Haase: *Zeit. Krist.* LXVIII, p. 82 (1928).
[12] Larsen: *U. S. Geol. Surv. Bull.* 679 (1921).

AgI has several crystal modifications. A sphalerite type **(miersite)** is stable up to 137° C; a wurtzite type **(iodyrite)** from 137° to 146°, an isometric type above 146°; still other types have been reported.[13] PD 3.75, 2.30, 3.98; 9–374*.[13a]

AgI (Miersite) is isometric with $a = 6.491\ kX$. U.C. 4. Crystals tetrahedral with perfect {011} cleavage. H. 2.5. G. 5.68. Isotropic with[12] $n = 2.20$. Color and streak canary-yellow. May exhibit anomalous birefringence. Forms a complete series of mix-crystals with CuI. PD 3.75, 2.30, 1.96; 9–399*.[13a]

AgI (Iodyrite) is hexagonal with $a = 4.58, c = 7.49\ kX$. U.C. 2. Crystals usually prismatic or tabular and distinctly hemimorphic with perfect basal cleavage. H. 1.5. G. 5.69. M.P. 552° C. Soluble in NH_4OH. Uniaxial positive with[14] $n_O = 2.185$ C, 2.218 D, 2.328 F, $n_E = 2.229$ D, $n_E - n_O = 0.011$ D. Again:[12] $n_O = 2.21$, $n_E = 2.22$, $n_E - n_O = 0.010$. May be slightly biaxial and produce abnormal green interference colors. Color yellow to yellowish green. Inverts to an isometric phase at 146° C. Miscible with 10 mol. per cent (or even more) of AgBr, retaining hexagonal symmetry. PD see Iodyrite and Miersite.[13a]

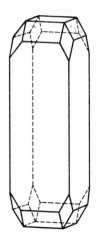

Fig. 3-3. A crystal habit of HgCl.

HgCl (Calomel) is tetragonal with $c/a = 2.437$. Crystals prisms (see Fig. 3-3) or basal plates with distinct {100} cleavage. H. 1–2. G. 7.15. M.P. 302° C. Volatile. Uniaxial positive with $n_O = 1.9556$ Li, 1.9733 Na, 1.9909 Tl, $n_E = 2.6006$ Li, 2.6559 Na, 2.7129 Tl, $n_E - n_O = 0.6826$ Na. Color white or yellowish. PD 3.16, 4.14, 1.96; 4–0581.

[13] Tammann: *Zeit. phys. Chem.* LXXV, p. 733 (1911); Barth and Lunde: *Zeit. phys. Chem.* CXXII, p. 293 (1926).

[13a] Identity of polymorph uncertain.

[14] Merwin: *Int. Crit. Tables,* VII (1930). *J. Am. Chem. Soc.* XLII, p. 2432 (1920).

NH₄Cl (Salammoniac) is isometric with $a = 3.859\ kX$ and the CsCl space lattice for N and Cl. Crystals usually trapezohedral with poor {111} cleavage. H. 1.5–2. G. 1.53. Isotropic with $n = 1.638$ C, 1.6426 D, 1.6529 F (Grailich). Again:[15] $n = 1.639 \pm 0.001$. Colorless. Soluble in H_2O. Inverts at 156° C. to the NaCl space lattice (with G. 1.27) and decomposes at 350° C. NH₄Cl can apparently intercrystallize with metallic chlorides, but Neuhaus[16] has shown that the metallic chloride (often $FeCl_3$) is present in submicroscopic crystals regularly arranged and no isomorphous series exists. PD 2.74, 3.87, 1.58; 7–7.

NH₄Br is isometric with the CsCl space lattice. Crystals tetrahedral with G. 2.44. Isotropic with[17] $n = 1.7075$ C, 1.7108 D, 1.7163 F. Again:[17a] $n = 1.7124$ D. White or colorless. Above 109° C. it inverts to the NaCl space lattice. PD 2.87, 4.06, 1.66, 4–0618.

NH₄F is hexagonal[9] in plates and prisms.[4] G. 1.315. Uniaxial positive with $n_O < 1.328$, $n_E - n_O = 0.001$. Again:[17a] $n_O = 1.3147$ D, $n_E = 1.3160$. PD 3.85, 3.39, 3.59; 8–32.

CsICl₂ has two crystal phases. One is trigonal with $c/a = 0.964$. Crystals often thin basal plates of rhombohedral units. G. 3.86. M.P. 230° C. Uniaxial positive with[18] $n_O = 1.637$, $n_E = 2.15$, $n_E - n_O = 0.513$. Color pale orange.

NaHF₂ is trigonal in rhombohedrons of 74°36′, often twinned. Uniaxial positive with[18] $n_O = 1.32$, $n_E = 1.33$, $n_E - n_O = 0.01$. PD 2.75, 2.03, 4.59; 6–0479.

KHF₂ is tetragonal with $c/a = 0.601$. Crystals basal plates with {111}, etc. Uniaxial negative[18] with $n_O = 1.354$, $n_E = 1.342$, $n_O - n_E = 0.012$. PD 2.60, 2.38, 2.18, 1–1095.

NH₄HF₂ is orthorhombic with $a:b:c = 0.971:1:0.863$. Crystals pseudo-tetragonal and sometimes cubic in aspect; also basal tablets or long prismatic. G. 1.5. X = c; Y = a. $(-)2V$ = near 0°, $n_X = 1.385 \pm 0.003$, $n_Y = 1.390 \pm 0.003$, $n_Z = 1.394 \pm 0.003$, $n_Z - n_X = 0.009$ (Vigfusson).[19] Again:[9] $(-)2V = 40°$, $n_X = 1.368\pm$, $n_Y = 1.385\pm$, $n_Z = 1.387\pm$, $n_Z - n_X = 0.019\pm$ (Merwin). PD 2.76, 2.64, 2.61; 3–0763.

NaH is isometric with the NaCl space lattice. Crystals acicular. G. 0.92. M.P. 800° C. with decomposition. Isotropic with[20] $n = 1.470$. PD 2.83, 2.44, 1.73; 2–0809.

[15] Merwin in Wyckoff: *Am. Jour. Sci.* CCIV, p. 469 (1922).
[16] Neuhaus: *Chem. Erde*, V, p. 529 (1930).
[17] Measured by V. A. Vigfusson at the University of Wisconsin.
[17a] Wulff: *Zeit. phys. Chem.* B, X, p. 347 (1930).
[18] C. D. West: *pers. comm.*, Nov. 2, 1936.
[19] V. A. Vigfusson: *pers. comm.*, Sept. 30 and Nov. 29, 1930.
[20] Bode: *Zeit. phys. Chem.* B, VI, p. 251 (1930).

KH is isometric with the NaCl space lattice. Crystals acicular. G. 1.43–1.47. Isotropic with[20] $n = 1.453$. PD 3.30, 2.86, 2.02; 3–0454.

NaCN is isometric with the NaCl space lattice. Crystals cubic. M.P. 564° C. Isotropic with $n = 1.452$. Colorless. PD 2.95, 2.09, 1.78; 4–0665.

KCN is isometric. G. 1.52. M.P. 635° C. Crystals often cubes or octahedrons. Isotropic with[19] $n = 1.410 \pm 0.003$. Colorless. Very poisonous. PD 3.26, 2.31, 3.77; 4–0547.

NaK(CN)₂ is isometric. Colorless. Isotropic with[9] $n = 1.465\pm$.

AgCN crystallizes in prisms[9] which are probably uniaxial. G. 3.95. Optic sign positive. $n_O = 1.685\pm$, $n_E = 1.94$, $n_E - n_O = 0.255\pm$. White. PD 3.00, 3.70, 2.33; 1–0859.

KAg(CN)₂ (?) is trigonal with $c/a = 2.07$. No good cleavage. Uniaxial positive[21] with $n_O = 1.625$, $n_E = 1.63$, $n_E - n_O = 0.005$.

K₃Cu(CN)₄ is trigonal in rhombohedral forms. Uniaxial negative with $n = 1.5185$ Li, 1.5215 Na, 1.5285 blue, $n_O - n_E =$ very weak.

NaCNO is hexagonal[9] with rhombohedral cleavage. Uniaxial positive with $n_O = 1.389$, $n_E = 1.627$, $n_E - n_O = 0.238$. Colorless.

KCNO is tetragonal[18] with $c/a = 0.577$. Crystals basal tablets with {111}. G. 2.056. No cleavage seen. Uniaxial negative with $n_O = 1.552$, $n_E = 1.377$, $n_O - n_E = 0.173$. Colorless.

NaCNS forms[19] clear prismatic crystals, probably orthorhombic, with X parallel elongation. $(-)2V = 82° \pm 3°$ calc., $n_X = 1.545 \pm 0.005$, $n_Y = 1.625 \pm 0.005$, $n_Z = 1.695 \pm 0.005$, $n_Z - n_X = 0.150 \pm 0.01$. Colorless. PD 3.20, 3.49, 2.96; 1–0741.

KCNS forms[19] long prismatic crystals, probably monoclinic with $Z \wedge c = 16°\pm$. $(-)2V = 68° \pm 3°$ calc., $n_X = 1.532 \pm 0.003$, $n_Y = 1.660 \pm 0.005$, $n_Z = 1.730 \pm 0.005$, $n_Z - n_X = 0.198 \pm 0.01$. Colorless. PD 2.97, 2.78, 2.79; 9–388.

NH₄CNS is monoclinic[22] with $a:b:c = 2.035:1:2.367$, $\beta = 117°2'$. Crystals {100} plates or prisms with perfect {100} and {10$\bar{1}$} cleavages. $Y = b$,[19] $Z \wedge c = 22°$. $(-)2V = 23° \pm 3°$ calc., r < v strong, and also inclined dispersion. $n_X = 1.546 \pm 0.003$, $n_Y = 1.685 \pm 0.003$, $n_Z = 1.692 \pm 0.003$, $n_Z - n_X = 0.146 \pm 0.006$. Again:[22] $X \wedge \perp \{10\bar{1}\} = 18°$. PD 3.66, 3.11, 2.99; 1–0511.

LiNH₂ is isometric. Crystals often cubes modified by a tetrahedron.[18] G. 1.178. M.P. 373–5° C. Isotropic with $n = 1.610$. Colorless or stained. PD 2.91, 1.78, 2.52; 6–0418.

NaNH₂ is biaxial with good cleavage. M.P. 210° C. $(+)2V =$ moderate,

---

[21] Indices measured by Bolland (*Sitz. Akad. Wiss. Wien*, CXIX, p. 275, 1910) on "potassium silver cyanide" of unknown formula.

[22] Groth: *Chem. Krist.* II, p. 3 (1908).

r > v. $n_X = 1.500$, $n_Y = 1.527$, $n_Z = 1.562$, $n_Z - n_X = 0.062$. Colorless or stained. PD 5.20, 1.96, 3.18; 3–0123.

2. Hydrated Halides, etc., of Monovalent Bases. Formula Type AX·nH₂O

KF·2H₂O is pseudo-hexagonal and probably monoclinic. Optic orientation unknown.[9] (+)2V = very large. $n_X = 1.345\pm$, $n_Y = 1.352$, $n_Z = 1.363\pm$, $n_Z - n_X = 0.018\pm$. Colorless. PD 3.01, 2.58, 4.42; 1–0854.

NaBr·2H₂O is monoclinic[23] with $a = 6.59$ kX, $b = 10.20$, $c = 6.51$, $\beta = 112°05'$, U.C. 4. Crystals short six-sided prisms or thick basal plates. G. 2.166 (calc. 2.28). Y = b. (−)2V = very large with weak inclined dispersion. $n_X = 1.5128$, $n_Y = 1.5192$, $n_Z = 1.5252$ D. $n_Z - n_X = 0.0124$. Colorless.

LiI·3H₂O is hexagonal[24] with $c/a = 0.731$. Crystals short prisms. Plastic with no cleavage. G. 3.48. Loses water and melts at 73° C. Uniaxial negative with $n_O = 1.655$, $n_E = 1.625$, $n_O - n_E = 0.030$. Colorless or yellowish. PD 4.20, 2.79, 3.73; 1–0411.

3. Anhydrous Halides, etc., of Divalent Bases. Formula Type AX₂

MgF₂ (Sellaite) is tetragonal with $a = 4.660$, $c = 3.078$ kX. U.C. 2. Crystals prismatic with perfect {010} and {110} cleavages. H. 5. G. 3.15. Uniaxial positive with[25] $n_O = 1.378$, $n_E = 1.390$, $n_E - n_O = 0.012$. Colorless to white. PD 3.27, 2.23, 1.71; 6–0290.

CaF₂ (Fluorite) is isometric with a space lattice as shown in Fig. 3-4. Crystals often cubic, as in Fig. 3-5, or octahedral, with perfect {111} cleavage and common twinning on {111} (see Fig. 3-6). H. 4. G. 3.18. Fuses at 1360° C. with red flame color. Soluble in H₂SO₄ with evolution of HF. Isotropic with[26] $n = 1.4325$ C, 1.43385 D, 1.4370 F. Colorless or stained green, purple, etc. Often shows weak birefringence probably due to strain. It may contain Y or Ce to about Y, Ce:Ca = 1:2; with about[27] 17 per cent (Y, Ce)F₃: G. 3.40, $n = 1.448$. PD 1.93, 3.15, 1.65; 4–0864.

ZnF₂ is tetragonal or hexagonal. G. 4.84. M.P. 872° C. Uniaxial positive[28] with $n_O = 1.510$, $n_E = 1.526$, $n_E - n_O = 0.016$. PD 3.33, 2.61, 1.75; 7–214.

SrF₂ is isometric with the CaF₂ space lattice. G. 4.24. M.P. 1190° C.

[23] Wooster: *Nature* CXXX, p. 698 (1932) [*Strukturb.* II, p. 209].
[24] West: *Zeit. Krist.* LXXXVIII, p. 198 (1934).
[25] Sella: *Acc. Linc. Mem.* IV, p. 455 (1887).
[26] Merwin: *Am. Jour. Sci.* CLXXXII, p. 429 (1911).
[27] Zambonini: *Riv. min.* XLV, p. 148 (1915).
[28] Ingerson and Morey: *Am. Min.* XXXVI, p. 778 (1951).

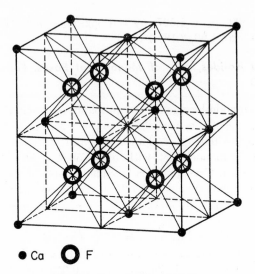

Fig. 3-4. Space lattice of CaF₂.

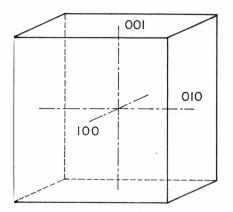

Fig. 3-5. A crystal habit of CaF₂.

Isotropic with[30] $n = 1.438$ D. Again:[29] $n = 1.442 \pm 0.001$ D. Miscible in all proportions[31] with CaF_2. PD 3.35, 2.05, 1.75; 6–0262.

CdF₂ is isometric[32] with the CaF_2 space lattice. G. 6.64. M.P. 1100° C. Isotropic with $n = 1.56$. Miscible in all proportions with CaF_2 with rectilinear variation of the refractive index. PD 3.11, 1.90, 1.62; 5–0567.

[29] Wulff and Heigl: *Zeit. Krist.* LXXVII, p. 98 (1931).

[30] Thilo: *Zeit. Krist.* LXV, p. 720 (1927); Wulff: *Zeit. Elektrochem.* XXXIV, p. 611 (1928).

[31] Rumpf: *Zeit. phys. Chem.* B, VII, p. 148 (1930).

[32] Goldschmidt: *Skr. Norsk. Vid. Akad.* I, p. 84 (1926).

BaF$_2$ is isometric[29] with G. 4.89. M.P. 1280° C. Isotropic with $n = 1.475$. Again:[5] $n = 1.4741$ D. PD 3.58, 2.19, 1.87, 4–0452.

CaBeF$_4$ is tetragonal[33] with $a = 6.90$, $c = 6.07$ Å. Uniaxial with $n = 1.355$.

MgZnF$_4$ is uniaxial positive with[28] $n_O = 1.40$ *ca.*, $n_E = 1.41$ *ca.*, $n_E - n_O = 0.01$ *ca.* M.P. 1185° C.

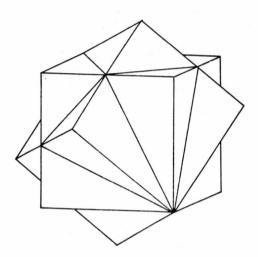

Fig. 3-6. Penetration spinel twin in CaF$_2$.

CaZnF$_4$ is uniaxial negative with[28] $n_O = 1.465$, $n_E = 1.455$, $n_O - n_E = 0.010$. M.P. 796° C.

SrZnF$_4$ is uniaxial negative with[28] mean index $= 1.455$, $n_O - n_E < 0.009$. M.P. 729° C.

BaZnF$_4$ is uniaxial negative with[28] mean index $= 1.544$, $n_O - n_E = 0.004\pm$. M.P. 790° C.

MnZnF$_4$ is uniaxial positive with[28] $n_O = 1.487$, $n_E = 1.517$, $n_E - n_O = 0.030$. M.P. 897° C.

ZnClF is biaxial with[28] $(+)2V = 70°$ *ca.*, mean index $= 1.70$, $n_Z - n_X < 0.009$. M.P. 689° C.

SrClF is tetragonal[34] with good basal cleavage and G. 4.62. M.P. 962° C. Uniaxial negative with $n_O = 1.651$, $n_E = 1.627$, $n_O - n_E = 0.024$.

BaClF is tetragonal with[34] good basal cleavage and G. 5.93. M.P. 1008° C. Uniaxial negative with $n_O = 1.640$, $n_E = 1.633$, $n_O - n_E = 0.007$. PD 3.77, 3.09, 2.35; 3–0304.

[33] Hahn: *N. Jahrb. Min. Abhand.* Bd. LXXXVI, p. 1 (1953).

[34] Winter: *Inaug. Diss. Leipzig.* 1913. *Tables Ann. Const. Phys.* IV, p. 1063, 1067, (1922).

PbClF (Matlockite) is tetragonal with $a = 4.09$, $c = 7.21$ kX. Crystals basal tablets with perfect {001} cleavage. H. 2.5–3. G. 7.12. M.P. 601° C. Uniaxial negative with[35] $n_O = 2.145$ Na, 2.191 (486), $n_E = 2.006$ Na, 2.039 Tl, $n_O - n_E = 0.139$ Na. Sometimes biaxial probably due to strain. Colorless or yellow, amber or green. Colorless in section.

MgCl₂ (Chloromagnesite) is hexagonal with $a = 3.58$, $c = 17.59$ kX. Crystals basal plates. G. 2.325. M.P. 708° C. Uniaxial negative with[12] $n_O = 1.675$, $n_E = 1.59$, $n_O - n_E = 0.085$. Colorless. PD 2.56, 1.82, 2.96; 3–0854.

CaCl₂ (Hydrophilite) is orthorhombic[36] and pseudo-tetragonal with $a = 6.24$, $b = 6.43$, $c = 4.20$ kX. G. 2.2. M.P. 772° C. Perfect prismatic cleavage and lamellar twinning on {110}. (+)2V = moderate,[37] $n_X = 1.600$, $n_Y = 1.605$, $n_Z = 1.613$, $n_Z - n_X = 0.013$. The substance may react with index liquids containing turpentine, etc., but it does not react with α-monobromnaphthalene nor with paraffin oil. PD 4.49, 3.05, 2.33; 1–0338.

CaCl₂ forms a brown-yellow powder which is hygroscopic. G. 3.05. M.P. 498° C. Uniaxial negative. $n_O{}^{29} = 1.542$, $n_E = 1.531$, $n_O - n_E = 0.011$.

ZnCl₂ is uniaxial and positive[9] with $n_O = 1.687$, $n_E = 1.713$, $n_E - n_O = 0.026$. Colorless. Also said to be isometric with[38] G. 2.91 and M.P. 262° C. PD 3.06, 4.79, 1.86; 1–0822.

SrCl₂ is isometric[30] with G. 3.08 and M.P. 872° C. Isotropic with $n = 1.6499$ D. PD 2.47, 4.03, 2.10; 6–0537.

FeCl₂ (Lawrencite) is hexagonal in basal plates with $a = 3.57$, $c = 17.51$ kX. U.C. 3. Perfect basal cleavage. Uniaxial negative with[39] $n_O = 1.567$, $n_O - n_E$ is rather weak. Color green to brown or yellow. Made by sublimation. PD 2.54, 5.9, 1.80; 1–1106.

BaCl₂ is monoclinic (inverts to isometric at 925°); G. 3.856. (+)2V = near[30] 90°. $n_X = 1.73024$, $n_Y = 1.73611$, $n_Z = 1.74196$, $n_Z - n_X = 0.01172$. PD 2.85, 2.59, 2.46; 2–0794*.

HgCl₂ is orthorhombic with $a:b:c = 0.725:1:1.070$. Crystals equant or thin basal tablets with perfect {011} and poor {001} cleavages. G. 6.22. M.P. 153° C. X = c, Y = a.[14] (−)2V = 85°, $n_X = 1.725$, $n_Y = 1.859$, $n_Z = 1.965$, $n_Z - n_X = 0.240$. PD 4.35, 2.99, 4.10; 4–0331.

PbCl₂ (Cotunnite) is orthorhombic with $a = 7.67$, $b = 9.15$, $c = 4.50$ kX. U.C. 4. Perfect basal cleavage. H. 2.5. G. 5.8. Soluble in hot water.

---

[35] Bannister: *Min. Mag.* XXIII, p. 587 (1934).

[36] van Bever and Nieuwenkamp: *Zeit. Krist.* XC, p. 374 (1935).

[37] Slawson: *Am. Min.* XIV, p. 160 (1929). But Wulff and Heigl[29] give $n_X = 1.531$, $n_Z = 1.542$ for CaCl₂; is this really CaCl₂·2H₂O?

[38] *Handb. Chem. Phys.* 1940, p. 436 and p. 518.

[39] Larsen: *U. S. Geol. Surv. Bull.* 679 (1921). Index too low as compared with MgCl₂— perhaps hydrated?

$Y = b$,[40] $Z = c$. $(+)2V = 66°12'$ Na, $n_X = 2.179$ Li, 2.199 Na, $n_Y = 2.192$ Li, 2.217 Na, $n_Z = 2.260$ Na, $n_Z - n_X = 0.061$ Na. Colorless, greenish or yellowish. PD 3.58, 3.89, 2.78; 5–0416.

PbBr$_2$ is orthorhombic[41] with $a:b:c = 0.588:1:1.183$. Crystals columnar parallel a with perfect basal cleavage. G. 6.62. M.P. 373° C. X $= c$, Y $= b$. $(+)2V = $ large, $n_X = 2.434$, $n_Y = 2.476$, $n_Z = 2.553$, $n_Z - n_X = 0.119$. Color white. PD 2.92, 3.75, 2.64; 5–0608.

CaI$_2$ is hexagonal with $c/a = 0.8599$. Crystals tabular with basal cleavage. G. 5.67. Uniaxial negative with[42] $n_O = 1.743$ Na, $n_E = 1.652$, $n_O - n_E = 0.091$. Colorless in thin plates; thick ones are weakly pleochroic in bluish or brownish tints. Inverts to a monoclinic phase (with G. 5.305) before melting at 388° C. PD 3.49, 2.24, 2.00; 4–0481.

HgI$_2$ is dimorphous; one phase is orthorhombic with $a:b:c = 0.649:1:?$. Crystals prismatic with {001}. G. 6.22. Forms isomorphous mix-crystals with HgBr$_2$ which have perfect basal cleavage. The acute bisectrix is b and Y $= c$. Color yellow with weak pleochroism—X = Y < Z. The other phase is tetragonal with $c/a = 2.008$. Crystals basal tablets or pyramidal; twinning on {102}. Perfect {001} cleavage. G. 6.30. Uniaxial negative with[14] $n_O = 2.600$ C, 2.711 (600), 2.748 D, $n_E = 2.375$ C, 2.438 (600), 2.455 D, $n_O - n_E = 0.293$ D. Also biaxial with 2E up to 30°. Color red with X orange-red, Z blood-red. PD 3.57, 4.12, 2.19; 4–0454/5 [which polymorph?].

Hg(CN)$_2$ is tetragonal with $c/a = 0.459$. Crystals short prismatic with a sphenoid or, rarely, a base. G. 4.00. Poor {100} cleavage. Uniaxial negative with[43] $n_O = 1.645$, $n_E = 1.492$, $n_O - n_E = 0.153$. PD 3.73, 4.85, 2.52; 7–213.

4. Hydrated Halides, etc., of Divalent Bases. Formula Type AX$_2$·nH$_2$O

MgCl$_2$·6H$_2$O (Bischofite) is monoclinic with $a:b:c = 1.387:1:0.854$, $\beta = 93°42'$. Crystals short prismatic. H. 1–2. G. 1.59. Bitter taste. Decomposes at 116–8° C. Deliquescent. X $= b$, Y $\wedge c = 9.5°$. $(+)2V = 79°24'$, r > v weak.[44] $n_X = 1.495$, $n_Y = 1.507$, $n_Z = 1.528$, $n_Z - n_X = 0.033$ Na. Colorless or white. PD 4.10, 2.65, 2.88; 1–0431.

CaCl$_2$·4H$_2$O is stable between 14° and 45°. It has three crystal phases.[45]

[40] Stöber: *Acad. roy. Belg. Cl. Sc.* Bull. Ser. 3 XXX, p. 345 (1895).
[41] Nieuwenkamp and Bijvoet: *Zeit. Krist.* LXXXIV, p. 49 (1933).
[42] A. F. Kirkpatrick, Amer. Cyanamid Co., pers. comm.
[43] Chamot and Mason: *Chem. Microscopy.* I, p. 330 (1931).
[44] Görgey: *Min. Mitt.* XXIX, p. 200 (1910).
[45] Shepelev, Lyashenko and Druzhinin: *Dokl. Akad. Nauk.* U.S.S.R. LXXV, p. 379 (1950). [*Chem. Abst.* XLV, p. 9980 (1951)].

One is triclinic and granular with $(-)2V = 63°$, $n_X = 1.532$, $n_Y = 1.560$, $n_Z = 1.571$, $n_Z - n_X = 0.039$. A second phase is orthorhombic in needles with Z parallel with elongation and $(-)2V = 5°$. $n_X = 1.506$, n_Y nearly $= n_Z = 1.530$, $n_Z - n_X = 0.024$. A third phase is orthorhombic(?) in six-sided plates with $(-)2V = 68°$, $n_X = 1.447$, $n_Y = 1.477$, $n_Z = 1.491$, $n_Z - n_X = 0.044$. Another report gives[23] $n_1 = 1.566$, $n_2 = 1.548$. PD 2.63, 2.22, 4.70; 1–1080.

CaCl$_2$·6H$_2$O is trigonal with $c/a = 0.505$. Crystals prismatic with perfect basal and prismatic cleavages. G. 1.68. M.P. 30° C. Uniaxial negative with $n_O = 1.417$, $n_E = 1.393$, $n_O - n_E = 0.024$. Colorless. Again:[23] $n_O = 1.5504$, $n_E = 1.4949$. PD 2.16, 3.93, 2.78; 1–1220.

CaMg$_2$Cl$_6$·12H$_2$O (Tachyhydrite) is trigonal with[46] $c/a = 1.761$. Perfect $\{10\bar{1}1\}$ cleavage. H. 2. G. 1.67. Deliquescent. Uniaxial negative with $n_O = 1.520$, $n_E = 1.512$ Na, $n_O - n_E = 0.008$. Color pale yellow. Made from a solution[47] of MgCl$_2$ and large excess of CaCl$_2$. PD 2.60, 3.09, 3.80; 1–1092.

MnCl$_2$·2H$_2$O is monoclinic[48] with $a:b:c = 1.094:1:0.421$, $\beta = 130°48'$. Crystals long prisms. Perfect $\{110\}$ and good $\{001\}$ cleavages. H. 1. G. 2.31. Easily deformed. $X = b$, $Z \wedge c = -32°$. $(+)2V = 72°$, $n_X = 1.584$, $n_Y = 1.611$, $n_Z = 1.666$ Na, $n_Z - n_X = 0.082$. PD 2.80, 5.59, 4.39; 3–0743*.

FeCl$_2$·2H$_2$O is monoclinic[48] with $\beta = 130°30'$. Crystals long prisms. Cruciform twinning on $\{001\}$. Soft. G. 2.387. $X = b$, Z (or Y?) $\wedge c = -38°$. $n_Y = 1.6435$. Colorless or pale green. PD 4.80, 5.60, 3.50; 1–0277*.

CoCl$_2$·2H$_2$O is monoclinic[48] with $a:b:c = 1.111:1:0.420$, $\beta = 130°31'$. Crystals long prisms; twinning on $\{302\}$. Good $\{110\}$ and distinct $\{001\}$(?) cleavages. G. 2.477. $X = b$, $Z \wedge c = -33°$. $(+)2V = 78°$ calc., $n_X = 1.626 \pm 0.002$, $n_Y = 1.662$, $n_Z = 1.721$ Na, $n_Z - n_X = 0.095$. Color dark violet with X inky blue, Y clear carmine red, Z strong carmine red. Formed from CoCl$_2$·6H$_2$O by drying in a desiccator at 50° C. Hydrates easily. PD 2.73, 5.49, 4.27; 3–0786.

NiCl$_2$·2H$_2$O is orthorhombic[48] with $a:b:c = 0.784:1:0.391$. Crystals long prisms; cruciform twinning. Perfect $\{110\}$ and good $\{001\}$ cleavages. H. 1. G. 2.58. Easily deformed. $X = b$, $Y = a$. $(-)2V = 72°$ ca., $n_X = 1.620$, $n_Y = 1.723$, $n_Z = 1.783$, $n_Z - n_X = 0.163$. Pleochroic with X pale yellow to brown, Y and Z canary yellow-green. PD 2.44, 5.40, 4.42; 1–1143.

SrCl$_2$·6H$_2$O is hexagonal with $c/a = 0.515$. Crystals prismatic with perfect basal cleavage. G. 1.93. Uniaxial negative with $n_O = 1.5364$ Na,

[46] Jung: *Cent. Min.* 1926 A, p. 273.
[47] de Schulten: *C. R.* III, p. 928 (1890).
[48] Neuhaus: *Zeit. Krist.* XCVIII, p. 112 (1938).

$n_E = 1.4866, n_O - n_E = 0.0498$. Again:[49] $n_O = 1.5356, n_E = 1.4857, n_O - n_E = 0.0499$ D. Colorless. PD 6.89, 3.54, 3.98; 6–0073.

SrBr$_2$·6H$_2$O is hexagonal. Crystals prismatic.[18] G. 2.358. Uniaxial negative with $n_O = 1.557, n_E = 1.535, n_O - n_E = 0.022$. Colorless. PD 4.12, 3.60, 2.26; 6–0176.

CuCl$_2$·2H$_2$O (Eriochalcite) is orthorhombic with $a = 7.38, b = 8.04, c = 3.72$ kX. U.C. 2. Crystal aggregates of fibers often grooved and bent. Perfect {110} and good {001} cleavages. H. 2.5. G. 2.55. X = b, Y = c.[9] $(+)2V = 80°40'$, r < v. $n_X = 1.644, n_Y = 1.684, n_Z = 1.742, n_Z - n_X = 0.098$. Again:[50] $(+)2V = 86°14'$, $n_X = 1.644, n_Y = 1.683, n_Z = 1.731, n_Z - n_X = 0.087$. Color bluish green; pleochroic with X pale blue, Y pale tawny green, Z pale yellow-green. PD 5.40, 4.03, 2.63; 1–0217.

MnCl$_2$·4H$_2$O (α-phase) is monoclinic with $a{:}b{:}c = 1.141{:}1{:}1.641$, $\beta = 110°46'$. Crystals basal tablets with a pyramid or prismatic with negative[19] elongation. Twinning common. $(+)2V = 78° \pm 3°$ calc., r < v moderate. $n_X = 1.555, n_Y = 1.575, n_Z = 1.607 \pm 0.003, n_Z - n_X = 0.052$. PD 4.37, 4.91, 2.90; 1–0362.

NiCl$_2$·6H$_2$O is monoclinic with $a{:}b{:}c = 1.468{:}1{:}0.943$, $\beta = 122°30'$. Crystals {100} tablets with {110} and {001}. Perfect basal cleavage. X ∧ $c = +8°\pm$. Y = b. $(+)2V$ very large,[51] $n_X = 1.535, n_Y = ?, n_Z = 1.61, n_Z - n_X = 0.075$. PD 5.50, 4.85, 3.53; 1–0200.

SrCl$_2$·2H$_2$O is probably monoclinic with[49] G. 2.37. $(+)2V$ = small, $n_X = 1.5942 \pm 0.0002, n_Y = 1.5948 \pm 0.0004, n_Z = 1.6172 \pm 0.0001, n_Z - n_X = 0.0230$. PD 3.20, 2.66, 2.10; 3–0500.

CdCl$_2$·2.5H$_2$O is monoclinic with $a{:}b{:}c = 1.177{:}1{:}1.112$, $\beta = 95°48'$. Crystals varied with distinct {001} cleavage. G. 3.327. Y = b, Z ∧ $c = +1°40'$. $(+)2V = 56°42'$ red, $56°27'$ Na, r > v weak; $n_Y = 1.6428$ red, 1.6513 Na, $n_Z - n_X = ?$. Colorless. Another phase is also monoclinic.

BaCl$_2$·2H$_2$O is monoclinic with $a{:}b{:}c = 0.618{:}1{:}0.655$, $\beta = 91°5'$. Crystals octagonal tablets parallel to {010}, twinned on {001} or {100}. No good cleavage. G. 3.09. Y = b, Z ∧ $c = 8°$. $(+)2V = 84°50'$ red, $83°46'$ Na; $n_X = 1.635$ Na, $n_Y = 1.641$ red, 1.646 Na, $n_Z = 1.660$ Na, $n_Z - n_X = 0.025$ Na. Again:[29] $n_X = 1.6291, n_Y = 1.6419, n_Z = 1.6583, n_Z - n_X = 0.0292$. Colorless. PD 4.48, 2.91, 2.54; 1–0342.

BaBr$_2$·2H$_2$O is monoclinic with $a{:}b{:}c = 1.45{:}1{:}1.16$, $\beta = 113°30'$. Crystals short prismatic (see Fig. 3-7) or basal tablets or columnar by elongation of {11$\bar{1}$}. Poor {100}, {10$\bar{1}$} or {001} cleavages. G. 3.69. Y = b,

---

[49] Wulff and Heigl: *Zeit. Krist.* LXXVII, p. 100 (1931).

[50] Neuhaus: *Zeit. Krist.* XCVII, p. 28 (1937).

[51] Indices measured by Bolland (*Sitz. Akad. Wiss. Wien* CXIX, p. 275, 1910) on "nickel chloride" of unknown formula.

$Z \wedge c = +89°35'$ Na. $(+)2V = 83°30'$ Li, $83°49'$ Na, $84°8'$ Tl. $n_X =$
1.7067 C, 1.7129 D, 1.7282 F, $n_Y = 1.7205$ C, 1.7266 D, 1.7418 F, $n_Z =$
1.7382 C, 1.7441 D, 1.7588 F, $n_Z - n_X = 0.0312$ D. Colorless. Formed
from H_2O solution; crystals easily deformed.

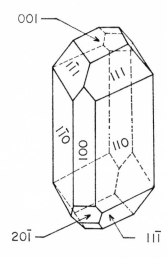

Fig. 3-7. A crystal habit of $BaBr_2 \cdot 2H_2O$.

$BaCdCl_4 \cdot 4H_2O$ is triclinic with $a:b:c = 0.855:1:0.513$, $\alpha = 92°35'$,
$\beta = 106°18'$ $\gamma = 88°26'$. Crystals short prismatic with twinning resembling that of plagioclase. Perfect $\{110\}$ and $\{1\bar{1}0\}$ cleavages. G. 2.97. X
nearly normal to $\{110\}$; optic plane nearly vertical with extinction at 11°
on (110), 6° on (010), 2.5° on (100) and 4.5° on $(1\bar{1}0)$. $(-)2V = 61°1'$,
r < v. $n_Y = 1.638$ red, 1.651 Na, 1.664 blue, $n_Z - n_X$ not very strong.
Again:[52] $n_X = 1.610$, $n_Y = 1.646$, $n_Z = 1.653$ all ± 0.003, $n_Z - n_X = 0.043$.

$BaCdBr_4 \cdot 4H_2O$ is isomorphous with $BaCdCl_4 \cdot 4H_2O$ with the same
cleavages and twinning. G. 3.69. Optic orientation differs only 1° or 2°.
$(-)2V = 70°13'$, r < v. $n_Y = 1.693$ red, 1.702 Na, $n_Z - n_X = ?$

$Cd_2MgCl_6 \cdot 12H_2O$ is orthorhombic with $a:b:c = 0.913:1:0.304$. Crystals
prismatic with probable $\{100\}$ and $\{010\}$ cleavages. Deliquescent. Y = a,
Z = c. $(+)2V =$ very large, r < v weak. $n_X = 1.49\pm$, $n_Y = 1.5268$ red,
1.5331 Na, $n_Z = 1.5728$ red, 1.5769 Na, $n_Z - n_X = 0.08\pm$.

$ZnF_2 \cdot 4H_2O$ is biaxial negative[28] with $2V = 50°$ ca., $n_X = 1.46$ ca.,
$n_Y = 1.468$ calc., $n_Z = 1.47$ ca., $n_Z - n_X = 0.01$ ca. Soluble in NH_4OH.
Decomposes below 100° C. PD 4.91, 4.13, 2.99; 1–0253.

$Cu_2(OH)_3Cl$ (Atacamite) is orthorhombic with $a = 6.01$, $b = 9.13$,
$c = 6.84$ kX. U.C. 4. Crystals often prismatic. Perfect $\{010\}$ and fair $\{101\}$

[52] Quodling and Mellor: *Zeit. Krist.* CII, p. 146 (1939).

cleavages. H. 3–3.5. G. 3.78. X = b,[53] Y = a. (−)2V = 75°, r < v strong. n_X = 1.831, n_Y = 1.861, n_Z = 1.880, $n_Z − n_X$ = 0.049 Tl. Color bright green, streak apple-green. Weakly pleochroic with X pale green, Y yellowish green, Z grass-green. Found in boiler deposits. Made by heating Cu_2O with $FeCl_3$ solution in a sealed tube.[54] PD 5.40, 5.00, 2.82; 2–0146.

$Cu_2(OH)_3Cl$ (Paratacamite) is hexagonal with a = 13.65, c = 13.95 kX. Good rhombohedral cleavage. H. 3. G. 3.74. Uniaxial positive[55] with n_O = 1.842, n_E = 1.848, $n_E − n_O$ = 0.006. Often biaxial (due to strain) with 2V up to about 50° and r > v. Made[55] by reaction of Cu with salt water. PD 5.74, 2.41, 2.48; 4–0193.

$Pb(OH)Cl$ (Laurionite) is orthorhombic with[56] a = 7.1, b = 9.7, c = 4.05 kX. U.C. 4. Elongated along c. Distinct {011} cleavage. H. 2–2.5. G. 6.24. X = a, Y = b. (−)2V = large,[53] n_X = 2.077, n_Y = 2.116, n_Z = 2.158, $n_Z − n_X$ = 0.081. Colorless to white. PD 3.30, 4.01, 2.52; 6–0268.

$PbCu(OH)_2Cl_2(?)$ (Percylite) is isometric(?). Crystals usually cubic or dodecahedral with cubic cleavage. H. 2.5. G. 2.25. F. 1. Isotropic[12] with n = 2.05 ± .01. Color blue. Also birefringent[57] in some cases, cause not known. Made by the reaction of $Pb(OH)_2$ on a solution of $CuCl_2$.

$Pb(Cu,Ag)Cl_2(OH)_2·H_2O$ (Boléite) is tetragonal[58] with a = 15.4, c = 62 kX. Crystals equant and pseudo-isometric. Perfect {001}, good {101} and poor {100} cleavages. H. 3–3.5. G. 5.05. Uniaxial negative with[12] n_O = 2.05, n_E = 2.03, $n_O − n_E$ = 0.02. Again[59] n = 2.081 and 2.087 in different parts of a zoned crystal. Color deep blue; in section bluish green and not pleochroic. PD 4.40, 3.83, 3.13; 2–0240.

$MgPt(CN)_4·7H_2O$ is tetragonal with c/a = 0.61. Perfect basal cleavage. Uniaxial positive with[60] n_O = 1.5585 C, 1.5608 D, n_E = 1.905 C, 1.91 D, $n_E − n_O$ = 0.35 D. Color carmine-red with O more, and E less, bluish. Surface color on {100} metallic greenish. Strongly pleochroic; phosphorescent.

$MgPt(CN)_4·C_3H_8O_3·5H_2O$ is monoclinic with $a:b:c$ = 0.965:1:0.492, β = 94°4′. Crystals short prismatic (vertically striated) with distinct {001} cleavage. The optic plane is normal to {010} for Li and parallel to {010} for Na and Tl light. X ∧ c = 24° for A, 30° for D, 36° for E and 68° for G

[53] Smith: *Min. Mag.* XII, p. 106 (1899).

[54] Mellor: vol. III, p. 178 (1923).

[55] Frondel: *Min. Mag.* XXIX, p. 34 (1950).

[56] Palache's $a\ b\ c$ (*Min. Mag.* XXIII, p. 573, 1934) changed to $c\ a\ b$ to make $b > a > c$.

[57] Friedel: *Bull. Soc. Franc. Min.* XV, p. 96 (1892).

[58] Hocart: *Zeit. Krist.* LXXIV, p. 20 (1930).

[59] Hadding: *Geol. För. Förh.* XLI, p. 175 (1919). Formula doubtful; sometimes written $Pb_9Cu_8Ag_3Cl_{21}(OH)_{16}·2H_2O$.

[60] Gaubert: *Bull. Soc. Franc. Min.* XL, p. 177 (1917).

light. $(-)2V = 17°39'$ Na, $34°18'$ Tl, $60°$(blue). $n_Y = 1.584$ Na, 1.589 Tl, $n_Z - n_X = ?$

CaNi(CN)$_4$·5H$_2$O is orthorhombic with[61] $a:b:c = 0.911:1:0.361$. Crystals show $\{010\}$, $\{100\}$, $\{120\}$, $\{111\}$. Perfect $\{100\}$ cleavage. Soluble in H$_2$O. G. 1.83. X = c, Y = a. $(-)2E = 70°40'$ (646), $71°20'$ (591), $78°40'$ (541). For $\lambda = 646$: $n_X = 1.529, n_Y = 1.612, n_Z = 1.632, n_Z - n_X = 0.103$. For $\lambda = 578$: $n_X = 1.5405, n_Y = 1.617, n_Z = 1.638, n_Z - n_X = 0.0975$. For $\lambda = 546$: $n_X = 1.5515, n_Y = 1.623, n_Z = 1.645, n_Z - n_X = 0.0935$. Color brown.

CaPd(CN)$_4$·5H$_2$O is orthorhombic with[61] $a:b:c = 0.895:1:0.350$. Crystals long parallel c with $\{120\}$, $\{100\}$, $\{111\}$. Perfect $\{100\}$ cleavage. G. 2.02. Soluble in H$_2$O. X = c, Y = a. $(-)2V = 68°$. For $\lambda = 646$: $n_X = 1.532, n_Y = 1.598, n_Z = 1.632$. For $\lambda = 591$: $n_X = 1.539, n_Y = 1.602, n_Z = 1.639, n_Z - n_X = 0.100$. For $\lambda = 541$: $n_X = 1.549, n_Y = 1.605, n_Z = 1.645$. Colorless.

CaPt(CN)$_4$·5H$_2$O is orthorhombic[61] with $a:b:c = 0.899:1:0.349$. Crystals prismatic with $\{120\}$, $\{100\}$ and $\{010\}$ and perfect $\{100\}$ cleavage. G. 2.61. X = a, Y = b. For 588mμ $(+)2V = 48°10'$, $n_X = 1.623$, $n_Y = 1.644, n_Z = 1.767, n_Z - n_X = 0.144$. For 486 m$\mu$: $(+)2V = 30°23'$, $n_X = 1.636, n_Y = 1.658, n_Z = 2.030\pm$, $n_Z - n_X = 0.394\pm$. Color green, not distinctly pleochroic; fluorescent.

Ca$_2$Fe(CN)$_6$·12H$_2$O is triclinic with $a:b:c = 1.054:1:0.841$, $\alpha = 97°9'$, $\beta = 89°57'$, $\gamma = 107°24'$. Perfect $\{001\}$ cleavage. G. 1.68. Optic plane nearly normal to $\{001\}$; an optic axis nearly normal to $\{010\}$. The normal to $\{010\}$ makes an angle of $16°18'$ (Na) with Z and $77°10'$ with X. A normal to $\{100\}$ makes an angle of $59°31'$ with Z and $71°21'$ with X. $(+)2V = 85°12'$ Na, r > v. $n_X = 1.5646$ Li, 1.5700 Na, 1.5753 Tl, $n_Y = 1.5764$ Li, 1.5818 Na, 1.5871 Tl, $n_Z = 1.5902$ Li, 1.5961 Na, 1.6017 Tl, $n_Z - n_X = 0.0261$ Na. Color yellow. PD 5.1, 5.5, 4.70; 1–0237.

Ca[N(CN)$_2$]$_2$·2H$_2$O loses water at[62] $100°$ C. $(+)2V = 50°$ calc. $n_X = 1.405$, $n_Y = 1.480$. $n_Z = 1.82$, $n_Z - n_X = 0.415$.

SrNi(CN)$_4$·5H$_2$O is monoclinic[61] with $a:b:c = 0.676:1:0.474$, $\beta = 92°23'$. Good basal cleavage. G. 2.03. Soluble in H$_2$O. Crystals show $\{110\}$, $\{001\}$, $\{111\}$. X $\wedge$ c = $14°$, Y = b. $(-)2E = 50°$, r < v. For $\lambda = 578$: $n_X = 1.492, n_Y = 1.612, n_Z = 1.6235, n_Z - n_X = 0.1315$. For $\lambda = 546$: $n_X = 1.499, n_Y = 1.6155, n_Z = 1.630$. Color brown.

SrPd(CN)$_4$·5H$_2$O is monoclinic[61] with $a:b:c = 0.682:1:0.468$, $\beta = 97°18'$. Crystals show $\{110\}$, $\{001\}$, $\{111\}$. Good $\{001\}$ cleavage. G. 2.17. Soluble in H$_2$O, X $\wedge$ c = $+12.5°$, Y = b. $(-)2E = 66°$. For $\lambda = 578$:

---

[61] Brasseur and de Rossenfosse: *Mem. Acad. roy. Belg. Cl. Sci.* XVI, 1937.
[62] Nagy: *Chem. Abst.* XLV, p. 10521 (1951).

$n_X = 1.495$, $n_Y = 1.6025$, $n_Z = 1.612$, $n_Z - n_X = 0.117$. For $\lambda = 546$: $n_X = 1.499$, $n_Y = 1.607$, $n_Z = 1.618$. Colorless.

SrPt(CN)$_4$·5H$_2$O is monoclinic[61] with $a:b:c = 0.682:1:0.463$, $\beta = 95°7'$. Crystals {010} tablets often twinned on {100}. G. 2.70. Soluble in H$_2$O. Perfect {001} cleavage. X $\wedge$ $c = 19°$ (594), $21°$ (565), $25°$ (544), $32°$ (505), $45°$ (474), $59°$ (460). $(-)2E = 106°40'$. For $\lambda = 578$: $n_X = 1.547$, $n_Y = 1.613$, $n_Z = 1.637$, $n_Z - n_X = 0.090$. For $\lambda = 546$: $n_X = 1.557$, $n_Y = 1.619$, $n_Z = 1.641$. Positive for $\lambda = 436$. Colorless, with blue fluorescence.

BaNi(CN)$_4$·4H$_2$O is monoclinic[61] with $a:b:c = 0.872:1:0.494$, $\beta = 104°50'$. G. 2.383. Soluble in H$_2$O. X $\wedge$ $c = 8°$ (590), $14°$ (488). Y $= b$. $(-)2V = 4°40'$. For $\lambda = 646$: $n_X = 1.558$, $n_Y = 1.652$, $n_Z = 1.652$. For $\lambda = 591$: $n_X = 1.569$, $n_Y = 1.658$, $n_Z = 1.658$, $n_Z - n_X = 0.089$. For $\lambda = 486$: $n_X = 1.608$, $n_Y = 1.6715$, $n_Z = 1.6715$. Color orange-yellow.

BaPd(CN)$_4$·4H$_2$O is monoclinic[61] with $a:b:c = 0.871:1:0.483$, $\beta = 104°25'$. G. 2.574. Crystals {010} plates long parallel c with {110}, {011}. X $\wedge$ $c = 6°$ (644), $6.5°$ (590), $10°$ (474), $20°$ (426). Z $= b$. $(-)2V = 28°50'$. For $\lambda = 646$: $n_X = 1.570$, $n_Y = 1.642$, $n_Z = 1.647$. For $\lambda = 578$: $n_X = 1.583$, $n_Y = 1.646$, $n_Z = 1.651$, $n_Z - n_X = 0.068$. For $\lambda = 436$: $n_X = 1.651$, $n_Y = 1.668$, $n_Z = 1.674$.

BaPt(CN)$_4$·4H$_2$O is monoclinic[61] with $a:b:c = 0.869:1:0.479$, $\beta = 103°54'$. Crystals prismatic or {010} tablets. G. 3.01. Y $= b$, Z $\wedge$ $c +1°$. $(+)2V = 25°21'$ (646), $20°20'$ (541). For $\lambda = 646$: $n_X = 1.662$, $n_Y = 1.670$, $n_Z = 1.833$. For $\lambda = 578$: $n_X = 1.666$, $n_Y = 1.6745$, $n_Z = 1.919$, $n_Z - n_X = 0.253$. For $\lambda = 546$: $n_X = 1.672$, $n_Y = 1.6806$, $n_Z = 2.001$, $n_Z - n_X = 0.329$. Color clear green. Also may be yellow with Z darkest. Surface color on (110) blue or violet. Emerald green fluorescence on (001).

5. Halides, etc., of Trivalent Bases, Hydrated and Anhydrous. Formula Type AX$_3$·nH$_2$O

C$_2$Cl$_6$ is orthorhombic[63] with $a:b:c = 0.568:1:0.316$. Crystals {100} tablets without cleavage. G. 2.091. X $= c$, Y $= a$. $(+)2V = 38°$, r $<$ v. $n_X = 1.590$. $n_Y = 1.598$ calc., $n_Z = 1.668$, $n_Z - n_X = 0.078$. Clear and colorless. It inverts to a triclinic phase at 43°, and to an isometric phase (with G. 1.94) at 71°, melting at 185° C.

AlF$_3$·H$_2$O (Fluellite) is orthorhombic with $a = 11.40$, $b = 21.14$, $c = 8.52$ kX. Poor {010} and {111} cleavages. H. 3. G. 2.17. The optic plane[64] is {001}, X $= a$. $(+)2V =$ very large. $n_X = 1.473$, $n_Y = 1.490$, $n_Z = 1.511$, $n_Z - n_X = 0.038$. Again:[64] $n_X = 1.489$, $n_Y = 1.495$, $n_Z = 1.506$, $n_Z -$

[63] West: *Zeit. Krist.* LXXXVIII, p. 195 (1934).
[64] Larsen and Berman: *U. S. Geol. Surv. Bull.* 848 (1934).

$n_X = 0.017$. The variation in indices may be due to partial replacement of F by OH. Colorless. PD 6.60, 3.29, 2.66; 2–0121.

AlCl$_3$·6H$_2$O (Chloraluminite) is rhombohedral with $c/a = 0.534$. Deliquescent in air. Uniaxial negative[65] with $n_O = 1.560$, $n_E = 1.507$, $n_O - n_E = 0.053$. Colorless. Made from H$_2$O solution.[66] PD 3.30, 3.25, 2.31; 8–453.

AlBr$_3$·6H$_2$O is isomorphous[18] with AlCl$_3$·6H$_2$O. G. 2.27. Uniaxial negative with $n_O = 1.605$, $n_E = 1.555$, $n_O - n_E = 0.050$. PD 3.84, 3.59, 3.38; 1–0480.

AsI$_3$ is rhombohedral with $c/a = 2.998$. Crystals usually six-sided basal plates with perfect {0001} cleavage. Uniaxial negative with[9] $n_O = 2.59 \pm C$, $n_E = 2.23\pm$, $n_O - n_E = 0.36\pm$. Color deep red. PD 3.22, 3.58, 2.08; 7–272.

SbBr$_3$ is orthorhombic[67] with $a:b:c = 0.781:1:1.165$. Crystals {001} tablets with good {010} cleavage. G. 4.15. Very deliquescent. Index n very high, much above 1.74. Optically negative. $n_Z - n_X =$ very strong. Colorless with luster and dispersion like that of diamond. PD 5.20, 3.18, 2.98; 1–0235.

SbI$_3$ has three crystal phases; the low temperature trigonal crystals are often in six-sided basal plates. G. 4.85. Uniaxial negative[9] with $n_O = 2.78$ Li, $n_E = 2.36\pm$, $n_O - n_E = 0.42\pm$. Color deep ruby red. PD 3.30, 2.55, 2.16; 7–273.

GdCl$_3$·6H$_2$O is monoclinic[68] with $a:b:c = 1.473:1:1.219$, $\beta = 93°40'$. Crystals often {010} tablets with {110}, {011}, etc. Perfect {100} cleavage. Hygroscopic. G. 2.424. $Y = b$, $Z \wedge c = -50°$. $(-)2V = 75°\pm$, $n_X = 1.565$, $n_Y = 1.570$, $n_Z = 1.575$, $n_Z - n_X = 0.010$. One optic axis nearly normal to the cleavage. Colorless. PD 3.42, 2.41, 3.97; 3–0392.

SmCl$_3$·6H$_2$O is monoclinic[69] with $a = 8.00$, $b = 6.62$, $c = 9.60$, $\beta = 93°40'$. Crystals often {010} tablets with {110}, {011}, etc. Perfect {100} cleavage. Hygroscopic. G. 2.414. $Y = b$, $Z \wedge c = -33°$. An optic axis nearly normal to the cleavage. $(-)2V =$ large, $n_X = 1.564$, $n_Y = 1.569$, $n_Z = 1.573$, $n_Z - n_X = 0.009$. Colorless in thin flakes, but thicker crystals are greenish yellow with $X > Z$.

[65] Takahashi *et al.*: *Jour. Geol. Soc. Tokyo*, XXXV, p. 439 (1928).

[66] Mellor: V, pp. 314, 316 (1920).

[67] Slawson: *Am. Min.* VII, p. 173 (1922).

[68] Pabst: *Am. Jour. Sci.* XXII, p. 426 (1931).

[69] Iveronova, Tarasova, and Umanskii, *Izvest. Akad. Nauk S.S.S.R., Ser Fiz.*, XV, p. 164 (1951), quoted by Wyckoff, *Crystal Structures*, Ch. X, Table p. 33a (suppl.) Interscience, New York, 1948, . . . , 1960.

6. Halides, etc., of Tetravalent Bases. Formula Type AX_4

GeBr$_4$ is isometric[70] in octahedral crystals. G. 3.13. M.P. 26°. Isotropic with $n = 1.6269$.

SeCl$_4$ is isometric. Crystals cubic. G. 3.75–3.85. M.P. 305° C. Deliquescent. Isotropic with $n = 1.807$. Color whitish yellow.

SnI$_4$ is isometric. Crystals often octahedral. G. 4.70. Isotropic[9] with $n = 2.063 \pm$ Li, 2.106 $\pm$ Na, 2.161 $\pm$ Tl. Color red. PD 3.54, 2.17, 3.07; 6–0232.

ZrF$_4$ is monoclinic prismatic[71] with $a:b:c = 0.959:1:0.774$, $\beta = 94°30'$. Crystals show {100}, {110}, {011}, etc. G. 4.54. Indices are 1.57 and 1.60. Again[72] $(-)2V = ?$, $n_Y = 1.59$. (Apparently $n_X = 1.57$ and $n_Z = 1.60$.—A. N. W.)

HfF$_4$ is monoclinic[72] with $a:b:c = 0.967:1:0.774$, $\beta = 94°26'$. Crystals show {100}, {001}, {110}, {011}, etc. G. 7.13. Indices are 1.54 and 1.58 from a prism with faces {011} and {001}.

7. Anhydrous Halides, etc., of Monovalent and Divalent Bases. Formula Type $A_mB_nX_{m+2n}$

LiBeF$_3$ is orthorhombic (?)[73] in fibers with cleavage and extinction parallel length. Mean index $n = 1.33$ ca. PD 2.21, 2.08, 3.19; 9–344.

Li$_2$BeF$_4$ is orthorhombic[73] with $a = 10.08$, $b = 12.45$, $c = 4.92$ Å. Crystals basal plates. M.P. $> 375°$ C. Optically biaxial with Y $= c$ and mean index $n = 1.34$ ca.

LiNaB$_2$F$_6$ is monoclinic[73] with $a = 9.71$, $b = 8.89$, $c = 5.22$, $\beta = 105°$. Crystals acicular along c with cleavage parallel to c. M.P. 280° C. Y $= b$. $(+)2V = ?$; mean index $n = 1.33$ ca.

Na$_2$BeF$_4$ has several crystal phases.[73] The high temperature α-phase fuses at about 600° C. It is hexagonal with $a = 5.27$, $c = 6.96$ Å. G. 2.60. An α'-phase is orthorhombic with $a = 5.22$, $b = 9.40$, $c = 6.72$ Å. G. 2.64. On cooling it inverts to the β-phase at 290° C. and to the γ-phase at 190° C. The β-phase is monoclinic with $a = 5.5$, $b = 6.75$, $c = 9.3$ Å., $\beta = 95°$. U.C. 4. G. ≈ 2.65. The γ-phase is orthorhombic with $a = 4.89$, $b = 10.90$, $c = 6.56$ Å. G. 2.48. Another phase (called γ^2) is hexagonal with $a = 8.98$, $c = 4.93$ Å. M.P. $< 600°$ C. This may be a hydrate. All the phases have very weak birefringence. PD 2.93, 2.65, 2.44; 3–0660* [which polymorph?].

NaK$_3$FeCl$_6$ (Rinneite) is hexagonal-scalenohedral with $a = 11.86$, $c = 13.81$ kX. Crystals basal tablets or short prismatic. Good {11$\bar{2}$0}

[70] Dennis and Hance: *Chem. News*, CXXIV, p. 67 (1922).
[71] Hevesy and Dullenkopf: *Zeit. anorg. Chem.* CCXX, p. 161 (1935).
[72] Schulze: *Zeit. Krist.* LXXXIX, p. 477 (1934).
[73] Hahn: *N. Jahrb. Min. Abh. Bd.* LXXXVI, p. 1 (1953).

cleavage. H. 3. G. 2.35. Uniaxial positive[74] with $n_O = 1.5836$ Li, 1.5886 Na, 1.5930 Tl, $n_E = 1.5842$ Li, 1.5894 Na, 1.5939 Tl, $n_E - n_O = 0.0008$ Na. Colorless when pure, but often rose, violet, yellow or brown.

K_2MgF_4 is tetragonal[75] with $a = 3.977$, $c = 13.16$ Å. G. 2.71. Uniaxial negative with $n_O = 1.379$, $n_E = 1.377$, $n_O - n_E = 0.002$. PD 2.20, 6.61, 1.65; 6–0589.

$KCaCl_3$ (Chlorocalcite) is probably orthorhombic[76] and is pseudo-isometric. Cleavage cube-like, but with one direction better than the other two. H. 2.5–3. May show lamellar twinning parallel with "cubic" faces Optic plane normal to a "cubic" face. $(-)2V = ?$, $n_Y = 1.52$ ca., $n_Z - n_X$ = weak. Color white or stained violet.

K_4MnCl_6 (Chlormanganokalite) is hexagonal with $c/a = 0.5797$. Crystals rhombohedral. H. 2.5. G. 2.31. Uniaxial positive with mean index $n = 1.59$, $n_E - n_O$ = very weak. Color yellow. PD 2.55, 2.69, 5.90; 3–0856.

K_2PdCl_4 is tetragonal with $c/a = 0.410$. Crystals prismatic with {110} and {111}. Uniaxial negative with[18] $n_O = 1.715$, $n_E = 1.537$, $n_O - n_E = 0.178$. Again:[77] $n_O = 1.710$, $n_E = 1.523$, $n_O - n_E = 0.187$. Color brown; pleochroic with O > E strong.

K_4CdCl_6 is hexagonal with $c/a = 0.607$. Crystals rhombohedral with perfect rhombohedral cleavage. Twinning common. Uniaxial positive with $n_O = 1.5841$ B, 1.5906 D, 1.5965 E, 1.6208 H, $n_E = 1.5842$ B, 1.5907 D, 1.5966 E, 1.6210 H. $n_E - n_O = 0.0001$ D.

K_2PtCl_4 is tetragonal with $c/a = 0.416$. Crystals prismatic. G. 3.3. Uniaxial negative[78] with $n_O = 1.693$, $n_E = 1.548$, $n_O - n_E = 0.145$. Again:[18] $n_O = 1.690$, $n_E = 1.557$, $n_O - n_E = 0.133$. Also:[78a] $n_O = 1.683$, $n_E = 1.553$, $n_O - n_E = 0.130$. Bolland[79] found that "potassium platinum chloride" of unknown formula was uniaxial positive with $n_O = 1.64$, $n_E = 1.67$, $n_E - n_O = 0.03$ and had a dark red-brown color with flakes clear violet, O being brighter than E and slightly greenish. PD 6.94, 3.16, 3.55; 9–367.

$(NH_4)_2FeCl_4$ is isometric[80] and isotropic with $n = 1.6439$ D.

[74] Boeke: *N. Jahrb. Min.* II, p. 39 (1909).

[75] Brehler and Winkler: *Heidelb. Beit. Min. Pet.* p. 6 (1954). Also De Vries and Roy: *J. Am. Chem. Soc.* LXXV, p. 2479 (1953).

[76] Renner: *Centralb. Min.* 1912, p. 106; Zambonini: *Mineralogia Vesuviana*, p. 50 (1910), p. 99 (1935).

[77] Mellor and Quodling: *Proc. Roy. Soc. N. So. Wales* LXX, p. 205 (1936).

[78] Bokii and Burovaya: *Trudy Inst. Krist.* p. 47 (1947); [*Chem. Abst.* XLIV, p. 7704 (1950)].

[78a] Mellor and Quodling: *Proc. Roy. Soc. N. So. Wales* LXIX, p. 167 (1935).

[79] Bolland: *Sitz. Akad. Wiss. Wien* CXIX, p. 275 (1910).

[80] Landolt-Börnstein: *Tabellen*, 1924.

$(NH_4)_2ZnCl_4$ is orthorhombic with $a:b:c = 0.722:1:0.570$. Crystals {010} platelets. G. 1.88. Y = c. Z = a. $(+)2V = 53°48'$, r > v weak. $n_Y = 1.5055$ D. Colorless. Formed from H_2O solution with excess of NH_4Cl. Again:[42] $(+)2V = 33°$, $n_X = 1.585$, $n_Y = 1.590$, $n_Z = 1.600$, $n_Z - n_X = 0.015$. PD 5.20, 2.76, 3.12; 2–0155.

$(NH_4)_3ZnCl_5$ is orthorhombic with $a:b:c = 0.782:1:0.692$. Crystals columnar or {010} tablets or equant. G. 1.81. Y = c, Z = a. $(+)2V = 46°10'$, r > v weak. $n_Y = 1.538$. Colorless. Made from H_2O solution. PD 3.15, 5.8, 2.46; 2–0548.

$(NH_4)_3(UO_2)F_5$ is tetragonal with $c/a = 0.9\pm$. Crystals pyramidal; often with cruciform twinning. G. 4.26. Uniaxial negative(?)[80a] with $n_O = 1.495$, $n_E = 1.49$, $n_O - n_E = 0.005$.

$Cs_2(UO_2)Cl_4$ is triclinic[80a] with (010) $\wedge$ (110) = $49°7'$ and (010) $\wedge$ (011) = $40°31'$; crystals like gypsum, much twinned. $Z' \wedge c$ in (010) = $15°$. A prism parallel to c gives $n_1 = 1.695$, $n_2 = 1.625$ and a prism parallel to a gives $n_3 = 1.614$, $n_4 = 1.691$. Color yellow.

NH_4ZnF_3 is uniaxial positive[28] with $n_O = 1.47$, $n_E = 1.481$, $n_E - n_O = 0.011$. Decomposes below 150° C.

$(NH_4)_2PdCl_4$ forms dark green needles[81] with bronze iridescence. Uniaxial negative with $n_O = 1.736$, $n_E = 1.544$, $n_O - n_E = 0.192$. Again:[18] $n_O = 1.723$, $n_E = 1.553$, $n_O - n_E = 0.170$. PD 7.21, 3.67, 4.26; 7–201.

$(NH_4)_2PtCl_4$ is tetragonal[78] with $a/c = 0.60$. Uniaxial negative with $n_O = 1.706$, $n_E = 1.574$, $n_O - n_E = 0.132$.

Rb_2PdCl_4 is tetragonal. Crystals prismatic. Uniaxial negative[18] with $n_O = 1.715$, $n_E = 1.533$, $n_O - n_E = 0.182$. Color brown with O > E strong.

Cs_2CuCl_4 is orthorhombic with $a:b:c = 0.786:1:0.614$. Crystals short prisms with {110}, {111}, {120}, {010}, etc. No distinct cleavage. Y = a, Z = c. $(+)2V = 83°46'$ calc., $n_X = 1.625$, $n_Y = 1.648$, $n_Z = 1.678$, $n_Z - n_X = 0.053$, all ±0.002. Faintly pleochroic with X and Y clear yellow, Z orange.

Cs_2PdCl_4 is tetragonal.[18] Crystals prismatic. Uniaxial negative with $n_O = 1.720$, $n_E = 1.560$, $n_O - n_E = 0.160$. Color brown with O > E strong.

$CsHgCl_3$ is orthorhombic (and isometric?). Rhombic crystals have $a:b:c = 0.577:1:0.409$; extremely weak birefringence with mean index $n = 1.779$ Li, 1.791 Na. Isometric (?) crystals are octahedral with no

[80a] Optics by Bolland (*Sitz. Akad. Wiss. Wien* CXIX, p. 275, 1910) on "ammonium uranium fluoride" of unknown formula.

[81] Bokii and Lyashenko: *Trudy Inst. Krist.* p. 29 (1947); *Chem. Abst.* XLIV, p. 7703–4 (1950).

good cleavage, but are weakly birefringent with extinction parallel to the diagonals of the cube.

$K_2Zn(CN)_4$ is isometric[81a] in octahedrons. G. 1.673. n = 1.406 Li, 1.413 Na, 1.417 Tl. Colorless.

$K_2Cd(CN)_4$ is isometric[81a] and octahedral. G. 1.824. n = 1.415 Li, 1.4213 Na, 1.425 Tl.

$K_2Hg(CN)_4$ is isometric[81a] and octahedral. G. 2.438. Isotropic with n = 1.451 Li, 1.458 Na, 1.461 Tl.

$K_2Zn(CN)_4$ and $K_2Cd(CN)_4$ form mix-crystals[81a]; for 20.76 per cent $K_2Zn(CN)_4$ G. is 1.789 and n = 1.4191 Na at 25° C.; for 39.41 per cent $K_2Zn(CN)_4$ G. is 1.768 and n = 1.4175 Na; for 60.02 per cent $K_2Zn(CN)_4$ G. is 1.744 and n = 1.416; for 81.13 per cent $K_2Zn(CN)_4$ G. is 1.682 and n = 1.4141.

$K_2Zn(CN)_4$ and $K_2Hg(CN)_4$ form mix-crystals[81a] in which for 53.21 per cent $K_2Zn(CN)_4$ G. is 1.962 and n = 1.452 Na at 25° C.; for 65.42 per cent $K_2Zn(CN)_4$ G. is 1.883 and n = 1.447; for 76.08 per cent $K_2Zn(CN)_4$ G. is 1.801 and n = 1.443; for 88.36 per cent $K_2Zn(CN)_4$ G. is 1.738 and n = 1.436.

$K_2Cd(CN)_4$ and $K_2Hg(CN)_4$ form mix-crystals[81a] in which for 22.00 per cent $K_2Cd(CN)_4$ G. is 2.261 and n = 1.451 Na at 25° C.; for 39.40 per cent $K_2Cd(CN)_4$ G. is 2.151 and n = 1.441; for 61.29 per cent $K_2Cd(CN)_4$ G. is 2.005 and n = 1.435; for 82.10 per cent $K_2Cd(CN)_4$ G. is 1.927 and n = 1.428.

$KHg(CNS)_3$ is orthorhombic[81b] in acicular crystals with (011) $\wedge$ (0$\bar{1}$1) = 158°$\pm$. X = c, Y = a. (−)2V = 65° − 70°, r < v strong. n_X = 1.735, n_Y = 1.82, "n_Z = 1.84, est." (but the given $n_Z - n_X$ = 0.150 and the optic angle and sign indicate that n_Z should be close to 1.88).

$K_2Hg(CNS)_4$ is monoclinic[81a]; crystals varied in habit with 110 $\wedge$ 1$\bar{1}$0 = 80°$\pm$, β = 106°$\pm$. X $\wedge$ a = 22°, Y near c, Z = b. (−)2V = nearly 90°, r > v strong. n_X = 1.645, n_Y = 1.80 (est.) n_Z = 1.9+ (est.), $n_Z - n_X$ = 0.255(est.)

$Cs_3Ag_2Ba(CNS)_7$ is tetragonal with c/a = 0.906. Crystals short prismatic with {201}. Perfect basal cleavage. G. 3.03. Uniaxial negative with n_O = 1.7761, n_E = 1.6788, $n_O - n_E$ = 0.0973.

$Cs_3Cu_2Ba(CNS)_7$ is tetragonal with c/a = 0.918. Crystals short prismatic with {201} and {001}. Perfect basal cleavage. G. 2.92. Uniaxial negative with n_O = 1.8013 Na, n_E = 1.6882, $n_O - n_E$ = 0.1131.

$Cs_3Cu_2Sr(CNS)_7$ is tetragonal with c/a = 0.916. Crystals short pris-

[81a] Carozzi: *Gazz. Chim. Ital.*, LVI, p. 180 (1926); [*Tables Ann. Const. Phys.*, VII, No. 2, p. 1489, (1930)].

[81b] Mason and Forgeng: *Jour. Phys. Chem.* XXXV, p. 1123 (1931).

matic with $\{201\}$ and $\{001\}$. Perfect basal cleavage. G. 2.88. Uniaxial negative with $n_O = 1.8535$, $n_E = 1.6982$, $n_O - n_E = 0.1553$.

8. Hydrated Halides, etc., of Monovalent and Divalent Bases. Formula Type $A_m B_n X_{m+2n} \cdot p H_2 O$

KMgCl$_3 \cdot$6H$_2$O (Carnallite) is orthorhombic[82] with $a = 9.54$, $b = 16.02$, $c = 22.52$ kX. U.C. 12. Crystals six-sided pyramidal. No good cleavage. Lamellar twinning not rare. H. 2.5. G. 1.60. X $= c$, Y $= b$. $(+)2V = 70°$, r $<$ v. $n_X = 1.4665$, $n_Y = 1.4753$, $n_Z = 1.4937$, $n_Z - n_X = 0.0272$ Na. Colorless, white, or stained red or rarely yellow or blue. PD 3.30, 2.92, 4.65; 8–75.

KMgBr$_3 \cdot$6H$_2$O is orthorhombic pseudo-tetragonal with no cleavage; twinning on $\{110\}$. H. 2. Y $= c$, Z $= b$. $(+)2V = 87°$, $n_Y = 1.535$, $n_Z - n_X = $ very strong. Colorless. Mix-crystals with KMgCl$_3 \cdot$6H$_2$O (15 to 85 per cent) are tetragonal, uniaxial positive, $n_O = 1.52\pm$, $n_O - n_E = $ very weak, like leucite, increasing with increase of Cl.

K$_2$CuCl$_4 \cdot$2H$_2$O (Mitscherlichite) is tetragonal[83] with $a = 7.45$, $c = 7.88$ kX. U.C. 2. Crystals pyramidal or short prismatic. H. 2.5. G. 2.418. Uniaxial negative with[84] $n_O = 1.6485$ (578), 1.6636 (492), $n_E = 1.6133$ (578), 1.6235 (492), $n_O - n_E = 0.0352$ (578). Again: $n_O = 1.6365$ Na, $n_E = 1.6148$, $n_O - n_E = 0.0217$. Color greenish blue; pleochroic with O sky-blue, E grass-green, but colorless or nearly so in section. Also biaxial and probably orthorhombic with twinning on $\{110\}$ in four sectors in which the optic plane is parallel with the diagonal (in $\{001\}$) and 2H $= 25°$. PD 2.64, 5.4, 2.71; 1–1073.

K$_2$HgCl$_4 \cdot$H$_2$O is orthorhombic with $a:b:c = 0.707:1:0.766$. Crystals prismatic or $\{110\}$ tablets. X $= a$, Y $= c$. $(-)2V = 78°25'$, r $>$ v strong, $n_X = 1.648$ Na, $n_Y = 1.678$, $n_Z = 1.699$, $n_Z - n_X = 0.051$.

(NH$_4$)$_2$MnCl$_4 \cdot$2H$_2$O is pseudo-isometric[48] and uniaxial negative (or may be biaxial with 2V reaching 10°). Crystals dodecahedral in aspect. Distinct $\{100\}$ and $\{001\}$ cleavages. G. 1.91–1.92. $n_O = 1.644$ Na, $n_E = 1.607$, $n_O - n_E = 0.037$. Pink in mass. PD 2.78, 2.70, 1.88; 2–0844.

(NH$_4$)$_2$CoCl$_4 \cdot$2H$_2$O has[85] $n_X = 1.640$, $n_Y = ?$, $n_Z = 1.682$, $n_Z - n_X = 0.042$.

Cs$_2$MnCl$_4 \cdot$2H$_2$O is triclinic (?) in long plates formed of $\{001\}$ and $\{100\}$

[82] Busz: *N. Jahrb. Min. Festb.* p. 121 (1907).

[83] Hendricks and Dickinson: *J. Am. Chem. Soc.* XLVIII, p. 2149 (1927).

[84] Ehringhaus: *N. Jahrb. Min. Bl. Bd.* XLI, p. 342 (1917).

[85] Kurnakov, Luzhnaya, and Kuznetsov: *Bull. Acad. Sci. U.R.S.S., Ser. Chim.* 1937, p. 577.

at an angle of $84°33'$; good $\{001\}$ cleavage. Extinction[86] on plates at $45°$ to edge. $n'_X = 1.64$, $n_Y = ?$, $n'_Z = 1.65$, $n'_Z - n'_X = 0.01$.

$(NH_4)_2CuCl_4 \cdot 2H_2O$ is tetragonal with $c/a = 0.742$. Crystals pyramidal or pseudo-dodecahedral with $\{111\}$ and $\{100\}$. G. 2.01. Uniaxial negative[50] with $n_O = 1.671$, $n_E = 1.641$, $n_O - n_E = 0.030$. Blue; pleochroic with O very pale yellow green, E weak pure blue. PD 5.5, 2.68, 2.75; 1–0211. Also may be biaxial with 2H up to $16°$ and twinning on $\{110\}$.

$(NH_4)_2(UO_2)Cl_4 \cdot 2H_2O$ is triclinic[86a] with $a:b:c = 0.61:1:0.56$, $\alpha = 99°$, $\beta = 102°$, $\gamma = 89°$. Crystals $\{011\}$ or $\{010\}$ tablets. $n'_X = 1.566$–1.574, $n'_Y = 1.633$, $n'_Z = 1.637$, $(-)2V = $ small, $n'_Z - n'_X = 0.063$–0.071. Color yellow with X colorless, Y deep yellow.

$Li_2K_2Fe(CN)_6 \cdot 3H_2O$ is monoclinic with $a:b:c = 0.962:1:0.747$, $\beta = 96°8'$. Crystals $\{100\}$ tablets, long parallel to c. Twinning on $\{100\}$. $X \wedge c = -44°$, $Y = b$. $(+)2V = 66°31'$ Li, $65°56'$ Na, $65°22'$ Tl. $n_X = 1.5883$ Na, $n_Y = 1.6007$, $n_Z = 1.6316$, $n_Z - n_X = 0.0433$.

$LiKPt(CN)_4 \cdot 3H_2O$ is orthorhombic with $a:b:c = 0.715:1:0.444$. Crystals prismatic with no good cleavage. $Y = a$, $Z = c$. $(+)2V = 19°$, $r > v$ distinct. For 656 $m\mu$: $n_X = 1.6183$, $n_Y = 1.6217$, $n_Z = 2.0405$, $n_Z - n_X = 0.4217$. For 588 $m\mu$: $n_X = 1.6237$, $n_Y = 1.6278$, $n_Z = 2.2916$, $n_Z - n_X = 0.6679$. Color red; pleochroic with X and Y orange yellow, Z red.

$LiRbPt(CN)_4 \cdot 3H_2O$ is orthorhombic with $a:b:c = 0.715:1:0.448$. Crystals prismatic. $Y = a$, $Z = c$. $(+)2V = 12°40'$, $r > v$ distinct. For 656 $m\mu$: $n_X = 1.6153$, $n_Y = 1.6176$, $n_Z = 1.827$, $n_Z - n_X = 0.2117$. For 588 $m\mu$: $n_X = 1.6204$, $n_Y = 1.6233$, $n_Z = 1.9310$, $n_Z - n_X = 0.3106$. Color yellow; fluorescence green; pleochroic with X and Y light yellow, Z gold yellow.

$NaKPt(CN)_4 \cdot 3H_2O$ is monoclinic with[87] $a:b:c = 0.852:1:0.472$, $\beta = 95°8'$. Crystals prismatic. The optic plane is nearly normal to the edge of $\{011\}$. $(+)2V = $ very small. $n_X = 1.6088$ D, $n_Y = 1.61\pm$, $n_Z = 1.90\pm$, $n_Z - n_X = 0.29\pm$. Color orange.

$Na_4Fe(CN)_6 \cdot 10H_2O(?)$ is monoclinic with $a:b:c = 0.852:1:0.787$, $\beta = 97°34'$. Crystals prismatic with indistinct $\{110\}$ cleavage. G. 1.46. $Y = b$. $Z \wedge c = +74°$. $(+)2V = 81°25'$ Na; $r > v$ weak; $n_X = 1.5193$ Na, $n_Y = 1.528$ red, 1.5295 Na, 1.536 green, $n_Z = 1.5436$ Na, $n_Z - n_X = 0.0243$ Na. Color yellow with $Y > X > Z$. Formed from H_2O solution. PD 7.4, 2.04. 3.51: 1–0095.

[86] Optic data by Bolland (*Sitz. Akad. Wiss. Wien* CXIX) on "Cæsium manganese chloride" of unknown formula.

[86a] Nichols and Howes: *Carn. Inst. Publ.* 298, p. 218 (1919).

[87] Gaubert: *Bull. Soc. Franc. Min.* XL, p. 181 (1917). Bolland (*Sitz. Akad. Wiss. Wien* CXIX, p. 275, 1910) gives $n_Z = 1.95$, $n_Z - n_X = 0.335+$.

Na$_2$Pt(CN)$_4$·3H$_2$O is triclinic[88] with $a:b:c = 1.701:1:0.809$, $\alpha = 94°57'$, $\beta = 92°18'$, $\gamma = 89°1'$. Crystals prismatic, twinned on {100}. Perfect {001} and poor {110} cleavages. G. 2.633. For $\lambda = 578$: $(-)2V = 23°30'$, r > v strong. $n_X = 1.541$, $n_Y = 1.608$, $n_Z = 1.611$, $n_Z - n_X = 0.070$. For $\lambda = 546$: $n_X = 1.549$, $n_Y = 1.612$, $n_Z = 1.615$. For $\lambda = 436$: $n_X = 1.608$, $n_Y = 1.641$. $n_Z = 1.644$. X $\wedge$ $\perp$ {001} = 9°30'. X $\wedge$ $\perp$ {100} = 87° in (001) $\wedge$ (0$\bar{1}$0). Y $\wedge$ $\perp$ {001} = 93°, Y $\wedge$ $\perp$ {100} = 18°. Z $\wedge$ $\perp$ {001} = 99°, Z $\wedge$ $\perp$ {100} = 108°. Extinction from the trace of the optic plane in {001} is at 41° to (100) in (100) $\wedge$ (1$\bar{1}$0) in Na light; the same extinction angle is 26° greater in red than in blue light. Colorless.

K$_4$Fe(CN)$_6$·3H$_2$O is monoclinic with $a:b:c = 0.3936:1:0.3943$, $\beta = 90°2'$. Crystals prismatic; apparently pseudo-tetragonal about b; see Fig. 3-8. Twinning on {100} or {001}. Perfect {010} cleavage. G. 1.9. X $\wedge$ $c =$

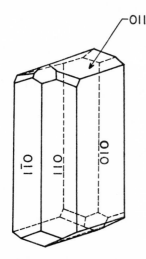

Fig. 3-8. Pseudotetragonal habit of potassium ferrocyanide.

$+31° 50'$, Z $= b$. $(-)2V = 78°10'$ Na, r > v = very weak. $n_Y = 1.5772$, $n_Z - n_X = ?$.[89] Color yellow. PD 2.92, 2.22, 2.09; 1–0923.

K$_2$Ni(CN)$_4$·3H$_2$O is triclinic[90] with $a:b:c = 1.700:1:0.832$, $\alpha = 95°28'$, $\beta = 92°27'$, $\gamma = 89°24'$. Crystals often twinned and pseudo-hexagonal. X $\wedge$ $\perp$ {110} = 72°, X $\wedge$ $\perp$ {010} = 79°, X $\wedge$ $\perp$ {001} = 13°. Y $\wedge$ $\perp$ {110} = 31°, Y $\wedge$ $\perp$ {010} = 58°, Y $\wedge$ $\perp$ {001} = 77°. $(-)2V = 21°$. For $\lambda = 578$ mμ: $n_X = 1.4657$, $n_Y = 1.5915$, $n_Z = 1.5955$, $n_Z - n_X = 0.1298$.

[88] Brasseur and de Rassenfosse: *Bull. Roy. Soc. Liege*, VIII, p. 24 (1939); *Chem. Zent.* 1939, II, p. 3941. See also Baumhauer: *Zeit. Krist.* XLIX, p. 113 (1911).
[89] Bolland: (*Sitz. Akad. Wiss. Wien* CXIX, 1910, p. 275) gives $n_Z - n_X = 0.005$.
[90] Brasseur and de Rassenfosse: *Zeit. Krist.* XCVII, p. 239 (1937).

For $\lambda = 546$ mμ: $n_X = 1.4707$, $n_Y = 1.5965$, $n_Z = 1.6005$, $n_Z - n_X = 0.1298$.

$K_4Ru(CN)_6 \cdot 3H_2O$ is monoclinic with $a:b:c = 0.394:1:0.395$, $\beta = 90°6'$. Crystals {010} plates with {110} and {011}, and perfect {010} cleavage. $X \wedge c = +32°10'$. $Z = b$. $(-)2V = 54°$, $n_Y = 1.5837$ Na. Colorless.

$K_4Os(CN)_6 \cdot 3H_2O$ is monoclinic with $a:b:c = 0.393:1:0.394$, $\beta = 90°6'$. Crystals {010} plates with perfect {010} cleavage. $X \wedge c = +30° 10'$, $Z = b$. $(-)2V = 47°$, $n_Y = 1.6071$. Colorless.

$K_2Pt(CN)_4 \cdot 3H_2O$ is orthorhombic with $a:b:c = 0.879:1:0.274$. Crystals short prismatic without cleavage. $Y = a$, $Z = c$. $(+)2E = 78°$ red, 40° blue. $n'_X = 1.615$,[91] $n_Y = ?$, $n_Z' = 1.62$, $n'_Z - n'_X = 0.005$. Colored and fluorescent. PD 8.0, 3.28, 4.00; 1–0084.

$(NH_4)_4Fe(CN)_6 \cdot 2NH_4Cl \cdot 3H_2O$ is trigonal with $c/a = 1.032$. Crystals rhombohedral with no distinct cleavage. G. 1.49. Uniaxial negative with $n_O = 1.6067$ Li, 1.6198 Na, 1.6241 Tl, $n_E = 1.5881$ Li, 1.5922 Na, 1.5964 Tl, $n_O - n_E = 0.0276$ Na. Color yellow.

$Rb_2Pt(CN)_4 \cdot 3H_2O(?)$ is monoclinic[92] with $a:b:c = 0.931:1:0.533$, $\beta = 99°48'$. Crystals {100} tablets or prismatic. $X = b$. Z nearly $= c$. $(+)2V =$ moderate, with distinct horizontal dispersion. $n'_X = 1.6072$ C, 1.6111 He yellow, $n_Y = 1.62\pm$, $n'_Z = 1.662$ C, 1.696 He yellow, $n'_Z - n'_X = 0.055$ C, 0.085 He yellow. Color pale green, weakly fluorescent in blue. Alters easily to colorless.

$Na_2Co(CNS)_4 \cdot 8H_2O$ **(Julienite)** is tetragonal[93] with $a = 19.00$, $c = 5.47$ Å. U.C. 4. Crystals acicular. G. 1.65. Uniaxial positive with $n_O = 1.556$, $n_E = 1.645$, $n_E - n_O = 0.089$. Color blue. Crystallizes from water solution. PD 3.55, 3.23, 1.38; 2–0372.

9. Anhydrous Halides, etc., of Monovalent and Trivalent Bases. Formula Type $A_mB_nX_{m+3n}$

Li_3FeF_6 is isometric[93a] and isotropic with $n = 1.42$. Soluble in HCl.

$Li_3Na_3Al_2F_{12}$ **(Cryolithionite)** is isometric with $a = 12.097$ kX. U.C. 8. Crystals dodecahedral; distinct {011} cleavage. H. 2.5–3. G. 2.77. M.P. 710° C. Isotropic with $n = 1.3395$ Na. Colorless to white. PD 1.96, 4.29, 2.21; 2–1282.

Na_3AlF_6 **(Cryolite)** is monoclinic with $a = 5.39$, $b = 5.59$, $c = 7.76$ kX,

[91] Indices measured by Bolland (*Sitz. Akad. Wiss. Wien* CXIX, p. 275, 1910) on "potassium platinum cyanide" of unknown formula.

[92] Baumhauer: *Zeit. Krist.* XLIX, p. 113 (1911). Bolland (*Sitz. Akad. Wiss. Wien* CXIX, p. 275, 1910) gives for "rubidium platinum cyanide": $n_X = 1.56$, $n_Y = 1.71$. $n_Z = 1.95+$.

[93] Preisinger: *Tsch. Min. Pet. Mitt. Ser. 3, Bd. 3*, p. 376 (1953); *Min. Abst.* XII, p. 337 (1954).

[93a] Nielsen: *Zeit. anorg. Chem.* CCXXIV, p. 84 (1935).

$\beta = 90°11'$. U.C. 2. Composition varies in synthetic material, toward $2.95NaF \cdot AlF_3$.[94] Crystals cubic in aspect. Twinning very common, often repeated. No cleavage, but $\{110\}$ and $\{001\}$ parting. H. 2.5. G. 2.97. M.P. 1020° C. Inverts to an isometric phase at about 560° C. Y = b,[95] Z $\wedge$ $c = 44°$. $(+)2V = 43°$, r $<$ v. $n_X = 1.3376$, $n_Y = 1.3377$, $n_Z = 1.3387$, $n_Z - n_X = 0.0011$. Again: X = b; $n_X = 1.3385$, $n_Y = 1.3388$, $n_Z = 1.3396$, $n_Z - n_X = 0.0011$. Colorless to white or stained brown, red or black. Colorless in section. PD 1.94, 2.76, 2.33; 8–73*.

$Na_5Al_3F_{14}$ **(Chiolite)** is tetragonal with $a = 7.005$, $c = 10.39$ kX. U.C. 2. Perfect $\{001\}$ and distinct $\{011\}$ cleavages. H. 3.5–4. G. 2.99. Uniaxial negative[96] with $n_O = 1.3486$, $n_E = 1.3424$, $n_O - n_E = 0.0062$. White or colorless. PD 2.91, 5.18, 2.32; 2–0749.

$NaBF_4$ **(Ferruccite)** is orthorhombic[97] with $a = 6.25$, $b = 6.77$, $c = 6.82$ kX. U.C. 4. Crystals basal tablets or equant. Good $\{100\}$, $\{010\}$ and $\{001\}$ cleavages. H. 3. G. 2.496. Y = b, Z = a. $(+)2V = 11°25'$, $n_X = 1.301$, $n_Y = 1.3012$ calc., $n_Z = 1.3068$, $n_Z - n_X = 0.0058$. Colorless to white. Taste bitter and acid.

KBF_4 **(Avogadrite)** is orthorhombic with $a:b:c = 1.5796:1:1.283$. Crystals basal tablets sometimes elongated parallel b or a. G. 2.505. X = c, Y = b. $(-)2V = $ large, n_X[98] $= 1.3231$ (677), 1.3239 Na, $n_Y = 1.3236$ (677), 1.3245 Na, $n_Z = 1.3247$ Na, $n_Z - n_X = 0.0008$ Na. Colorless. Another phase is isometric. PD 3.37, 2.89, 2.10; 2–0448*.

$CsBF_4$ is isotypic with KBF_4 with G. 3.305 and mean $n = 1.36$ Na. It forms mix-crystals with KBF_4 at least to about 19 per cent $CsBF_4$. PD 2.27, 3.35, 3.73; 9–394.

K_2LiAlF_6 is hexagonal[99] with $a = 5.574$, $c = 13.648$ Å. U.C. 3. Stable to 470° C. Basal and rhombohedral cleavages. G. 3.00. Uniaxial negative with $n_O = 1.391$, $n_E = 1.390$, $n_O - n_E = 0.001$. Inverts to isometric at 470°; then closely similar to K_2NaAlF_6.

K_2NaAlF_6 **(Elpasolite)** is isometric with $a = 8.093$ kX. U.C. 4. Crystals equant with $\{111\}$, $\{100\}$. No cleavage. H. 2.5. G. 3. Isotropic with $n = 1.376$. Colorless. PD 2.86, 2.02, 2.34; 8–70*.

$KAuBr_4$ is monoclinic[77] with $a:b:c = 0.797:1:0.361$, $\beta = 94°26'$. Crystals $\{010\}$ or $\{001\}$ tablets or prismatic; often twinned on $\{100\}$. X $\wedge$ c = $+13°$, Y = b. $(-)2V = $ very small, $n_X < 1.74 < n_Y < n_Z$, $n_Z - n_X = $ strong. Marked pleochroism; through $\{010\}$, carmine red and dark brown.

[94] Scott: *J. Counc. Sci. Ind. Res. Australia* XIX, p. 442 (1946) [*Min. Abst.* X, p. 257].
[95] Cesàro and Mélon: *Bull. Acad. Belg. Cl. Sc.* 362 (1936).
[96] Bøggild: *Zeit. Krist.* LI, p. 591 (1912).
[97] Carobbi: *Per. Mineral.* IV, p. 410 (1933).
[98] Zambonini: *Atti Accad. Lincei Rom.* (6), III, p. 644 (1926).
[99] Winkler: *Festschr. Mineral.* Bd. 31, p. 7 (1952).

$(NH_4)_2MnF_5$ is orthorhombic[100] with $a:b:c = 0.576:1:0.742$. G. 2.37. {010} cleavage. $X = c$, $Y = b$. $(-)2V = ?$, $n_X = 1.46$, $n_Y = ?$, $n_Z = 1.50$, $n_Z - n_X = 0.04$.

$(NH_4)_3ScF_6$ is tetragonal[100] with $c/a = 1.02$. G. 1.80. Uniaxial negative with $n_O < 1.47$, $n_O - n_E =$ weak.

$Cs_3Tl_2Cl_9$ is hexagonal with $c/a = 0.826$. Uniaxial negative with $n_O = 1.772$ Li, 1.784 Na, 1.792 Tl, $n_E = 1.762$ Li, 1.774 Na, 1.786 Tl, $n_O - n_E = 0.010$ Na.

$K_3Cr(CN)_6$ is monoclinic with $a:b:c = 1.287:1:0.805$, $\beta = 90°3'$. Crystals prismatic; lamellar twinning on {100}; {100} cleavage. G. 1.71. $Y = b$, $Z \wedge c = 0°\pm$. $(+)2V = 46°$, $r < v$, $n_X = 1.5176$ Li, 1.5221 Na, 1.5268 Tl, $n_Y = 1.5198$ Li, 1.5244 Na, 1.5292 Tl, $n_Z = 1.5324$ Li, 1.5373 Na, 1.5423 Tl, $n_Z - n_X = 0.0152$ Na. Color clear yellow.

$K_3Mn(CN)_6$ is monoclinic with $a:b:c = 1.289:1:0.801$, $\beta = 90°7'$. Crystals prismatic; twinning on {100}; {100} cleavage. $Y = b$, $Z \wedge c = 0°\pm$. $(+)2V = 43°$, $r < v$ marked, $n_X = 1.5527$ Li, $n_Y = 1.5547$, $n_Z = 1.5710$, $n_Z - n_X = 0.0183$. Weakly pleochroic with X brick red, Y scarlet, Z blood red.

$K_3Fe(CN)_6$ is monoclinic with $a:b:c = 1.288:1:0.801$, $\beta = 90°6'$. Crystals prismatic with {110}, {100}, {322}, {12$\bar{2}$}, {111} (see Fig. 3-9); often

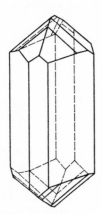

Fig. 3-9. A crystal habit of potassium ferricyanide. (After Groth.)

twinned on {100}. Perfect {100} cleavage. G. 1.85. $Y = b$, $Z \wedge c = +3°53'$. $(+)2V = 49°$, $r < v$ marked, $n_X = 1.5591$ B, 1.5660 D, $n_Y = 1.5615$ B, 1.5689 D, $n_Z = 1.5759$ B, 1.5831 D, $n_Z - n_X = 0.0171$ D. Pleochroic with X orange to clear red, Y hyacinth to cherry red, Z cherry red, and X < Z < Y. PD 4.14, 3.09, 2.94; 1-0423.

$K_3Rh(CN)_6$ is monoclinic with $a:b:c = 1.286:1:0.811$, $\beta = 90°29'$.

[100] Kasporava: *Tables Ann. Intern. Const.* V(1925).

Crystals prismatic, often twinned on $\{100\}$; also pyramidal. $Y = b$, $Z \wedge c = 0°\pm$. $(+)2V = 39°$, $r < v$; $n_X = 1.5498$ Na, $n_Y = 1.5513$, $n_Z = 1.5634$, $n_Z - n_X = 0.0136$. Colorless.

$K_2NaFe(CN)_6$ is monoclinic prismatic.[101] Crystals equant prismatic. No good cleavage. G. 1.85 ca. $Y = b$, $Z \wedge c = 40°$ ca. $(+)2V = 31°$, $n_X = 1.580 \pm 0.003$, $n_Y = 1.581 \pm 0.003$, $n_Z = 1.591 \pm 0.003$, $n_Z - n_X = 0.011$ ca. Color orange red, weakly pleochroic yellow to orange. Again:[102] $n_X = 1.5815 \pm 0.0005$, $n_Z = 1.590 \pm 0.001$.

$(NH_4)_2NaFe(CN)_6$ is monoclinic prismatic with β about 120°. Crystals equant or vertically long. G. 1.52–1.53. $Y = b$, $Z \wedge c = 20°$ in obtuse β. $(+)2V = 10°$, $n_X = 1.584 \pm 0.003$, $n_Y = 1.587 \pm 0.003$, $n_Z = 1.598 \pm 0.003$, $n_Z - n_X = 0.014$.

10. Hydrated Halides, etc., of Monovalent and Trivalent Bases. Formula Type $A_mB_nX_{m+3n} \cdot pH_2O$

$NaAuCl_4 \cdot 2H_2O$ is orthorhombic[103] with $a:b:c = 0.700:1:0.546$. Crystals six-sided prisms having $\{110\}$, $\{010\}$, $\{111\}$ and $\{021\}$. $(+)2V = ?$, $n_X = 1.545$, $n_Y = ?$, $n_Z = 1.75+$, $n_O - n_X = 0.205+$. Serves as a microchemical test for gold.

$KAuCl_4 \cdot 2H_2O$ is orthorhombic[79] with $a:b:c = 0.859:1:?$. Crystals basal tablets long parallel a, with $\{110\}$, $\{010\}$. $(+)2V = $ small, $n_X = 1.55$, $n_Y = 1.56$, $n_Z = 1.69$, $n_Z - n_X = 0.14$.

$KAuBr_4 \cdot 2H_2O$ is monoclinic with $a:b:c = 0.797:1:0.710$, $\beta = 94°24'$, Crystals vertically long with $\{100\}$, $\{010\}$, $\{110\}$, $\{111\}$. G. 4.1. $X \wedge c = -20°$. Apparently negative. $n_X = 1.67$, $n_Z - n_X = $ extreme.

$K_2FeCl_5 \cdot H_2O$ (Erythrosiderite) is orthorhombic with[104] $a = 9.924$. $b = 13.75$, $c = 6.93$ Å. U.C. 4. Perfect $\{120\}$ and $\{101\}$ cleavages. G. 2.37. $X = b$, $Y = c$. $(+)2V = 62°$, $r > v$ strong.[64] $n_X = 1.715$, $n_Y = 1.75$, $n_Z = 1.80$, $n_Z - n_X = 0.085$. Color ruby red to brownish red; in section weakly pleochroic.

$(NH_4)_2FeCl_5 \cdot H_2O$ (Kremersite) is orthorhombic with $a:b:c = 0.685:1:0.702$. Good $\{110\}$ and $\{011\}$ cleavages. Crystals pseudo-octahedral in aspect. G. 2.00. $Y = c$, $Z = b$. $(+)2V = 78°$ ca., $r < v$ strong.[48] $n_X = 1.750$, $n_Y = 1.775$, $n_Z = 1.814$, $n_Z - n_X = 0.064$. Color garnet-red. Pleochroic with X and Z pale yellow-green, Y deep red-orange. PD 5.70, 2.82, 4.95; 1–0187 (?).

$(NH_4)_3RhCl_6 \cdot H_2O$ is orthorhombic[78] with $a:b:c = 0.874:1:0.497$. Posi-

---

[101] Unpublished data from E. F. Williams, American Cyanamid Co.

[102] Unpublished data from D. W. Davis of the American Cyanamid Co.

[103] Optic data by Bolland (*Sitz. Akad. Wiss. Wien* CXIX, p. 275, 1910) on "sodium gold chloride" of unknown formula.

[104] *abc* changed to *bac* to make $b > a > c$.

tive elongation. $(-)2V = 70°$, $n_X = 1.740$, $n_Y = 1.750$, $n_Z = 1.756$, $n_Z - n_X = 0.016$. Color red.

$(NH_4)_3IrCl_6 \cdot H_2O$ is orthorhombic[81] with $a:b:c = 0.868:1:0.496$. Crystals prismatic with Z parallel length. $(-)2V = 66°$, $n_X = 1.706$, $n_Y = 1.714$, $n_Z = 1.718$, $n_Z - n_X = 0.012$.

$Na_3Fe(CN)_6 \cdot 2H_2O$ is deliquescent.[105] $(-)2V = 77°$ ca., $n_X = 1.531$, $n_Y = 1.549$, $n_Z = 1.560$, $n_Z - n_X = 0.029$. Color red.

11. Halides, etc., of Monovalent and Tetravalent Bases. Formula Type $A_mB_nX_{m+4n} \cdot pH_2O$

$Li_2SiF_6 \cdot 2H_2O$ is monoclinic.[38] G. 2.33. Only two indices reported: $n_1 = 1.296$, $n_2 = 1.300$, $n_2 - n_1 = 0.004$.

Na_2SiF_6 **(Malladrite)** is hexagonal with $c/a = 1.333$. Crystals basal plates with small pyramids. G. 2.75. Uniaxial negative with[106] $n_O = 1.3125$, $n_E = 1.3089$, $n_O - n_E = 0.0036$. Again:[106a] $n_O = 1.312$, $n_E = 1.309$, $n_O - n_E = 0.003$. Colorless. Basal sections of artificial crystals may show six biaxial sectors with the optic plane parallel to the prism faces and $Z = c$. Crystals serve as microchemical test for Na.

K_2SiF_6 **(Hieratite)** is isometric with $a = 8.168$ kX. U.C. 4. Crystals often octahedral. Perfect {111} cleavage. G. 2.665. Isotropic with[106] $n = 1.339$. Again:[106a] $n = 1.347$. May contain some Al which raises the index. Forms mix-crystals with $(NH_4)_2SiF_6$ and probably with Rb, Cs and Tl salts. It serves as a test for K. By evaporation of a solution at about 10° C. hexagonal crystals are formed which have $c/a = 1.60$. G. 3.08. Perfect basal cleavage and uniaxial negative character with weak birefringence. Colorless. PD 4.70, 2.35, 2.88; 7–217.

$(NH_4)_2SiF_6$ **(Cryptohalite)** is isometric with $a = 8.337$ kX. U.C. 4. Crystals often octahedral. Perfect {111} cleavage. G. 2.028. Isotropic[107] with $n = 1.3682$ C, 1.3696 D, 1.3723 F. Colorless. By evaporating a solution at about 5° C., hexagonal crystals form (which are called[108] **bararite** in nature); they have $a = 5.76$, $c = 4.77$ kX. U.C. 1. Crystals are basal tablets with perfect basal cleavage. G. 2.15. Uniaxial negative[107] with $n_O = 1.406$, $n_E = 1.391$, $n_O - n_E = 0.015$ Na. PD 4.84, 2.42, 2.10; 7–13.

Na_2GeF_6 is hexagonal with[106a] $a = 8.99$, $c = 5.12$ Å. Uniaxial negative with $n_O = 1.327$, $n_E = 1.324$, $n_O - n_E = 0.003$. It forms mix-crystals with Na_2SiF_6 in all proportions. With 28 per cent Na_2SiF_6 $n_O = 1.331$, $n_E =$

---

[105] Unpublished data from R. W. Stafford of the American Cyanamid Co.

[106] Raiteri: *Atti Accad. Linc. Rom.* XXXI, p. 112 (1922). Also *Zeit. anorg. Chem.* LXXXVII, p. 55 (1914).

[106a] Cipriani: *Rend. Soc. Min. Ital.* X, p. 253 (1954).

[107] Christie: *Rec. Geol. Surv. India* LIX, p. 233 (1926).

[108] Palache and Frondel: *Dana's System of Mineralogy*, Vol. 2, p. 106 (1951).

1.329, $n_O - n_E = 0.002$. With 48 per cent Na_2SiF_6 $n_O = 1.322$, $n_E = 1.320$, $n_O - n_E = 0.002$. With 67 per cent Na_2SiF_6 $n_O = 1.319$, $n_E = 1.317$, $n_O - n_E = 0.002$.

K_2GeF_6 is hexagonal with[106a] $a = 9.38$, $c = 5.77$ Å. Uniaxial negative with $n_O = 1.383$, $n_E = 1.381$, $n_O - n_E = 0.002$. PD 3.77, 2.16, 4.89; 7–241.

Na_2TiF_6 is hexagonal[108a] with $a = 9.20$, $c = 5.13$ Å. Seems to intercrystallize freely with Na_2GeF_6. Uniaxial negative with $n_O = 1.419$, $n_E = 1.412$, $n_O - n_E = 0.007$.

$(NH_4)_2GeF_6$ is hexagonal.[109] Crystals short prisms or basal plates. G. 2.564. Uniaxial negative with $n_O = 1.428$, $n_E = 1.425$, $n_O - n_E = 0.003$. PD 5.07, 3.49, 2.25; 7–240.

Cs_2GeCl_6 is isometric,[110] often octahedral, with G. 3.45 and $n = 1.68$.

K_2ZrF_6 is monoclinic[111] with $a:b:c = 0.573:1:0.597$, $\beta = 90°20'$. Crystals prismatic with $\{001\}$ cleavage. G. 3.58. Lamellar twinning on $\{100\}$ and $\{001\}$. Soluble in hot H_2O. $Y = b$, $Z \wedge c = 45°$. $(+)2V = 60°$, $n_X = 1.454$, $n_Y = 1.465$, $n_Z = 1.498$, $n_Z - n_X = 0.044$. Colorless.

K_3ZrF_7 is isometric;[111a] crystals octahedral. Isotropic with $n = 1.408$.

$(NH_4)_3ZrF_7$ is isometric.[111b] Crystals octahedral. Isotropic with $n = 1.433$ D. PD 5.44, 4.71, 3.33; 7–24.

K_2SnCl_6 is isometric; crystals octahedral with perfect $\{111\}$ cleavage. G. 2.69. Isotropic with $n = 1.6517$ C, 1.6574 D, 1.6717 F. Colorless.

$(NH_4)_2SnCl_6$ is isometric. Crystals octahedral. G. 2.40. Isotropic with $n = 1.690$ D. Colorless. PD 5.81, 5.03, 2.52; 7–198.

K_2HfF_6 is monoclinic and isomorphous with K_2ZrF_6. Minimum (measured) $n = 1.449$ (probably n_X); maximum 1.461 (probably n_Y). Colorless.

K_3HfF_7 is isometric.[111c] Crystals octahedral. Isotropic with $n = 1.403$.

$(NH_4)_3HfF_7$ is isometric. Octahedral. Isotropic with $n = 1.426$ D.

K_2PtCl_6 is isometric.[106] Crystals octahedral or cubic with good $\{111\}$ cleavage. G. 3.6–3.7. Isotropic with $n = 1.827$ (557 mμ). Color yellow.

$(NH_4)_2PtCl_6$ is isometric. Crystals octahedral with perfect $\{111\}$ cleavage. G. 3.0. Isotropic[112] with $n = 1.8$: again,[81] $n > 1.780$, deep yellow. PD 5.70, 4.93, 2.97; 7–218.

$NH_4CH_3PtCl_6$ is isometric and isotropic[112] with $n = 1.74$.

[108a] Cipriani: *Per. Miner.* XXIV, p. 361 (1956).

[109] Dennis, Staneslow and Forgeng: *J. Am. Chem. Soc.* LV, p. 4392 (1933).

[110] Laubengayer, Billings and Newkirk: *J. Am. Chem. Soc.* LXII, p. 546 (1940).

[111] Kerr-Lawson: *Univ. Toronto Studies, Geol. Ser.* XX, p. 63 (1925).

[111a] *Int. Crit. Tab.* I, p. 156 (1926).

[111b] *Ibid.* I, p. 114 (1926).

[111c] Böggild, in v. Hevesy: *Kgl. Danske Selsk. Math.fys.-Med.* VI, No. 7, p. 50 (1925).

[112] Moore and Gatewood: *J. Am. Chem. Soc.* XLV, p. 145 (1923), and Gatewood: *J. Am Chem. Soc.* XLV, p. 3059 (1923).

$Li_2Pt(CN)_6$ has[113] Z parallel to elongation with one index $n > 1.95$ and another $n = 1.59$.

$K_2Pt(CN)_6$ is rhombohedral with $c/a = 1.32$. Crystals have $\{0001\}$, $\{10\bar{1}1\}$, $\{2\bar{2}01\}$, etc. Uniaxial negative with $n_O = 1.861$ (668 mμ), 1.890 (588 mμ), $n_E = 1.781$ (668 mμ), 1.820 (588 mμ), $n_O - n_E = 0.070$ (588 mμ).

$K_2Pt(CNS)_6$ is rhombohedral[114] with $a = 6.733$, $c = 10.26$ kX. U.C. 1. G. 2.49. Uniaxial negative with $n_O = 1.861$ (668 mμ), 1.890 (588 mμ), $n_E = 1.781$(668 mμ), 1.820 (588 mμ), $n_O - n_E = 0.070$ (588 $m\mu$).

12. Halides, etc., of Monovalent and Pentavalent Bases. Formula Type $A_mB_nX_{m+5n}$

K_2TaF_7 is monoclinic with[115] $a:b:c = 0.6718:1:0.9198$, $\beta = 90°15'$; crystals acicular parallel to the vertical axis with $\{010\}$ and $\{110\}$ faces prominent. G. 4.06. $X = b$; $Z \wedge c = 32°$. $(-)2V = ?$, $n_X = 1.414$, $n_Y = ?$, $n_Z = 1.418$, $n_Z - n_X = 0.004$.

K_2NbF_7 is monoclinic with[115] $a:b:c = 0.6711:1:0.9209$, $\beta = 90°12'$; crystals acicular parallel to c and often flattened parallel to (010). G. 3.21. The optic plane and X are probably normal to $\{010\}$; $Z \wedge c = 34°$. $n_X = 1.437$, $n_Y = ?$, $n_Z = 1.440$, $n_Z - n_X = 0.003$.

13. Halides, etc., of Divalent and Trivalent (with or without Monovalent) Bases. Formula Type $A_mB_nX_{2m+3n} \cdot \pm pH_2O$ or $AB_mC_nX_{1+2m+3n} \cdot \pm pH_2O$

$Zn(BF_4)_2$ is probably uniaxial[116] with $n > 1.36$, $n_1 - n_2 = 0.011$.

$NaCaAlF_6 \cdot H_2O$ is dimorphous; one phase is pachnolite and the other is thomsenolite. **Pachnolite** is monoclinic with $a = 12.12$, $b = 10.39$, $c = 15.68$ kX, $\beta = 90°20'$. U.C. 16. Crystals prismatic. Poor basal cleavage. H. 3. G. 2.98. $X = b$,[64] $Z \wedge c = 69°$. $(+)2V = 76°$, r < v weak, with strong horizontal dispersion. $n_X = 1.411$, $n_Y = 1.413$, $n_Z = 1.420$, $n_Z - n_X = 0.009$. Colorless. PD 3.95, 1.97, 2.79; 5–0356. **Thomsenolite** is also monoclinic, but with $a = 5.57$, $b = 5.50$, $c = 16.10$ kX, $\beta = 96°27'$. U.C. 4. Crystals often prismatic. Perfect basal and distinct prismatic cleavages. H. 2. G. 2.98. $X \wedge c = -52°$, $Z = b$.[117] $(-)2V = 50°$, r < v weak.

[113] Bolland: *Sitz. Akad. Wiss. Wien* CXIX, p. 275 (1910).

[114] Hendricks and Merwin: *Am. Jour. Sci.* XV, p. 487 (1928).

[115] Goldschmidt in Hevesy: *Kgl. Danske Videns. Selsk. Math. fys. Med.* VI, No. 7, p. 56 (1925). Zambonini: *Soc. Min. Fr. Livre Jubilaire*, 1930, p. 443. Zambonini states that $Z = b$, but also states that $Z \wedge c = 32°$, for K_2TaF_7.

[116] Deverin: *Bull. Soc. Vaud* LVI, p. 545 (1928).

[117] Bøggild: *Zeit. Krist.* LI, p. 591 (1912).

$n_X = 1.4072$, $n_Y = 1.4136$, $n_Z = 1.4150$, $n_Z - n_X = 0.0078$. Colorless. PD 4.02, 1.96, 2.00; 5–0343. A substance which is probably either pachnolite or thomsenolite[118] has been made by reaction of powdered cryolite with $CaCl_2$ solution.

$Mg(BF_4)_2$ is hexagonal, rhombohedral.[116] Uniaxial with $n < 1.36$, $n_1 - n_2 = 0.014$.

$Ca(BF_4)_2$ is orthorhombic[116]. $(-)2V$ = very small. $n_Y < 1.36$, $n_Z - n_X = 0.002$.

$Mn(BF_4)_2$ is pseudo-trigonal.[116] Biaxial with 2V small. $n_Z = 1.359$, $n_Z - n_X = 0.013$.

$Co(BF_4)_2$ is almost uniaxial;[116] pink and weakly pleochroic with X > Z. $n = 1.40\pm$. $n_Z - n_X = 0.014$.

$Ni(BF_4)_2$ is pseudo-trigonal.[116] 2V very small. $n_X > 1.47$, $n_Y = 1.48\pm$, $n_Z < 1.50$.

$Sr(BF_4)_2$ is dimorphous.[116] One phase is isometric with $n < 1.44$. One phase is orthorhombic and biaxial.

$Cu(BF_4)_2 \cdot 6H_2O$ is monoclinic and closely related to $Cu(ClO_4)_2$. $6H_2O$. G. 2.175. $X \wedge c = 59°$, $Z = b$. $(-)2V$ = large, with marked crossed dispersion giving anomalous interference colors near extinction in (010) sections or plates. Mean index, $n = 1.50$ ca.

$Sr_3Fe_2F_{12} \cdot 2H_2O$ is orthorhombic[119] in tablets. G. 3.71. Soluble in hot water. X normal to tablets. $(-)2V = 55°$ calc. $n_X = 1.473$, $n_Y = 1.480$, $n_Z = 1.482$, $n_Z - n_X = 0.009$.

$BaFeF_5 \cdot H_2O$ is orthorhombic[119] in tablets. G. 3.94. Soluble in hot water. X normal to tablets. $(+)2V = 20°$ calc., $n_X = 1.502$, $n_Y = 1.503$, $n_Z = 1.513$, $n_Z - n_X = 0.011$.

$Y_2Pt_3(CN)_{12} \cdot 21H_2O$ is orthorhombic with $a:b:c = 0.892:1:0.616$. Crystals basal plates with perfect {001} cleavage. Twinning on {110}. $Y = b$,[92] $Z = c$. $(+)2V = 15°\pm$ Na, $n'x = 1.5899$ He red, 1.5907 C, $n_Y = ?$, $n_Z = 2.058$ He red, 2.055 C, $n_Z - n_X = 0.46$ C. Color deep red; pleochroic in violet and orange tints.

$Ce_2Pt_3(CN)_{12} \cdot 18H_2O$ is monoclinic with[120] $a:b:c = 0.581:1:0.553$, $\beta = 107°33'$. Crystals prismatic with no good cleavage. Twinning on {100}. G. 2.66. $(+)2V = 70°$ est. $n_X = 1.65$, $n_Y = 1.66$, $n_Z = 1.68$, $n_Z - n_X = 0.03$. Color pale yellow with bluish fluorescence.

---

[118] Lemberg: *Zeit. deutsche geol. Ges.* XXVIII, p. 620 (1876).

[119] Nielsen: *Zeit. anorg. Chem.* CCXXVI, p. 222 (1936).

[120] Optic data by Bolland (*Sitz. Akad. Wiss. Wien* CXIX, p. 275, 1910) on "cerium platinum cyanide" of unknown formula.

14. Halides, etc., of Divalent and Tetravalent Bases. Formula Type $A_mB_nX_{2m+4n} \cdot pH_2O$

$MgSiF_6 \cdot 6H_2O$ is trigonal[121] with $c/a = 0.517$. Crystals prismatic to rhombohedral with perfect $\{11\bar{2}0\}$ cleavage. G. 1.76. Uniaxial positive with $n_O = 1.3427$ C, 1.3439 D, 1.3473 F, $n_E = 1.3587$ C, 1.3602 D, 1.3634 F, $n_O - n_E = 0.0163$ D. Colorless. Crystals serve in a microchemical test for Mg. PD 4.79, 4.22, 2.64; 1–0284.

$MnSiF_6 \cdot 6H_2O$ is trigonal with[121] $c/a = 0.504$. Crystals prismatic with perfect $\{11\bar{2}0\}$ cleavage. G. 1.86. Uniaxial positive with $n_O = 1.3552$ C, 1.3570 D, 1.3605 F, $n_E = 1.3721$ C, 1.3742 D, 1.3774 F, $n_E - n_O = 0.0172$ D. Color pink. Made by reaction of HF on manganese silicates.

$FeSiF_6 \cdot 6H_2O$ is trigonal[121] with $c/a = 0.503$. Crystals like those of $MgSiF_6 \cdot 6H_2O$. Uniaxial positive with $n_O = 1.3619$ Li, 1.3638 Na, 1.3656 Tl, $n_E = 1.3828$ Li, 1.3848 Na, 1.3867 Tl, $n_E - n_O = 0.0210$ Na. Made by reaction of HF on iron silicates. Crystals serve as a microchemical test for Fe.

$NiSiF_6 \cdot 6H_2O$ is trigonal[121] with $c/a = 0.514$. Crystals long prismatic with perfect $\{11\bar{2}0\}$ cleavage. G. 2.13. Uniaxial positive with $n_O = 1.3876$ C, 1.3910 D, 1.3950 F, $n_E = 1.4036$ C, 1.4066 D, 1.4105 F, $n_E - n_O = 0.0156$ D. Color apple green. PD 4.65, 4.13, 2.57; 8–8. Made by reaction of HF on nickel silicates.

$CoSiF_6 \cdot 6H_2O$ is trigonal[121] with $c/a = 0.522$. Crystals prismatic to rhombohedral with distinct $\{11\bar{2}0\}$ cleavage. G. 2.09. Uniaxial positive with $n_O = 1.3817$ C, $n_E = 1.3872$, $n_E - n_O = 0.0055$. Color red.

$CuSiF_6 \cdot 6H_2O$ is trigonal[121] with $c/a = 0.540$. Crystals thick prismatic, unstable, with poor $\{11\bar{2}0\}$ cleavage. G. 2.21. Uniaxial negative with $n_O = 1.4074$ C, 1.4092 D, 1.4138 F, $n_E = 1.4062$ C, 1.4080 D, 1.4124 F, $n_O - n_E = 0.0012$ D. Color blue.

$ZnSiF_6 \cdot 6H_2O$ is trigonal[121] with $c/a = 0.517$. Crystals prismatic with perfect $\{11\bar{2}0\}$ cleavage. G. 2.14. Uniaxial positive with $n_O = 1.3808$ C, 1.3824 D, 1.3860 F, $n_E = 1.3938$ C, 1.3956 D, 1.3992 F, $n_E - n_O = 0.0132$ D. Colorless. PD 4.68, 4.16, 2.59; 8–42.

$MgSnCl_6 \cdot 6H_2O$ is trigonal with $c/a = 0.508$. Crystals rhombohedral with perfect $\{11\bar{2}0\}$ cleavage. G. 2.08. Uniaxial positive with $n_O = 1.5715$ C, 1.5885 D, $n_E = 1.583$ C, 1.597 D, $n_E - n_O = 0.0085$ D. Colorless.

---

[121] The studies of Böhm (*Zeit. anorg. Chem.* XLIII, 1905, p. 330) and of Edmister and Cooper (*J. Am. Chem. Soc.* XLII, 1920, p. 2419) make it probable that the supposed silicofluorides of Co, Ni, Mn and Cu are actually acid fluorides, containing no Si, of the type $RF_2 \cdot 5HF \cdot 6H_2O$. By inference the other silicofluorides are questioned.

15. Oxyhalides, etc., of Divalent Bases. Formula Type $mAO \cdot nAX_2 \cdot pH_2O$

Hg_3OCl_4 is isometric[122] in dodecahedrons or octahedrons. G. 6.39. Isotropic with $n = 2.001$ Na.

$Ca_2OCl_2 \cdot 3H_2O$ (?) is tetragonal[123] with $a = 12.04$, $c = 8.65$ Å. U.C. 8. Uniaxial positive with $n_O = 1.535$, $n_E = 1.63$, $n_E - n_O = 0.095$. Colorless.

$Ca_2OCl_2 \cdot 2H_2O$ is hexagonal[9] and prismatic. Uniaxial negative with $n_O = 1.638\pm$, $n_E = 1.634\pm$, $n_O - n_E = 0.004\pm$. Colorless.

$Ca_2OCl_2 \cdot H_2O$ is hexagonal in prisms and basal plates with basal cleavage. Uniaxial negative with[124] $n_O = 1.628$, $n_E = 1.623$, $n_O - n_E = 0.005$. Colorless.

$Ca_4O_3Cl_2 \cdot 15H_2O$ is orthorhombic with[124] $a:b:c = 0.804:1:?$. Crystals acicular along c and flattened on $\{100\}$ with $\{100\}$ and $\{010\}$ cleavages. $Y = b$; $Z = c$. $(-)2V = 44°6'$. $n_X = 1.481$ calc., $n_Y = 1.536 \pm 0.003$, $n_Z = 1.543 \pm 0.003$, $n_Z - n_X = 0.062$. Colorless. PD 4.08, 2.75, 2.61; 2–0280.

$Ca_5O_4Cl_2 \cdot 14H_2O(?)$ is orthorhombic[9] with perfect basal cleavage. $X = a$. $(-)2V = 45°$, $n_X = 1.517$, $n_Y = 1.532$, $n_Z = 1.537$. $n_Z - n_X = 0.020$. Colorless. Similar crystals probably containing CO_2 have $n_X = 1.478$, $n_Y = 1.544$, $n_Z = 1.558$, $n_Z - n_X = 0.080$. (Are these the $Ca_4O_3Cl_2 \cdot 15H_2O$ salt?—A.N.W.).

$Ca_4O_3Br_2 \cdot 15H_2O$ is orthorhombic.[124] Crystals acicular along c and flattened on $\{100\}$ with $\{100\}$ and $\{010\}$ cleavages. $Y = b$; $Z = c$. $(+)2V =$ large. $n_X = ?$, $n_Y = 1.555 \pm 0.002$, $n_Z - n_Y = 0.004$ at most. (These data require that $n_Z - n_X$ shall be very weak, 0.007 at most, in contrast with data for the preceding Cl_2 salt. A.N.W.).

$Ca_4O_3I_2 \cdot 15H_2O$ is orthorhombic.[124] Crystals acicular along c and flattened on $\{100\}$ with $\{100\}$ and $\{010\}$ cleavages. $Y = b$; $Z = c$. $(+)2V = ?$, $n_X = ?$, $n_Y = 1.575 \pm 0.002$, $n_Z = 1.595 \pm 0.002$.

$Ca_2OBr_2 \cdot 3H_2O$ is orthorhombic.[124] Crystals acicular along c and flattened on $\{100\}$ with $\{100\}$, $\{010\}$ and $\{001\}$ cleavages. $Y = b$; $Z = c$. $(+)2V = ?$, $n_X = ?$, $n_Y = 1.623$, $n_Z = 1.645$.

$Ca_4O_3(CNS) \cdot 12.5H_2O$ is orthorhombic.[124] Acicular along c and flattened on $\{100\}$ with $\{100\}$ and $\{010\}$ cleavages. $Y = b$. $X = c$ and $Z = a$ in sodium light and $X = a$ and $Z = c$ in lithium light. For Na: $(+)2V = 12°12'$, $n_X = 1.586 \pm 0.002$, $n_Y = 1.587 \pm 0.002$, $n_Z = 1.622$ calc., $n_Z - n_X = 0.036$. For Li: $(-)2V = 17°52'$, $n_X = 1.530$ calc., $n_Y = 1.5866 \pm 0.002$, $n_Z = 1.588$, $n_Z - n_X = 0.058$.

[122] Carozzi: *Gazz. Chim. Ital.* LVI, p. 175 (1926).
[123] Bunn: *Chemical Crystallography*, 1946, p. 283.
[124] Pehrman and Mylius: *Acta Acad. Math. Phys.* VIII, No. 9 (1935).

$Pb_3O_2Cl_2$ **(Mendipite)** is orthorhombic with $a = 9.50$, $b = 11.87$, $c = 5.87$ kX. Perfect {110} and good {100} and {010} cleavages. H. 2.5. G. 7.24. X = a;[12] Y = b. $(+)2V$ = nearly 90°, r < v strong. $n_X = 2.24$, $n_Y = 2.27$, $n_Z = 2.31$, $n_Z - n_X = 0.07$. Elongation +. Colorless or nearly so. PD 3.09, 3.04, 2.78; 8–111.

Hg_2OCl **(Terlinguaite)**[125] is monoclinic with $a = 11.63$, $b = 5.76$, $c = 9.28$ kX, $\beta = 105°\ 37'$. Crystals prismatic. Perfect {$\overline{1}01$} cleavage. H. 2.5. G. 8.725. Optic plane parallel[12] with b and inclined $-7°$ to c. $(-)2V = 20°$, r < v extreme. $n_X = 2.35$ Li, $n_Y = 2.64$, $n_Z = 2.66$, $n_Z - n_X = 0.31$. Color yellow, rarely brown. Slightly pleochroic in green and yellow. PD 3.26, 2.51, 2.81; 2–0481.

16. Oxyhalides of Trivalent Bases. Formula Type AOX

$BiOCl$ **(Bismoclite)** is tetragonal with[126] $a = 3.89$, $c = 7.37$ kX. Crystals basal plates with perfect basal cleavage. H. 2–2.5. G. 7.717. Uniaxial negative with $n_O = 2.15$, $n_E = ?$, $n_O - n_E$ = strong. Color pale cream, grayish, yellowish, brown. Made by slow hydrolysis of $BiCl_3$ in HCl. PD 3.44, 2.68, 2.75; 6–0249.

$BiO(OH,Cl)$ **(Daubréeite)** is tetragonal. BiOCl and BiOOH intercrystallize in all proportions; with Cl > OH it is called bismoclite and with OH > Cl it is daubréeite.[127] With[126] OH $\approx$ Cl: $a = 3.85$, $c = 7.40$ kX. Perfect basal cleavage. H. 2–2.5. G. 7.56 calc. Uniaxial negative (probably with very little Cl). $n_O = 1.91 \pm 0.01$ and $n_O - n_E = 0.01$ $ca.$ Color pale cream, grayish or yellowish brown. Made by precipitation of $BiCl_3$ solution with ammonia.

17. Oxyhalides, etc., of Tetravalent Bases. Formula Type $AOX_2 \cdot nH_2O$

$HfOCl_2 \cdot 8H_2O$ is uniaxial negative with[128] $n_O = 1.557$, $n_E = 1.543$, $n_O - n_E = 0.014$.

$ZrOCl_2 \cdot 8H_2O$ is tetragonal with [129] $c/a = 0.318$. Crystals prismatic with {100} cleavage. Soluble in HCl. Uniaxial positive with $n_O = 1.552$, $n_E = 1.563$, $n_E - n_O = 0.011$. PD 12.8, 3.60, 6.9; 1–0024.

---

[125] Terlinguaite has one divalent and one monovalent Hg.

[126] Bannister: *Min. Mag.* XXIV, p. 49 (1935).

[127] Palache, Berman and Frondel: *Dana's System of Mineralogy*, 7th Ed. Vol. II, p. 60, 1951.

[128] *Int. Crit. Tables*, I, p. 140 (1926).

[129] *Ibid.*, p. 114.

18. Oxyhalides, etc., of Divalent and Trivalent Bases. Formula Type ABO_2X or $A_4B_2O_6X_2 \cdot nH_2O$

$PbSbO_2Cl$ (Nadorite) is orthorhombic[130] with $a = 5.59$, $b = 12.20$, $c = 5.43$ Å, U.C. 4. Crystals {100} tablets elongated along b with perfect {100} cleavage. Twinning on {011} at 91°45'. H. 4. G. 7.02. F. 1.5. Soluble in HCl. X = b; Y = c. (+)2V = very large, r > v strong. $n_X = 2.30$ Li, $n_Y = 2.35$, $n_Z = 2.40$, $n_Z - n_X = 0.10$. Color smoky brown to brownish yellow. Made by fritting.[131]

19. Halides, etc., with Ammonia or Amine

$Pd(NH_3)_4Cl_2 \cdot H_2O$ is tetragonal.[81] Uniaxial negative with $n_O = 1.620$, $n_E = 1.557$, $n_O - n_E = 0.063$. Again:[77] $n_O = 1.619$, $n_E = 1.559$. Color pale yellow.

$[Pt(NH_3)_5Cl]Cl_3 \cdot H_2O$ is hexagonal with $a = 20.50$, $c = 6.64$ Å. Uniaxial positive[81] with $n_O > 1.718$, $n_E < 1.722$, $n_E - n_O < 0.004$.

$Co(NH_3)_6 \cdot Fe(CN)_6$ is trigonal.[132] Crystals prismatic. Uniaxial positive with $n_O = 1.662$, $n_E = 1.695$, $n_E - n_O = 0.033$.

$IrCl_3(NH_3)_4 \cdot H_2O$ is trigonal with $c/a = 0.645$. Crystals prismatic. Uniaxial positive with $n_O = 1.6576$, $n_E = 1.6666$, $n_E - n_O = 0.009$.

$Rh[(NH_3)_5Cl]Cl_2$ is orthorhombic and pseudo-tetragonal with $a:b:c = 0.784:1:0.0505$. Crystals {101} domatic with {120}. Fair {120} and {010} cleavages. G. 2.08. Y = c; Z = b. An optic axis visible through {120}. (+)2V = very large, r < v distinct. $n_X = 1.700$, $n_Y = 1.703$, $n_Z = 1.707$, $n_Z - n_X = 0.007$.

$Zn(NH_3)_2Cl_2$ is orthorhombic[133] with $a:b:c = 0.916:1:0.951$. Crystals {110} twinned plates or pseudo-tetragonal forms like pyramids on the b axis. Perfect {011} and {010} cleavages. H. 1. G. 1.95. Soluble in water. Y = b; Z = c. (−)2V = large (86° in glycerine). $n_Y = 1.618$ ca. Colorless. Formed in an electric battery. PD 5.80, 3.88, 2.92; 1–0165.

$Zn(NH_3)_6Cl_2$ is hexagonal[133] prismatic with perfect basal cleavage. H. 1. Soluble in water. Uniaxial negative with $n_O = 1.539$, $n_E = 1.530\pm$, $n_O - n_E = 0.009\pm$. Colorless. Formed in an electric battery.

$Pt(NH_3)_2O_2(OH)_2Cl_2$ forms pale yellow crystals[81] with (−)2V = 75°, $n_X = 1.690$, $n_Y = 1.730$, $n_Z = 1.756$, $n_Z - n_X = 0.066$.

$KPtCl_3 \cdot NH_3 \cdot H_2O$ is orthorhombic[104] with $a:b:c = 0.793:1:0.754$. Crystals prismatic with {011}; no good cleavage. X = c; Y = b. (−)2V = 64° ca. $n_X = 1.5438$, $n_Y = 1.5754$, $n_Z = 1.588\pm$, $n_Z - n_X = 0.044\pm$. Color

[130] Sillén and Melander: *Zeit. Krist.* CIII, p. 420 (1941).
[131] Bolfa, Pastant and Roubault: *C. R. Acad. Sci. Paris*, CCXXVIII, p. 1739 (1949)
[132] Steinmetz: *Zeit. Krist.* LVII, p. 242 (1922).
[133] Chudoba: *Cent. Min.* 1929 A, p. 139.

reddish yellow with X yellowish red, Y reddish yellow, Z yellow or red.

NH₃BF₃ is orthorhombic.[134] Crystals often have {110} and {001}. G. 1.864. M. P. 163° C. X = b; Y = a. 2V = 90° ± 3°, n_X = 1.335, n_Y = 1.34–1.35, n_Z = 1.36, $n_Z - n_X$ = 0.025. X = b, Y = a.

Co(NH₃)₆Cl₃ is monoclinic with $a:b:c$ = 0.988:1:0.650, β = 91°19′. Crystals {010} plates or equant with {210}, {010}, {10$\bar{1}$}, etc. No good cleavage. G. 1.704. The optic plane is normal to {010}; the acute bisectrix is nearly normal to {10$\bar{1}$}. Mean index n = 1.706, $n_Z - n_X$ = weak. Color brownish red, pleochroic. PD 3.60, 5.8, 2.48; 1–0522.

Pd(NH₃)₂Cl₂ (Trans-) forms dendrites[78] with n_1 = 1.718, $n_2 > 1.817$.

Pt(NH₃)₂Cl₂ (Trans-) is monoclinic. Crystals acicular or apparently rhombohedral.[81] X ∧ needle length = 19°. Z is in long diagonal of rhomb. n_X = 1.706, n_Y = 1.778, $n_Z > 1.790$, $n_Z - n_X > 0.084$. Color yellow.

Pt(NH₃)₂Cl₂ (Cis-) forms needles[81] with an extinction angle of 30°. (−)2V = 70°, n_X = 1.745, n_Y = 1.790, n_Z = 1.812, $n_Z - n_X$ = 0.067. Color yellow.

PtCONH₃Cl₂ (Cis-) is biaxial[81] with (+)2V = 74°, n_X = 1.722, n_Y = 1.745, n_Z = 1.790, $n_Z - n_X$ = 0.068. Color green-brown.

20. Compound (and also Acid) Halides, etc.

AsI₃·3S₈ is hexagonal with[135] c/a = 0.366. It has ditrigonal pyramidal symmetry. Uniaxial negative with n_O = 2.2756, n_E = 1.8501, $n_O - n_E$ = 0.4255 for λ = 650 and n_O = 2.3036, n_E = 1.8636, $n_O - n_E$ = 0.440 for λ = 589.

NiF₂·5HF·6H₂O is trigonal[14] with c/a = 2.01. Crystals flattened prisms with prismatic cleavage. Uniaxial positive with n_O = 1.390 C, 1.392 D, 1.395 F, n_E = 1.406 C, 1.408 D, 1.410 F, $n_E - n_O$ = 0.016. Color blue-green.

CoF₂·5HF·6H₂O is trigonal[14] with c/a = 1.04. Crystals flattened prisms with prismatic cleavage. G. 2.04. Uniaxial positive with n_O = 1.382 C, 1.384 D, 1.390 G′, n_E = 1.397 C, 1.399 D, 1.406 G′, $n_E - n_O$ = 0.015 D. Color orange-red.

Pt(NH₃)₅(SO₄)Cl₂ forms[78] crystals with symmetrical extinction and common twinning. n_1 = 1.673, n_2 = 1.710.

(NH₂OH)₂·H₂GeF₆·2H₂O is monoclinic[109] with β about 100°. Crystals equant with {110}, {100}, and {011}. G. 2.492. X ∧ a = 80°; Y = b. (−)2V = 60° ca., r > v fairly strong. n_X = 1.418, n_Y = 1.438, n_Z = 1.443, $n_Z - n_X$ = 0.025 Na.

(N₂H₄)₂·H₂GeF₆ is monoclinic[109] with β about 100°. Crystals prismatic with {100}, {001}. G. 2.406. Y = b. Extinction on (110) at 30°. (−)2V =

---

[134] Laubengayer and Condike: *J. Am. Chem. Soc.* LXX, p. 2274 (1948).
[135] West: *Zeit. Krist.* XCVI, p. 459 (1937).

near 90°. $n_X = 1.452$, $n_Y = 1.460$, $n_Z = 1.464$, $n_Z - n_X = 0.012$. (Indices and 2V are inconsistent. A.N.W.).

CuF$_2$·5HF·6H$_2$O is monoclinic[14] with three cleavages. G. 2.41. Loses water easily. Extinction parallel to one cleavage and much inclined to another. Negative elongation. $(-)2V = 32°$, $n_X = 1.395$, $n_Y = 1.440$, $n_Z = 1.444$, $n_Z - n_X = 0.049$. Color greenish blue with X < Y = Z.

IV. Oxides

Oxides are classed as simple,[1] multiple and compound. Hydroxides are considered separately. The arrangement in order of decreasing A to X ratio may be outlined as follows:

A. SIMPLE OXIDES

α. ANHYDROUS

1. Formula Type A_2X

Li_2O is isometric with the CaF_2 space lattice. Distinct $\{111\}$ cleavage. G. 2.01. M.P. above 1625° C., but it sublimes below 1000° C. and oxidizes

---

[1] Oxides are considred to be "simple" if they contain only one metal or two (or more) metals whose ions are near enough in size to occupy equivalent positions in the crystal structure. Compound oxides contain one (or more) anions besides oxygen (and hydroxyl).

to Li_2O_2 at lower temperatures. Soluble in water. Isotropic[1a] with $n = 1.644$; also anisotropic (from strain?). Colorless or stained yellow by Li_2O_2.

Cu_2O **(Cuprite)** is isometric with the CaF_2 space lattice. Poor octahedral cleavage. H. 3.5–4. G. 5.975. M.P. 1235° C. Isotropic with $n = 2.534$ B, 2.558 C, 2.705 D, 2.963 F. Color bright red. Made by heating copper in air. PD 2.47, 2.14, 1.51; 5–0667.

H_2O **(Ice)** is hexagonal with $a = 7.82$, $c = 7.36$ kX. U.C. 12. Complete crystals rare; skeleton crystals (snow) very common in cold winters, often as basal tablets, hexagonal stars, dendrites, etc. H. 1.5, increasing to 4 at $-44°$ C. and to about[2] 6 at $-78.5°$ C. G. 0.918. Melts at 0° C. to water which has G. 1. and $n = 1.333$ and vaporizes (to steam) at 100° C. Ice is uniaxial positive with[3] $n_O = 1.3071$ C, 1.3091 D, 1.3133 F, $n_E = 1.3086$ C, 1.3104 D, 1.3147 F, $n_E - n_O = 0.0014$ F. (data for $-3°$ C.). Under varying high pressures six other crystal phases of H_2O are known; one is isometric ($a = 6.36$; stable at 100° C.), one tetragonal, and a third orthorhombic. Optic data are lacking. Colorless (to pale blue in mass).

2. Formula Type AX

MgO (Periclase) is isometric with the NaCl space lattice. $a = 4.203$ kX. U.C. 4. Crystals cubic or octahedral with perfect cubic and poor octahedral cleavages. H. 5.5. G. 3.56. M.P. 2800° C. Isotropic with[4] $n = 1.7335$ C, 1.7366 D, 1.7475 F. Colorless, made from fusion. It forms a complete series of mix-crystals with FeO, NiO or CoO; with 25 per cent FeO the color is yellow; with 50 per cent it is brown. PD 2.11, 1.49, 1.22; 4–0829.

CaO (Lime) is isometric with the NaCl space lattice. $a = 4.797$ kX. Crystals cubic with perfect cubic cleavage. H. 3.5. G. 3.32. M.P. 2570° C. Soluble in acid. Hydrates easily. Isotropic[5] with $n = 1.833$ C, 1.837 D, 1.846 (530). Reversible inversion at about 420° C., both phases being isotropic. Colorless. PD 2.41, 1.70, 2.78; 4–0777.

MnO (Manganosite) is isometric with $a = 4.436$ kX. U.C. 4. Crystals often octahedral with fair cubic cleavage. H. 5.5. G. 5.36. Isotropic with[6] $n = 2.16$ (red), 2.19 (green). Again:[7] $n = 2.23$. Color emerald green on fresh fracture, becoming black on exposure. Streak brown. Made from fusion. PD 2.99, 3.69, 2.41; 7–58.

FeO (Wüstite) is isometric with the NaCl space lattice. $a = 4.29$ kX.

[1a] Jaeger and van Klooster: *Proc. K. Akad. Wet. Amsterdam*, XVI, p. 857 (1914).

[2] Blackwelder: *Am. J. Sci.* CCXXXVIII, p. 61 (1940).

[3] Ehringhaus: *N. Jahrb. Min. Bl. Bd.* XLI, p. 364 (1917).

[4] Haase: *Zeit. Krist.* LXV, p. 509 (1927).

[5] Ferguson and Merwin: *Am. J. Sci.* CXCVIII, p. 81 (1919).

[6] Ford: *Am. J. Sci.* XXXVIII, p. 502 (1914).

[7] Lapin: *Trav. Inst. Petrog. Acad. Sci. U.R.S.S.*, 1938, No. 13, p. 225 [*Min. Abst.* VII, p. 285].

U.C. 4. G. 5.5. M.P. 1370° C. Isotropic with[8] $n = 2.32$. Color black, nearly opaque. Forms a complete series of mix-crystals with MgO, having rectilinear variation of the refractive index. Thus, with MgO:FeO = 33:67, $n = 2.12$ and with MgO:FeO = 64:36, $n = 1.95$, and in general, $n = 1.737 + 0.583x$ where x = atomic proportion Fe/(Mg + Fe). PD 2.15, 2.49, 1.52; 6–0615.

NiO (Bunsenite) is isometric with the NaCl space lattice. $a = 4.171\ kX$. U.C. 4. Crystals often octahedral. H. 3.5. G. 6.8. F. 7. Isotropic with[9] $n = 2.27$ Li. Color deep green or brownish black. Found in slags. PD 2.09, 2.41, 1.48; 4–0835.

SrO is isometric with the NaCl space lattice. $a = 5.144\ kX$. Crystals cubic with perfect cubic cleavage. G. 4.75. Isotropic with[10] $n = 1.856$ C, 1.870 D, 1.880 (535). Colorless. Forms mix-crystals with CaO. PD 2.58, 2.98, 1.83; 6–0520.

CdO is isometric with the NaCl space lattice. $a = 4.689\ kX$. U.C. 4. Crystals octahedral or cubic with {111} (?) cleavage. H. 3. G. 8.15. Isotropic with[9] $n = 2.49$ Li. Color brown or red to black. PD 2.71, 2.35, 1.66; 5–0640. Found in the muffles of zinc ovens.

BaO is isometric with the NaCl space lattice. Crystals cubic with perfect cubic cleavage. $a = 5.523\ kX$. G. 5.72. Isotropic with[10] $n = 1.958$ C, 1.980 Na, 2.002 (520). Again:[10a] $n = 2.16 \pm 0.05$. Colorless. PD 3.20, 2.75, 1.95; 1–0746.

BeO (Bromellite) is hexagonal[11] with $a = 2.68$, $c = 4.36\ kX$. U.C. 2. Crystals prismatic with distinct {10$\bar{1}$0} cleavage. H. 9. G. 3.02. Uniaxial positive with $n_O = 1.719$, $n_E = 1.733$, $n_E - n_O = 0.014$. Color white. PD 2.36, 2.34, 2.19; 4–0843. Made by sublimation.

ZnO (Zincite) is hexagonal with $a = 3.242$, $c = 5.176\ kX$. U.C. 2. Perfect {10$\bar{1}$0} cleavage; basal parting. H. 4. G. 5.66. M.P. 1670° C. Soluble in HCl. Uniaxial positive with[12] $n_O = 1.990$ Li, 2.013 Na, 2.056 (530); $n_E = 2.005$ Li, 2.029 Na, 2.056 (530); $n_E - n_O = 0.016$ Na (natural zincite, 99.63% ZnO). Colorless to deep red. Not pleochroic. Commonly fluorescent in ultraviolet light. A common furnace product. PD 2.48, 2.82, 2.60; 5–0664.

HgO (Montroydite) is orthorhombic with $a = 3.513$, $b = 5.504$, $c = 3.296\ kX$. Crystals long prismatic or equant or varied. Perfect {010}

---

[8] Bowen and Schairer: *Am. J. Sci.* XXIX, p. 151 (1935).

[9] H. E. Merwin: *Pers. Comm.*, Mar. 25, 1931.

[10] Spangenberg: *Naturwiss.*, XV, p. 266 (1927).

[10a] Eskola: *Am. J. Sci.* IV, p. 331 (1922).

[11] Aminoff: *Zeit. Krist.* LXII, p. 113 (1925).

[12] Merwin: *Am. Soc. Testing Materials* XVII, pt. 2, p. 494 (1917); also Berman: *Am. Min.* XII, p. 168 (1927).

cleavage. H. 2.5. G. 11.2. X = a (?), Z = c. (+)2V = large.[13] n_X = 2.37 ± 0.02, n_Y = 2.5, n_Z = 2.65 ± 0.02, $n_Z - n_X$ = 0.28 ± 0.04 Li. Color deep red; streak yellow-brown; in section orange-red to pale yellow. Made by heating mercury in air. PD 2.87, 2.83, 2.41; 9–381.

PbO (Litharge) is tetragonal with a = 3.986, c = 5.011 kX. U.C. 2. Crystals basal tablets with perfect {110} cleavage. H. 2. G. 9.13. F. 1.5. Soluble in HNO_3. Uniaxial negative with[14] n_O = 2.665, n_E = 2.535, $n_O - n_E$ = 0.13 Li. Color red; light orange red in section. PD 3.12, 2.81, 1.87; 5–0561. Artificial "red lead" is commonly a mixture of litharge and massicot.

PbO (Massicot) is orthorhombic with[15] a = 5.476, b = 5.876, c = 4.743 kX. U.C. 4. Perfect {100} cleavage. H. 2. G. 9.56. F. 1.5. Soluble in HNO_3. Y = a(?). 2V near 90° with strong dispersion[12] (+ for red, − for blue). n_X = 2.51, n_Y = 2.61, n_Z = 2.71, $n_Z - n_X$ = 0.20 Li. Color yellow with X (or Y ?) light sulfur-yellow, Z deep yellow. A furnace product. PD 3.07, 2.95, 2.74; 5–0570.

CuO (Tenorite) is monoclinic with a = 4.653, b = 3.410, c = 5.108 kX, β = 99°32′. U.C. 4. Crystals lath-shaped or basal plates; often twinned; {001} and {111} cleavages. H. 3.5. G. 6.45. F. 3. Soluble in HCl. Y = b; Z near c. (−?)2V = large,[16] n_Y = 2.63 (red), 2.84 (white), 3.18 (blue), $n_Z - n_X$ = strong. Color and streak iron gray to black. Absorption very strong (Y < Z) and Y light brown, Z nearly opaque brown. Made by heating CuCl in oxygen. PD 2.52, 2.32, 2.53; 5–0661.

3. Formula Type A_2X_3

B_2O_3 is isometric.[17] G. 1.805. M.P. 294° C. Isotropic with n = 1.458. Like ice in contracting on melting; the glass has G. 1.844 and n = 1.464. Colorless. Obtained by dehydrating H_3BO_3 in a vacuum. B_2O_3 also has a hexagonal phase[18] with a = 4.33, c = 8.39 Å. G. 2.46. Uniaxial negative with n_O = 1.648, n_E = 1.615, $n_O - n_E$ = 0.033. PD 2.10, 2.78, 2.23; 6–0634*.

Y_2O_3 is isometric; crystals are rectilinear plates. Isotropic with[19] n = 1.910 ± 0.002. Very hygroscopic. PD 3.06, 1.87, 1.60; 5–0574.

Al_2O_3 has three or more crystal phases.

α-Al_2O_3 (Corundum) is hexagonal scalenohedral with a = 4.751, c = 12.97 kX. Crystals basal plates limited by the rhombohedron or varied.

[13] Larsen: *U. S. Geol. Surv. Bull.* 679 (1921).
[14] Larsen and Berman: *U. S. Geol. Surv. Bull.* 848 (1934).
[15] *abc* changed to *acb* to make $b > a$ with c as the polar axis.
[16] Tunell, Posnjak and Ksanda: *Zeit. Krist.* XC, p. 120 (1935).
[17] Cole: *J. Am. Cer. Soc.* XVIII, p. 55 (1935).
[18] Hendricks: *J. Wash. Acad. Sci.* XXXIV, p. 241 (1944).
[19] Yoder and Keith: *Am. Min.* XXXVI, p. 519 (1951).

No cleavage, but may have basal parting. H. 9. G. 4. M.P. 2050° C. Insoluble in acids. Uniaxial negative with[20] $n_O = 1.7653$ C, 1.7686 D, 1.7760 F, $n_E = 1.7573$ C, 1.7604 D, 1.7677 F, $n_O - n_E = 0.0082$ D. Colorless or blue (sapphire), red (ruby) or black (emery). Asterism rather rare, due to oriented needles (of rutile?). Deeply colored crystals are pleochroic with O > E and O blue, E emerald green to yellow-green in sapphire and O deep purple, E light yellow in ruby. Ruby is colored by chromium; sapphire by Co and Ti. Corundum is made by melting bauxite. PD 2.09, 2.55, 1.60; 10–173.

β-Al_2O_3 is hexagonal in triangular or hexagonal plates with perfect basal cleavage. G. 3.31. Uniaxial negative with[21] $n_O = 1.665 - 1.680$, $n_E = 1.63 - 1.65$, $n_O - n_E = 0.023 - 0.045$. Colorless. β-Al_2O_3 is unstable (or metastable?) unless it contains a little Na_2O; perhaps it is really $Na_2Al_{22}O_{34}$. Found in reaction layers of ceramic refractories. PD 1.40, 11.9, 2.68; 10–414.

γ-Al_2O_3 is isometric[22] with G. 3.47 and $n = 1.696$. It is unstable at ordinary temperatures. PD 1.98, 1.40, 2.39; 10–425. "Amorphous" Al_2O_3 has G. $1.65 - 1.69$ and $n = 1.68$. Colorless.

Cr_2O_3 is hexagonal scalenohedral with[23] $a = 4.95$, $c = 13.57$ Å. G. 5.2. Crystals equant prismatic to basal tablets. Twinning common, often on {0001}. Distinct rhombohedral cleavage. Uniaxial positive[12] with $n = 2.5\pm$ Li. Green in thin plates. PD 2.67, 2.48, 1.67; 6–0504*. Miscible in all proportions with Fe_2O_3. Found in refractory mixes.

α-Fe_2O_3 (Hematite) is hexagonal scalenohedral with $a = 5.029$, $c = 13.73$ kX. Crystals rhombohedral or basal plates. May have basal parting. H. 5. G. 5.2. M.P. 1350° C. Soluble in HCl. Uniaxial negative with[24] $n_O > 2.95$ Li, $n_E = 2.74$, $n_O - n_E = 0.21+$. Also[12] $n_O = 3.01$ Li, $n_E = 2.78$, $n_O - n_E = 0.23$. Hematite is steel gray to iron black in crystals; deep red in mass; opaque except in thin flakes which are blood-red with O brownish red, E yellowish red. PD 2.69, 2.51, 1.61; 6–0502. Made by sublimation and by fusion. Fe_2O_3 inverts promptly at 678° C. and is said to invert also at −40° C., but optic data on these forms are lacking. It is miscible in all proportions with Cr_2O_3. Al_2O_3 can dissolve in Fe_2O_3 up to about 12 per cent, but very little Fe_2O_3 can enter Al_2O_3. By partial deoxidation (17.8 per cent FeO) $n_E = 2.71$ and (with 16.1 FeO) $n_O - n_E = 0.16+$. Partially hydrated Fe_2O_3, called **hydrohematite** or **turgite**,

[20] Melczer: *Zeit. Krist.* XXXV, p. 561 (1901); also Brauns: *Cent. Min., A.*, p. 233 (1926).

[21] Brownmiller and Bogue: *Am. J. Sci.* XXIII, p. 501 (1932).

[22] Hansen and Brownmiller: *Am. J. Sci.* CCXV, p. 229 (1928).

[23] Wilde and Rees: *Trans. Brit. Cer. Soc.* XLII, p. 123 (1943).

[24] Sosman and Hostetter: *J. Am. Cer. Soc.* XXXVIII, p. 807 (1916).

is often fibrous; it may have G. 4.5–5 and n_O = 2.5–2.7, n_E = 2.3–2.6, $n_O - n_E$ = 0.1–0.2.

Sb_2O_3 has two crystal phases.

α-Sb_2O_3 (Senarmontite) is isometric with a = 11.14 kX. U.C. 16. Crystals octahedral with poor octahedral cleavage. H. 2–2.5. G. 5.5. Isotropic with[25] n = 2.073 Li, 2.087 Na. Often shows strong anomalous birefringence usually in zones or segments. Colorless or grayish white. PD 3.22, 1.97, 2.79; 5–0534. Made from fusion below 570° C.

β-Sb_2O_3 (Valentinite) is orthorhombic with $a:b:c$ = 0.394:1:0.434. Crystals prismatic or tabular, often in stellate groups. Perfect prismatic {110} and poor {010} cleavages. H. 2.5–3. G. 5.76. X = a, Y = c and Z = b for red light; X = a, Y = b, Z = c for green light. (−)2V = very small,[25] about 0° for yellow, r < v. n_X = 2.18, n_Y = 2.35, n_Z = 2.35, $n_Z - n_Y$ = 0.17. Colorless to white or stained. PD 3.14, 1.80, 4.59; 3–0530. Formed by sublimation or quenching melts heated above 570° C. Valentinite is the stable phase at lower temperatures.

α-As_2O_3 (Claudetite) is monoclinic with $a:b:c$ = 0.409:1:0.349. β = 94°20′. Crystals {010} plates resembling gypsum. Perfect {010} cleavage. Flexible. H. 2.5. G. 4.15. Y = b,[25] Z $\wedge$ c = 6° $ca.$ (+)2V = 58° calc., r < v. n_X = 1.87, n_Y = 1.92, n_Z = 2.01, $n_Z - n_X$ = 0.14. Colorless to white. It is the stable phase at an unknown temperature above 100° C.

β-As_2O_3 (Arsenolite) is isometric with a = 11.05 kX. U.C. 16. Crystals octahedral with perfect octahedral cleavage. H. 1.5. G. 3.87. Isometric with[25] n = 1.748 Li, 1.755 Na. May show anomalous birefringence. Color white or stained. PD 3.20, 6.39, 2.54; 4–0566. Made by sublimation below about 200° C.

Bi_2O_3 has four crystal phases.

γ-Bi_2O_3 (Sillenite) is isometric with a = 10.08 kX. Massive. Soft. G. 8.8. Isotropic with[26] n > 2.42. Color olive drab to green. Transparent in thin flakes. PD 3.22, 1.74, 2.73; 6–0312.

α-Bi_2O_3 (Bismite) is monoclinic with a = 5.83, b = 8.14, c = 7.48, β = 112°56′. U.C. 4. Massive. H. 4.5. G. 9.2+. M.P. 860° C. Biaxial with strong dispersion and indices above 2.43. Color grayish green to bright yellow. Transparent in very thin fragments. PD 3.23, 2.68, 1.67; 6–0307.

Two other phases of Bi_2O_3 are known, but optic data are not available.

4. Formula Type AX₂

UO_2 (Uraninite) is isometric with a = 5.47 Å. Crystals octahedral or cubic; rarely dodecahedral; usually massive. Fracture uneven to conchoidal. H. 5–6. G. 10.95 (artif). In nature the mineral commonly oxidizes, usually

---

[25] Des Cloizeaux: *Manuel de Minéralogie* 1862 and 1874.
[26] Frondel: *Am. Min.* XXVIII, p. 521 (1943).

to about U_3O_8; this decreases the specific gravity to about 8–10; often altered to an amorphous "metamict" state (pitchblende) with about 2–$5H_2O$ and G. about 6–8. F. = 7. Soluble in HNO_3. Not magnetic. Usually opaque; otherwise dark green, yellowish or dark brown. Streak brownish black, gray or olive green. In polished sections light gray with a brownish tint. Reflection percentages: red 12.5, orange 12.5, green 15. PD 3.16, 1.93, 2.74; 5–0550. Made by fusion of uranium oxide in borax[26a] and in other ways.

ThO_2 (Thorianite) is isometric with a = 5.61 kX. U.C. 4. Crystals often cubic with poor cubic cleavage. H. 6.5. G. 9.7. M.P. 3050° C. Isotropic with a variable index, averaging[13] n = 2.20. Color dark gray to black; reddish brown in thin splinters. PD 3.23, 1.69, 1.98; 4–0556. Forms a complete series of mix-crystals with UO_2. Strongly radioactive. Made by fusion in borax.

TiO_2 has three crystal phases, rutile, anatase and brookite.

α-TiO_2 (Rutile) is tetragonal with a = 4.58, c = 2.95. U.C. 2. Crystals prismatic, often acicular; vertically striated. Twinning common on {011} or varied. Distinct {110} and poor {100} cleavages. H. 6–6.5. G. 4.23. M.P. 1825° C. Uniaxial positive with[27] n_O = 2.6505 (546), 2.6211 (579), 2.5890 (623), 2.5555 (691), n_E = 2.9467 (546), 2.9085 (579), 2.8712 (623), 2.8294 (691), $n_E - n_O$ = 0.2874 (579). The indices vary also with change of temperature, as follows: at 25° C. n_O = 2.6124, n_E = 2.8993, $n_E - n_O$ = 0.2869; at 110° C. n_O = 2.6087, n_E = 2.8920, $n_E - n_O$ = 0.2833; at 300° C. n_O = 2.5992, n_E = 2.8770, $n_E - n_O$ = 0.2778. Color usually brown or red, but colorless in thin flakes. Colored crystals pleochroic with 0 < E. PD 3.25, 1.69, 2.49; 4–0551*.

β-TiO_2 (Anatase or Octahedrite) is tetragonal with a = 3.73, c = 9.37 kX. U.C. 4. Crystals pyramidal or rarely tabular {001}. Perfect basal and {011} cleavages. H. 5.5–6. G. 3.90. Uniaxial negative with[27] n_O = 2.5612, n_E = 2.4880, $n_O - n_E$ = 0.0732 at 25° C. Na; n_O = 2.5580, n_E = 2.4872, $n_O - n_E$ = 0.0708 at 150° C. Na and n_O = 2.5520, n_E = 2.4853, $n_O - n_E$ = 0.0667 at 450° C. Na. Often biaxial with small 2V (due to strain?). Color variable, but often brown (or yellow, blue or green); pleochroism usually weak and may be either O < E or O > E. PD 3.51, 1.89, 2.38; 4–0477*. Made by reaction of $TiCl_4$ or TiF_4 with H_2O vapor below 760° C.

The γ-phase (brookite), to be described later, is orthorhombic.

SnO_2 (Cassiterite) is tetragonal with a = 4.72, c = 3.17 kX. U.C. 2. Crystals short prismatic, pyramidal, or long prismatic. Common {011} twinning. Poor {100} cleavage. H. 6–7. G. 6.99. Uniaxial positive with[28]

[26a] Hillebrand: *U. S. Geol. Surv. Bull.* 113, p. 37 and 41 (1893).

[27] Schröder: *Zeit. Krist.* LXVII, p. 485 (1928).

[28] Ecklebe: *N. Jahrb. Min. Bl. Bd.* LXVI, p. 47 (1932).

$n_O = 2.0239$, $n_E = 2.1188$, $n_E - n_O = 0.0949$ for $\lambda = 496$; $n_O = 2.0006$, $n_E = 2.0972$, $n_E - n_O = 0.0966$ for $\lambda = 585$; $n_O = 1.9899$, $n_E = 2.0874$, $n_E - n_O = 0.0975$ for $\lambda = 653$. Also: $n_O = 2.0007$, $n_E = 2.0980$, $n_E - n_O = 0.0973$ at 16° C. for $\lambda = 578$, and $n_O = 2.0409$, $n_E = 2.1275$, $n_E - n_O = 0.0866$ at 535° C. Color of crystals yellow to brown; rarely red, gray or white; color in section colorless to brown; less commonly red or green. Absorption O < E. PD 3.35, 2.64, 1.77; 5–0467. Made from fusion.

PbO₂ (Plattnerite) is tetragonal with $a = 4.931$, $c = 3.367$. U.C. 2. Crystals prismatic; often dense or fibrous. No cleavage. H. 5.5. G. 8.9–9.36. Decomposes at 290° C. Uniaxial negative with[13] $n_O = 2.30 \pm .05$ Li; weak birefringence. Color jet black. In transmitted light cloudy and nearly opaque. Basal sections may show six biaxial segments. When made by fusion of lead oxide in potash the color is dark brown. PD 3.50, 2.80, 1.86; 8–185. Made by fusing PBO in KOH.

SeO₂ is tetragonal or hexagonal when crystallized in selenium. G. 3.96. Acicular. Uniaxial positive:[29] $n > 1.76$, $n_E - n_O = $ strong. PD 3.73, 3.01, 4.17; 4–0429. Another phase is monoclinic.

GeO₂ is tetragonal with[30] $a = 4.395$, $c = 2.852\ kX$. U.C. 2. Crystals short prisms. Insoluble. G. 6.24. Uniaxial positive with $n_O = 1.99$, $n_E = 2.05$–2.10 (est.), $n_E - n_O = 0.006$–0.011 (est.). Colorless. PD 3.11, 2.40, 1.62; 9–379*. Another phase is hexagonal[31] with $a = 4.972$, $c = 5.648\ kX$. Crystals rhombohedrons resembling cubes. G. 4.28. Soluble. Uniaxial positive with $n_O = 1.695$, $n_E = 1.735$, $n_E - n_O = 0.040$. When fused to glass[31a] it has G. 3.638, H. 4.5–5 and $n = 1.603$ C; 1.607 D, 1.6176 F. Colorless. PD 3.43, 2.37, 4.32; 4–0497/8* (which polymorph?).

SiO₂ (Quartz, etc.) has surprisingly many crystal phases. The high-temperature phase (**β-cristobalite**) is isometric; crystals octahedral or cubic or skeletal with common twinning on {111}. H. 6–7. G. 2.27–2.35. M.P. 1710° C. Insoluble in HCl. Isotropic above 200° to 275° C. with $n = 1.486$. It is stable above 1470° C. and metastable to about 250° C. PD 4.15, 2.53, 1.64; 4–0359* (at 500° C.). If the slow inversion to tridymite does not occur at about 1470° C., the substance inverts very easily to a tetragonal(?) phase (α-cristobalite) at a temperature between 275 and 200° C.; low cristobalite is uniaxial negative with $n_O = 1.487$, $n_E = 1.484$, $n_O - n_E = 0.003$. Complex lamellar twinning is common. Colorless. PD 4.04, 2.49, 2.85; 4–0379*.

The moderate temperature phase of SiO₂, called **tridymite,** is hexagonal above 117° C. (with $c/a = 1.653$) and orthorhombic (α-tridymite) below that temperature with $a = 9.88$, $b = 17.1$, $c = 16.3$ Å. U.C. 64. It is the

[29] Brownmiller: *Am. Min.* XII, p. 43 (1927).
[30] Laubengayer and Morton: *J. Am. Chem. Soc.* LIV, p. 2303 (1932).
[31] Zachariasen: *Zeit. Krist.* LXVII, p. 226 (1928).
[31a] Dennis: *Zeit. anorg. Chem.* CLXXIV, p. 97 (1928).

stable phase of SiO_2 between 870° and 1470° C. It inverts to quartz below 870° C. and to cristobalite above 1470° C. but these changes are very sluggish and tridymite may exist for long periods as a metastable form. This has permitted measurement of the melting point (1670° C.) and the study of the mineral at ordinary temperatures. α-Tridymite may invert on heating to a phase called β_1-tridymite at 117° C. and to another phase called β_2-tridymite at 163° C. But both these phases are hexagonal and uniaxial, the change at 163° C. being perhaps from hemihedral to holohedral symmetry. On cooling the inversions show some lag. Crystals of tridymite are usually six-sided basal plates with common wedge-like twinning in sectors (as seen on 001) as in aragonite and cordierite, the optic plane being normal to the external boundary. α-Tridymite has indistinct prismatic cleavage and basal parting. H. 7. G. 2.27. Y = a, Z = c. (+)2V = 35°. n_X = 1.469, n_Y = 1.469, n_Z = 1.473, $n_Z - n_X$ = 0.004. Again:[32] (+)2V = 76°15′, n_X = 1.471, n_Y = 1.472, n_Z = 1.474, $n_Z - n_X$ = 0.003. Also:[33] n_X = 1.470, n_Y = 1.480, n_Z = 1.483, $n_Z - n_X$ = 0.004. Colorless. PD 4.30, 4.08, 3.81; 3–0227*. Made from fusion in fluxes. Tridymite seems to vary in composition.

The low-temperature phase of SiO_2 is α-**quartz**; it is trigonal trapezohedral with a = 4.903, c = 5.393 Å. U.C. 3. Crystals usually short prismatic terminated by two rhombohedrons; often twinned. No cleavage. H. 7. G. 2.65. Insoluble in acids except HF. Uniaxial positive with n_O = 1.5419 C, 1.5442 D, 1.5497 F, n_E = 1.5509 C, 1.5533 D, 1.5590 F, $n_E - n_O$ = 0.0091. Composition and indices very constant in natural as well as artificial crystals. Refringence and birefringence decrease very slowly with increase of temperature. PD 3.34, 4.26, 1.82; 5–0490*. At 573° C. low-temperature α-quartz inverts to β-quartz and this change is reversed[34] promptly on cooling. β-**quartz** is hexagonal trapezohedral with a = 5.01, c = 5.47 Å. U.C. 3. It has good $\{10\bar{1}1\}$ and $\{10\bar{1}0\}$ cleavages. At 580° C. it has n_O = 1.5329 D, n_E = 1.5405, $n_E - n_O$ = 0.0066. PD 3.42, 1.85, 1.57; 7–346*. Quartz undergoes a second inversion at 870° C. to tridymite, which inverts at 1470° C. to cristobalite, but these changes are very sluggish.

SiO_2 (**Keatite** or **Silica K**) has been made[35] at 380–585° C. and 5000–18000 pounds per square inch water-vapor pressure. It is tetragonal with a = 7.46, c = 8.59 Å. U.C. 12. G. 2.50. Uniaxial negative with n_O = 1.522, n_E = 1.513, $n_O - n_E$ = 0.009. Stable to 1100° C.

SiO_2 (**Coesite** or **silica C**) has been crystallized from a mixture of equal parts of Na_2SiO_3 and $(NH_4)_2HPO_4$ at 500–800° C. and 35000 atmospheres.[36]

[32] Heide: *Cent. Min.* 1823, p. 69.
[33] Barth and Kvalhein: *Norsk Videns. Akad. Oslo*, XXII p. 1 (1944).
[34] Wyckoff: *Am. J. Sci.* CCXI, p. 101 (1926).
[35] Keat: *Science*, CXX, p. 328 (1954).
[36] Coes: *Science*, CXVIII, p. 131 (1953).

It is monoclinic[36a] with $a = 7.23$, $b = 12.52$, $c = 7.23$ Å, $\beta = 120°$. U.C. 17. H. 8. G. 3.01. Insoluble in HF, but dissolved in fused $(NH_4)HF_2$. Changes to silica glass and cristobalite at 1700° C. Biaxial with oblique extinction in the common six-sided plates. $(+)2V = 54°$. $n_X = 1.599$ (calc.)? $n_Z = 1.604$, $n_Z - n_X = 0.014$ ($n_Y = 1.593$, calc. from these data). PD 3.09, 3.43, 6.20; 8–18*. Pseudo-tetragonal twins[36a] on $\{021\}$.

SiO₂ glass has G. 2.19 and $n = 1.4588$. The natural substance, called **lechatelierite** is produced when lightning strikes quartz sand and fuses tiny tubes (fulgurites) in it.

A fibrous variety of SiO_2 called **Chalcedony,** has the same crystal structure as quartz,[37] but has H. 6 and G. 2.55–3.63, apparently with $n_O = 1.537$ (1.533–1.539), $n_E = 1.530$, $n_O - n_E = 0.007$, but the sign is uncertain and the substance may be biaxial, since the fibers in some cases seem to have ± elongation, parallel to Y or extinction at 29°.

TeO₂ (Tellurite) is orthorhombic with $a = 5.50$, $b = 11.75$, $c = 5.59$ Å. U.C. 8. H. 2. G. 5.91. X = b, Y = a. $(-)2V = $ large. $n_X = 2.00$ Li, $n_Y = 2.18$, $n_Z = 2.35$, $n_Z - n_X = 0.35$. Color white. Made from fusion. Another phase is tetragonal. PD 3.28, 3.72, 3.01; 9–433*.

γ-TiO₂ (Brookite) is orthorhombic with $a = 5.436$, $b = 9.166$, $c = 5.135$ kX. U.C. 8. Crystals $\{010\}$ platelets or prismatic; rarely pyramidal. Poor $\{120\}$ cleavage. H. 5.5–6. G. 4.14 ± .06. Very high refringence and birefringence and also extraordinary dispersion of the optic axes so that the optic plane is (001) for red and yellow light[38] (with r < v) and (100) for green and blue light (with r > v); the optic angle is 0° at about $\lambda = 555$ at 25° C. Z = b in all cases. Brookite shows abnormal interference colors and no good extinction.

At[27] 25° C. $n_X = 2.5831$, $n_Y = 2.5843$, $n_Z = 2.7004$, $n_Z - n_Y = 0.1173$ Na.
At 300° C. $n_X = 2.5880$, $n_Y = 2.5897$, $n_Z = 2.6762$, $n_Z - n_X = 0.0882$ Na.
At 600° C. $n_X = 2.5924$, $n_Y = 2.5981$, $n_Z = 2.6610$, $n_Z - n_X = 0.0686$ Na.

λ	671.6	589	579.1	555 ±	546.1	491.6	$n_F - n_C$
$(+)2E$	58°7′		25°48′	0°		68°16′	
n_X	2.5405	2.5831	2.5895		2.6154	2.6717	0.1341
n_Y	2.5443	2.5843	2.5904		2.6159	2.6770	0.1373
n_Z	2.6519	2.7004	2.7091		2.7402	2.8090	0.1623
$n_Z - n_X$	0.1114	0.1173	0.1196		0.1248	0.1373	0.0282

Color brown, yellowish, reddish, black. In section weakly pleochroic in

---

[36a] Ramsdell: *Am. Min.* XL, p. 975 (1955).

[37] Washburn and Navias: *Proc. Nat. Acad. Sci.* VIII, p. 1.

[38] Rastall (*Geol. Mag.* LXXV, p. 433, 1938) reports one case with the optic plane (001) for all colors.

yellow or brown tints; for example: X and Y orange, Z lemon yellow or X cinnamon brown, Y and Z clove brown. PD 3.47, 2.90, 1.38; 3–0380*. Brookite inverts to rutile at about 700° C. Another phase is anatase. Both of these other phases have already been discussed.

ZrO₂ (Baddeleyite) is monoclinic with $a = 5.21$, $b = 5.26$, $c = 5.575$ kX. $\beta = 99°7'$. Crystals varied, often twinned. Good basal and poor {010} and {110} cleavages. H. 6.5. G. 5.6±. M.P. 2700° C. X $\wedge$ $c = 13°$, Y $= b$. $(-)2V = 30°$, r > v. $n_X = 2.13$, $n_Y = 2.19$, $n_Z = 2.20$, $n_Z - n_X = 0.07$. Colorless to brown with X yellow, brown or green, Y oil green or reddish brown, Z brown. PD 3.16, 2.84, 2.62; 7–343. Made from fusion of ZrO_2 in borax. It inverts to a tetragonal phase at about 1008° C., and to a hexagonal phase at about 1900° C.; an isometric phase[39] has been reported; optic properties unknown.

5. Formula Type A₂X₅

P₂O₅ has at least three crystal phases.[39a] One phase is tetragonal; G. 2.89 ca.; uniaxial positive with $n_O = 1.599$, $n_E = 1.624$, $n_E - n_O = 0.025$. Colorless. A metastable phase is orthorhombic with a good cleavage parallel with the optic plane and a poor cleavage normal thereto. $(-)2V = 65°$. $n_X = 1.545$, $n_Y = 1.578$, $n_Z = 1.589$, $n_Z - n_X = 0.044$. Another metastable phase is hexagonal with G. 2.28–2.32. Uniaxial positive with $n_O = 1.469$, $n_E = 1.471$, $n_E - n_O = 0.002$. PD 5.40, 5.20, 3.02; 1–0213*.

β. HYDRATED

1. Formula Type AX₂·nH₂O

Sb₂O₄·nH₂O (or $Sb_3O_6(OH)$?) **Stibiconite(?)** is isometric. Massive or in powder or crusts. H. 4–5.5. G. 5–5.58. Isotropic with a remarkably great range in refractive index,[13] from $n = 1.60$ to 2.00, perhaps due to variations in content of water. PD 2.96, 5.93, 1.81; 10–388. Often mixed with birefringent fibrous material, perhaps cervantite. Color pale yellow to yellowish or reddish white. An isometric compound, $Sb_3O_6(OH)$, with $a = 10.28$ Å, has been made by heating antimonic acid.

2UO₂·7H₂O(?) (Ianthinite) is orthorhombic with $a:b:c = 0.9996:1:1.2964$. Crystals basal plates or prismatic along b. Perfect {001} cleavage. H. 2–3. G. 4.94. X $= c$; Y $= b$. $(-)2V =$ small. $n_X = 1.674$, $n_Y = 1.90$, $n_Z = 1.92$, $n_Z - n_X = 0.246$. Again:[40] $n_Y = 1.88$, $n_Z = 1.91$. Color violet-black (alters on edges to yellow). Pleochroic with X colorless, Y violet, Z dark violet. PD 7.60, 3.79, 3.59; 8–307*. [Composition quite

---

[39] Bauer: *N. Jahrb. Min. Bl. Bd.* LXXV, p. 159 (1939).

[39a] Hill, Faust and Reynolds: *Am. J. Sci.* CCXLII, p. 542 (1944).

[40] Branche, Chervet and Guillemin: *Bull. Soc. Fr. Min.* LXXIV, p. 457 (1951).

uncertain—another analysis leads to the formula[41] $3CaO \cdot 2CO_2 \cdot 7(UO_{2.83})$ $\cdot 10H_2O$.]

2. Formula Type $AX_3 \cdot nH_2O$

$4UO_3 \cdot 5H_2O$ is orthorhombic.[41] Perfect {001}, good {010} and poor {100} cleavages. H. 3–4. Y = b; Z = c. $(-)2V = 48°$, $n_X = 1.79$ calc., $n_Y = 1.89$, $n_Z = 1.91$, $n_Z - n_X = 0.12$. Strong pleochroism.

$4UO_3 \cdot 9H_2O$ (Schoepite) is orthorhombic with $a = 14.40$, $b = 16.89$, $c = 14.75$ kX. Crystals often tabular or short prisms. Perfect {001} cleavage. H. 2–3. G. 6.5. X = c; Y = b. $(-)2V = 89°$, r > v.[42] $n_X = 1.690$, $n_Y = 1.714$, $n_Z = 1.733$, $n_Z - n_X = 0.045$. Color yellow. PD 7.49, 3.26, 3.64; 8–396.

$7UO_3 \cdot 11H_2O$ (Becquerelite) is orthorhombic with[43] $a = 13.93$, $b = 14.84$, $c = 12.34$ Å. Crystals {010} tablets long parallel with c. Perfect {010} cleavage. H. 2–3. G. 5.2. X = b; Y = c. $(-)2V = 31°$, r > v.[44] $n_X = 1.735$, $n_Y = 1.820$, $n_Z = 1.830$, $n_Z - n_X = 0.095$. Color amber to brownish yellow; pleochroic with X colorless, Y light yellow, Z dark yellow. Made at room temperature[45] from solutions. PD 7.50, 3.22, 3.75; 8–299.

$WO_3 \cdot H_2O$ (or H_2WO_4) (Tungstite) is orthorhombic. Crystals tiny scales or prisms with perfect basal cleavage. H. 2.5. G. 5.5(?). F. 7. Soluble in KOH or NH_4OH but not in acids. X = c; Z = b.[46] $(-)2V = 27°$, r < v distinct. $n_X = 1.82$, $n_Y = ?$, $n_Z = 2.04$, $n_Z - n_X = 0.22$,[46] absorption X < Y < Z. Again:[13] $n_X = 2.09$, $n_Y = 2.24$, $n_Z = 2.26$, $n_Z - n_X = 0.17$, absorption Z < Y < X. This difference may be due to the fact that the indices change as the water is driven off; tungstite begins to lose water at 120° C. and so attempts to determine the indices with melts which become liquid only above this temperature may give inaccurate results. Color golden yellow to green. Luster pearly. Absorption Y < X < Z. PD 3.49, 2.68, 2.56; 6–0242. Made by heating hydrotungstite to 100° C. for several days.

$WO_3 \cdot 2H_2O$ (or $H_2WO_4 \cdot H_2O$) (Hydrotungstite) is monoclinic(?) with poor {010} cleavage. Crystals platy. Multiple twinning on {1$\bar{1}$0} very common. H. 2. G. 4.6. Soluble in NH_4OH, but not in acids. X $\wedge$ normal to {001} = 3° ca.; Y = b. $(-)2V = 52°$ ca.; r < v. $n_X = 1.70$, $n_Y = 1.95$, $n_Z = 2.04$, $n_Z - n_X = 0.34$. Color green with X colorless, Y yellow-green, Z dark green. Made from a solution[46] of $(NH_4)_6W_7O_{24} \cdot 6H_2O$ in water treated with HCl. PD 3.46, 2.30, 3.30; 6–0244.

[41] Bignand: *Bull. Soc. Fr. Min. Crist.* LXXVIII, p. 1 (1955).
[42] Walker: *Am. Min.* VIII, p. 67 (1923).
[43] $a\,b\,c$ changed to $a\,c\,b$ to make $b > a > c$.
[44] Palache and Berman: *Am. Min.* XVIII, p. 20 (1933).
[45] Gruner: *Am. Min.* XXXVIII, p. 342 (1953).
[46] Kerr and Young: *Am. Min.* XXIX, p. 192 (1944).

B. HYDROXIDES AND OXIDES CONTAINING HYDROXYL

1. Formula Type AX

LiOH is tetragonal with[47] $a = 3.55$, $c = 4.33$ kX. U.C. 2. Perfect basal and distinct prismatic cleavages. G. 1.46. Uniaxial negative with $n_O = 1.464$, $n_E = 1.452$, $n_O - n_E = 0.012$ for $\lambda = 589$. Colorless. PD 2.73, 3.47, 1.78; 4–0708.

NaOH is orthorhombic(?) in grains or basal plates with perfect {001} and poor prismatic cleavages, the latter at an angle of about 90°. Extinction[48] on (001) bisects the angle between the cleavages. G. 2.13. Z = c. $(-)2V = 50° \pm 10°$. $n_X = 1.457$, $n_Y = 1.470$, $n_Z = 1.472$, $n_Z - n_X = 0.015$. Colorless. PD 2.35, 1.70, 1.65; 1–1173.

NaOH·2H₂O(?) is orthorhombic(?) in {001} blades long parallel to a with {110} and domes.[48] Good basal cleavage. Angle between prism faces is $92° \pm 2°$. X = c, Y = a. $(-)2V = 45° \pm 5°$. $n_X = 1.435$, $n_Y = 1.470$, $n_Z = 1.475$, all $\pm .004$, $n_Z - n_X = 0.040$. Colorless. PD 5.90, 2.49, 2.69; 3–89*(?).

KOH is orthorhombic with[49] $a = 3.95$, $b = 4.03$, $c = 11.4$ Å. Prismatic cleavage angle of 94°. G. 2.05. X = a, Y = c, $(+)2V = $ large, $n_X = 1.486$, $n_Y = 1.492$, $n_Z = 1.497$, $n_Z - n_X = 0.011$. Colorless. PD 2.69, 1.98, 2.93; 1–1054.

2. Formula Type AX₂

Sr(OH)₂·8H₂O is tetragonal with $c/a = 0.64$. Crystals basal plates with {001} and {110} cleavages; twinning common on {110}, {101} or {210}. G. 1.885. Uniaxial negative with $n_O = 1.499$, $n_E = 1.476$, $n_O - n_E = 0.023$. Colorless. PD 2.02, 4.29, 2.76; 1–1263.

Mg(OH)₂ (Brucite) is hexagonal with $a = 3.125$, $c = 4.75$ kX. Crystals basal plates with perfect basal cleavage. H. 2.5. G. 2.39. F. 7. Soluble in HCl. Uniaxial positive[50] with $n_O = 1.559$, $n_E = 1.580$, $n_E - n_O = 0.021$. Again: $n_O = 1.5662$, $n_E = 1.5853$, $n_E - n_O = 0.0191$.[51] Color white. Often anomalously biaxial with small 2V, or showing abnormal interference colors due to marked change in birefringence with wave length. PD 2.37, 4.77, 1.79; 7–239. After heating above 400° C. MgO remains,[52] which is uniaxial negative with G. 3.666, $n_O = 1.644$, $n_E = 1.634$, $n_O - n_E = 0.010$.

[47] Ernst: *Zeit. phys. Chem.* XX, p. 65 (1933).

[48] Morey and Burlew: *Am. J. Sci.* XXXV, p. 185 (1938).

[49] Ernst and Schober: *Nachr. Akad. Wiss. Göttingen, Math. Phys. Kl. Abt.* 1947, No. 2, p. 49. *Chem. Abst.* XLIII, p. 7771 (1944).

[50] Bauer: *N. Jahrb. Min. Bl. Bd.* II, p. 73 (1883).

[51] Westphal, in Ehringhaus: *N. Jahrb. Min. Bl. Bd.* XLI, p. 371 (1917).

[52] Westphal: *Inaug. Diss.* Leipzig, 1913.

Ca(OH)$_2$ (Portlandite[53]) is hexagonal with $a = 3.585$, $c = 4.895$ kX. U.C. 1. Crystals basal plates with perfect basal cleavage. H. 2. G. 2.23. Uniaxial negative with[53a] $n_O = 1.574$, $n_E = 1.545$, $n_O - n_E = 0.029$ Na. Colorless. PD 2.63, 4.90, 1.93; 4–0733.

Mn(OH)$_2$ (Pyrochroite) is hexagonal with $a = 3.34$, $c = 4.68$ kX. Crystals basal tablets or rhombohedral with perfect basal cleavage. H. 2.5. G. 3.25. Uniaxial negative with $n_O = 1.723$, $n_E = 1.681$, $n_O - n_E = 0.042$. May have small 2V. Colorless, but easily altered to brown, and then absorption is O > E. PD 4.72, 1.37, 2.45; 8–171.

Zn(OH)$_2$ is orthorhombic with $a:b:c = 0.605:1:0.576$. Crystals prismatic or varied with no distinct cleavage. $X^{54} = c$, $Y = b$; $(-)2V = 50°40'$, r > v distinct; $n_X = 1.5705$, $n_Y = 1.5777$, $n_Z = 1.5796$, $n_Z - n_X = 0.0091$. Again:[55] $X = b$, $Y = a$, 2V = large. Also:[56] $Z = c$, $(-)2V$ large, r > v; $n_X = 1.570$, $n_Y = 1.578$, $n_Z = 1.580$, $n_Z - n_X = 0.010$. PD 4.38, 3.27, 2.71; 1–0360.

Ba(OH)$_2$·8H$_2$O is monoclinic with $a:b:c = 0.999:1:1.278$, $\beta = 98°56'$. Crystals complex, often flattened parallel to {001} or long parallel to a with perfect basal cleavage. G. 2.18. Loses H$_2$O at 78° C. (then G. 4.50) and fuses at 780° C. X nearly normal to {001}. $Z = b$. $(-)2V = 8°33'$ Na. $n_X = 1.471$, $n_Y = 1.5017$, $n_Z = 1.502$, $n_O - n_X = 0.031$. Colorless. PD 6.00, 4.62, 2.78; 1–0151.

BO(OH) has three crystal phases.[57] The high temperature α-phase may be grown from the vapor. It is orthorhombic[58] with $a = 1.507$, $b = 8.015$, $c = 1.503$ Å. Crystals basal plates with a prism angle of 78°30'. Perfect basal cleavage. G. 1.86. $X = c$; $Y = a$. $(-)2V^{57} = 23°$, $n_X < 1.376$, $n_Y = 1.514$, $n_Z = 1.521$. $n_Z - n_X > 0.145$. Again:[58] $n_X = 1.378$, $n_Y = 1.503$, $n_Z = 1.507$, $n_Z - n_X = 0.129$. Another (β) phase is monoclinic[57] with $a:b:c = 0.804:1:1.785$, $\beta = 120°12'$. G. 2.044. Perfect basal and distinct {101} cleavages. $Y = b$; $Z \wedge c = 5°$ red, 4.5° blue. $(-)2V = 35°$, r < v. $n_X = 1.434$, $n_Y = 1.570$, $n_Z = 1.588$, $n_Z - n_X = 0.154$. Again:[53] $n_X = 1.450$, $n_Y = 1.574$, $n_Z = 1.579$, $n_Z - n_X = 0.129$. A third phase ("most stable") is isometric,[57] often dodecahedral. G. 2.486. Isotropic with $n = 1.619$. All phases react rapidly with acetone, methyl alcohol or acetonitrile; they are colorless or white. PD 3.12, 5.93, 3.49; 9–15 (which phase?).

[53] Tilley: *Min. Mag.* XXII, p. 419 (1933).

[53a] Merwin in Ashton and Wilson: *Am. J. Sci.* XIII, p. 209 (1927).

[54] Unpub. data by F. T. Jensen (Univ. of Wis., 1933) on crystals furnished by H. Berman.

[55] Megaw: *Zeit. Krist.* XC, p. 283 (1935).

[56] C. D. West, *pers. comm.* Nov. 2, 1936.

[57] Kracek, Morey, and Merwin: *Am. J. Sci.* XXXV-A, p. 143 (1938).

[58] Tazaki: *J. Sci. Hiroshima Univ.* Ser. A, X, p. 37 (1940), *abc* changed to *cab*.

AlO(OH) (Boehmite) is orthorhombic[59] with $a = 3.69$, $b = 12.24$, $c = 2.86$ kX, U.C. 4, structure like that of lepidocrocite. Crystals thin, lenticular, flattened on {001}; usually massive. H. 3.5–4. G. 3.01–3.06 (3.11 calc.). {010} cleavage. Probably X $= a$ (elongation), Y $= c$, Z $= b$. $(+)2V^{60} =$ about 80°, $n_X = 1.646$, $[n_Y(\text{calc.}) = 1.652]$, $n_Z = 1.661$, $n_Z - n_X = 0.015$. Again:[61] $(-)2V = $ small, $n_X = n_Y = 1.649$, $n_Z = 1.665$, $n_Z - n_X = 0.016$. Earlier reports give mean index $n = 1.624$ to 1.645, but the reasons for such variation are unknown, and the reports are considered doubtful. Colorless or white. PD 6.11, 3.16, 2.35; 5–0190.

AlO(OH), made by heating $Al(OH)_3$ to about 200° C. for 50 hours, is amorphous with $n = 1.565$. When made by hydrating Al_2O_3 in steam at 125 atmospheres it has G. 3.06, $n = 1.65$ and $n_Z - n_X = $ weak—not like diaspore nor boehmite.

FeO(OH) (Lepidocrocite) is orthorhombic[62] with $a = 3.87$, $b = 12.51$, $c = 3.06$ kX. U.C. 4. Crystals {010} scales; or fibrous along a. Perfect {010} and good {001} cleavages. H. 5. G. 4.09. X $= b$, Y $= c$. $(-)2V = 83°$, $n_X = 1.94$, $n_Y = 2.20$, $n_Z = 2.51$, $n_Z - n_X = 0.57$. Color ruby-red to reddish brown. Pleochroic with X nearly colorless (to clear yellow in thicker grains), Y and Z orange to yellow to red orange (in thicker grains). Absorption X $<$ Y $<$ Z. PD 6.26, 3.29, 2.47; 8–98.

MnO(OH) (Manganite) is monoclinic[63] with $a = 8.86$, $b = 5.24$, $c = 5.70$ kX, $\beta = 90°$. U.C. 8. Pseudo-orthorhombic. Crystals striated prisms often grouped. Perfect {010} and good {001} cleavages. H. 4. G. 4.33. Y $= b$, Z $= c^{14}$; again,[64] Z $\wedge c = 4°$. $(+)2V = $ small, r $>$ v, very strong. $n_X = 2.25$ Li, $n_Y = 2.25 \pm .02$, $n_Z = 2.53$, $n_Z - n_X = 0.28$. Mass color steel gray to iron black; color in flakes for X and Y reddish brown, Z red brown with X and Y $<$ Z. PD 3.40, 2.64, 2.28; 8–99. Alters readily to pyrolusite.

LaOOH[65] is anisotropic with ill-defined crystal form and low birefringence. $n = 1.798 \pm .006$. The principal X-ray powder-pattern lines that differ from lines due to La_2O_3 are at $d = 2.959$, 2.042, 3.533, 3.243. Made hydrothermally.

NdOOH[65] forms lathlike crystals with positive elongation and parallel extinction. Birefringence low to moderate; $n = 1.850 \pm .008$. The principal

[59] Reichertz and Yost: *J. Chem. Phys.* (Am. Inst. Phys.) XIV, p. 495 (1946), *abc* changed to *cba*.

[60] Bohnstedt-Kupletskaya and Vlodavetz: *C. R. Acad. Sci. U.R.S.S.* XLIX, p. 587 (1945) [*Min. Abst.* X, p. 144].

[61] Ervin and Osborn: *J. Geol.* LIX, p. 381 (1951).

[62] Posnjak and Merwin: *Am. J. Sci.* XLVII, p. 311 (1919).

[63] Buerger: *Zeit. Krist.* XCV, p. 163 (1936).

[64] Mügge: *Centb. Min.* p. 1 (1922).

[65] Shafer and Roy: *Jour. Amer. Ceram. Soc.* XLII, p. 563 (1959).

powder lines are at d = 6.005, 2.974, 3.007, 1.981. Made hydrothermally.

SmOOH[65] forms lathlike crystals with parallel extinction and positive elongation. Birefringence moderate; n = 1.860 ± .008. The principal powder lines are at d = 1.948, 5.894, 2.929, 4.040, 1.169. Made hydrothermally.

YOOH[65] forms fibrous crystal grains with parallel extinction, positive elongation. Birefringence low to moderate; n = 1.845 ± .008. The principal X-ray powder lines are at d = 2.891, 3.986, 5.671, 4.076, 2.783. Made hydrothermally.

3. Formula Type AX$_3$

Al(OH)$_3$ (Gibbsite) is monoclinic with a = 8.624, b = 5.060, c = 9.700 kX, β = 94°34'. U.C. 4. Crystals often six-sided basal plates. Perfect basal cleavage. H. 2.5–3.5. G. 2.40. X = b, Z $\wedge$ c^{13} = $-25°$. (+)2V = 0°±. n_X = 1.566, n_Y = 1.566, n_Z = 1.587, n_Z − n_X = 0.021. Above 56° C. Y = b and Z $\wedge$ c = $-45°$ (red). Again:[66] n_X = n_Y = 1.577, n_Z = 1.595, n_Z − n_X = 0.018. Color white with pearly luster. PD 4.85, 4.37, 2.39; 7–324. Also called hydrargillite. See also bayerite.

Al(OH)$_3$ (Bayerite) is produced by rapid precipitation[66] of alumina from solution. X-ray study shows that it is not the same as gibbsite. It is weakly birefringent with a mean index n = 1.583 if dried at 110° C. and 1.55 if dried with alcohol and ether. PD 4.73, 2.22, 4.37; 8–96.

B(OH)$_3$ (Sassolite) is triclinic[57] with a = 7.04, b = 7.04, c = 6.56 kX, α = 92°30', β = 101°10', γ = 120°. U.C. 4. Crystals basal six-sided tablets or, rarely, acicular. Perfect basal cleavage. Flexible. H. 1. G. 1.48. Decomposes at 185° C. Soluble in water. X inclined 2° from normal to (001). X $\wedge$ c = 16°. The optic plane makes an angle on (001) of 17° ± 2° with (100) and 43° ± 2° with (1$\bar{1}$0). (−)2V = 10°. n_X = 1.337, n_Y = 1.461, n_Z = 1.462, n_Z − n_X = 0.125. Again:[13] n_X = 1.340, n_Y = 1.456, n_Z = 1.459, n_Z − n_X = 0.119. Color white or stained. PD 3.18, 6.04, 1.59; 9–335.

La(OH)$_3$[65] is uniaxial positive with positive elongation. n_O = 1.740, n_E = 1.768 ± .005. Stable below about 480° C. and 10,000 lbs. per sq. in. pressure of water vapor. A high-density form stable at higher pressures and temperatures has low to moderate birefringence and n = 1.760 ± .015. PD 2.962, 3.662, 2.071, 5.067, and 2.110.

Nd(OH)$_3$[65] is uniaxial positive with positive elongation. n_O = 1.740, n_E = 1.768 ± .005. Stable to a little above 400° C. under hydrothermal conditions. A high-density form stable at higher temperature and pressures above 10,000 lbs. per sq. in. water-vapor pressure has low birefringence and n = 1.78 ± .02. PD 3.930, 2.614, 2.970, 7.885, 3.375.

[66] Achenbach: *Chem. Erde*, VI p. 307 (1931).

Sm(OH)$_3$[65] is uniaxial positive with positive elongation. $n_O = 1.740$, $n_E = 1.768 \pm .005$. Stable below nearly 400° C. under hydrothermal conditions. A high-density form stable at higher temperature and pressures above 10,000 lbs. per sq. in. water-vapor pressure has low birefringence and $n = 1.780 \pm .015$. PD 2.583, 3.723, 3.089, 5.566, 2.089.

Y(OH)$_3$[65] is uniaxial positive with positive elongation. $n_O = 1.676$, $n_E = 1.714 \pm .005$. Stable at 300° C. under 2000 lbs. per sq. in. pressure of water vapor, and at increasing temperatures as the pressure is increased, to about 380° C. and 18,000 lbs. per sq. in. water-vapor pressure. There seems to be no dense polymorph analogous to those of the corresponding compounds of La, Nd, and Sm. PD 8.12, 4.09, 3.07; 9–62.

4. Miscellaneous Hydroxides

Na$_2$Sn(OH)$_6$ is hexagonal[66a] with $a = 5.956$, $c = 14.13$ Å. U.C. 3. G. 3. Crystals basal plates. Decomposes at about 250° C. Uniaxial positive with $n_O = 1.568$, $n_E = 1.582$, $n_E - n_O = 0.014$. PD 2.52, 4.75, 1.85; 1–1115.

Ca$_3$Al$_2$(OH)$_{12}$ (Hydrogrossularite)[66b] is isometric with $a = 12.56$ Å., in dodecahedral or octahedral crystals. Isotropic, with $n = 1.604 \pm .002$. Isomorphous with grossularite in the garnet group. Made hydrothermally. PD 2.71, 1.62, 3.03; 3–0801*.

4CaO·3Al$_2$O$_3$·3H$_2$O[66b] is biaxial. $(-)2V = $ large, and $n_Z - n_X = 0.005$. PD 3.59, 3.24, 1.572, 2.084, 2.156, 3.007.

C. MULTIPLE OXIDES

α. ANHYDROUS

1. Formula Type A$_m$B$_n$X$_p$ with $(m + n):p \approx 1:1$

KAlO$_2$ is isometric.[67] Crystals octahedral. Extremely hygroscopic. Isotropic with $n = 1.603$. Colorless. It may take some Ca$_4$Al$_2$Fe$_2$O$_{10}$ in solid solution raising the index to 1.625. PD 2.72, 1.57, 1.21; 2–0897.

LiFeO$_2$ is isometric[68] above 600° C. and anisotropic when crystallized below that temperature. The isometric form does not invert on cooling. Its crystals are octahedral with G. 4.368 and $n = 2.40 \pm .04$ Li. PD 2.07, 1.47, 2.39; 2–1237*.

Li$_2$TiO$_3$ is isometric.[69] G. 3.42. Isotropic with $n = 2.087$ Na. PD 2.07,

---

[66a] Krc: *Anal. Chem.* XXIII, p. 675 (1951).

[66b] Majumdar and Roy: *Jour. Amer. Ceram. Soc.* XXXIX, p. 434 (1956).

[67] Brownmiller: *Am. J. Sci.* XXIX, p. 260 (1935).

[68] Posnjak and Barth: *Phys. Rev.* XXXVIII, p. 2234 (1931).

[69] Kordes: *Zeit. Krist.* XCII, p. 139 (1935).

1.46, 1.19; 8–249. It forms mix-crystals in all proportions with 3MgO, the refractive index decreasing regularly from 2.087 to 1.7366 (the index of MgO).

LiAlO₂ forms plates or grains with G. 2.554. M.P. 1900–2000° C. Uniaxial negative[70] with $n_O = 1.624$, $n_E = 1.606$, $n_O - n_E = 0.018$. It may take some SiO_2 in crystal solution lowering the indices even to $n_O = 1.586$, $n_E = 1.570$, $n_O - n_E = 0.016$. PD 1.39, 2.37, 1.52; 1–1306.

NaAlO₂ is orthorhombic(?),[21] often twinned. M.P. 1650° C. $(-)2V = 30°$. $n_X = 1.566$, $n_Y = 1.575$, $n_Z = 1.580$, $n_Z - n_X = 0.014$. Colorless. PD 2.59, 2.54, 2.93; 2–0985.

Na₂ZrO₃ is probably orthorhombic.[71] Crystals six-sided plates produced by pseudo-hexagonal twinning. G. 4.0. $(-)2V = ?$. $n_X = 1.720$, $n_Y = ?$, $n_Z > 1.80$, $n_Z - n_X > 0.08$. Made by fusion at 1110° C. and slow cooling. PD 2.31, 1.66, 1.62; 8–242.

HAlO₂ (Diaspore) is orthorhombic with $a = 4.40$, $b = 9.39$, $c = 2.84$ kX. U.C. 4. Crystals often {010} platelets elongated along c; also foliated massive. Perfect {010} and good {110} cleavages. H. 6.5–7. G. 3.3–3.5. $X = c$, $Y = b$;[72] $(+)2V = 84-85°$. $n_X = 1.702$, $n_Y = 1.722$, $n_Z = 1.750$, $n_Z - n_X = 0.048$. Colorless or faintly tinted, but it may contain up to about 5 per cent Fe_2O_3 and then it is pleochroic with brown color and $X < Y < Z$. PD 3.99, 2.32, 2.13; 5-0355.

HFeO₂ (Goethite) is orthorhombic with $a = 4.64$, $b = 10.0$, $c = 3.03$ kX. U.C. 4. Prismatic and striated or tabular or fibrous. Perfect {010} and good {100} cleavages. H. 5–5.5. G. 4.28 (crystals), 3.3–4.3 (massive). $Y = a$ (red) and c (yellow), $Z = c$ (red) and a (yellow). $(-)2V =$ small to medium[72a] (0° at $\lambda = 610-620$), r > v strong. $n_X = 2.260$ Na, $n_Y = 2.393$, $n_Z = 2.398$, $n_Z - n_X = 0.138$. The optic angle changes with change of temperature, being 0° at 610–620° C. Pleochroic with X yellow, Y brownish yellow, Z orange yellow. PD 4.21, 2.69, 2.44; 8–97. Fibrous varieties show anomalous optical effects probably due to impurities between the fibers. Impure aggregates may be apparently isotropic with $n = 2.00 \pm$ to 2.15 $\pm$.

NaCa₄Al₃O₉ is orthorhombic (pseudo-isometric)[21] in six- or eight-sided polyhedrons with common twinning. Dissociates at 1508° C. to CaO and liquid. $(-)2V =$ medium. $n_X = 1.702 \pm 0.003$, $n_Y = 1.708$ ca., $n_Z = 1.710$, $n_Z - n_X = 0.008$. Colorless. PD 2.67, 1.55, 2.19; 2–0929.

Na₄Ca₃Al₁₀O₂₀ is stable to 1630° C. Granular. $(+)2V = ?$; mean index[21] $n = 1.592$, $n_Z - n_X = 0.005$ ca. Colorless. PD 2.57, 4.19, 3.90; 2–1003.

[70] Weyberg: *Cent. Min.* 1906, p. 645. Hatch: *Am. Min.* XXVIII, p. 471 (1943).
[71] D'Ans and Löffler: *Zeit. anorg. Chem.* CXCI, p. 1 (1930).
[72] Michel-Lévy and Lacroix: *Les Minéraux des Roches*, 1888.
[72a] Nuffield and Peacock: Univ. Toronto Stud., Geol. Ser. XLVII, p. 53 (1942).

2. Formula Type $A_mB_nX_p$ with $(m + n){:}p \approx 3{:}4$

LiAl$_5$O$_8$ is isometric with the spinel[72b] space lattice. G. 3.606. Isotropic with $n = 1.735$ D. Colorless. PD 2.39, 1.40, 1.98; 3–0911.

SPINEL GROUP

The spinel group has about a dozen end-member formulas but these are not all miscible in all proportions, indeed Fe''' replaces Al or Cr probably only to a limited extent, but Al can be replaced by Cr in any proportion. All the crystals of the spinel group are isometric. All may contain an excess of the trivalent base. The chief compounds are:

MgAl$_2$O$_4$	Spinel proper	
FeAl$_2$O$_4$	Hercynite	
MgCr$_2$O$_4$	Magnesiochromite	
FeCr$_2$O$_4$	Chromite	Spinel
ZnAl$_2$O$_4$	Gahnite	
MnAl$_2$O$_4$	Galaxite	
CoAl$_2$O$_4$	Artificial	

FeFe$_2$O$_4$	Magnetite proper	
MgFe$_2$O$_4$	Magnesioferrite	
MnFe$_2$O$_4$	Jacobsite	Magnetite
ZnFe$_2$O$_4$	Franklinite	
CdFe$_2$O$_4$	Artificial	

MgAl$_2$O$_4$ (Spinel) is isometric with $a = 8.080\,kX$. U.C. 8. Crystals often octahedral. Twinning on {111} common. Poor octahedral cleavage; cubic cleavage (or parting?) is usual in boules.[73] H. 8. G. 3.55 (3.578 calc.). M.P. 2135° C. Isotropic with $n = 1.7161$ (623), 1.7190 (578), 1.7322 (436) for the pure substance. PD 2.44, 2.02, 1.43; 5–0672*. The natural mineral is very rarely pure; MgAl$_2$O$_4$ is miscible in all proportions with FeAl$_2$O$_4$ and ZnAl$_2$O$_4$ and probably with MnAl$_2$O$_4$ and CoAl$_2$O$_4$. Miscibility is possible[73] in artificial crystals with MgCr$_2$O$_4$, FeCr$_2$O$_4$, ZnCr$_2$O$_4$ and MnCr$_2$O$_4$, but in nature these do not seem to form complete series. With 75 mol. per cent[74] Al$_2$Al$_4$O$_9$ (to 25 per cent MgAl$_2$O$_4$) $n = 1.7261$ (623), 1.7288 (578), 1.7428 (436). With 9 per cent MgFe$_2$O$_4$ in solution $n = 1.76$ Na. SiSiO$_4$ in solution may lower the index to 1.718. Colorless or blue or red from Mn, Fe, etc.; blue varieties are said to have higher indices than red types.[75] Crystals are

---

[72b] Kordes: *Zeit. Krist.* XCI, p. 193 (1935).
[73] Wilde and Rees: *Trans. Brit. Cer. Soc.* XLII, p. 123 (1943).
[74] Rinne: *N. Jahrb. Min.* LVIII A, p. 43 (1928).
[75] Gaubert: *Bull. Soc. Fr. Min.* L, p. 504 (1927).

often birefringent, probably from strain. $MgAl_2O_4$ glass has $n = 1.67-1.68$. Made from fusion for use as a gem.

$FeAl_2O_4$ (Hercynite) is isometric with $a = 8.119$ kX. U.C. 8. Crystals octahedral. Usually massive. H. 7.5. G. 4.39. M.P. 1750° C. Isotropic[76] with $n = 1.83$. Color black; streak dark grayish green. Properties of the $MgAl_2O_4$-$FeAl_2O_4$-$ZnAl_2O_4$ system are shown in Fig. 4-1. PD 2.45, 2.02, 1.43; 3-0894*.

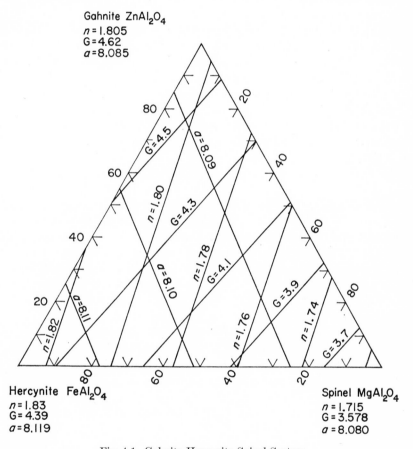

Gahnite $ZnAl_2O_4$
$n = 1.805$
$G = 4.62$
$a = 8.085$

Hercynite $FeAl_2O_4$
$n = 1.83$
$G = 4.39$
$a = 8.119$

Spinel $MgAl_2O_4$
$n = 1.715$
$G = 3.578$
$a = 8.080$

Fig. 4-1. Gahnite-Hercynite-Spinel System.

$MgCr_2O_4$ (Magnesiochromite) is isometric. G. 4.39. M.P. > 1800° C. Isotropic[15] with $n = 1.90$. Again: $n = 2.035$. Forms mix-crystals with $MgAl_2O_4$, $FeCr_2O_4$, etc. Color pale gray-green. PD 2.49, 1.47, 1.59; 9-353.

[76] Bowen and Schairer: *J. Geol.* XLVI, p. 397 (1938).

FeCr$_2$O$_4$ (Chromite) is isometric with a = 8.344 kX. U.C. 8. No cleavage. H. 5.5. G. 5.09. M.P. > 1800° C. Forms mix-crystals with MgCr$_2$O$_4$, FeAl$_2$O$_4$, etc. Isotropic with n = 2.12. With much MgAl$_2$O$_4$, n = 1.83. Color black; streak brown. Opaque except in thin splinters. Made by fusing the mixed oxides. PD 2.51, 1.91, 1.61; 4–0759*.

ZnAl$_2$O$_4$ (Gahnite) is isometric with a = 8.085 kX. U.C. 8. Crystals octahedral. H. 7.5. G. 4.62. Isotropic with[15] n = 1.805. Again:[77] n = 1.782 (natural material, probably impure). Color green to black, rarely blue. PD 2.44, 2.86, 1.43; 5–0669.

MnAl$_2$O$_4$ (Galaxite) is isometric with a = 8.271 kX. U.C. 8. Massive. H. 7.5. G. 4.03. Isotropic with n = 1.848 calc. Natural galaxite[78] (Mn$_{.90}$Fe$_{.05}$Mg$_{.05}$)(Al$_{.77}$Fe$_{.23}$)$_2$O$_4$ has G. 4.234 and n = 1.923. Color brown to black. PD 2.49, 2.92, 1.46; 10–310.

CoAl$_2$O$_4$ is isometric with[79] n > 1.78 (red), n = 1.74 (blue). This is the "cobalt blue" pigment of commerce.

FeFe$_2$O$_4$ (Magnetite) is isometric with a = 8.374 kX. U.C. 8. Crystals often octahedral or dodecahedral. Good octahedral parting. H. 5.5–6.5. G. 5.175. M.P. 1590° C. Isotropic with n = 2.42 Na. Color black; streak black. Opaque except in very thin splinters. Strongly magnetic. PD 2.53, 1.48, 2.97; 7–322. Apparently miscible in all proportions with MgFe$_2$O$_4$, ZnFe$_2$O$_4$, NiFe$_2$O$_4$ and MnFe$_2$O$_4$. Also FeFe$_2$O$_4$ may be changed artificially in whole or in part to **Fe$_2$O$_3$ (maghemite or oxymagnite).** Oxymagnite has about the structure of magnetite; has G. 4.74 calc., H. 5, and is isotropic with n = 2.52–2.74. Color brown to yellow. PD 2.52, 1.48, 2.95; 4–0755.

MgFe$_2$O$_4$ (Magnesioferrite) is isometric with a = 8.366 kX. U.C. 8. Crystals usually octahedral; often massive or granular. No cleavage. H. 6–6.5. G. 4.5. M.P. 1580°–1610° C. Soluble in HCl. Isotropic[80] with n = 2.39 Na. Color red. Strongly magnetic. PD 2.74, 2.10, 1.70; 8–479.

ZnFe$_2$O$_4$ (Franklinite) is isometric[80a] with a = 8.423 kX. U.C. 8. Crystals often octahedral. H. 5.5. G. 5.2. Poor octahedral parting. Isotropic[13] with n = 2.36 ca. Li. Color iron black; streak reddish brown to black. Opaque except in very thin splinters. Weakly magnetic. PD 2.55, 1.50, 1.99; 10–467.

CdFe$_2$O$_4$ is isometric[80] with G. 5.8. Isotropic with n = 2.39 ± .02Li. PD 2.62, 3.08, 1.67; 1–1083.

ZnGa$_2$O$_4$ is isometric. G. 6.15 calc. Isotropic with n = 1.74. PD 1.48, 2.52, 1.67; 3–1155.

[77] Simpson: *J. Roy. Soc. W. Australia* XVI, p. 25 (1930).

[78] Ross and Kerr: *Am. Min.* XVII, p. 15 (1932).

[79] Merwin: *Proc. Am. Cer. Soc.* XXXVIII, p. 2 (1917).

[80] Roberts and Merwin: *Am. J. Sci.* XXI, p. 145 (1931).

[80a] Clark, Ally and Badger: *Am. J. Sci.* XXII, p. 539 (1931).

Mg$_2$TiO$_4$ is isometric with M.P. 1732° C. Isotropic[81] with n = 1.959. PD 2.55, 2.10, 1.50; 3–0858.

Ca$_3$Al$_2$O$_6$ is isometric.[82] Conchoidal fracture. H. 6. Isotropic with n = 1.710. Also reported as pseudo-isometric[21] and isotropic or nearly so. Colorless. PD 2.70, 1.91, 1.56; 8–516.

Sr$_3$Al$_2$O$_6$ is isometric[83] in trapezohedrons. Isotropic with n = 1.728. PD 2.81, 1.62, 1.99; 9–44*.

Ba$_3$Al$_2$O$_6$ Spherulitic tablets[97] soluble in water. G. 4.54. Biaxial with n_Y = 1.735, n_Z − n_X = 0.009.

Ca$_5$Al$_6$O$_{14}$ is isometric.[82] H. 5. M.P. 1455° C. No cleavage. Isotropic with n = 1.608. As glass n = 1.662. With 1 per cent Na$_2$O, n = 1.59. With 2 per cent K$_2$O, n = 1.593. Another phase is probably orthorhombic. 2V = large. n_X = 1.687, n_Z = 1.692, n_Z − n_X = 0.005.

BaAl$_2$O$_4$ is isometric. Crystals dodecahedral with no cleavage. G. 3.99. M.P. 1820° ± 20° C. Soluble in water. Isotropic with[84] n = 1.683 ± .002. Colorless. PD 3.17, 4.56, 2.62; 2–0545.

CaFe$_2$O$_4$ is tetragonal or hexagonal.[85] It dissociates at 1216° C. Crystals long acicular. Uniaxial negative with n_O = 2.465 Li, 2.58 Na, n_E = 2.345 Li, 2.43 Na, n_O − n_E = 0.15 Na. Color in mass black; deep red in powder, not pleochroic. Formed from glass at 1190° C. It may take as much as 10 per cent CaAl$_2$O$_4$ in crystal solution; then it has n_O = 2.25 Li, n_E = 2.13, n_O − n_E = 0.12. PD 2.66, 2.52, 1.51; 8–100.

MnMn$_2$O$_4$ (Hausmannite) is tetragonal with a = 5.75, c = 9.42 kX. U.C. 4. Crystals pseudo-octahedral; granular. Perfect basal cleavage. H. 5.5. G. 4.84. Uniaxial negative with[86] n_O = 2.45 ± .02 Li, n_E = 2.15 ± .02 n_O − n_E = 0.30 ± .04. Color brownish black; not pleochroic. Streak chestnut-brown. Opaque except in thin splinters. Made by heating MnO in air. PD 2.47, 2.74, 1.54; 8–17*.

ZnMn$_2$O$_4$ (Hetaerolite) is tetragonal with a = 5.74, c = 9.15 kX. U.C. 4. Crystals pyramidal, also massive. Poor basal cleavage. H. 6. G. 5.18. Uniaxial negative with[13] n_O = 2.35, n_E = 2.10, n_O − n_E = 0.25. Color black; streak dark brown. Opaque except in thin splinters which are reddish brown with O < E. Made from fusion. PD 2.46, 2.70, 1.52; 7–354.

Pb$_3$O$_4$ (Minium) is tetragonal[86a] with a = 8.80, c = 6.56 Å. H. 2.5. G. 8.9–9.2. F. 1.5. Uniaxial negative. Mean index[15] n = 2.42 ± 0.02 Li. n_O −

[81] Coughanour and De Prosse: *J. Res. Bur. Stand.* LI, p. 85 (1953).

[82] Hansen, Brownmiller and Bogue: *J. Am. Chem. Soc.* L, p. 396 (1928).

[83] Toropov: *Dokl. Acad. Sci. U.S.S.R.* XXIII, p. 74 (1939) [*Min. Abst.* VII, p. 486].

[84] Toropov: *Dokl. Acad. Sci. U.S.S.R.* I, p. 147 (1935) [*N. Jahrb. Min.* 1935, I, p. 220].

[85] Sosman and Merwin: *J. Wash. Acad. Sci.* VI, p. 532 (1916).

[86] Larsen in Miser and Fairchild: *J. Wash. Acad. Sci.* X, p. 1 (1920).

[86a] Bystrom and Westgren: *Ark. Kemi. Min. Geol.* XVIB, No. 19 (1943) [*Struc. Rep.* XI 238].

n_E = weak. Color red. Streak orange yellow. Strongly pleochroic in thin section, with O nearly colorless, E deep reddish brown. Commonly shows abnormal green interference colors. PD 3.38, 2.90, 2.79; 8–19. Made by heating PbO in air.

$MgBeAl_4O_8$ is uniaxial negative with[87] n_O = 1.722–1.725, n_E = 1.715–1.718, $n_O - n_E$ = 0.007. Colorless. PD 2.43, 2.05, 1.43; 8–11.

$PbAl_2O_4(?)$ is uniaxial negative with[88] n_O = 1.91, n_E = 1.85, $n_O - n_E$ = 0.06. PD 3.09, 4.44, 2.23; 3–0562.

$BeAl_2O_4$ (Chrysoberyl) is orthorhombic with a = 5.47, b = 9.39, c = 4.42 kX. U.C. 4. Crystals basal tablets or varied; twinning on {130} common. Good prismatic cleavage. H. 8.5. G. 3.75. M.P. between 1855° and 1880° C. X = c, Y = b. (+)2V = 70°, r > v. n_X = 1.732, n_Y = ?, n_Z = 1.741, $n_Z - n_X$ = 0.009 (artificial). Averages with some iron:[89] n_X = 1.746, n_Y = 1.748, n_Z = 1.756, $n_Z - n_X$ = 0.010. Optic angle variable, may be as low as 10°. At high temperature Y = a. Color green; rarely yellow or red. Pleochroic with (for example) X columbine-red, Y orange yellow, Z emerald-green. One variety, a gem stone called alexandrite, is emerald-green in day light but columbine-red in artificial light. Made from fusion. PD 2.09, 1.62, 3.23; 10–82.

$CaAl_2O_4$ is orthorhombic[90] or monoclinic. Prismatic to fibrous. Distinct prismatic cleavage. Pseudo-hexagonal twinning on {130}. H. 6.5. G. 2.98. M.P. 1600° C. Soluble in HCl. X = c; Y = b. (−)2V = 56°. n_X = 1.643, n_Y = 1.655, n_Z = 1.663, $n_Z - n_X$ = 0.020. Colorless. Formed from fusion. It may take as much as 15 per cent $CaFe_2O_4$ in crystal solution; then it has n_X = 1.70±, n_Z = 1.72±, $n_Z - n_X$ = 0.020±. Important in cements.

$SrAl_2O_4$ has pseudo-hexagonal twinning[83] with perfect cleavage in one direction. Biaxial with n_X = 1.649, n_Y = ?, n_Z = 1.663, $n_Z - n_X$ = 0.014. PD 3.14, 3.05, 2.98; 9–39.

$Ca_2Fe_2O_5$ is orthorhombic.[91] It dissociates at 1436° C. (+)2V = moderate. n_X = 2.20 Li, 2.25 Na, n_Y = 2.22 Li, n_Z = 2.29 Li, $n_Z - n_X$ = 0.09 Li. Color yellow-brown with X > Y = Z. It forms mix-crystals with $Ca_2Al_2O_5$ at least to $Ca_6Al_4Fe_2O_{15}$.

$Ca_4Al_2Fe_2O_{10}$ (Brownmillerite) is orthorhombic.[92] G. 3.77. M.P. 1415° C. (−)2V = 75° calc. n_X = 1.96 Li, n_Y = 2.01, n_Z = 2.04, $n_Z - n_X$ =

[87] Geller, Yavorsky, Steierman and Creamer: *J. Res. Nat. Bur. Stand.* XXXVI, p. 277 (1946). [*Min. Abst.* XI, p. 369 (1951).]

[88] Geller and Bunting: *J. Res. Nat. Bur. Stand.* XXXI, p. 255 (1943).

[89] Palache, Berman and Frondel: *Dana's System of Mineralogy* I, p. 718 (1944).

[90] Rankin and Merwin: *J. Am. Chem. Soc.* XXXVIII, p. 568 (1916). Carstens: *Zeit. Krist.* LXIII, p. 473 (1926).

[91] Agrell: *J. Iron Steel Inst. London* CLII, p. 19 (1945).

[92] Bogue: *Chemistry of Portland Cement*, 1947.

0.08. It may have MgO in solid solution; then $n_X = 1.92$, $n_Y = ?$, $n_Z = 1.97$, G. 3.72. Pleochroic with X yellow-brown, Z brown. Also said to be monoclinic with a very small extinction angle. Found in Portland cement.

$Ca_6Al_4Fe_2O_{15}$ is orthorhombic.[93] Crystals tabular. Decomposes at 1365° C. $(-)2V$ = small. $n_X = 1.94$, $n_Y = ?$, $n_Z = 1.99$, $n_Z - n_X = 0.05$. Found in Portland cement mixes.

$CaCr_2O_4$ is orthorhombic(?). M.P. 2000° C. $\pm$. Biaxial.[94] Extinction parallel with cleavage and elongation. Refractive indices very high. Green and pleochroic. Found in chrome-dolomite refractories. Polymorphous. PD 5.51, 2.76, 2.29; 9-151*.

$CaAl_4O_7$ has two crystal phases.[76] The α-phase is monoclinic.[95] H. 6.5. Melts incongruently at about 1765° C. Z $\wedge$ elongation[96] = 39°. $(+)2V = 0°-5°$. $n_X \approx n_Y = 1.617$, $n_Z = 1.651$, $n_Z - n_X = 0.035$. The β-phase is probably orthorhombic; it is unstable. Prismatic cleavage. H. 5.5-6. Z parallel elongation. $(-)2V = 35°$, r > v strong. $n_X = 1.662$, $n_Y = 1.671$, $n_Z = 1.674$, $n_Z - n_X = 0.012$. Colorless. Made from fusion. PD 3.52, 2.61, 4.44; 7-82.

$SrAl_4O_7$ is monoclinic(?) in prisms with extinction[84] reaching 45°. $(+)2V$ = large. $n_X = 1.614$, $n_Y = ?$, $n_Z = 1.640$, $n_Z - n_X = 0.026$, $\therefore n_Y = 1.625$ ca.

$Ca_3Fe_2O_6$ is monoclinic.[91] Crystals acicular with a small extinction angle to Z. n_X decidedly greater than 1.73; $n_Z - n_X = 0.017$ ca. Metallic and dead black in reflected light. Opaque to deep ruby red in tiny needles.

Ca_2GeO_4 is triclinic.[98] Crystals are white or slightly greenish. $n_X = 1.724$, $n_Y = ?$, $n_Z = 1.739$, $n_Z - n_X = 0.015$.

3. Formula Type $A_mB_nX_p$ with $(m+n){:}p \approx 2{:}3$

$SrTiO_3$ is isometric with[99] $a = 3.90$ Å. Conchoidal fracture. H. 6-6.5. G. 5.12. M.P. 2080° C. Isotropic with $n = 2.380$ C, 2.409 D, 2.488 F. $n_F - n_C = 0.108$. Color often dark blue to black; but when fully oxidized water-white. Slight impurities cause various colors including yellow, red and blue. PD 2.76, 1.95, 1.59; 5-0634.

[93] Swayze: *Am. J. Sci.*, CCXLIV, p. 1 and 65 (1946).

[94] Rigby: *Thin Section Mineralogy of Ceramic Materials* (1948).

[95] Goldsmith: *J. Geol.* LVI, p. 80 (1948) and *Am. Min.* XXXIV, p. 471 (1949). Goldsmith shows that the compound formerly described as $Ca_3Al_{10}O_{18}$ is actually $CaAl_4O_7$.

[96] Sundius: *Symposium on Chemistry of Cements*, p. 395 (1938).

[97] Carlson and Wells: *J. Res. Nat. Bur. Stand.* XLI, p. 103 (1948).

[98] Zhuravlev: *Dokl. Akad. Nauk. U.S.S.R.* LIX, p. 1145 (1948). [*Chem. Abst.* XLII, p. 7186 (1948)].

[99] Merker: *Min. Eng.* VII, p. 645 (1955).

CaAl$_{12}$O$_{19}$ is hexagonal with $a = 5.536$, $c = 21.825$. G. 3.54–3.9. Uniaxial negative[100] with $n_O = 1.757$, $n_E = 1.750$, $n_O - n_E = 0.007$ (with very little SiO$_2$, TiO$_2$, and Fe$_2$O$_3$). With[100] SiO$_2$ 2.08, TiO$_2$ 8.78, Fe$_2$O$_3$ 0.75 per cent., $n_O = 1.790$, $n_E = 1.780$, $n_O - n_E = 0.010$. Colorless to blue or green. PD 1.39, 2.48, 2.11; 7–85.

SrAl$_{12}$O$_{19}$ has perfect basal cleavage. It is uniaxial negative with $n_O = 1.702$, $n_E = 1.694$, $n_O - n_E = 0.008$. Colorless. PD 2.63, 2.48, 2.11; 10–66.

BaAl$_{12}$O$_{19}$ is hexagonal with basal cleavage. G. 3.69. Uniaxial negative with[84] $n_O = 1.702$, $n_E = 1.694$, $n_O - n_E = 0.008$.

Na$_2$Al$_{12}$O$_{19}$ is hexagonal with G. 3.33. Uniaxial negative with[101] $n_O = 1.686$, $n_E = 1.650$, $n_O - n_E = 0.036$. Again: $n_O = 1.670$, $n_E = 1.633$, $n_O - n_E = 0.037$. Colorless.

K$_2$Al$_{12}$O$_{19}$ (β-alumina) is hexagonal. G. 2.40. Uniaxial negative with[101] $n_O = 1.696$, $n_E = 1.660$, $n_O - n_E = 0.036$. Again:[102] $n_O = 1.668$, $n_E = 1.64$, $n_O - n_E = 0.028$. Colorless. PD 1.40, 2.51, 2.69; 1–1301.

FeTiO$_3$ (Ilmenite) is hexagonal with $a = 5.083$, $c = 14.04$ kX. Crystals often basal tablets. H. 5.5–6. G. 4.72 $\pm$ .04. Uniaxial negative with high indices and very strong birefringence. Color iron black; streak black. Opaque except in very thin splinters, which transmit only red light. Percentage reflection for all colors: 18. Probably forms a complete series of mix-crystals with MgTiO$_3$ and also with MnTiO$_3$. PD 2.74, 1.72, 2.54; 3–0781.

MgTiO$_3$ (Geikielite) is hexagonal with $a = 5.086$, $c = 14.093$ kX. H. 5–6. G. 4.05. M.P. 1630° C. Rhombohedral cleavage. Uniaxial negative with[13] $n_O = 2.31$, $n_E = 1.95$, $n_O - n_E = 0.36$. Again[81] $n_O = 2.28$, $n_E = 1.95$. Color brownish black; in thin section purplish red with O < E, faint. PD 2.72, 2.22, 2.53; 6–0494.

MnTiO$_3$ (Pyrophanite) is hexagonal with $a = 5.126$, $c = 14.333$. Crystals fine scales. Perfect $\{02\bar{2}1\}$ cleavage. H. 5–6. G. 4.54. Uniaxial negative with[13] $n_O = 2.481$ Na, $n_E = 2.210$ Na, $n_O - n_E = 0.271$ Na. Also $n_O = 2.441$ Li. Color deep blood-red; yellowish red in section; not pleochroic. PD 2.79, 2.58, 1.75; 2–0846.

Al$_2$TiO$_5$ is orthorhombic with[103] $a = 9.60$, $b = 9.63$, $c = 3.60$ Å. G. 3.62. M.P. 1890° C. Parallel extinction. $n_X = 1.98$, $n_Z = 2.04$, $n_Z - n_X = 0.06$. Again: $n_X = 2.025$, $n_Z = 2.06$, $n_Z - n_X = 0.035 - 0.04$. PD 2.66, 1.60, 4.74; 9–252.

[100] Filonenko: *C. R. Acad. Sci. U.R.S.S.* XLVIII, p. 430 (1945) [*Min. Abst.* IX, p. 282].

[101] Tropov and Stukalova: *Dokl. Akad. Sci. U.S.S.R.* XXIV, p. 459 (1939).

[102] Kato and Yamaguchi: *J. Jap. Ceram. Assoc.* LI, p. 465, 543, 586, 640 (1943) [*Chem. Abst.* XLV, p. 7755 (1951)].

[103] Yamaguchi: *J. Jap. Ceram. Assoc.* LII, p. 6 (1944) [*Chem. Abst.* XLV, p. 7925 (1951)].

Ca$_3$Ti$_2$O$_7$ has parallel extinction and positive elongation.[104] Uniaxial (or nearly so) and negative. $n_O = 2.22$, $n_E = 2.16$, $n_O - n_E = 0.06$. PD 1.95, 4.9, 9.7; 6–0698.

BaTiO$_3$ has at least three crystal phases.[105] The stable phase above 120° C. is isometric[105a] with $n = 2.40$ at 20° C., 2.46 at 120° C. and 2.42 at 140° C. Another phase is tetragonal, but optic data are not known. A third phase (stable below 5° C.) is biaxial orthorhombic with[106] $(-)2V = $ large, $n_X = 2.395$, $n_Y = 2.401$, $n_Z = 2.406$, $n_Z - n_X = 0.011$ at 20° C. $(-?)2V = $ large, $n_X = 2.40$, $n_Y = 2.405$, $n_Z = 2.410$, $n_Z - n_X = 0.010$ at 90° C. $(-?)2V = $ large, $n_X = 2.456$, $n_Y = 2.46$, $n_Z = 2.466$, $n_Z - n_X = 0.010$ at 115° C. The birefringence is[107] 0.056 at 20° C., 0.038 at 90° C. and 0.018 at 115° C. PD 2.83, 2.31, 2.00; 5–0626.

CaTiO$_3$ (Perovskite) is pseudo-isometric and orthorhombic (or monoclinic?). Crystals apparently cubic, rarely octahedral. Poor {001} cleavage. H. 5.5. G. 4.01, increasing to 4.88 when Ce replaces some Ca. Isotropic or weakly birefringent. $Y = c$, $X = a$ in the orthorhombic interpretation or $Y = b$, $Z \wedge c$ (or a) $= 45°$ in the monoclinic interpretation. $(+)2V = 90°\pm$, r > v, mean index[13] $n = 2.38$ (or, with Ce, 2.30–2.37; with Cb, $2.33 \pm .02$). Often contains rare earths and may contain Cb, Na, Fe, Mg, etc. Color black or brown or yellow. Black samples opaque except in thin splinters. PD 2.70, 1.91, 1.56; 9–365*.

PbZrO$_3$ is orthorhombic[105a] (like one phase of BaTiO$_3$). $X = a$, $Y = b$, $Z = c$. $(-)2V$ near 90°. n_Z about 2.2, $n_Z - n_X = 0.039$. (Therefore, $n_Y \approx 2.180$ and $n_X = 2.161$. A.N.W.). PD 2.94, 1.70, 1.46; 3–0655.

MgTi$_2$O$_5$ is biaxial with[108] M.P. 1652° C., $n_X = 2.19$, $n_Y = ?$, $n_Z = 2.32$, $n_Z - n_X = 0.13$. Again:[81] $(-)2V = 70°$ calc., $n_X = 2.11$, $n_Y = 2.19$, $n_Z = 2.23$, $n_Z - n_X = 0.12$. Formed in slags rich in titanium. PD 3.51, 2.75, 1.88; 9–16.

Fe$_2$TiO$_5$ (Pseudobrookite) is orthorhombic with $a = 9.79$, $b = 9.93$, $c = 3.725$ kX. U.C. 4. Crystals {100} tablets or prismatic and vertically striated. Distinct {010} cleavage. H. 6. G. 4.39. $X = b$, $Y = c$. $(+)2V = 50°\pm$, r < v. $n_X = 2.38$ Li, $n_Y = 2.39$, $n_Z = 2.42$, $n_Z - n_X = 0.04$. Color brown with $X < Y > Z$. Formed as a sublimation product. PD 3.48, 2.75, 4.90; 9–162.

TiTi$_2$O$_5$ (Anosovite) is orthorhombic with[108] $a = 3.747$, $b = 9.465$, $c = $

---

[104] Fisk: *J. Am. Ceram. Soc.* XXXIV, p. 9 (1951) [*Chem. Abst.* XLV, p. 2643 (1951)].

[105] Matthias and von Hippel: *Phys. Rev.* LXXIII, p. 268 (1948).

[105a] Jona, Shirane and Pepinsky: *Phys. Rev.* XCVII, p. 1581 (1955).

[106] Bush, Fleury and Merz: *Helv. Phys. Acta*, XXI, p. 212 (1948).

[107] Merz: *Phys. Rev.* LXXVI, p. 1221 (1949).

[108] Belyankin and Lapin: *Dokl. Akad. Sci. U.S.S.R.* LXXX, p. 421 (1951) [*Min. Abst.* XI, p. 415]. Also Rusakov and Zhdanov: *Dokl. Akad. Sci. U.S.S.R.* LXXVI, p. 411 (1951) [*Min. Abst.* XI, p. 415].

9.715 Å. It may contain some Mg, Fe, Mn, Al. G. > 4.19 (calc. 4.29). $n_X = 2.19$, $n_Y = ?$, $n_Z = 2.32$, $n_Z - n_X = 0.13$. Color black. X-ray pattern nearly the same as that of $MgTi_2O_5$, but the maximum content of Mg is $MgO:TiO_2 = 1:44$. Composition is somewhat in doubt. Formed in titanium-rich slags. PD 3.46, 2.70, 1.85; 9–309.

4. Formula Type $A_mB_nX_p$ with $(m + n):p \approx 1:2$

KReO₄ is tetragonal with[109] $c/a = 1.582$. Crystals pyramidal. Uniaxial positive with $n_O = 1.643$, $n_E = 1.673$, $n_E - n_O = 0.030$. PD 3.40, 5.19, 2.12; 8–44.

KMnO₄ is orthorhombic[110] with $a = 7.394$, $b = 9.098$, $c = 5.730$ Å. U.C. 4. G. 2.70. (2.74). Y $= a$; Z $= c$. $(+)2V = 80°$. $n_X = 1.765$, $n_Y = 1.78$, $n_Z = 1.81$, $n_Z - n_X = 0.045$ for λ 10000 Å. For $\lambda = 5893$ Å: $n_X = 1.80 \pm 0.02$, $n_Y = ?$, $n_Z = 1.85 \pm 0.02$, $n_Z - n_X = 0.05\pm$. Color black to purple. Opaque except in thin splinters. PD 3.22, 3.57, 2.95; 7–23.

β. HYDRATED

1. Formula Type $A_mB_nX_p \cdot xH_2O$ with $(m + n):p \approx 1:1$

Ca₄Al₂O₇·12–14H₂O has at least three phases. The α-phase[111] forms pseudo-hexagonal plates with $(-)2V = 10°$, $n_X = 1.520\pm$, n_Y nearly $= n_Z = 1.535 - 1.539$, $n_Z - n_X = 0.015 - 0.019$. The β-phase is often twinned; it has $(-)2V = 14°$, $n_X = 1.505 - 1.507$, n_Y nearly $= n_Z = 1.532 - 1.535$, $n_Z - n_X = 0.027 - 0.028$. A third phase is uniaxial negative with[112] $n_O = 1.549$, $n_E = 1.527 - 1.533$, $n_O - n_E = 0.016 - 0.022$. The mineral, **hydrocalumite,** has the same composition,[112a] but it is considered to be a hydrous hydroxide—**Ca₄Al₂(OH)₁₄·6H₂O**. It is monoclinic with $a = 9.6$, $b = 11.4$, $c = 16.84$ kX, $\beta = 111°$. U.C. 4. It has perfect basal cleavage and one poor cleavage inclined 60° to (100). H. 3. G. 2.15. X $\wedge c < 3°$; Y $= b$. $(-)2V = 24° \pm 2°$. $n_X = 1.535$, $n_Y = 1.553$, $n_Z = 1.557$, $n_Z - n_X = 0.022$. Colorless. PD 8.33, 7.73, 4.02; 2–0077* (which phase?).

Ca₄Al₂O₇·8H₂O is uniaxial negative[112] with $n_O = 1.519$, $n_E = 1.506$, $n_O - n_E = 0.013$. Colorless.

Ca₆Al₂O₉·33H₂O forms needles with X parallel with the elongation. Uniaxial negative with[113] $n_O = 1.475$, $n_E = 1.466$, $n_O - n_E = 0.009$. Colorless.

[109] Machatschki: *Zeit. Krist.* LXXII, p. 541 (1930).
[110] McCrone: *Anal. Chem.* XXII, p. 1459 (1950).
[111] Assarsson: *Zeit. anorg. Chem.* CC, p. 385 (1931).
[112] Wells, Clarke and McMurdie: *J. Res. Nat. Bur. Stand.* XXX, p. 367 (1943).
[112a] Tilley: *Min. Mag.* XXIII, p. 607 (1934).
[113] Flint and Wells: *J. Res. Nat. Bur. Stand.* XXX, p. 471 (1944).

$Ca_5Al_2O_8 \cdot 34H_2O$ is hexagonal.[111] Uniaxial negative with $n_O = 1.487$, $n_E = 1.480$, $n_O - n_E = 0.007$. Colorless.

2. Formula Type $A_mB_nX_p \cdot xH_2O$ with $(m + n):p \approx 3:4$

$BaAl_2O_4 \cdot H_2O$ is isometric. Crystals dodecahedral. Isotropic with[114] $n = 1.644$. Colorless.

$Ca_3Al_2O_6 \cdot 6H_2O$ is isometric with[115] G. 2.52. Isotropic with $n = 1.604$. Colorless. PD 5.16, 2.30, 2.04; 3–0125*.

$Ca_3Fe_2O_6 \cdot 6H_2O$ is isometric hexoctahedral with[116] $a = 12.74$ Å. Isotropic with $n = 1.710$. Isomorphous with $Ca_3Al_2O_6 \cdot 6H_2O$. Another phase is hexagonal with $n = 1.61–1.66$.

$Zn_2Mn_4O_8 \cdot H_2O$ **(Hydrohetaerolite)** is apparently tetragonal; often fibrous along [110]. Cleavage parallel to axis [110]. H. 5.5–6. G. 4.6(?). Uniaxial negative with[13] $n_O = 2.26 \pm .02$, $n_E = 2.10 \pm .02$, $n_O - n_E = 0.16$. Color dark brown to black; streak brown. Opaque except in thin splinters which are dark brown. PD 2.47, 2.66, 1.51; 9–459.

$Ca_3Al_2O_6 \cdot 18H_2O$ is orthorhombic[117] in needles with vertical striations. Often in rosettes. Negative elongation. Cleavage normal to the optic plane. $(-)2V = 75°$ ca. $n_X = 1.479 \pm .003$, $n_Y = 1.489 \pm .002$, $n_Z = 1.495 \pm .003$, $n_Z - n_X = 0.016$. Colorless.

$BaAl_2O_4 \cdot 2H_2O$ forms flat plates,[114] often aggregated, with parallel extinction. $(+)2V = ?$. $n_X = 1.610$, $n_Y = ?$, $n_Z = 1.613$, $n_Z - n_X = 0.003$.

$BaAl_2O_4 \cdot 4H_2O$ forms prisms,[114] often twinned. $(+)2V = 40°$ calc.; $n_X = 1.625$, $n_Y = 1.628$, $n_Z = 1.650$, $n_Z - n_X = 0.025$.

$BaAl_2O_4 \cdot 6H_2O$ (with slight excess of Ba) forms needles,[114] probably orthorhombic, with Z parallel with elongation. $(+)2V = ?$, $n_X = 1.535$, $n_Y = ?$, $n_Z = 1.540$, $n_Z - n_X = 0.005$.

$BaAl_2O_4 \cdot 7H_2O$ forms thin nearly rectangular flakes[114] with Z parallel with the elongation. $n_X = 1.538$, $n_Y = ?$, $n_Z = 1.556$, $n_Z - n_X = 0.018$.

$Ba_2Al_2O_5 \cdot 5H_2O$ forms monoclinic(?) crystals[118] nearly equant. G. 3.42. $(+)2V = 75°$ calc. $n_X = 1.642$, $n_Y = 1.655$, $n_Z = 1.676$, $n_Z - n_X = 0.034$. PD 2.07, 6.11, 1.76; 2–1232.

$CaAl_2O_4 \cdot 10H_2O$ forms hexagonal plates[119] with negative elongation. G. 1.95. Mean refractive index is 1.48. With $6–8H_2O$ it is uniaxial positive with $n_O = 1.489$ Na, $n_E = 1.507$, $n_E - n_O = 0.018$. Colorless when pure.

$Ca_2Al_2O_5 \cdot 7–9H_2O$ is hexagonal in thin basal plates, often spherulitic. G.

---

[114] Carlson and Wells: *J. Res. Nat. Bur. Stand.* XLI, p. 103 (1948).

[115] Thorvaldson and Grace: *Canad. J. Res.* I, p. 36 (1929).

[116] Flint, McMurdie and Wells: *J. Res. Nat. Bur. Stand.* XXVI, p. 13 (1941).

[117] Mylius: *Acta Acad. Abo, Math. Phys.* VII, No. 3 (1933).

[118] Geller and Bunting: *J. Res. Nat. Bur. Stand.*, XXXI, p. 255 (1943).

[119] Assarsson: *Zement* XXVI, p. 293 (1937).

1.95. Uniaxial negative with[112] $n_O = 1.522$, $n_E = 1.502$, $n_O - n_E = 0.020$. Again:[119] $n_O = 1.519$, $n_E = 1.506$, $n_O - n_E = 0.013$. Also reported with $(-)2V = 7°$. Colorless.

$Ca_3Al_2O_6 \cdot 10-12H_2O$ is hexagonal. Uniaxial negative with[112] notable variation in the indices (due to variation in H_2O?); for example: with $11H_2O$, $n_O = 1.530$, $n_E = 1.510$, $n_O - n_E = 0.020$; with[115] $?H_2O$: $n_O = 1.520$, $n_E = 1.504$, $n_O - n_E = 0.016$. Colorless. This is said to be an intimate mixture[112] of $Ca_2Al_2O_5 \cdot 8H_2O$ and $Ca_4Al_2O_7 \cdot 13H_2O$ in equal portions. PD 7.65, 3.77, 2.86; 2–0083.

3. Formula Type $A_mB_nX_p \cdot xH_2O$ with $(m + n):p \approx 1:2$

$(Ca,Na_2)U_2O_7 \cdot nH_2O$ **(Clarkeite)** often contains some Pb and K and there may be a complete $Ca-Na_2$ series.[120] H_2O is common, but was probably absent in the synthetic product. H. 4–5. G. 6.39. The mean refractive index is above 2.00 for the Ca compound and about 1.84 for the Na compound. An intermediate sample found in nature as an alteration product of uraninite (UO_2) has $(-)2V = 30-50°$, $n_X = 1.997$, $n_Y = 2.098$, $n_Z = 2.180$, $n_Z - n_X = 0.117$. Color yellow to brown. Made from uranyl nitrate solutions and $CaCO_3$ or CaO at about 260° C. PD 3.17, 3.34, 5.77; 8–315.

$CuO \cdot UO_3 \cdot 2H_2O$ **(Vandenbrandeite)** is triclinic. Crystals basal plates or laths. Perfect {001} cleavage with distinct cleavage normal to it and another poor cleavage. H. 4. G. 5.03. An optic axis nearly normal to {001}; $Z \wedge$ elongation[121] $= 40°\pm$. $(-?)2V = $ large. $n_X = 1.77 \pm .02$, $n_Y = 1.78 \pm .02$, $n_Z = 1.80 \pm .02$, $n_Z - n_X = 0.03$. Again:[121a] $n_X = 1.765 \pm .005$, $n_Y = 1.792 \pm .002$, 2V near 90° for triclinic natural material with $a = 7.84$, $b = 5.43$, $c = 6.09$ kX, $\alpha = 91°52'$, $\beta = 102°00'$, $\gamma = 89°37'$. PD 4.44, 5.26, 2.97; 8–325*.

4. Formula Type $A_mB_nX_p \cdot xH_2O$ with $(m + n):p \approx 2:5$

$PbO \cdot 4UO_3 \cdot 5H_2O(?)$ **(Fourmarierite)** is orthorhombic with[122] $a:b:c = 0.982:1:0.811$. Crystals {010} plates, long parallel to c. Perfect {010} cleavage. H. 3–4. G. 6.05. $X = b$; $Y = a$. $(-)2V$ large, $r > v$ strong.[15] $n_X = 1.85$, $n_Y = 1.92$, $n_Z = 1.94$, $n_Z - n_X = 0.09$. Color red to brown; pleochroic with X colorless, Y pale yellow, Z yellow. Made from solution at 100° C. PD 3.08, 3.43, 1.90; 8–303*.

$PbO \cdot 3UO_3 \cdot 2H_2O(?)$ **(Curite)** is orthorhombic with $a = 12.52$, $b = 12.98$, $c = 8.35$ Å. Crystals prismatic; usually massive. {100} cleavage. H. 4–5. G. 7.2. $X = b$; $Y = a$. $(-)2V = $ large, $r > v$ strong. $n_X = 2.06$,

[120] Gruner: *Am. Min.* XXXIX, p. 836 (1954).

[121] Schoep: *Ann. Mus. Congo Belge* I, No. 3, p. 25 (1932).

[121a] Milne and Nuffield, *Am. Min.*, p. 394 (1951).

[122] *abc* changed to *cab* to make $b > a > c$.

$n_Y = 2.11$, $n_Z = 2.15$, $n_Z - n_X = 0.09$. Again:[122a] $n_X = 2.05$, $n_Y = 2.08$, $n_Z = 2.12$, $n_Z - n_X = 0.07$. Color orange-red; pleochroic with X pale yellow, Y light red-orange, Z dark red-orange. Made from solution[123] at 180° C. and higher, PD 6.28, 3.97, 3.14; 8–292.

D. COMPOUND OXIDES

NaCaCb$_2$O$_6$F (Pyrochlore) is isometric hexoctahedral. $a = 10.37$ Å. Crystals octahedral; also granular. Octahedral cleavage (or parting?) distinct to poor. H. 5–5.5. G. 4.5±. Isotropic with[13] $n = 1.96$, increasing with tenor of Ta. Forms a continuous series of mix-crystals with NaCaTa$_2$O$_6$F (microlite) and usually contains other elements including K, Mg, Fe, Mn, Ce, La, Ti, etc. Colorless, yellow, brown. May show weak anomalous birefringence or a zonal structure in shades of brown or yellow. The index probably decreases with alteration by hydration; on ignition n increases to 2.0–2.2. PD 1.84, 1.57, 1.19; 3–1100.

(Na,Ca)$_2$Ta$_2$O$_6$(O,OH,F) (Microlite) is isometric[124]. $a = 10.42$ Å. Crystals octahedral with poor octahedral cleavage. G. 6.12. Isotropic with[124] $n = 2.055$. Forms mix-crystals with NaCaCb$_2$O$_6$F, and usually contains other elements including K, Mg, Fe, Mn, Ce, La, Ti, etc. Colorless, yellow, brown, etc. The index probably decreases with alteration by hydration; on ignition (changing from the metamict to the crystalline state) n increases to 2.0–2.2. PD 1.57, 1.84, 3.00; 3–1139.

Mg$_6$Al$_2$(OH)$_{16}$CO$_3$·4H$_2$O (Hydrotalcite) is hexagonal with $a = 6.13$, $c = 46.15$ Å. U.C. 3. Crystals basal tablets. Massive or lamellar. Perfect basal cleavage. H. 2. G. 2.06. Uniaxial negative with[125] $n_O = 1.511$, $n_E = 1.495$, $n_O - n_E = 0.016$. Also small 2V due to strain. Again:[125] $n_O = 1.510$–1.518, $n_E = 1.494$–1.504, $n_O - n_E = 0.012$–0.017. Colorless. Found in boiler deposits.

Ca$_4$Al$_2$O$_6$Cl$_2$·10H$_2$O is hexagonal[125a] in basal plates with $c/a = 2.067$. Uniaxial negative with $n_O = 1.550$, $n_E = 1.535$, $n_O - n_E = 0.015$. Again:[117] $n_O = 1.552$, $n_E = 1.533$, $n_O - n_E = 0.019$. Colorless. Below 36° C. it is monoclinic and pseudo-hexagonal in basal plates with complex twinning and $a:b:c = 0.579:1:1.378$, $\beta = 92°40'$. G. 1.89. Y = b; an optic axis is nearly normal to (001).

Ca$_4$Al$_2$O$_6$Br$_2$·8–10H$_2$O is hexagonal.[117] Crystals basal plates. Uniaxial negative. With 8H$_2$O: $n_O = 1.570$, $n_E = 1.558$, $n_O - n_E = 0.012$. With 10H$_2$O: $n_O = 1.556$, $n_E = 1.546$, $n_O - n_E = 0.010$. Colorless.

[122a] Branche, Chervet and Guillemin, *Bull. Soc. Fr. Min. Crist.* LXXIV, p. 457 (1951).
[123] Gruner: *Am. Min.* XXXVIII, p. 342 (1953).
[124] Pecora, Switzer, Barbosa and Myers: *Am. Min.* XXXV, p. 899 (1950).
[125] Frondel: *Am. Min.* XXVI, p. 295 (1941).
[125a] Wells: *J. Res. Nat. Bur. Stand.* I, p. 951 (1928).

$Ca_4Al_2O_6I_2 \cdot 8H_2O$ is hexagonal.[117] Crystals platy spherulites. Uniaxial negative with $n_O = 1.575 \pm 0.002$, $n_E = 1.572 \pm 0.002$, $n_O - n_E = 0.003$. Colorless.

$Ca_4Al_2O_6 \cdot CO_2 \cdot 11H_2O$ forms hexagonal plates. Uniaxial negative[126] with $n_O = 1.552$, $n_E = 1.532$, $n_O - n_E = 0.020$. Colorless.

$Ca_4Al_2O_6(NO_3)_2 \cdot 10H_2O$ forms hexagonal plates often in spherulitic groups. Uniaxial positive with[117] $n_O = 1.502$, $n_E = 1.532$, $n_E - n_O = 0.030$. Colorless.

$Ca_4Al_2O_6 \cdot (ClO_3)_2 \cdot 10H_2O$ forms hexagonal plates often in spherulitic groups. Uniaxial (positive?) with[117] $n_O = 1.519$–1.521, $n_E = 1.521$, $n_E - n_O = 0.002$–0.000. Colorless.

$Ca_4Al_2O_7 \cdot (CH_3 \cdot CO_2)_2 \cdot 8H_2O$ forms thin hexagonal plates mostly in spherulitic groups. Uniaxial negative with[117] $n_O = 1.549$, $n_E = 1.538$, $n_O - n_E = 0.011$. Colorless.

$Ca_4Al_2O_7 \cdot SO_3 \cdot 12H_2O$ forms hexagonal plates often in spherulitic groups. Uniaxial negative with[127] $n_O = 1.504$, $n_E = 1.488$, $n_O - n_E = 0.016$.

$Ca_4Al_2O_7 \cdot SiO_2 \cdot 12H_2O$ is hexagonal. Uniaxial negative with[128] $n_O = 1.538$, $n_E = 1.523$, $n_O - n_E = 0.015$.

$Ca_5Al_2O_8(IO_3)_2 \cdot 22H_2O$ forms long needles, probably hexagonal. Uniaxial negative with $n_O = 1.521$, $n_E = 1.496$, $n_O - n_E = 0.025$.

$Ca_6Al_2O_9 \cdot (IO_3)_2 \cdot 33H_2O$ forms long needles, probably hexagonal. Very weakly birefringent with mean $n = 1.471$.

$Mg_4Al_{10}Si_2O_{23}$ (**Sapphirine**) is monoclinic with $a = 9.70$, $b = 14.55$, $c = 10.05$ Å, $\beta = 111°27'$. H. 7.5. G. 3.4–3.5. Incongruent melting[128] at 1475° C. Y $= b$; Z $\wedge$ c $= 6°$–$9°$. Mg may be replaced, at least in part, by Fe. With very little Fe (only 0.65 per cent FeO): $(-)2V = 68°49'$, $n_X = 1.7055$, $n_Y = 1.7088$, $n_Z = 1.7112$ (red), $n_Z - n_X = 0.0057$. With 3.09 FeO: $(-)2V = 50°30'$, $n_X = 1.714$, $n_Y = 1.719$, $n_Z = 1.720$ Na, $n_Z - n_X = 0.006$. With 9.08 FeO : $(-)2V$ rather large, $n_X = 1.729$ Na, $n_Y = ?$, $n_Z = 1.734$, $n_Z - n_X = 0.005$. Color pale blue (darker with Fe). Made from fusion.

[126] Jones: *Symposium on Chemistry of Cements*, p. 231 (1938).

[127] Lerch, Aston and Bogue: *J. Res. Nat. Bur. Stand.* II, p. 715 (1929).

[128] Keith and Schairer: *J. Geol.* LX, p. 181 (1952).

V. Carbonates, Nitrates, and Halates

All artificially produced carbonates, nitrates and halates whose optical properties have been measured are included. An outline classification follows:

A. ACID CARBONATES

(NH_4)HCO_3 (Teschemacherite) is orthorhombic with $a = 7.29$, $b = 10.79$, $c = 8.76$ kX. Space group $Pccn$. U.C. 8. Crystals prismatic or equant. Perfect $\{110\}$ cleavages at 68°. H. 1.5. G. 1.57. F. 5.5, but volatile.

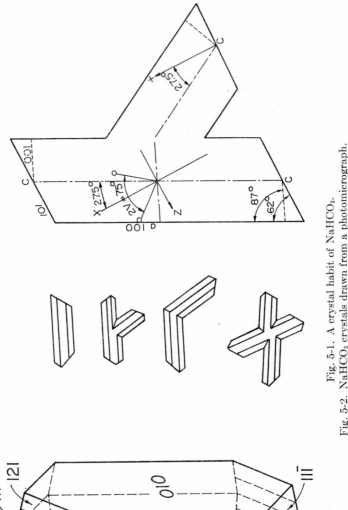

Fig. 5-1. A crystal habit of NaHCO₃.
Fig. 5-2. NaHCO₃ crystals drawn from a photomicrograph.
Fig. 5-3. Optic orientation of NaHCO₃ twin.

$X = a,$[1,2] $Y = b.$ $(-)2V = 41°38'$, $r < v$ weak. $n_X = 1.4227$, $n_Y = 1.5358$, $n_Z = 1.5545$, $n_Z - n_X = 0.1318$ Na. Colorless. Made from H_2O solution in closed vessels. PD 3.00, 5.34, 3.62; 9–415.

NaHCO$_3$ (Nahcolite) is monoclinic with $a = 7.51$, $b = 9.70$, $c = 3.53 kX$, $\beta = 93°19'$. Space group $P2_1/n$. Crystals {010} tablets with {110}, {111} and {11$\bar{1}$}; see Figs. 5-1, 5-2, 5-3; often twinned on {101}. Perfect {101}, good {111} and poor {100} cleavages. H. 2.5. G. 2.21. $X \wedge c = +27.5°$, $Y = b.$ $(-)2V = 75°$ $ca.$, $r > v$ weak. $n_X = 1.380$, $n_Y = 1.500$, $n_Z = 1.586$, $n_Z - n_X = 0.206$. Again:[3] $n_X = 1.376$, $n_Y = 1.500$, $n_Z = 1.582$, $n_Z - n_X = 0.206$. Since the extinction angle is about half the angle between the c axes in {101} twins, the substance may be recognized by the peculiar condition that both parts of the twin go to extinction simultaneously.[4] The substance is colorless. It is commonly called *baking soda*. PD 2.94, 2.61, 2.21; 3–0653.

KHCO$_3$ (Kalicinite) is monoclinic with $a = 15.01$, $b = 5.69$, $c = 3.68 kX$, $\beta = 104°30'$. U.C. 4. Space group $P2_1/a$. Crystals often prismatic, with {100}, {001} and {101} cleavages. Soft. G. 2.16. F. easy. Soluble in water. $X \wedge c = +30°$; $Y = b.$ $(-)2V = 81.5°$. n_X[5] $= 1.380$ Na, $n_Y = 1.482$, $n_Z = 1.573$, $n_Z - n_X = 0.193$ Na. Also: $n_X = 1.379$ C, 1.383 F, $n_Y = 1.4794$ C, 1.487 F, $n_Z = 1.569$ C, 1.581 F. Colorless to white. Made by passing CO_2 into an aqueous solution of K_2CO_3. PD 2.84, 3.68, 2.62; 1–0976.

Na$_3$H(CO$_3$)$_2$·2H$_2$O (Trona) is monoclinic with[5a] $a = 20.41$, $b = 3.49$, $c = 10.31$ Å, $\beta = 106°20'$. Space group $C2/c$ or Cc. Crystals {001} tablets

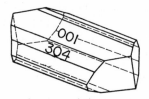

Fig. 5-4. A crystal habit of $HNa_3(CO_3)_2·2H_2O$.

elongated along b. Perfect {100} and good {10$\bar{1}$} cleavages. H. 3. G. 2.13. $X = b$;[6] $Z \wedge c = 83°$. $(-)2V = 72°$, $r < v$ marked. n_X[6] $= 1.412$, $n_Y = 1.492$, $n_Z = 1.540$, $n_Z - n_X = 0.128$. Again:[5a] $n_X = 1.418$, $n_Y = 1.492$,

[1] Lang: *Sitz. Akad. Wiss. Wien*, XLV (II), p. 112 (1862).
[2] Larsen: *U. S. Geol. Surv. Bull.* 679, 1921.
[3] H. E. Merwin: *pers. comm.*, Mar., 25, 1931.
[4] H. L. Robson: *pers. comm.*, Dec. 3, 1930.
[5] Merwin: *Intern. Crit. Tables* VII, 1930.
[5a] Brown, Peiser and Turner-Jones: *Acta Cryst.* II, p. 167 (1949).
[6] Larsen and Berman: *U. S. Geol. Surv. Bull.* 848 (1934).

$n_Z = 1.543$, $n_Z - n_X = 0.125$. Colorless. Made from solution in water containing much NaCl and Na_2SO_4 at $50°$–$85°$ C. PD 3.06, 2.66, 9.42; 2–0601*.

$MgKH(CO_3)_2 \cdot 4H_2O$ is triclinic. Crystals {010} tablets with {110} and {101}. Extinction angle on {010} is $32°$. $(-)2V = 65°$ calc. r > v; $n_X^7 = 1.430$, $n_Y = 1.51$, $n_Z = 1.542$, $n_Z - n_X = 0.112$. Colorless. Made by treating a suspension of $MgCO_3 \cdot 3H_2O$ in a solution of KCl or K_2SO_4 with CO_2.

B. NORMAL CARBONATES

1. Formula Type A_2CO_3 (and $ABCO_3$)

α. ANHYDROUS

$LiNaCO_3$ is hexagonal[8] in prismatic crystals. Uniaxial negative with $n_O = 1.538$, $n_E = 1.406$, $n_O - n_E = 0.132$. Colorless.

Li_2CO_3 is monoclinic with $a:b:c = 1.672:1:1.244$, $\beta = 114°25'$. Crystals prismatic. Perfect {001} and distinct {101} cleavages. Common twinning on {100}. G. 2.11. M.P. 618°. X $\wedge$ c nearly $0°$; Z = b. $(-)2V = 15°$ ca., $n_X = 1.428$, $n_Y = 1.567$, $n_Z = 1.572$, $n_Z - n_X = 0.144$ Na. Colorless. Made from fusion or by heating a saturated solution. PD 2.83, 4.18, 2.93; 9–359.

Na_2CO_3 made from fusion shows lamellar twinning.[9] $(-)2V = 34° \pm 3°$, $n_X = 1.415$, $n_Y = 1.535$, $n_Z = 1.546$, $n_Z - n_X = 0.131$. Colorless. PD 2.36, 2.96, 2.60; 1–1166.

K_2CO_3 made from fusion shows lamellar twinning with very oblique extinction.[9] $(-)2V = 35° \pm 5°$, $n_X = 1.426 \pm .004$, $n_Y = 1.531 \pm .002$, $n_Z = 1.541 \pm .002$, $n_Z - n_X = 0.115 \pm .006$. Colorless. PD 2.80, 2.61, 2.97; 1–1001.

β. HYDRATED

$Na_2CO_3 \cdot H_2O$ (Thermonatrite) is orthorhombic with[10] $a = 6.44$, $b = 10.72$, $c = 5.24$ kX. U.C. 4. Space group $Pmmm$. Crystals basal laminæ or {010} tablets; often forms crusts. Poor {010} cleavage. H. 1.5. G. 2.25. F. 1.5. X = b;[3] Y = c. $(-)2V = 48°$, r < v weak. $n_X^2 = 1.420$, $n_Y = 1.506$, $n_Z = 1.524$, $n_Z - n_X = 0.104$. Again:[3] $n_X = 1.420$, $n_Y = 1.509$, $n_Z = 1.525$, $n_Z - n_X = 0.105$. Colorless or white. Made from solution in water at temperatures between $32°$ and $112°$ C. PD 2.77, 2.37, 2.75; 8–448.

[7] Bayliss and Koch: *Austral. J. Appl. Sci.* III, p. 237 (1952). [*Chem. Abst.* XLVI, p. 10557 (1952)].

[8] Eitel and Skaliks: *Zeit. anorg. Chem.* CLXXXIII, p. 263 (1929).

[9] H. E. Merwin: *pers. comm.* Mar. 25, 1931.

[10] Colby and Harper: *Zeit. Krist.* LXXXIX p. 191 (1934).

Na₂CO₃·2.5H₂O is orthorhombic with[11] $a:b:c = 0.794:1:0.439$. Crystals acicular prismatic (often in sheaves), terminated by two planes making an angle of 134°. G. 2.05. X = c. (−)2V = large, $n_X = 1.435$, $n_Y = 1.492$, $n_Z = 1.547$, all ±.003, $n_Z - n_X = 0.112$. Colorless. Formed from evaporation of a solution of Solvay soda at 18°–25° C.

2K₂CO₃·3H₂O is monoclinic with[12] $a:b:c = 0.993:1:0.854$, $\beta = 111°24'$, and an extinction angle of 15°–20°. (+)2V = 66°, $n_X = 1.474$, $n_Y = 1.483$, $n_Z = 1.510$, $n_Z - n_X = 0.036$. K₂CO₃·nH₂O (probably the same) has[13] (+)2V = 60°–65° ca., $n_X = 1.476 \pm .003$, $n_Y = 1.486 \pm .003$, $n_Z = 1.514 \pm .003$, $n_Z - n_X = 0.038$. PD 2.76, 3.01, 6.90; 1–1014.

Na₂CO₃·10H₂O (Natron) is monoclinic with $a:b:c = 1.483:1:1.400$, $\beta = 121°8'$. Crystals {010} tablets with distinct {001} and poor {010} cleavages. H. 1–1.5. G. 1.46–1.47. M.P. 34.5°. X = b;[2] Z ∧ c = +41° ca. (−)2V = 71°, r > v weak with crossed dispersion. $n_X = 1.405$, $n_Y = 1.425$, $n_Z = 1.440$, $n_Z - n_X = 0.035$. Colorless to white or stained. Effloresces rapidly in dry air, changing to the monohydrate. PD 2.89, 5.3, 4.03; 1–0938.

2. Formula Type ACO₃

α. ANHYDROUS

MgCO₃ (Magnesite) is hexagonal-scalenohedral with $a = 4.58$, $c = 14.92 \, kX$. Space group $R\bar{3}c$. Crystals rare; usually massive. Perfect {10$\bar{1}$1} cleavage. H. 4. G. 3.00. Uniaxial negative with[14] $n_O = 1.700$, $n_E = 1.509$, $n_O - n_E = 0.191$. Colorless or white when pure. MgCO₃ is miscible in all proportions with FeCO₃ and ZnCO₃ and CoCO₃, but has only limited miscibility with CaCO₃ and MnCO₃. In crystals with Mg:Fe = 1:1, $n_O = 1.788$, $n_E = 1.570$, $n_O - n_E = 0.218$. Made by heating CaCO₃ with MgCl₂ or MgSO₄ solution in a closed tube at 160–200° C. PD 2.74, 2.10, 1.70; 8–479.

CaCO₃ has three crystal phases; the commonest one is calcite; another is aragonite; a rare one is vaterite.

CaCO₃ (Calcite) is hexagonal-scalenohedral with[14a] $a = 4.9898$, $c = 17.060$ Å at 18° C. Space group $R\bar{3}c$. The cell commonly used in morphological descriptions[14b] has $a' = 4a$ and $c' = c$, in which the cleavage is {10$\bar{1}$1} [the cleavage is {10$\bar{1}$4} with reference to the actual unit cell].

---

[11] Pabst: *Am. Min.* XV, p. 69 (1930).
[12] Milton and Axelrod: *Am. Min.* XXXII, p. 607 (1947).
[13] Data from E. F. Williams: American Cyanamid Co., 1943.
[14] Wayland: *Am. Min.* XXVII, p. 614 (1942).
[14a] Andrews: *Min. Mag.* XXIX, p. 85 (1950) on commercial "Specpure" calcite.
[14b] H. Winchell: *Am. J. Sci.* CCLIV, p. 65 (1956).

Crystals are extremely varied in habit: 328 crystal-forms are known and 296 more are considered uncertain.[14c] Perfect $\{10\bar{1}1\}$ cleavage. Parting common on $\{01\bar{1}2\}$, rare on $\{0001\}$. See Figs. 5-5 and 5-6. H. 3. G. 2.71. F. 7, but calcite dissociates at 900° C. Under pressures above 110 atmos-

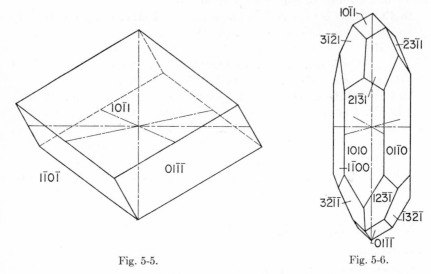

Fig. 5-5.   Fig. 5-6.

Figs. 5-5, 5-6. Crystal habits of CaCO₃, calcite.

pheres it melts at 1290° C. Soluble in cold dilute HCl with effervescence. Uniaxial negative with n_O = 1.6544 C, 1.6584 D, 1.6678 F, n_E = 1.4846 C, 1.4864 D, 1.4908 F, $n_O - n_E$ = 0.1720 D. Colorless. Easily made from bicarbonate solution. CaCO₃ is miscible probably in all proportions with MnCO₃, but only in very limited amounts with FeCO₃, ZnCO₃, CoCO₃, or MgCO₃. Made by precipitation from solution. PD 3.04, 2.29, 2.10; 5–0586.

MnCO₃ (Rhodochrosite) is hexagonal-scalenohedral with a = 4.73, c = 15.51 kX. Space group $R\bar{3}c$. Crystals rhombohedral, but rare. Perfect $\{10\bar{1}1\}$ cleavage. H. 3.5–4. G. 3.70, but varying with variations in composition (Ca, Fe, Mg replacing some Mn). Uniaxial negative with[14] n_O = 1.816, n_E = 1.597, $n_O - n_E$ = 0.219 (when pure). With Mn:Fe = 1:1, n_O = 1.845, n_E = 1.615. With Mn:Ca = 1:1, n_O = 1.737, n_E = 1.542. Color pink, red, gray, brown. Colorless (or pale red) in section. Made by heating CaCO₃ with MnCl₂ or MnSO₄ solution in a closed tube at 150–200° C. PD 2.84, 3.66, 1.76; 7–268.

[14c] Palache: *Calcite: An angle table and critical list*, cited by Palache, Berman, and Frondel: *Dana's System of Mineralogy*, Part II, p. 158 (1951).

FeCO₃ (Siderite) is hexagonal-scalenohedral with $a = 4.71$, $c = 15.43\ kX$. Space group $R\bar{3}c$. Crystals rhombohedral or varied. Perfect $\{10\bar{1}1\}$ cleavage. H. 4 *ca.* G. 3.96 (pure), decreasing with Mn, Mg, Ca replacing some Fe. Uniaxial negative with[14] $n_O = 1.875$, $n_E = 1.633$, $n_O - n_E = 0.242$. With Fe:Mg = 1:1, $n_O = 1.788$, $n_E = 1.570$. Color brown, gray, green, etc. In section colorless to yellow or brown. PD 2.79, 1.73, 3.59; 8–133. Made by reaction of $(NH_4)_2CO_3$ and $FeCl_2$ at red heat.

CoCO₃ (Cobaltocalcite) is hexagonal-scalenohedral with $a = 4.67$, $c = 15.13\ kX$. Space group $R\bar{3}c$. Usually massive. H. 4. G. 4.13. Uniaxial negative[2] with $n_O = 1.855$, $n_E = 1.60$, $n_O - n_E = 0.255$. Color rose-red, altering to gray, brown or black. In transmitted light O is violet red, E rose-red. PD 2.77, 1.71, 3.65; 1–1020. Made by heating $CoCl_2$ with carbonates at 150° C. in a closed tube.

ZnCO₃ (Smithsonite) is hexagonal-scalenohedral with $a = 4.65$, $c = 14.95\ kX$. Space group $R\bar{3}c$. Crystals rhombohedral; often massive. Good $\{10\bar{1}1\}$ cleavage. H. 4–4.5. G. 4.43 but varying (4.0–4.45) with composition and condition. Uniaxial negative with[15] $n_O = 1.842$ Li, 1.848 Na, 1.855 Tl, $n_E = 1.619$ Li, 1.621 Na, 1.624 Tl, $n_O - n_E = 0.227$ Na. Color gray or varied. In section colorless or nearly so. May contain some Ca, Fe, Mg, Cu, etc. replacing Zn. PD 2.75, 3.55, 1.70; 8–449.

CaCO₃ (Vaterite) is hexagonal with $a = 4.12$, $c = 8.56\ kX$; in platelets or skeletal groups resembling snowflakes. G. 2.64. Uniaxial positive with[16] $n_O = 1.550$, $n_E = 1.640$–1.650, $n_E - n_O = 0.090$–0.100. Colorless or white. PD 2.73, 3.29, 3.58; 1–1033. Made by causing crystallization of gelatinous $CaCO_3$ at 5° in the presence of much K_2CO_3.

CaCO₃ (Aragonite) is orthorhombic with $a = 4.94$, $b = 7.94$, $c = 5.72\ kX$. Space group $Pmcn$. U.C. 4. Crystals often prismatic, varied with common twinning. Good $\{010\}$ cleavage. H. 3.5–4. G. 2.94. X = c,[17] Y = a. $(-)2V = 18°4'$ C, $18°8'$ D, $18°20'$ F. $n_X = 1.5279$ C, 1.5300 D, 1.5346 F, $n_Y = 1.6772$ C, 1.6810 D, 1.6900 F, $n_Z = 1.6815$ C, 1.6854 D, 1.6947 F, $n_Z - n_X = 0.1554$ D. Colorless. Metastable at ordinary temperatures; inverts to calcite at about 400° C. May contain some Pb, Sr, Zn replacing Ca. PD 3.40, 1.98, 3.27; 5–0453. Made from solutions of calcium salts with alkali carbonates.

SrCO₃ (Strontianite) is orthorhombic with $a = 5.12$, $b = 8.40$, $c = 6.08\ kX$. Space group $Pmcn$. U.C. 4. Crystals prismatic or varied. Common twinning. Good $\{110\}$ cleavage. H. 3.5. G. 3.75, but often less due to presence of some Ca replacing Sr (*e.g.* 3.63 with 6 per cent of CaO). X = c,

[15] Mountain: *Min. Mag.* XXI, p. 51 (1926).
[16] Donnay: *Soc. Geol. Belg. Bull.* LIX, p. B215 (1936).
[17] Mülheims: *Zeit. Krist.* XIV, p. 229 (1888).

$Y = b.$ $(-)2V = 7°7'$ calc.[18] Na, r < v very weak. $n_X = 1.5181$ Li, 1.5199 Na, 1.5219 Tl, $n_Y = 1.6624$ Li, 1.6666 Na, 1.6704 Tl, $n_Z = 1.6640$ Li, 1.6685 Na, 1.6728 Tl, $n_Z - n_X = 0.1486$ Na. Colorless. Inverts to a hexagonal phase at 929° C. and fuses at 1497° C. The natural substance nearly always contains some Ca. PD 3.54, 3.45, 2.05; 5–0418. Forms a complete series[19] with $BaCO_3$.

$BaCO_3$ (Witherite) is orthorhombic with $a = 5.25$, $b = 8.83$, $c = 6.54$ kX. Space group $Pmcn$. U.C. 4. Crystals twinned on {110} to pseudo-hexagonal forms usually pyramidal. H. 3–3.5. G. 4.29. X = c, Y = b. $(-)2V = 16°$, r > v very weak. $n_X{}^{20} = 1.529$, $n_Y = 1.676$, $n_Z = 1.677$. $n_Z - n_X = 0.148$. Colorless. Inverts to a hexagonal phase at 811° C. and to an isometric phase at 982° C. which melts at 1740° C. Artificial crystals form a complete series with $SrCO_3$ and a series up to Ca:Ba $\approx$ 1:2 with $CaCO_3$. PD 3.72, 3.68, 2.15; 5–0378.

$PbCO_3$ (Cerussite) is orthorhombic with $a = 5.17$, $b = 8.48$, $c = 6.13$ kX. Space group $Pmcn$. U.C. 4. Crystals varied, often {010} tablets, pyramidal or equant. Pseudo-hexagonal twinning very common. Good {110} and {021} cleavages. H. 3–3.5. G. 6.55. X = c, Y = b. $(-)2V = 9°$ Na, r > v strong. Uniaxial at 15° C. for $\lambda = 415$ mμ. $n_X{}^{21} = 1.8037$, $n_Y = 2.0763$, $n_Z = 2.0780$, $n_Z - n_X = 0.2743$ Na. Colorless or stained. Often present in commercial "white lead." PD 3.59, 3.50, 2.49; 5–0417.

β. HYDRATED

$MgCO_3 \cdot 3H_2O$ (Nesquehonite) is orthorhombic with $a = 7.68$, $b = 11.93$, $c = 5.39$ kX. Space group $Pmmm$. U.C. 4. Crystals prismatic with perfect {110} and poor {001} cleavages. H. 2.5. G. 1.85. Soluble in cold HCl with effervescence. X = a. Y = c. Optic axes nearly normal to the {110} cleavages. $(-)2V = 53°$, r < v weak. $n_X = 1.417$ calc.,[22] $n_Y = 1.503 \pm 0.001$, $n_Z = 1.527 \pm 0.001$, $n_Z - n_X = 0.110$. Colorless. PD 6.50, 3.86, 2.61; 1–0130. Made by reaction of alkali carbonates with a Mg salt.

$MgCO_3 \cdot 5H_2O$ (Lansfordite) is monoclinic with $a = 12.48$, $b = 7.55$, $c = 7.34$ kX, $\beta = 101°46'$. Space group $P2_1/m$. U.C. 4. Crystals prismatic with perfect {001} cleavage. H. 2.5. G. 1.69. Soluble in cold HCl with effervescence. $(-)2V{}^{22} = 59°48'$, $n_X = 1.456$, $n_Y = 1.469$, $n_Z = 1.508$, $n_Z - n_X = 0.052$. Colorless. Made (with nesquehonite) by reaction of alkali carbonates with $MgCl_2$.

[18] Indices measured by Beykirch: *N. Jahrb. Min. Bl. Bd.* XIII, p. 427 (1901) on crystals with 5.95 per cent CaO.

[19] Cork and Gerhard: *Am. Min.* XVI, p. 71 (1931).

[20] Mallard: *Bull. Soc. Fr. Min.* XVIII, p. 7 (1895).

[21] Dübigk: *N. Jahrb. Min. Bl. Bd.* XXXVI, p. 214 (1913).

[22] Fenoglio: *Per. Min.* VI, p. 1 (1935).

CaCO$_3$·6H$_2$O is monoclinic with $a:b:c = 1.02:1:?$, $\beta = 108°?$. Crystals basal plates or short prisms. G. 1.77. Y $= b$, Z $\wedge c = +17°$ with distinct inclined dispersion. $(-)2V = 38°$. $n_X = 1.460$, $n_Y = 1.535$, $n_Z = 1.545$, $n_Z - n_X = 0.085$. Colorless. Formed at 0° from aqueous solutions containing CaCO$_3$ and also KOH. Changes easily by dehydration to CaCO$_3$·5H$_2$O and CaCO$_3$·3H$_2$O ? and then CaCO$_3$.

3. Formula Type AB(CO$_3$)$_2$

CaMg(CO$_3$)$_2$ (Dolomite) is hexagonal with $a = 4.83$, $c = 15.92$ kX. Space group $R\bar{3}$. U.C. 3. Crystals rhombohedral or prismatic. Twinning varied, not rare. Perfect $\{10\bar{1}1\}$ cleavage. H. 3.5–4. G. 2.85, increasing to about 3 with Mg:Fe $= 1:1$. Uniaxial negative with[23] $n_O = 1.679$, $n_E = 1.502$, $n_O - n_E = 0.177$. Colorless. PD 2.88, 1.78, 1.80; 5–0622. CaMg(CO$_3$)$_2$ forms a continuous series with CaFe(CO$_3$)$_2$ and a considerable (perhaps continuous) series with CaMn(CO$_3$)$_2$. With Mg:Fe $= 1:1$, $n_O = 1.721$, $n_E = 1.528$, $n_O - n_E = 0.193$. But Ca can be replaced also (in part) by some Fe and Mn. Made from solutions of Ca and Mg carbonates under pressure of at least 10 atmospheres of CO$_2$.

CaFe(CO$_3$)$_2$ (Ferrodolomite) is hexagonal with $a = 4.82$, $c = 16.11$ kX. Crystals rhombohedral, often with $\{0001\}$. Perfect $\{10\bar{1}1\}$ cleavage. H. 3.5–4. G. 3.2. F. 7. Uniaxial negative with $n_O = 1.765$, $n_E = 1.555$, $n_O - n_E = 0.210$. Colorless to brown.

CaBa(CO$_3$)$_2$ (Alstonite) is orthorhombic with $a = 4.99$, $b = 8.77$, $c = 6.11$ kX.[24] Crystals commonly pseudo-hexagonal pyramids or prisms by twinning. Poor $\{110\}$ cleavage. H. 4–4.5. G. 3.67 (may be 3.70 with some Sr replacing Ca). X $= c$, Y $= a$. $(-)2V = 7°$, r $>$ v weak.[25] $n_X = 1.525$, $n_Y = 1.673$, $n_Z = 1.673$, $n_Z - n_X = 0.148$. Colorless, white or pink. It may contain some Sr, replacing Ba. PD 3.68, 3.12, 2.13; 3–0322*.

4. Formula Type A$_2$(CO$_3$)$_3$·nH$_2$O

(La,Ce)$_2$(CO$_3$)$_3$·8H$_2$O (Lanthanite) is orthorhombic with $a = 9.50$, $b = 17.1$, $c = 9.00$ kX. U.C. 8. Thin to thick basal tablets. Perfect $\{010\}$ cleavage. H. 2.5–3. G. 2.7. X $= b$,[2] Y $= c$. $(-)2V = 63°$ $ca.$, r $<$ v very weak. $n_X = 1.53$ $ca.$, $n_Y = 1.587$, $n_Z = 1.613$, $n_Z - n_X = 0.083$ $ca.$ Colorless. Made by reaction of (La,Ce) hydroxide with NaHCO$_3$ solution and CO$_2$.

[23] Hawkes and Smythe: *Min. Mag.* XXIV, p. 65 (1935).

[24] Gossner and Mussgnug: *Cent. Min.* 1930A, p. 220; axial transformation $abc \rightarrow bac$ here.

[25] Bellanca: *Per. Min.* XII, p. 127 (1941).

5. Formula Type $A_mB_n(CO_3)_p$ with $(m + n):p \approx 3:2$

α. ANHYDROUS

$Na_2Mg(CO_3)_2$ is hexagonal[8] with $c/a = 3.33$ and distinct prismatic cleavage. G. 2.734. M.P. 677° C. under a pressure of 1240 kg/cm². Uniaxial negative with $n_O = 1.594$, $n_E = 1.54$, $n_O - n_E = 0.054$. Colorless. PD 2.61, 1.89, 2.73; 4–0737.

$Na_2Ca(CO_3)_2$ is hexagonal[8] in basal plates with perfect basal cleavage. G. 2.54. M.P. 812° C. in CO_2 gas. Uniaxial negative with $n_O = 1.547$, $n_E = 1.504$, $n_O - n_E = 0.043$. May have small optic angle due to strain. Stable in air. Colorless.

$K_2Mg(CO_3)_2$ is probably hexagonal[8] with prismatic cleavage. G. 2.671. Uniaxial negative with $n_O = 1.597$, $n_E = 1.47$, $n_O - n_E = 0.127$. Colorless. The glass has G. 2.39 and $n = 1.496$.

$K_2Ca(CO_3)_2$ **(Fairchildite)** is hexagonal in basal plates with distinct basal cleavage. G. 2.465. M.P. 813° C. in CO_2 gas. Uniaxial negative with[12] $n_O = 1.530$, $n_E = 1.48$ $ca.$, $n_O - n_E = 0.05\pm$. Colorless. PD 3.19, 2.64, 6.64; 6–0321*. Seems to form complete series with similar compounds containing Na, Ba or Sr. Made by treating $CaCO_3$ with strong solutions of KOH or K_2CO_3 (59 per cent at 19°).

β. HYDRATED

$Na_6Zn_8(CO_3)_{11} \cdot 8H_2O$ is isometric.[26] Crystals tetrahedral. Isotropic with $n = 1.540$. Colorless.

$K_6Ca_2(CO_3)_5 \cdot 6H_2O$ **(Buetschliite)** is probably hexagonal.[12] Crystals barrel-shaped along c. Uniaxial negative with $n_O = 1.595$, $n_E = 1.455$, $n_O - n_E = 0.140$. Colorless. PD 2.86, 3.03, 2.69; 6–0428. Made by hydration of fairchildite.

$Na_2Ca(CO_3)_2 \cdot 2H_2O$ **(Pirssonite)** is orthorhombic with $a = 11.32$, $b = 20.06$, $c = 6.00$ Å. U.C. 8. Crystals short prismatic or {010} tablets, etc. H. 3–3.5. G. 2.35. X = a, Y = c.[27] (+)2V = 31°11′ Li, 31°26′ Na, 31°27′ Tl, r < v slight. $n_X = 1.5043$ Na, $n_Y = 1.5056$ Li, 1.5095 Na, 1.5115 Tl, $n_Z = 1.5710$ Li, 1.5751 Na, 1.5789 Tl, $n_Z - n_X = 0.0694$. Colorless. PD 2.50, 5.10, 2.65; 2–1051.

$K_2Mg(CO_3)_2 \cdot 4H_2O$ is orthorhombic.[7] Crystals plates or tablets with six sides. (+)2V = 65° $ca.$, r < v. $n_X = 1.465$, $n_Y = 1.485$, $n_Z = 1.535$, $n_Z - n_X = 0.070$. Colorless. Made by treating $MgKH(CO_3)_2$ with $MgCO_3$ in solution.

$Na_2Ca(CO_3)_2 \cdot 5H_2O$ **(Gaylussite)** is monoclinic with $a:b:c = 1.4897:1:1.4441$, $\beta = 101°33′$. Crystals often elongated along a with {001},

---

[26] C. D. West: *pers. comm.* Nov. 2, 1936.

[27] Pratt: *Am. J. Sci.* II, p. 123, 126 (1896). Foshag: *Am. Min.* XVIII, p. 431 (1933).

{011}, {111}, etc. Perfect {110} cleavage. H. 2.5–3. G. 1.99. X = b; Z $\wedge$ c^{27} = $-15°$. $(-)2V = 34°$, r < v and crossed dispersion. n_X = 1.4435, n_Y = 1.5156, n_Z = 1.5233, $n_Z - n_X$ = 0.0798 Na. Colorless. It is a stable phase in the system Na_2CO_3–$CaCO_3$–H_2O. PD 6.41, 3.18, 2.70; 2–0122.

$Na_2Cu(CO_3)_2 \cdot 3H_2O$ (Chalconatrite) is monoclinic(?). Crystals six-sided plates; also laths. H. low. G. 2.27. Y parallel length of laths; Z normal to plates and apparently Z $\wedge$ c very small. $(+?)2V$ = large.[27a] n_X = 1.483, n_Y = 1.530, n_Z = 1.576, $n_Z - n_X$ = 0.093. Color greenish blue and pleochroic with X nearly colorless, Y pale blue, Z blue. Made by grinding copper acetate in a solution of sodium carbonate, then filtering, washing, and drying. PD 6.92, 4.15, 3.68; 10–442*.

C. CARBONATES CONTAINING HYDROXYL OR HALOGEN OR EXTRA OXYGEN

1. Formula Type $A_m(CO_3)_p Z_q$

$Pb_2Cl_2(CO_3)$ (Phosgenite) is tetragonal with a = 8.139, c = 8.856 Å. U.C. 4. Crystals prismatic or varied. H. 2–3 varying with the crystal direction. G. 6.13. Distinct {001} and {110} cleavages. Uniaxial positive[28] with n_O = 2.1181, n_E = 2.1446, $n_E - n_O$ = 0.0265 Na. Color white, brown, rose, gray, greenish. In thick sections it may show O reddish and E greenish. PD 2.82, 2.23, 3.64; 9–494.

$(BiO)_2(CO_3)$ (Bismutite) is tetragonal with a = 3.859, c = 13.658 kX. U.C. 2. Usually massive or in crusts. Basal cleavage. H. 2.5–3.5. G. 8.15, but varying to 6.1. Refractive index varies[29] from 2.12 to about 2.30, due to varying non-essential water content; birefringence moderate. Fibers have parallel extinction and positive elongation. Color usually yellow, but may be gray, green or brown. PD 2.95, 2.14, 1.62; 4–0666.

$Pb_3(OH)_2(CO_3)_2$ (Hydrocerussite) is hexagonal with a = 8.97, c = 23.8 kX. U.C. 3. Crystals thin to thick tabular or pyramidal. Perfect basal cleavage. H. 3.5. G. 6.8. Uniaxial negative with[2] n_O = 2.09, n_E = 1.94, $n_O - n_E$ = 0.15. Colorless. Chief component of "white lead." PD 2.63, 3.60, 3.28; 10–401*.

$Cu_3(OH)_2(CO_3)_2$ (Azurite) is monoclinic with a = 4.96, b = 5.83, c = 10.27 kX, β = 92°25'. Space group $P2_1/c$. U.C. 2. Crystals varied, often with many forms. Good {011} and poor {100} cleavages. H. 3.5–4. G. 3.77. X = b,[2] Z $\wedge$ c = $-12°36'$. $(+)2V$ = 67°, r > v. n_X = 1.730, n_Y = 1.754, n_Z = 1.836, $n_Z - n_X$ = 0.106 Na. Color pale to dark blue. In section pale

[27a] Frondel and Gettens: *Science*, CXXII, p. 75 (1955).
[28] Smith: *Min. Mag.* XII, p. 107 (1899).
[29] Frondel: *Am. Min.* XXVIII, p. 521 (1943).

blue with X < Y < Z. PD 3.50, 5.15, 2.53; 3–0360*. Made by heating copper sulphate or nitrate with calcite in a closed tube.

$(UO_2)(CO_3)$ **(Rutherfordine)** is orthorhombic with[29a] $a = 4.85$, $b = 9.21$, $c = 4.30$ Å. Often finely fibrous. Soft. G. 4.82. Perfect {010} and good {001} cleavages. X = b; Y = c (elongation). (+)2V = 53° calc. $n_X = 1.715$, $n_Y = 1.730$, $n_Z = 1.795$, $n_Z - n_X = 0.080$. Color yellow, weakly pleochroic. Artificial crystals studied.[29b] PD 4.56, 4.25, 3.19; 9–163.

$Ni_3(OH)_4(CO_3)\cdot 4H_2O$ **(Zaratite)** is probably isometric with[30] $a = 6.15$ kX. U.C. 1. H. 3.5. G. 2.66. Forms incrustations. Isotropic with $n = 1.58$–1.60. Often mixed with fibrous material with positive elongation, parallel extinction and variable indices (due to strain or another phase). Color emerald green. Made by the action of $NiCl_2$ on $MgCO_3\cdot 3H_2O$.

$Cu_2(OH)_2(CO_3)$ **(Malachite)** is monoclinic with $a = 9.49$, $b = 12.00$, $c = 3.24$ Å, $\beta = 98°42'$. U.C. 4. Space group $P2_1/a$. Crystals rare, often twinned; massive. Perfect {$\bar{2}01$} and fair {010} cleavages. H. 3.5–4. G. 4.0, but often less, even to 3.6. X ∧ $c = 23.5°$; Y = b. (−)2V = 43° ± 2°, r < v distinct. $n_X{}^2 = 1.655$, $n_Y = 1.875$, $n_Z = 1.909$, $n_Z - n_X = 0.254$. Color green with X nearly colorless, Y yellow green, Z deep green. PD 2.86, 3.69, 5.06; 10–399. Formed on a copper anode by electrolysis of soluble carbonates.

$Mg_4(OH)_2(CO_3)_3\cdot 3H_2O$ **(Hydromagnesite)** is monoclinic with[31] $a:b:c = 1.121:1:0.947$, $\beta = 113°32'$. (Possibly orthorhombic.) Crystals {100} plates long parallel c. Perfect {010} cleavage. H. 2.5. G. 2.236. X ∧ $c = 47°9'$; Z = b. (+)2V = moderate, $n_X = 1.523$, $n_Y = 1.527$, $n_Z = 1.545$, $n_Z - n_X = 0.022$ Na. Colorless. PD 5.79, 2.90, 2.15; 8–179. Made from solution of magnesium sulfate or nitrate with alkali carbonates.

$Zn_5(OH)_6(CO_3)_2$ **(Hydrozincite)** is monoclinic with $a = 13.452$, $b = 6.307$, $c = 5.357$ kX, $\beta = 95°30'$. Space group $C2/m$ or Cm or $C2$. U.C. 2. Crystals rare, usually massive. Perfect {100} cleavage. H. 2–2.5. G. 4.0 $ca.$; mostly 3.5–3.8 for massive samples. X = b. Z ∧ $c = 13°$,[6] also Z ∧ $c = 40°$.[32] (−)2V = 40°, r < v distinct. $n_X = 1.640$, $n_Y = 1.736$, $n_Z = 1.750$, $n_Z - n_X = 0.110$.[2] Color white, gray, pale yellow, brown, pink. Colorless in section. $5ZnO\cdot 2CO_2\cdot 4H_2O$ easily made from solution of zinc salts and alkali carbonates.

2. Formula Type $A_m B_n (CO_3)_p Z_q$

$Na_3MgCl(CO_3)_2$ **(Northupite)** is isometric with $a = 13.99$ kX. U.C. 16. Space group $Fd3$. Crystals octahedral. No cleavage. H. 3.5–4. G. 2.366.

[29a] Clark and Christ: *Am. Min.* XLI, p. 844 (1956).
[29b] Cromer and Harper: *Acta Cryst.* VIII, p. 847 (1955).
[30] Fenoglio: *Per. Min.* V, p. 265 (1935).
[31] Rogers: *Am. J. Sci.* VI, p. 37 (1923).
[32] Prider: *Min. Mag.* XXVI, p. 60 (1941).

Soluble in acid with effervescence. Isotropic with[27] $n = 1.5117$ Li, 1.5144 Na, 1.5180 Tl. Again:[33] $n = 1.510$. Colorless. PD 2.69, 2.48, 8.00; 2–0916. Made by reaction of $MgCl_2$ and Na_2CO_3 and NaCl. Forms a complete series of mix-crystals with $Na_6Mg_2SO_4(CO_3)_4$.

$Na_3MgBr(CO_3)_2$ is isometric with $a = 14.17$ kX. Crystals octahedral. G. 2.67. Isotropic with[27] $n = 1.515$. Colorless.

$Ca(BiO)_2(CO_3)_2$ (Beyerite) is tetragonal with $a = 3.78$, $c = 21.77$ kX. U.C. 2. Space group $I4/mmm$. Crystals rectangular basal plates. H. 2–3. G. 6.56. No cleavage. Uniaxial negative with $n_O = 2.13 \pm .02$, $n_E = 1.99 \pm .02$, $n_O - n_E = 0.14$. Color yellow. In section pale yellow to colorless; not pleochroic. May be slightly biaxial (due to strain?). PD 2.84, 2.14, 1.75; 4–0693. Made by heating $BiNO_3$, $CaCO_3$ and urea in dilute HNO_3 in a bomb at 220° C.

$NaAl(CO_3)(OH)_2$ (Dawsonite) is orthorhombic with $a = 6.72$, $b = 10.34$, $c = 5.56$ Å. U.C. 4. Space group Ima. Crystals platy to acicular along c. H. 3. G. 2.44. Perfect $\{110\}$ cleavage. X $= a$,[34] Y $= c$. $(-)2V = 76°46'$ Na, r $<$ v weak. $n_X = 1.466$, $n_Y = 1.542$, $n_Z = 1.596$, $n_Z - n_X = 0.130$. Again:[35] $n_X = 1.462$, $n_Y = 1.537$, $n_Z = 1.589$, $n_Z - n_X = 0.127$. Colorless. Made by reaction of solutions of sodium aluminate and bicarbonate with excess of CO_2.

$(NH_4)_4(UO_2)(CO_3)_3$ is monoclinic with $a:b:c = 0.964:1:0.867$, $\beta = 99°17'$. Crystals prismatic with perfect $\{001\}$ cleavage. G. 2.77. $(-)2V$[36] $= ?$, $n_X' = 1.60$, $n_Z' = 1.625$, $n_Z' - n_X' = 0.025$. Color yellow.

$Na_2Ca(UO_2)(CO_3)_3 \cdot 6H_2O$ (Andersonite) is hexagonal with $a = 18.04$, $c = 23.90$ Å. U.C. 6. Space group $R\overline{3}$ or $R3$. Crystals pseudo-cubic. G. 2.8. Uniaxial positive[37] with $n_O = 1.520$, $n_E = 1.540$, $n_E - n_O = 0.020$. Color in mass bright green; in section: O colorless, E pale yellow. PD 13.0, 7.97, 5.68; 4–0080. Made by evaporating a solution containing K_2CO_3 and nitrates of Na, Ca and U.

$Mg_2(UO_2)(CO_3)_3 \cdot 18H_2O$ (Bayleyite) is monoclinic with $a = 26.65$, $b = 15.31$, $c = 6.53$ Å, $\beta = 93°4'$. Space group $P2_1/a$. U.C. 4. Crystals prismatic or acicular divergent groups. G. 2.05. X $\wedge$ c[37] $= 15°$. $(-)2V = 30°$ calc. $n_X = 1.455$, $n_Y = 1.490$, $n_Z = 1.500$, $n_Z - n_X = 0.045$. Color yellow with X pinkish, Y and Z pale yellow. Fluorescent in yellowish-green. PD 7.66, 13.1, 3.83; 4–0130. Made from solutions of uranyl nitrate, magnesium nitrate and potassium carbonate.

$CaMg(UO_2)(CO_3)_3 \cdot 12H_2O$ (Swartzite) is monoclinic with $a = 11.12$,

[33] Shiba and Watanabe: *C. R. Acad. Sci., Paris*, CXCIII, p. 1421 (1931).

[34] Graham: *Trans. Roy. Soc. Canada*, II (3), p. 165 (1908).

[35] Pelloux: *Per. Min.* III, p. 69 (1932).

[36] Optic data from Bolland: *Sitz. Akad. Wiss. Wien* CXIX, IIb, p. 275 (1910) on "ammonium uranyl carbonate" of unknown formula.

[37] Axelrod *et al.*: *Am. Min.* XXXVI, p. 1 (1951).

$b = 14.72$, $c = 6.47$ Å, $\beta = 99°26'$. Space group $P2_1/m$ or $P2_1$. U.C. 2. Crystals prismatic. G. 2.3. $(-)2V = 40°$ calc.[37] $n_X = 1.465$, $n_Y = 1.51$. $n_Z = 1.540$, $n_Z - n_X = 0.075$. Color green; in transmitted light X colorless, Y and Z yellow. PD 8.76, 5.50, 7.31; 4–0111. Obtained by seeding an evaporating solution of K_2CO_3 and nitrates of Ca, Mg and U.

D. COMPOUND CARBONATES

$Na_6Mg_2(SO_4)(CO_3)_4$ (Tychite) is isometric with $a = 13.87\ kX$. U.C. 8. Space group $Fd3$. No cleavage. H. 3.5–4. G. 2.588. Isotropic with[38] $n = 1.510$. Colorless. Made from reaction of $MgSO_4$ solution with a mixed solution of Na_2CO_3 and Na_2SO_4.

$Na_6Mg_2(CrO_4)(CO_3)_4$ is isometric with G. 2.506. Isotropic with[38] $n = 1.555$. Made from reaction of $MgCrO_4$ solution with a mixed solution of Na_2CO_3 and Na_2SO_4.

$Ag_2(CO_3)\cdot 4NH_3\cdot H_2O$ is orthorhombic[39] with $a{:}b{:}c = 0.577{:}1{:}0.768$, and pseudo-hexagonal. Crystals prismatic or pyramidal. Perfect {010} and {021} cleavages with distinct {001} and {110} partings. Common twinning on {110}. $Y = b$, $Z = c$. $(+)2V = 10°$, $r < v$ strong, the substance being uniaxial in the extreme red and having $2E = 36°$ for 435 mμ. $n_X = 1.66$, $n_Y = 1.66$, $n_Z = 1.68$, $n_Z - n_X = 0.023$ Na. Colorless. Unstable in air.

$Pb_4(SO_4)(CO_3)_2(OH)_2$ (Leadhillite) is monoclinic with $a = 9.07$, $b = 11.55$, $c = 20.70\ kX$, $\beta = 90°30'$. U.C. 8. Space group $P2_1/a$. Crystals often pseudo-hexagonal in thin to thick {001} plates and apparently rhombohedral. Twinning on {140} very common; also other types. Perfect basal cleavage. H. 2.5–3. G. 6.55. $X \wedge c = -5.5°$, $Z = b$. $(-)2V$ about 10° at room temperature; becomes uniaxial (for Na) at about 125° C. $n_X{}^2 = 1.87 \pm 0.01$, $n_Y = 2.00 \pm 0.01$, $n_Z = 2.01 \pm 0.01$, $n_Z - n_X = 0.14$ ca. Colorless, gray, pale green, blue or yellow. Colorless in sections. Made by heating $PbSO_4$ and $PbCO_3$ with water in a closed tube at 180° C.

E. NITRATES AND NITRITES

1. Formula Type ANO_3

α. ANHYDROUS

$LiNO_3$ is hexagonal with a rhombohedral angle of 74°20'. G. 2.33. Very hygroscopic. Uniaxial negative with[39a] extreme birefringence. $n_O = 1.735$,

---

[38] Penfield and Jamieson: *Am. J. Sci.* XX, p. 217 (1905).

[39] Gaudefroy: *Bull. Soc. Fr. Min.* XLVI, p. 20 (1923).

[39a] Fry: *U. S. Dept. Agric. Bull.* 1108, p. 11 (1922).

$n_E = 1.435$, $n_O - n_E = 0.300$. Colorless. Formed from hot water solution. PD 3.60, 2.13, 2.79; 8–466.

NaNO$_3$ (Soda-Niter) is hexagonal with $a = 5.07$, $c = 16.81$ kX. U.C. 6. Space group $R\bar{3}c$. Crystals rhombohedral, resembling calcite; massive. Perfect rhombohedral cleavage. H. 1.5–2. G. 2.27. F. 1; deflagrates on heating. Deliquescent. Uniaxial negative with extreme birefringence.[40] $n_O = $ 1.5793 B, 1.5874 D, 1.5954 E, 1.6260 H, $n_E = 1.3346$ B, 1.3361 D, 1.3374 E, 1.3440 H, $n_O - n_E = 0.2513$ D. Index on cleavage, $n'_E = 1.467$. Merwin[5] gives: $n_O = 1.5848$ D, $n_E = 1.3360$, $n_O - n_E = 0.2488$. Colorless or white. PD 3.03, 2.31, 1.90; 7–271. Made from water solution.

CsNO$_3$ is hexagonal with $c/a = 1.236$. Crystals prismatic with pyramids. Distinct basal cleavage. G. 3.69. Uniaxial positive with weak birefringence decreasing with lowering temperature. $n_O{}^{26} = 1.558$, $n_E = 1.560$, $n_E - n_O = 0.002$. Colorless. Inverts to an isometric phase at 161° C. PD 3.15, 4.47, 2.57; 9–403. Made from water solution at 14° C.

KNO$_3$ (Niter) is orthorhombic with $a = 5.42$, $b = 9.17$, $c = 6.45$ kX. U.C. 4. Space group $Pnma$. Isostructural with aragonite. Crystals prismatic or acicular. Twinning on $\{110\}$ common. Perfect $\{011\}$ and distinct $\{010\}$ and $\{110\}$ cleavages. H. 2. G. 2.1. F. 1. Deflagrates vividly on coal with violet flame color. X = c, Y = a. $(-)2V = 6°11'$ B, 7°12' D, 8°5' E, 10°22' H, r < v. $n_X = 1.3328$ B, 1.3346 D, 1.3365 E, $n_Y = 1.4988$ B, 1.5056 D, 1.5124 E, 1.5385 H, $n_Z = 1.4994$ B, 1.5064 D, 1.5135 E, $n_Z - n_X = 0.1718$ D. Merwin[5] gives: $n_X = 1.332$ D, $n_Y = 1.5038$, $n_Z = 1.5042$, $n_Z - n_X = 0.1722$ D. Colorless or white. PD 3.78, 3.73, 3.03; 5–0377*. Easily made from water solution. Inverts at 129° C. to a rhombohedral phase isostructural with NaNO$_3$. Other phases are known.

KNO$_3$ and **RbNO$_3$** form mix-crystals[41] from 0 to at least 50 per cent RbNO$_3$ in which 2E decreases from 10°51' with r < v in pure KNO$_3$ to 0° at about 32 per cent RbNO$_3$; with more RbNO$_3$ the optic angle opens in 010 attaining 2°48' with r > v in crystals with 37 per cent RbNO$_3$. The density increases from 2.11 for pure KNO$_3$ to 2.35 for 50 per cent RbNO$_3$.

RbNO$_3$ is orthorhombic with $a:b:c = 1.737:1:0.711$; very nearly hexagonal. Crystals prismatic with poor $\{001\}$ cleavage. G. 3.12. Y = b, Z = c. $(-)2V = $ small;[42] r > v. $n_X = 1.51$, $n_Y = 1.52$, $n_Z = 1.524$, $n_Z - n_X = 0.014$. Colorless. PD 3.10, 2.53, 1.96; 4–0608*. Made from water solution at 17° C.

NH$_4$NO$_3$ (Ammonia-Niter) is orthorhombic with $a = 4.96$, $b = 5.45$, $c = 5.75$ Å. Space group $Pmmn$. Crystals pseudo-tetragonal long prisms.

[40] Schrauf: *Sitz. Akad. Wiss. Wien* XLI, p. 787 (1860).

[41] Stortenbeker: *Rec. Trav. Chim. Pays-Bas* XXXIII, p. 90 (1914).

[42] Bolland (*Sitz. Akad. Wiss. Wien* CXIX, IIb, p. 275, 1910) gives $n_X = 1.535$, $n_Z = 1.54$.

Distinct $\{010\}$ cleavage. G. 1.725. X = b, Y = a. $(-)2V^{43} = 35°$, r < v weak. $n_X = 1.411$ (668), 1.413 (588), 1.416 (502), $n_Y = 1.605$ (668), 1.611 (588), 1.623 (502), $n_Z = 1.6296$ (668), 1.637 (588), 1.6494 (502), $n_Z - n_X = 0.224$. Colorless. PD: See below. Made from solution at ordinary temperature. Stable between $-18°$ and $+32°$ C. It inverts (on cooling) at $-18°$ C. to a hexagonal phase with $a = 15.9$ and $c = 5.75$; G. 1.71 at $-25°$ C. Uniaxial positive with $n_O = 1.493 \pm 0.007$, $n_E = 1.623 \pm 0.007$, $n_E - n_O = 0.130 \pm 0.014$. On heating it inverts at $50°$ C. to a tetragonal phase (stable between $84°$ and $125°$ C.) with $a = 5.74$ and $c = 5.00$ Å. G. 1.666. Uniaxial positive with[43] $n_O = 1.509$, $n_E = 1.585$, $n_E - n_O = 0.076$. The stable phase between $32°$ and $84°$ C. is orthorhombic with $a = 7.06$, $b = 7.66$, $c = 5.80$ Å. Space group $Pbnm$. U.C. 4. G. 1.66 at $40°$ C. Optic orientation unknown. $(-)2V = 80°$ calc. $n_X^{44} = 1.463 \pm .002$, $n_Y = 1.543 \pm .005$, $n_Z = 1.600 \pm .002$, $n_Z - n_X = 0.137 \pm .004$. With 19.3 per cent KNO_3 it has[45] $n_X = 1.46$, $n_Y = 1.54$, $n_Z = 1.60$, $n_Z - n_X = 0.14$. The tetragonal phase inverts to an isometric phase at $125°$ C. which has $a = 4.40$ Å.[46] U.C. 1. The latter has G. 1.594 and $n = 1.530 \pm 0.005$, measured at $130°$ C. Molten NH_4NO_3 has G. 1.42 and $n = 1.459 \pm 0.005$ measured at $175°$ C. PD 2.64, 3.25, 3.40; 8–499*, also 3.09, 2.72, 3.96; 8–452*, also two others at higher temperature.

AgNO₃ is orthorhombic sphenoidal with $a:b:c = 0.943:1:1.37$. Crystals thick basal plates. Twinning on $\{001\}$. G. 4.35. M.P. $209°$ C. Soluble in water. Y = a, Z = c. $(+)2V = 62°$, r < v strong $(2E = 126°37'$ red, $133°50'$ blue). $n_X = 1.729$, $n_Y = 1.744$, $n_Z = 1.788$, $n_Z - n_X = 0.059$. Colorless. PD 3.01, 3.67, 4.53; 6–0363. Inverts at $159°$ C. to a hexagonal(?) phase.

TlNO₃ is orthorhombic with $a:b:c = 0.511:1:0.651$. Crystals short prismatic, varied, with poor $\{010\}$ cleavage. G. 5.55. X = c, Y = b. $(-)2V = 52°38'$ red, $53°52'$ blue.[26] $n_X = 1.817$, $n_Y = 1.862$, $n_Z = 1.869$, $n_Z - n_X = 0.052$. Inverts at $80°$ C. to a hexagonal phase and at $151°$ C. to an isometric phase. Made from a water solution at about $20°$ C. PD 2.96, 4.40, 3.08; 7–187* (which polymorph?).

β. HYDRATED

LiNO₃·3H₂O is orthorhombic(?); crystals prismatic[47] with parallel extinction; the optic plane is normal to the elongation. $(-)2V = 55°$. $n_X = 1.365$, $n_Y = 1.490$, $n_Z = 1.523$, $n_Z - n_X = 0.158$.

[43] Bowen: *J. Phys. Chem.* XXX, p. 721 (1926).
[44] Hendricks, Deming and Jefferson: *Zeit. Krist.* LXXXV, p. 143 (1933).
[45] Whetstone: *Canad. J. Res.* XXVI B, p. 499 (1948).
[46] Hendricks, Posnjak and Kracek: *J. Am. Chem. Soc.* LIV, p. 2766 (1932).
[47] West: *Zeit. Krist.* LXXXVIII, p. 198 (1934).

2. Formula Type A(NO₃)₂

$Sr(NO_3)_2$ is isometric and tetartohedral in crystals like those of $Ba(NO_3)_2$. G. 2.99. Isotropic with $n = 1.586$,[48] 1.5878 Na.[49] Also weakly birefringent (due to strain?). Colorless. PD 4.48, 2.35, 2.25; 4–0310. Made from water solution above 25° C.

$Ba(NO_3)_2$ **(Nitrobarite)** is isometric and tetartohedral(?). $a = 8.11\ kX$. Space group $Pa3$ or $P2_13$. Crystals double tetrahedrons, modified cubes, etc. Twinning on {111}. No cleavage. G. 3.25. F. 1. Isotropic with $n = 1.5665$ C, 1.5711 D, 1.5825 F. Also weakly birefringent in sectors. Colorless. Forms mix-crystals in all proportions[50] with $Pb(NO_3)_2$. Easily made from water solution.

$Pb(NO_3)_2$ is isometric and tetartohedral like $Ba(NO_3)_2$. (Another phase is monoclinic.) G. 1.54. Isotropic with $n = 1.773$ C, 1.7815 D, 1.806 F. Again:[51] $n = 1.7700$ Li, 1.7807 D, 1.8068 Cd. Colorless. PD 2.45, 4.68, 2.34; 4–0773. Made from water solution. Forms mix-crystals in all proportions with[51] $Ba(NO_3)_2$.

$Mg(NO_3)_2 \cdot 6H_2O$ **(Nitromagnesite)** is monoclinic prismatic with $a:b:c = 0.5191:1:0.9698$, $\beta = 92°56'$. Crystals long prismatic. Perfect {110} cleavage. G. 1.46. $(-)2V = 5° \pm 1°$, r < v² weak. $n_X = 1.34 \pm 0.01$, $n_Y = 1.506 \pm 0.003$, $n_Z = 1.506 \pm 0.003$, $n_Z - n_X = 0.266$. Colorless or white. PD 4.40, 2.93, 3.29; 1–0349. Made from water solution.

$Ca(NO_3)_2 \cdot 4H_2O$ **(Nitrocalcite)** is monoclinic prismatic with $a:b:c = 1.5839:1:0.6876$, $\beta = 98°6'$. Crystals long prismatic. Cleavable. G. 1.90. X normal to a cleavage,[2] $(-)2V = 50° \pm 2°$, $n_X = 1.465 \pm 0.003$, $n_Y = 1.498 \pm 0.003$, $n_Z = 1.504 \pm 0.003$, $n_Z - n_X = 0.039$. Colorless. PD 5.2, 7.8, 2.89; 1–0229. Made from water solution.

$Co(NO_3)_2 \cdot 6H_2O$ is monoclinic with $a:b:c = 1.172:1:1.925$, $\beta = 101°0'$. Crystals basal tablets with perfect {001} (or {100}?) cleavage. The acute bisectrix makes an angle of about 18° with a normal to the cleavage. $(-)2E = 62.5°$. According to Bolland[52] "cobalt nitrate" (of unknown formula) is optically positive with $n'_X = 1.38(?)$ $n_Y = ?$, $n'_Z = 1.52(?)$, $n_Z - n_X = 0.14(?)$. Color red. PD 4.60, 3.29, 2.19; 1–0317.

[48] Yakowitz and Jorgenson: *Ind. Eng. Chem.* (Anal. Ed.) IX, p. 204 (1937).

[49] Behr: *N. Jahrb. Min.* 1903, I, p. 135. This value verified by E. T. Wherry: *pers. comm.*, Feb. 1928.

[50] Vegard and Dale: *Zeit. Krist.* LXVII, p. 148 (1928).

[51] Wulff and King: *Zeit. Krist.* LXXXVII, p. 72 (1934).

[52] Bolland: *Sitz. Akad. Wiss. Wien* CXIX, IIb, p. 275 (1910).

3. Formula Type $A_mB_n(NO_3)_p \cdot qH_2O$

$Mg_3Ce_2(NO_3)_{12} \cdot 24H_2O$ is hexagonal.[53] Crystals rhombohedral. Uniaxial negative with n_O = 1.5204 C, 1.5249 D, 1.5346 F, n_E = 1.5135 C, 1.5176 D, 1.5267 F, $n_O - n_E$ = 0.0073 D; F–C for n_O = 0.0142.

$Mg_3Nd_2(NO_3)_{12} \cdot 24H_2O$ is hexagonal.[53] Crystals rhombohedral. Uniaxial negative with n_O = 1.5228 C, 1.5266 D, 1.5368 F, n_E = 1.5156 C, 1.5192 D, 1.5286 F, $n_O - n_E$ = 0.0074; F–C for n_O = 0.0140.

$Mg_3Pr_2(NO_3)_{12} \cdot 24H_2O$ is hexagonal.[53] Crystals rhombohedral. Uniaxial negative with n_O = 1.5215 C, 1.5255 D, 1.5356 F, n_E = 1.5144 C, 1.5182 D, 1.5277 F, $n_O - n_E$ = 0.0073; F–C for n_O = 0.0141.

$Mg_3La_2(NO_3)_{12} \cdot 24H_2O$ is hexagonal.[53] Crystals rhombohedral. Uniaxial negative with n_O = 1.5180 C, 1.5220 D, 1.5319 F, n_E = 1.5112 C, 1.5150 D, 1.5242 F, $n_O - n_E$ = 0.0070 D; F–C for n_O = 0.0139.

F. NITRATES CONTAINING HYDROXYL OR HALOGEN

$Ca_4Al_2(NO_3)_2(OH)_{12} \cdot 4H_2O$ is hexagonal in basal plates often in spherulites. Uniaxial negative[54] with weak birefringence when immersed in water, but uniaxial positive[55] in immersion liquids; n_O = 1.502 ± 0.005, n_E = 1.532 ± 0.005, $n_E - n_O$ = 0.030. Colorless.

$Ca(OH)(VO_3) \cdot H_2O$ is orthorhombic[56] in needles along c and flattened on {100}; {100}, {010} and {001} cleavages. X = c, Y = b, (−)2V = 44° calc. n_X = 1.447 ± 0.002, n_Y = 1.564 ± 0.002, n_Z = 1.583 ± 0.002, $n_Z - n_X$ = 0.136. Colorless.

$Cu_2(OH)_3(NO_3)$ (Gerhardtite) is orthorhombic with $a:b:c$ = 0.9206:1:1.1498. Crystals thick basal tablets with pyramidal striations. Perfect {001} and good {100} cleavages. H. 2. G. 3.43. X = a, Y = b. (+)2V = very large,[6] r > v strong. n_X = 1.703, n_Y = 1.713, n_Z = 1.722, $n_Z - n_X$ = 0.019. Color green, with X and Y green, Z blue. PD 6.85, 3.44, 2.45; 3–0068. Made by heating a solution of the normal nitrate and in other ways. A monoclinic phase is also known.

$Hg(OH)(NO_3) \cdot 0.5H_2O$ is orthorhombic with $a:b:c$ = 0.698:1:0.519. Crystals {010} plates with {001}, {100}, {110}, etc. Perfect {010}, good {100} and distinct {120} cleavages. For mercury "oxydulnitrat" Bolland[52] gives parallel extinction and n_X = 1.69, n_Y = 1.72, n_Z = 1.92, $n_Z - n_X$ = 0.23. (+)2V = 70° calc. (PD: 5.60, 3.47, 3.75; 1–0196 for "$HgNO_3 \cdot H_2O$").

[53] Flint: *Zeit. Krist.* Ref. III, p. 94 (1931).

[54] Mylius: *Acta Acad. Abo. Math. Phys.* VII, No. 3 (1933).

[55] Is this due to change in hydration or to inversion?

[56] Pehrman and Mylius: *Acta Acad. Abo. Math. Phys.* VIII, No. 9 (1935).

G. NITRATES CONTAINING URANYL OR AMMONIA

$UO_2(NO_3)_2 \cdot 6H_2O$ is orthorhombic[57] with $a = 11.58$, $b = 13.20$, $c = 8.04$ Å. U.C. 4. G. 2.74–2.81. M.P. 60° C. Crystals usually vertically long. X = c, Y = b. $(-)2V = 46°$, r > v weak. $n_X = 1.482$, $n_Y = 1.494$, $n_Z = 1.572$, $n_Z - n_X = 0.090$. Again:[58] $n_X = 1.485$, $n_Y = 1.497$, $n_Z = 1.58$, $n_Z - n_X = 0.095$. Color yellow with X light yellow, Y yellow, Z yellow-green; also color siskin-green with yellowish green fluorescence and X clear yellow, Y greenish yellow, Z deep citron-yellow. PD 5.70, 4.33, 6.60; 1–0176.

$K_2(UO_2)(NO_3)_4$ is monoclinic[59] with $a:b:c = 0.639:1:0.619$, $\beta = 90° \pm$. Crystals basal plates or prismatic. G. 3.36. n_1 (vibration parallel to b) = 1.5422, n_2 (vibration in (010) at 26°34' from a toward c in the acute angle β) = 1.5349. Color green.

$(NH_4)_2(UO_2)(NO_3)_4 \cdot 2H_2O$ is monoclinic with[59] $a:b:c = 0.842:1:0.559$, $\beta = 85°5'$. Crystals resemble cubes modified by pyramids. No cleavage. G. 2.78. Dissociates at 140° C. Volatile. Z = b. $(-)2V = 45°$ calc. $n_X = 1.508$, $n_Y = 1.619$, $n_Z = 1.639$, $n_Z - n_X = 0.131$. Color sulfur-yellow.

$Ca(NH_3)_4(NO_3)_2$ is biaxial with[60] $(-?)2V = 45°$, $n_X = 1.475$, $n_Y = ?$, $n_Z = 1.510$, $n_Z - n_X = 0.035$ Na.

H. COMPOUND NITRATES

$Na_3(SO_4)(NO_3) \cdot H_2O$ **(Darapskite)** is monoclinic with $a:b:c = 1.5258:1:0.7514$, $\beta = 102°55'$. Crystals pseudo-tetragonal {100} tablets. Perfect {010} cleavage and {100} cleavage or parting. H. 2.5. G. 2.20. X = b, Z $\wedge$ $c = 12°$. $(-)2V = 27° \pm 1°$, r > v moderate.[2] $n_X = 1.391 \pm 0.005$, $n_Y = 1.481 \pm 0.003$, $n_Z = 1.486 \pm 0.003$, $n_Z - n_X = 0.095$. Colorless. Made by heating a water solution of Na_2SO_4 and $NaNO_3$ at temperature between 14° and 50° C.

I. NITRITES

$K_2PbCu(NO_2)_6$ is isometric.[61] Crystals cubic with smaller dodecahedral and trisoctahedral faces. Isotropic with $n =$ or somewhat greater than 1.80. Made by adding KNO_2 to a solution of $Na_2PbCu(NO_2)_6$.

[57] McCrone: *Anal. Chem.* XXI, p. 1151 (1949).

[58] C. D. West: *pers. comm.*, Nov. 2, 1936.

[59] Nichols and Howes: *Carn. Inst. Publ.* 298, p. 214 (1919). Rimbach (*Ber. Chem. Ges.* XXXVII, 1904, p. 472) has described orthorhombic and trigonal phases of ammonium, and two orthorhombic phases of potassium, uranyl nitrate.

[60] Portnow and Wassiliew: *Zeit. anorg. Chem.* CCXXI, p. 149 (1935).

[61] Mackenzie and Smith: *Rec. Trav. Chim. Pays-Bas*, LVII, p. 1211 (1938).

NaNO₂ is orthorhombic[62] with $a:b:c = 0.640:1:0.967$. Crystals {010} tablets, prismatic or columnar along b with perfect {101} cleavage. G. 2.15. $X = a$, $Y = b$. $(+)2V = 75°$. $n_X = 1.354$, $n_Y = 1.460$, $n_Z = 1.648$, $n_Z - n_X = 0.294$. Again:[63] $n_X = 1.340$, $n_Y = 1.425$, $n_Z = 1.655$, $n_Z - n_X = 0.315$. Colorless. PD 2.98, 2.79, 2.04; 6–0392.

K₂Cd(NO₂)₄ is orthorhombic with $a:b:c = 0.537:1:1.924$; pseudohexagonal. Crystals columnar prismatic or {010} tablets with distinct {110} cleavage. $Y = b$, $Z = c$. $(+)2V = 48°$. $n_X = 1.556$ calc., $n_Y = 1.565$, $n_Z = 1.608$, $n_Z - n_X = 0.052$ Na. Color pale yellow.

K₂Pt(NO₂)₄ is monoclinic with[64] $a = 7.74$, $b = 12.87$, $c = 9.24$ Å., $\beta = 96°15'$. G. 3.13. Acute bisectrix, X, nearly normal to a poor cleavage. Extinction on {110} at 6° to c in acute angle β. $(-)2E = 102°; 2V = 55°28'$ calc. For $\lambda = 578$: $n_X = 1.590$, $n_Y = 1.670$, $n_Z = 1.685$, $n_Z - n_X = 0.095$. For $\lambda = 546$: $n_X = 1.605$, $n_Y = 1.676$, $n_Z = 1.710$. $n_Z - n_X = 0.105$.

Sr(NO₂)₂·H₂O[65] is isometric. Crystals cubic with poor {111} cleavage. G. 2.99. Isotropic with $n = 1.589$ Na. Colorless. Formed from cold water solution.

Na₂Ru(NO₂)₅·2H₂O is monoclinic with $a:b:c = 1.508:1:1.022$, $\beta = 97°47'$. Crystals prismatic with no good cleavage. Twinning on {100} of the Carlsbad type. $Y = b$, $Z \wedge c = 84°18'$ Na, $84°34'$ Tl. $(+)2V = 24°50'$ Li, $25°14'$ Na, $25°37'$ Tl. $n_X = 1.5889$ Na, $n_Y = 1.5847$ Li, 1.5943 Na, 1.6041 Tl, $n_Z = 1.7163$ Na, $n_Z - n_X = 0.1274$ Na. Color orange with X yellow, Z orange.

J. NITRITES CONTAINING HALOGEN

K₂PtI₂(NO₂)₂·2H₂O is tetragonal with $c/a = 0.589$. Perfect {100} and distinct {001} cleavages. Uniaxial negative with $n_O = 1.7909$, $n_E = 1.6527$, $n_O - n_E = 0.1382$. Color reddish yellow with O orange, E greenish yellow.

K₂PtBr₂(NO₂)₂·H₂O is triclinic with $a:b:c = 0.992:1:1.317$, $\alpha = 90°58'$, $\beta = 91°43'$, $\gamma = 91°7'$. Crystals {001} (or {20$\bar{1}$}) tablets, or complex. Common twinning on {001}. One optic axis is nearly normal to {001}; the other, visible through {20$\bar{1}$}, makes an angle of 30°5' with a normal to this face. $X \wedge$ normal to {001} = 47°55'; $X \wedge$ normal to {20$\bar{1}$} = 63°10'; $Z \wedge$ normal to {001} = 42°7'; $Z \wedge$ normal to {20$\bar{1}$} = 32°27'. $(+)2V = 72°21'$. Axis A, visible through {001}, is very little dispersed with $r > v$. Axis B, visible through {20$\bar{1}$}, shows strong inclined dispersion with $r < v$. $n_X = 1.626$, $n_Y = 1.6684$, $n_Z = 1.757$, $n_Z - n_X = 0.131$ Na. Color yellow.

[62] Ziegler: *Phys. Rev.* XXXVIII, p. 1040 (1931).
[63] Bunn: *Chemical Crystallography*, p. 283, 1946.
[64] Lambot: *Bull. Soc. Roy. Sci. Liège* XII, p. 463 (1943).
[65] Not analyzed; perhaps more water.

K. NITRITES CONTAINING AMMONIA

KCo(NH₃)₂(NO₂)₄ is orthorhombic with $a:b:c = 0.878:1:0.519$. Crystals show $\{010\}$, $\{110\}$, $\{101\}$. G. 2.067. Again[58] G. 2.172. Good $\{110\}$ cleavage. $Y = a$, $Z = c$. $(+)2V$ = moderate, $r \gg v$. $n_X = 1.702$, $n_Y = 1.713$, $n_Z = 1.760$, $n_Z - n_X = 0.058$.

NH₄Co(NH₃)₂(NO₂)₄ is orthorhombic[66] with $a:b:c = 0.868:1:0.511$. Crystals prismatic with $\{110\}$, $\{101\}$. G. 1.972. No cleavage seen. For vibrations along c, $n > 1.74$ and < 1.78; for vibrations along either a or b, $n = 1.73\pm$. Therefore n_X and n_Y nearly $= 1.73$, $n_Z > 1.74$ and < 1.78, $Z = c$ and $(+)2V$ not large.

Rh(NH₃)₃(NO₂)₃ has symmetrical extinction.[67] $(+)2V = 69°$, $n_X = 1.700$, $n_Y = 1.720$, $n_Z = 1.780$, $n_Z - n_X = 0.080$. Color of crystals light yellow.

Pt(NH₃)₂ClNO₂(trans-) forms irregular crystals[67] with $(-)2V = 46°$ calc. $n_X = 1.764$, $n_Y = 1.786$, $n_Z = 1.790$, $n_Z - n_X = 0.026$.

Pt(NH₃)₂BrNO₂(trans-) has symmetrical extinction[67] with $n_X = 1.778$, $n_Y > 1.780$, $n_Z > 1.780$.

Pt(NH₃)₂Cl(NO₂)₃ is monoclinic[68] with $a:b:c = 0.97:1:0.56$, $\beta = 96°$. Crystals acicular. $(+)2V = 66°$. $n_X = 1.755$, $n_Y = 1.797$, $n_Z = 1.89$ calc., $n_Z - n_X = 0.135$. Color of crystals pale green.

Pt(NH₃)₂(NO₂)₂(cis-) is monoclinic[68] with $a:b:c = 0.821:1:1.030$, $\beta = 101°20'$. Crystals acicular. Twinning common. $X \wedge c = 42° - 45°$ in obtuse β; $Y = b$. $(+)2V = 80°$. $n_X = 1.711$, $n_Y = 1.742$, $n_Z = 1.790$, $n_Z - n_X = 0.079$. Color pale yellow.

Pt(NH₃)₂(NO₂)₂(trans-) has an extinction angle[68] of 20°. $(-)2V = 32°$. $n_X = 1.531$, $n_Y = 1.779$, $n_Z = 1.80$ ca., $n_Z - n_X = 0.269$ ca. Colorless.

KRh(NH₃)₂(NO₂)₄·0.5H₂O is triclinic[67] with $a:b:c = 1.205:1:0.903$, $\alpha = 95°18'$, $\beta = 118°36'$, $\gamma = 85°11'$. $(-)2V = 62°$. $n_X = 1.612$, $n_Y = 1.690$, $n_Z = 1.716$, $n_Z - n_X = 0.104$. Color of crystals light yellow.

L. HALATES

The halates include chlorates, bromates and iodates as well as hypochlorites, perchlorates, perbromates and periodates. A few complex and compound salts are known.

[66] Knaggs: *J. Chem. Soc. London* CXXI, p. 2069 (1922).
[67] Bokii and Burovaya: *Trudy Inst. Krist.* p. 29 (1947).
[68] Bokii and Lyashenko: *Trudy Inst. Krist.*, p. 21 and 37 (1947).

1. Formula Type $A_m(XO_2)_2 \cdot nH_2O$

$Ca(ClO_2)_2 \cdot 2H_2O$ is tetragonal.[68a] Uniaxial positive with $n_O = 1.53$, $n_E = 1.63$, $n_E - n_O = 0.10$. Colorless.

$Ca_3(ClO_2)_2(OH)_4$ is tetragonal.[68a] Uniaxial positive with $n_O = 1.51$, $n_E = 1.585$, $n_E - n_O = 0.075$. Colorless.

2. Formula Type $AXO_3(OH)_n$ with $n = 0$ or 1

$NaClO_3$ is isometric and tetartohedral. Crystals cubic or tetartohedral with no cleavage. Penetration twins common on $\{100\}$. G. 2.49. Soluble in water. Isotropic with $n = 1.5127$ C, 1.5151 D, 1.5216 F. Rotates the plane of polarization for 1 mm. of thickness $2.3°$ B, $3.1°$ D, $4.6°$ F. Colorless. Made from water solution. PD 2.94, 3.29, 1.76; 5–0610.

$NaBrO_3$ is isometric tetartohedral. Crystals tetartohedral, etc. G. 3.3. Soluble in water. Isotropic with $n = 1.6117$ for 672 mμ,[69] 1.617 for 579 mμ, 1.6268 for 492 mμ; again[70] $n = 1.5943 + Na$. Weakly birefringent in some cases (due to strain?). Rotates the plane of polarization for 1 mm. of thickness $1.4°$ B, $2.1°$ D, $3.75°$ F. Colorless. Made from water solution. PD 3.00, 1.79, 4.74; 6–0377.

$AgBrO_3$ is tetragonal with $c/a = 0.941$. Crystals prismatic columnar or pyramidal. Poor $\{110\}$ cleavage. G. 5.1–5.2. Uniaxial positive with $n_O = 1.8466$ Na, 1.860 (green), $n_E = 1.920$ Na, 1.9405 (green), $n_E - n_O = 0.0734$ Na. Color white. PD 2.95, 3.04, 3.48; 6–0385.

$KBrO_3$ is hexagonal rhombohedral with $c/a = 1.357$. Crystals rhombohedral. Poor basal cleavage. G. 3.32. Uniaxial negative with[26] $n_O = 1.68$, $n_E = 1.54$, $n_O - n_E = 0.14$. PD 3.21, 3.01, 4.39; 7–242.

$KClO_3$ is monoclinic with $a = 7.085$, $b = 5.585$, $c = 4.647$ Å,[71] $\beta\ 109°38'$. (Pseudo-trigonal and closely related to calcite and soda niter.) Crystals lamellar to equant basal tablets. Perfect basal and $\{110\}$ cleavages. Lamellar twinning on $\{001\}$. G. 2.32. Soluble in water. $Y \wedge a = 58.5°$ in obtuse angle β;[71] $Z = b$. $(-)2V = 28°$, with distinct horizontal dispersion. $n_X = 1.415$, $n_Y = 1.517$, $n_Z = 1.523$, $n_Z - n_X = 0.108$. Again:[72] $X \wedge c = +56°10'$, $(-)2V = 26°45'$. $n_X = 1.4099$, $n_Y = 1.5174$, $n_Z = 1.5241$, $n_Z - n_X = 0.1142$. Colorless. PD 3.45, 2.79, 2.86; 1–0599. Made from water solution.

KIO_3 is monoclinic with $a:b:c = 1.009:1:1.439$, $\beta = 90°45'$. Crystals commonly twinned in pseudo-cubic form with $\{110\}$, $\{001\}$, $\{100\}$, etc. No cleavage seen. G. 3.89 (or 3.98). M.P. 560° C. $(-)2V = $ small,[26] $r > v$.

[68a] *Handbook of Chemistry and Physics*, 1953, p. 492.

[69] Rose: *N. Jahrb. Min. El. Bd.* XXIX, p. 64 (1910).

[70] LeBlanc and Rowland: *Zeit. phys. Chem.* XIX, p. 277 (1896).

[71] McCrone: *Anal. Chem.* XXII, p. 1067 (1950).

[72] Porter: *Festsch. V. Goldschmidt*, 1928, p. 210.

$n_X = 1.700$, $n_Y = 1.828$, $n_Z = 1.832$, $n_Z - n_X = 0.132$. PD 3.16, 4.48, 2.23; 1–0776.

Cu(OH)IO$_3$ is orthorhombic[73] with $a:b:c = 0.712:1:1.707$. Crystals basal tablets with {010}, {110} and {101}. Distinct {100} cleavage. X = a, Y = b. (−)2V = small, r > v (uniaxial in blue). $n_X = 1.775 \pm 0.01$, $n_Y = 2.046 \pm 0.005$, $n_Z = 2.052 \pm 0.005$, $n_Z - n_X = 0.277$. Color green with X colorless, Y green, Z yellowish green. Dimorphous with **salesite** which is also orthorhombic with $a = 4.78$, $b = 10.77$, $c = 6.70$ Å with perfect {110} cleavages. H. 3. G. 4.77 (−)2V = 0°–5°, r > v, extreme. $n_X = 1.786$, $n_Y = 2.070$, $n_Z = 2.075$, $n_Z - n_X = 0.289$. Color bluish green.

3. Formula Type A(XO$_3$)$_2 \cdot n$H$_2$O

Mg(BrO$_3$)$_2 \cdot$6H$_2$O is isometric; crystals octahedral. G. 2.29. Loses water at 200° C. Isotropic with $n = 1.5139$ Na. Colorless.

Zn(BrO$_3$)$_2 \cdot$6H$_2$O is isometric. Crystals octahedral. G. 2.56. M.P. 100° C. Isotropic with $n = 1.5452$ Na. Color white.

Sr(ClO$_3$)$_2$ is orthorhombic with $a:b:c = 0.916:1:0.597$. Crystals pyramidal. G. 3.15. Decomposes at 120° C. X = c, Y = a. (−)2V = 72°21′, r > v. $n_X = 1.5636$ B, 1.5670 D, 1.5717 F, $n_Y = 1.6002$ B, 1.6047 D, 1.6116 F, $n_Z = 1.6210$ B, 1.6257 D, 1.6337 F, $n_Z - n_X = 0.0587$ D. Colorless.

Ba(ClO$_3$)$_2 \cdot$H$_2$O is monoclinic with $a:b:c = 1.142:1:1.198$, $\beta = 93°34′$. Crystals columnar prisms with perfect {011} and good {100} cleavages. G. 3.18. Y = b; Z $\wedge$ c = −24°. (+)2V = 55.5°, r < v weak. $n_X = 1.562$, $n_Y = 1.577$, $n_Z = 1.635$, $n_Z - n_X = 0.073$. Colorless. PD 6.00, 2.32, 3.35; 1–0155.

Ca(IO$_3$)$_2 \cdot$6H$_2$O is orthorhombic. M.P. 42° C. (+)2V = nearly 90° calc. $n_X = 1.604$, $n_Y = 1.644$, $n_Z = 1.686$, $n_Z - n_X = 0.082$. Colorless.

Ca(IO$_3$)$_2$ (Lautarite) is monoclinic prismatic with $a = 7.18$, $b = 11.38$, $c = 7.32$ kX, $\beta = 106°22′$. U.C. 4. Space group $P2_1/c$. Crystals short prismatic. Good {011} cleavage. H. 3.5–4. G. 4.59. X $\wedge$ c = +25°, Y = b.[6] (+)2V = nearly 90°, r > v moderate. $n_X = 1.792$, $n_Y = 1.840$, $n_Z = 1.888$, $n_Z - n_X = 0.096$. Colorless. PD 4.27, 3.04, 3.24; 1–0386. Made by fusing CaIO$_3 \cdot$H$_2$O in NaNO$_3$.

3Cu(IO$_3$)$_2 \cdot$2H$_2$O (Bellingerite) is triclinic pinacoidal[74] with $a = 7.22$, $b = 7.82$, $c = 7.92$ Å, α 105°6′, β 96°58′, γ 92°55′. U.C. 1. Space group $P\bar{1}$. Crystals thick {100} tablets with {110}, {2$\bar{1}$0}, {0$\bar{1}$2}, {010}, etc. H. 4. G. 4.89. On {100} extinction is very nearly parallel with the zone edge [0$\bar{1}$1] and X′ $\wedge$ [001] = 37°. (+)2V = medium, r > v strong. $n_X =$

---

[73] Palache, Jarrell and Richmond: *Am. Min.* XXIV, p. 388 (1939).
[74] Berman and Wolfe: *Am. Min.* XXV, p. 505 (1940).

1.890, $n_Y = 1.90$, $n_Z = 1.99$, $n_Z - n_X = 0.10$. Color light green with X and Y light bluish green, Z blue-green.

4. Formula Type $A(XO_3)_3 \cdot nH_2O$

$Sm(BrO_3)_3 \cdot 9H_2O$ is hexagonal[75] with $c/a = 0.562$. G. 2.845. Uniaxial negative with $n_O = 1.605$ D, 1.609 E, 1.614 F, $n_E = 1.551$ D, 1.555 E, 1.560 F, $n_O - n_E = 0.054$ D.

$Gd(BrO_3)_3 \cdot 9H_2O$ is hexagonal[75] with $c/a = 0.570$. G. 2.892. Uniaxial negative with $n_O = 1.605$ D, 1.609 E, 1.614 F, $n_E = 1.551$ D, 1.555 E, 1.560 F, $n_O - n_E = 0.054$ D.

5. Formula Type $AXO_4 \cdot nH_2O$

KIO_4 is tetragonal. Crystals pyramidal. G. 3.62. It is stable to 200° C. but loses oxygen at 300° forming KIO_3. Uniaxial positive[76] with $n_O = 1.6151$ C, 1.6205 D, 1.6346 F, $n_E = 1.6416$ C, 1.6479 D, 1.6651 F, $n_E - n_O = 0.0274$ D. PD 3.41, 5.22, 2.12; 8–472.

$LiClO_4 \cdot 3H_2O$ is hexagonal[77] with $a = 15.42$, $c = 5.42$ kX. Crystals prismatic with distinct basal and $\{11\bar{2}0\}$ cleavages. G. 1.89. M.P. 95° C. Uniaxial negative with $n_O = 1.483$, $n_E = 1.448$, $n_O - n_E = 0.035$. Colorless. PD 4.23, 2.85, 3.86; 8–156.

$NaClO_4$ is orthorhombic[78] and apparently isostructural with $CaSO_4$. G. 2.50. Optic orientation not reported. $(+)2V$ = small. $n_X = 1.4606$, $n_Y = 1.4617$, $n_Z = 1.4730$, $n_Z - n_X = 0.0124$. Colorless. PD 3.54, 3.97, 2.96; 8–494*.

$KClO_4$ is orthorhombic[79] with $a:b:c = 0.781:1:1.281$. Crystals thick basal tablets with perfect basal and $\{110\}$ cleavages. G. 2.524. Y = a, Z = b. $(+)2V = 50°15'$ C, 49°48' D, 48°48' F. $n_X = 1.4712$ C, 1.4731 D, 1.4774 F, $n_Y = 1.4718$ C, 1.4737 D, 1.4779 F, $n_Z = 1.4750$ C, 1.4769 D, 1.4812 F, $n_Z - n_X = 0.0038$ D. Colorless. PD 3.49, 3.15, 2.89; 7–211*. Made by reaction of K_2SO_4 with $Ba(ClO_4)_2$. Miscible in all proportions with $KMnO_4$.

NH_4ClO_4 is orthorhombic[79] with $a:b:c = 0.793:1:1.281$. Crystals short prisms or basal tablets with perfect $\{110\}$ and distinct $\{001\}$ cleavages. G. 1.95. Y = c, Z = b. $(+)2V = 69°34'$ C, 69°54' D, 70°45' F, r > v distinct. $n_X = 1.4798$ C, 1.4818 D, 1.4865 F, $n_Y = 1.4813$ C, 1.4833 D, 1.4881 F, $n_Z = 1.4859$ C, 1.4881 D, 1.4931 F, $n_Z - n_X = 0.0063$ D. Colorless. PD 4.58, 3.61, 3.25; 8–451*. Made by reaction of $(NH_4)_2SO_4$ with $Ba(ClO_4)_2$.

[75] Pabst: *Am. J. Sci.* XXVI, p. 72 (1933).

[76] Merwin: *Int. Crit. Tables* VII, p. 27 (1931).

[77] West: *Zeit. Krist.* XCI, p. 480 (1935).

[78] Wulff and Heigl: *Zeit. Krist.* LXXVII, p. 84 (1931).

[79] Tutton: *Proc. Roy. Soc.* A. 111, p. 462 (1926); also Wulff: *Zeit. Elektrochem.* XXXIV, p. 611 (1928) and Wulff and Heigl: *Zeit. Krist.* LXXVII, p. 84 (1931).

RbClO₄ is orthorhombic[79] with $a:b:c = 0.796:1:1.288$. Crystals thick basal tablets to prismatic and apparently sphenoidal with distinct basal and {110} cleavages. G. 3.014. $Y = a$, $Z = b$. $(+)2V = 55°12'$ C, $55°4'$ D, $54°33'$ F; r > v weak. $n_X = 1.4674$ C, 1.4692 D, 1.4732 F, $n_Y = 1.4684$ C, 1.4701 D, 1.4742 F, $n_Z = 1.4715$ C, 1.4731 D, 1.4774 F, $n_Z - n_X = 0.0039$ D. Colorless. PD 3.85, 2.73, 2.32; 2–0309 (at 300° C).

CsClO₄ is orthorhombic[79] with $a:b:c = 0.817:1:1.287$. Crystals basal tablets or short prisms with perfect basal and {110} cleavages. G. 3.327. $Y = a$, $Z = b$. $(-)2V = 62°30'$. $n_X = 1.4734$ C, 1.4752 D, 1.4797 F, $n_Y = 1.4770$ C, 1.4788 D, 1.4835 F, $n_Z = 1.4786$ C, 1.4804 D, 1.4852 F, $n_Z - n_X = 0.0052$. Colorless. PD 3.99, 2.83, 2.41; 2–0923 (at 230° C). Made by reaction of Cs_2SO_4 with $Ba(ClO_4)_2$.

TlClO₄ is orthorhombic[80] with $a:b:c = 0.798:1:1.290$. Crystals domatic with {110} cleavage. G. 4.96. $Y = c$, $Z = b$. $(+)2V = $ small. $n_X = 1.6370$ Li, 1.6427 D, 1.6557 Cd, $n_Y = 1.6389$ Li, 1.6445 D, 1.6578 Cd, $n_Z = 1.6484$ Li, 1.6541 D, 1.6681 Cd, $n_Z - n_X = 0.0114$. Colorless. PD 3.21, 3.05, 4.42; 9–406.

6. Formula Type A(XO₄)₂·nH₂O

Mg(ClO₄)₂·6H₂O is hexagonal[81] with $a = 15.52$, $c = 5.26$ kX. Crystals slender prisms with distinct basal cleavage. G. 1.98. Uniaxial negative with $n_O = 1.482$, $n_E = 1.458$, $n_O - n_E = 0.024$. Also may be biaxial (2V up to 16°) with twinning as in aragonite. Colorless. PD 2.85, 4.18, 3.91; 1–0969.

Mn(ClO₄)₂·6H₂O is hexagonal[81] with $a = 15.70$, $c = 5.30$ kX. Crystals prismatic with distinct basal cleavage. G. 2.10. Uniaxial negative with $n_O = 1.492$, $n_E = 1.475$, $n_O - n_E = 0.017$.

Fe(ClO₄)₂·6H₂O is hexagonal[81] with $a = 15.58$, $c = 5.24$ kX. Crystals prismatic with distinct basal cleavage. G. 2.15. Uniaxial negative with $n_O = 1.493$, $n_E = 1.478$, $n_O - n_E = 0.015$. Also may be biaxial with very small 2V and twinning as in aragonite. Color green.

Co(ClO₄)₂·6H₂O is hexagonal[81] with $a = 15.52$, $c = 5.20$ kX. Crystals prismatic with distinct basal cleavage. G. 2.20. Uniaxial negative with $n_O = 1.510$, $n_E = 1.490$, $n_O - n_E = 0.020$. Also may be biaxial with very small 2V and twinning as in aragonite. Color red or pink with O pale pink, slightly yellowish, E deep pink.

Ni(ClO₄)₂·6H₂O is hexagonal[81] with $a = 15.46$, $c = 5.17$ kX. Crystals prismatic with distinct basal cleavage. G. 2.25. Uniaxial negative with $n_O = 1.518$, $n_E = 1.498$, $n_O - n_E = 0.020$. Color greenish blue with O green, E dark bluish green.

[80] Wulff and Schaller: *Zeit. Krist.* LXXXVII, p. 43 (1934).

[81] West: *Zeit. Krist.* XCI, p. 480 (1935).

$Zn(ClO_4)_2 \cdot 6H_2O$ is hexagonal[81] with $a = 15.52$, $c = 5.20$ kX. Crystals prismatic with distinct basal cleavage. G. 2.25. Uniaxial negative with $n_O = 1.508$, $n_E = 1.487$, $n_O - n_E = 0.021$.

$Cd(ClO_4)_2 \cdot 6H_2O$ is hexagonal[81] with $a = 15.92$, $c = 5.30$ kX. Crystals prismatic with distinct basal cleavage. G. 2.37. Uniaxial negative with $n_O = 1.489$, $n_E = 1.480$, $n_O - n_E = 0.009$.

$Hg(ClO_4)_2 \cdot 6H_2O$ is hexagonal rhombohedral.[81] G. 2.79. Uniaxial negative with $n_O = 1.511$, $n_E = 1.509$, $n_O - n_E = 0.002$.

$Cu(ClO_4)_2 \cdot 6H_2O$ is monoclinic[81] with G. 2.245. Crystals prismatic or $\{100\}$ tablets. $X \wedge c = 23°$; $Z = b$. $(+)2V = 54°$. $n_X = 1.495$, $n_Y = 1.505$, $n_Z = 1.522$, $n_Z - n_X = 0.027$. Marked crossed dispersion giving anomalous interference colors near extinction in (010) sections.

$Ba(ClO_4)_2 \cdot 3H_2O$ is hexagonal[82] with $c/a = 1.33$. Crystals prismatic. Hygroscopic. G. 2.91. Uniaxial negative with $n_O = 1.5330$, $n_E = 1.5323$, $n_O - n_E = 0.0007$. PD 2.90, 3.65, 2.14; 1–0931.

$Ca(IO_4)_2 \cdot 6H_2O$ is orthorhombic[83] with $a:b:c = 0.647:1:0.277$. Crystals pyramidal or prismatic with $\{131\}$, $\{110\}$, $\{010\}$, $\{100\}$, etc. Poor $\{110\}$ cleavage. $Y = a$, $Z = c$. $(+)2V = 88°\pm$, r < v. $n_X = 1.604$, $n_Y = 1.644$, $n_Z = 1.686$, $n_Z - n_X = 0.082$ D.

7. Miscellaneous Halates

$Co(ClO_4)_2 \cdot 6NH_3$ is isometric. Crystals octahedral with distinct octahedral cleavage. Isotropic with $n = 1.430$ Na.

$Ni(ClO_4)_2 \cdot 6NH_3$ is isometric. Crystals octahedral with distinct octahedral cleavage. Isotropic with $n = 1.437$ Na. PD 4.04, 2.85, 2.19; 2–0284.

$Co(ClO_4)_3 \cdot 6NH_3$ is isometric[84] in modified octahedrons. G. 2.065. Isotropic with $n = 1.570$. Color yellow-brown.

$CoCl(ClO_4)_2 \cdot 6NH_3$ is rhombohedral[84] with $c/a = 1.93$. Crystals basal plates with poor $\{10\bar{1}1\}$ cleavage. G. 1.905. Uniaxial negative with $n_O = 1.610$, $n_E = 1.600$, $n_O - n_E = 0.010$. Color orange.

$Ca_4Al_2(ClO_3)_2(OH)_{12} \cdot 4H_2O(?)$ is hexagonal[54] in plates often in spherulites. Uniaxial negative in water, but changes[85] slowly to uniaxial positive in immersion liquids. $n_O = 1.521 \pm 0.002$, $n_E = 1.521 \pm 0.002$, $n_O - n_E =$ very weak.

$Ca_5Al_2(IO_3)_2(OH)_{15} \cdot 14H_2O(?)$ is probably hexagonal.[54] Uniaxial negative with $n_O = 1.521 \pm 0.003$, $n_E = 1.496 \pm 0.003$, $n_O - n_E = 0.025$.

$Ca_6Al_2(IO_3)_2(OH)_{18} \cdot 24H_2O(?)$ seems to be hexagonal.[54] Uniaxial negative with $n_O = 1.471 \pm 0.002$, $n_E = 1.471 \pm 0.002$, $n_O - n_E =$ very weak.

[82] Wulff and Heigl: *Zeit. Krist.* LXXVII, p. 84 (1931).

[83] Mélon: *Eull. Soc. Fr. Min.* LVIII, p. 343 (1935).

[84] C. D. West: *pers. comm.*, Nov. 2, 1936.

[85] Is this due to change of hydration or to change of phase or both?

$Al(NO_3)(IO_3)_2 \cdot 6H_2O$ is rhombohedral[86] with $c/a = 1.206$. Crystals basal tablets limited by $\{10\bar{1}0\}$, $\{10\bar{1}1\}$ and $\{10\bar{1}2\}$. No cleavage. Twinning on $\{10\bar{1}1\}$. G. 2.78. Soluble in water. Uniaxial positive with $n_O = 1.6516$, $n_E = 1.6987$. Colorless; transparent to porcelain-like.

$H_2K_2TeI_2O_{10} \cdot 2H_2O$ is rhombohedral with $c/a = 1.933$. Crystals rhombohedral with $\{0001\}$. Common twinning on $\{10\bar{1}1\}$. No good cleavage. Uniaxial negative with $n_O = 2.142$, $n_E = 2.030$, $n_O - n_E = 0.112$ Na.

$Ca_2(ClO_4)_2(OH)_2 \cdot 2H_2O$ is orthorhombic[87] in needles along c, flattened on $\{100\}$ with $\{100\}$, $\{001\}$, and $\{010\}$ cleavages. $X = c$, $Y = b$, $(-)2V = ?$. $n_X = 1.532 \pm 0.002$, $n_Y = 1.535 \pm 0.002$, $n_Z = ?$.

$Ca_4(ClO_4)_2(OH)_6 \cdot 12H_2O$ is orthorhombic[87] in needles a'ong c flattened on $\{100\}$ with $\{100\}$ and $\{010\}$ cleavages. $Y = b$, $Z = c$. $(-)2V = 66°26'$. $n_X = 1.490$ calc., $n_Y = 1.499 \pm 0.002$, $n_Z = 1.503 \pm 0.002$, $n_Z - n_X = 0.013$.

[86] Sztrokay: *Zeit. Krist.* XC, p. 38 (1935).
[87] Pehrman and Mylius: *Acta Acad. Abo, Math. Phys.* VIII, No. 9 (1935).

VI. Borates

Borates are here classified first by the presence or absence of other anionic elements or groups. Astonishingly few reports on optical properties of borates are accessible. One compound borate-silicate is included here. Other compound borates are given with the respective other anions.

A. BORATES

Al_3BO_6 is orthorhombic with $a:b:c = 0.974:1:0.679$. Crystals acicular. $Y = b$, $Z = c$. $(+)2V = 87°$, $n_X = 1.586$, $n_Y = 1.603$, $n_Z = 1.623$. $n_O - n_X = 0.037$. Colorless. Formed from fusion.

$(Mg,Fe)_2Fe'''BO_5$ (Ludwigite) is orthorhombic with $a:b:c = 0.6595:1:?$. Usually in fibrous masses. H. 5. G. 3.6 (without ferrous iron) to 4.7 (without Mg). Opaque except in thin splinters. $(+)2V = $ small,[1] $r > v$ extreme. $n_X = 1.83 \pm .01$, $n_Y = 1.83 \pm .01$, $n_Z = 1.97 \pm .01$, $n_Z - n_X = 0.14$ (with very little ferrous iron). With FeO $= 15.84$ per cent, $(+)2V = $ very small, $n_X = 1.85 \pm .01$, $n_Y = 1.85 \pm .01$, $n_Z = 2.02 \pm .02$, $n_Z - n_X = 0.17$. Color dark green to black with X and Y dark green, Z dark reddish brown to opaque. PD 2.67, 2.23, 2.18; 5–0648.

$Mg_3(BO_3)_2$ (Kotoite) is orthorhombic with $a = 5.41$, $b = 8.42$, $c = 4.51$. U.C. 2. Massive. Perfect $\{110\}$ cleavage; also $\{101\}$ parting. H. 6.5. G. 3.10. M.P. about 1340° C. $X = a$,[2] $Y = b$. $(+)2V = 21°$, $r > v$. $n_X = 1.652$, $n_Y = 1.653$, $n_Z = 1.673$, $n_Z - n_X = 0.021$. Colorless. Made by fusion.

$AlBO_3$ (Jeremejevite) is hexagonal with $a = 8.57$, $c = 8.17$ kX. U.C. 12. Crystals hexagonal prisms containing an inner part which is apparently monoclinic and optically biaxial. No cleavage. H. 6.5. G. 3.28. Uniaxial negative[3] with $n_O = 1.653$, $n_E = 1.640$, $n_O - n_E = 0.013$. The inner part has $(-)2V = 10°–30°$ ca.; $n_E = 1.640$, n_Y nearly $= n_Z = 1.653$, $n_Z - n_X = 0.013$. Colorless to pale yellowish brown. PD 4.27, 1.39, 2.19; 8–183.

$Ca_2B_2O_5$ is biaxial. M.P. 1304° C. $(-)2V = 25°$ calc. $n_X = 1.585$, $n_Y = 1.662$, $n_Z = 1.667$, $n_Z - n_X = 0.082$. Colorless. Made from fusion.

---

[1] Larsen: *U. S. Geol. Surv. Bull.* 679, 1921.

[2] Watanabe: *Tsch. Min. Mitt.* L, p. 441 (1939).

[3] Frondel: *Dana's System of Mineralogy*, II, p. 330 (1951).

Mn₃B₄O₉ is triclinic[4] with $a:b:c = 1.837:1:2.012$, $\alpha = 92°6'$, $\beta = 123°58'$, $\gamma = 76°26'$. Crystals prismatic with perfect {001} and distinct {010} cleavages. G. 3.61. An optic axis is parallel to (001); X makes an angle of 63° with a normal to (110), 27°43' with a normal to (001) and 29°11' with a normal to (100). $(-)2V = 55°47'$. $n_X = 1.617$, $n_Y = 1.738$, $n_Z = 1.776$, $n_Z - n_X = 0.159$. Made from fusion.

CaB₂O₄ is orthorhombic with $a = 6.19$, $b = 11.60$, $c = 4.28$ Å. U.C. 4. Crystals {100} plates elongated along c with perfect {100}, distinct {101} and poor {010} cleavages. G. 2.65. M.P. 1544° C. X $= a$, Y $= c$. $(-)2V = 51°$, $n_X = 1.540$, $n_Y = 1.656$, $n_Z = 1.682$, $n_Z - n_X = 0.142$. Color white. Made from fusion.

NaBO₂·2H₂O is triclinic[5] with $a = 6.78$, $b = 10.58$, $c = 5.88$ Å, $\alpha = 91°30'$, $\beta = 122°30'$, $\gamma = 89°$. Perfect {010} and {100} cleavages. G. 1.90. M.P. 130° C. $ca.$ Z nearly normal to (010), X' $\wedge$ $c = 43°$ in obtuse angle β; X' $\wedge$ $c = 4°$ in acute angle α. $(-)2V = 58°$, r > v = strong, $n_X = 1.439 \pm 0.002$, $n_Y = 1.473 \pm 0.002$, $n_Z = 1.484 \pm 0.002$, $n_Z - n_X = 0.045$. Colorless. PD 5.29, 3.80, 5.03; 6–0122. Made from aqueous NaOH solution.

MgB₂O₄·3H₂O (Pinnoite) is tetragonal with $a = 7.617$, $c = 8.190$ Å. U.C. 4. Crystals short prismatic; usually granular or fibrous. H. 3.5. G. 2.27. Uniaxial positive[6] with $n_O = 1.565$, $n_E = 1.575$, $n_E - n_O = 0.010$. Again:[7] $n_O = 1.562$, $n_E = 1.574$, $n_E - n_O = 0.012$. Color yellow. Made by mixing a solution of borax and one of MgCl₂·6H₂O, seeding with pinnoite and keeping at 100° C. for some days.

Na₂B₄O₇·5H₂O (Tincalconite) is hexagonal with $a = 11.20$, $c = 21.13$ kX. Crystals apparently octahedral with {0001} and {10$\bar{1}$1}. No cleavage. G. 1.88. Uniaxial positive with[8] $n_O = 1.461$, $n_E = 1.474$, $n_E - n_O = 0.013$. Colorless or white with vitreous luster. PD 2.94, 4.42, 2.21; 8–49. Made by boiling a solution of borax.

Na₂B₄O₇·4H₂O (Kernite) is monoclinic with $a = 15.52$, $b = 9.14$, $c = 6.96$ kX, $\beta = 108°52'$. Crystals nearly equant to elongated parallel with c; perfect {001} and {100} and fair {101} cleavages; cleavage fragments are elongated parallel with b. H. 2.5. G. 1.91. Fuses easily to clear glass. Slowly soluble in water. X $\wedge$ $c = +70.5°$, Z $= b$. $(-)2V = 80°$, r > v distinct. $n_X = 1.455$, $n_Y = 1.472$, $n_Z = 1.487$, $n_Z - n_X = 0.032$. Colorless or white. Made by heating borax in a closed tube at about 150° C. for several days, cooling, wetting and reheating to about 150° C.

---

[4] The formula is Mn₂B₂O₅ according to Le Chatelier: *C. R. Acad. Sci. Paris*, CXIII, 1891.

[5] Krc: *Anal. Chem.* XXIII, p. 806 (1951).

[6] Boeke: *Centb. Min.* 1910, p. 531.

[7] Schaller: *U. S. Geol. Surv. Bull.* 833, p. 81 (1952).

[8] Schaller: *U. S. Geol. Surv. Prof. Pap.* 158, p. 137 (1930).

$Na_2B_4O_7 \cdot 10H_2O$ (Borax) is monoclinic with $a = 11.82$, $b = 10.61$, $c = 12.30\ kX$, $\beta = 107°35'$. Crystals prismatic, resembling pyroxene. Twinning occurs on $\{100\}$. Perfect $\{100\}$ and distinct $\{110\}$ cleavages. H. 2. G. 1.70. $Y = b$,[9] $Z \wedge c = -56°$ (red), $-55°50'$ Na, $-54°39'$ (green). $(-)2V = 39°28'$ (red), $39°10'$ Na, $38°35'$ (green). $n_X = 1.4445$ C, 1.4467 D, 1.4517 F, $n_Y = 1.4669$ C, 1.4694 D, 1.4750 F, $n_Z = 1.4669$ C, 1.4724 D, 1.4778 F, $n_Z - n_X = 0.0257$ D. Colorless. PD 2.57, 2.84, 4.86; 1–1097. Made from an aqueous solution of boric acid and sodium carbonate at ordinary temperature. **Borax glass** is isotropic with $n = 1.5147$ Na.

$CaB_2O_4 \cdot 6H_2O$ is monoclinic[10] with $a:b:c = 1.2058:1:1.2063$, $\beta = 104°11'$. U.C. 2. Crystals equant with $\{111\}$, $\{100\}$, $\{001\}$, $\{201\}$, $\{110\}$, etc. Perfect $\{001\}$ cleavage. H. 2.5. G. 1.88. F. 1. $X = b$, $Z \wedge c = -3°$. $(-)2V = 77° \pm 5°$ calc. r > v. $n_X = 1.505$ (1.506), $n_Y = 1.511$, $n_Z = 1.515$ (1.514), $n_Z - n_X = 0.010$ (0.008). Colorless. Made from Portland cement mixed with four parts of $Ca_2B_6O_{11} \cdot 5H_2O$.

$NaCaB_5O_9 \cdot 5H_2O$ (Probertite) is monoclinic with $a = 13.88$, $b = 12.56$, $c = 6.609$ Å, $\beta = 107°40'$. U.C. 2. Crystals often in groups of needles. Perfect $\{110\}$ cleavage. H. 3.5. G. 2.14. Fuses easily with swelling. $Y = b$,[8] $Z \wedge c = -12°$. $(+)2V = 73°$, r > v. $n_X = 1.514$, $n_Y = 1.524$, $n_Z = 1.543$, $n_Z - n_X = 0.029$. Again:[8] $n_X = 1.515$, $n_Y = 1.525$, $n_Z = 1.544$. Colorless or white. PD 9.1, 2.78, 2.90; 4–0107. Made by heating a mixture of two parts of $NaCaB_5O_9 \cdot 8H_2O$ and one part of $Na_2B_4O_7 \cdot 10H_2O$ to about 60° C.

$NaCaB_5O_9 \cdot 8H_2O$ (Ulexite) is triclinic with $a = 8.71$, $b = 12.72$, $c = 6.69\ kX$, $\alpha = 90°16'$, $\beta = 109°8'$, $\gamma = 105°7'$. U.C. 2. Often in fibrous masses or crusts. Perfect $\{010\}$, good $\{1\bar{1}0\}$ and poor $\{110\}$ cleavages. H. 2.5. G. 1.96. $Y \wedge c$[8] = about 20°. $(+)2V = 73° \pm 1°$, $n_X = 1.493$, $n_Y = 1.505$, $n_Z = 1.519$, $n_Z - n_X = 0.026$. White or colorless. PD 12.3, 4.15, 7.8; 9–483.

$K_2CaB_8O_{14} \cdot 12H_2O$ is orthorhombic.[11] Crystals prismatic. G. 1.80. $n_X = 1.449$, $n_Y = ?$, $n_Z = 1.476$, $n_Z - n_X = 0.027$. Colorless.

$MgB_4O_7 \cdot 9H_2O$ is hexagonal. Uniaxial negative with[12] $n_O = 1.485$, $n_E = 1.442$, $n_O - n_E = 0.043$. Colorless.

$KB_5O_8 \cdot 4H_2O$ is orthorhombic hemimorphic[13] (Class C_{2v}) with $a:b:c = 0.9905:1:0.8105$. Crystals pyramidal with $\{111\}$, $\{100\}$, $\{001\}$, etc. Perfect $\{010\}$ and distinct $\{100\}$ cleavages. Crystals generally twinned on

[9] Dufet: *Bull. Soc. Fr. Min.* X, p. 218 (1887).

[10] Peacock and Vigfusson: *Univ. Toronto Stud., Geol. Ser.* XLII, p. 113 (1939).

[11] Gode: *Latv. P. S. R. Zin. Akad. Vestis*, 1952, No. 1 (54), p. 89 [*Chem. Abst.* XLVII, p. 8570 (1953)].

[12] Nikolaev and Chelishcheva: *Dokl. Akad. Sci. U.S.S.R.* VIII, p. 127 (1940). [*Min. Abst.* VIII, p. 257 (1941)].

[13] W. R. Cook, Cleveland, Ohio: *pers. comm.* March 20, April 5 and May 23, 1956.

$\{01\bar{1}\}$, occasionally on $\{00\bar{1}\}$. H. 2.5. G. 1.74. X = c; Y = b. $(+)2V = 70°$ calc. $n_X = 1.422$, $n_Y = 1.436$, $n_Z = 1.480$, $n_Z - n_X = 0.058$. Colorless. PD 5.50, 3.50, 3.30; 3–0107(?).

$NH_4B_5O_8 \cdot 4H_2O$ is orthorhombic (Class C_{2v}) with[13] $a = 11.324$, $b = 11.029$, $c = 9.235$ Å. Crystals pyramidal with $\{100\}$, $\{111\}$, $\{001\}$, etc. Distinct $\{100\}$ and $\{010\}$ cleavages. Often twinned on $\{01\bar{1}\}$; less often on $\{00\bar{1}\}$. H. 2.5. G. 1.57. X = c; Y = b. $(+)2V = 30°$ calc. r < v weak. $n_X = 1.427$, $n_Y = 1.431$, $n_Z = 1.486$, $n_Z - n_X = 0.059$. Colorless. Crystallizes readily from solution. As in the case of many other K and NH_4 salts, $KB_5O_8 \cdot 4H_2O$ and $NH_4B_5O_8 \cdot 4H_2O$ intercrystallize freely, the a axis increasing steadily in length, becoming equal to the b axis with about 25% NH_4 and notably longer in the pure NH_4 salt which is here described with $a > b$ to emphasize this condition.

$(NH_4)_2B_{10}O_{16} \cdot 5H_2O$ (Ammonioborite) is[13a] monoclinic(?) Forms platy groups. X is normal to the plates. Z makes an angle of 7° to 13° with the elongation of the plates. $(+)2V = 60°$, r < v weak. $n_X = 1.470$, $n_Y = 1.487$, $n_Z = 1.540$, $n_Z - n_X = 0.070$. Color white. Made by evaporating at 95° a water solution of $NH_4B_5O_8 \cdot 4H_2O$.

$CaB_6O_{10} \cdot 4H_2O$ forms a powder with[14] $n_X = 1.505$, $n_Y = ?$, $n_Z = 1.550$, $n_Z - n_X = 0.045$. Colorless.

$MgB_6O_{10} \cdot 7.5H_2O$ is uniaxial negative with[12] $n_O = 1.5081$, $n_E = 1.463$, $n_O - n_E = 0.045$. Colorless.

B. BORATES CONTAINING HALOGEN OR HYDROXYL

$Na_2BO_2Cl \cdot 2H_2O$ (Teepleite) is tetragonal with[15] $a = 7.27$, $c = 4.84 kX$. U.C. 2. Crystals basal tablets. H. 3–3.5. G. 2.07. Uniaxial negative with $n_O = 1.521$, $n_E = 1.503$, $n_O - n_E = 0.018$. Colorless or white. PD. 2.68, 2.01, 2.88; 2–0926.

$Mg_3B_7O_{13}Cl$ (Boracite) is orthorhombic with $a = 16.97$, $b = 16.97$, $c = 12.10 kX$ (pure); with some Fe replacing Mg: $a = 17.11$, $b = 17.11$, $c = 12.10$. U.C. 16. Crystals often cubic in aspect. No cleavage. H. 7–7.5. G. 2.93 (with some Fe, 2.97 ca.). $(+)2V = 82.5°$.[16] $n_X = 1.658$, $n_Y = 1.662$, $n_Z = 1.668$, $n_Z - n_X = 0.010$. Again:[17] $n_X = 1.6622$, $n_Y = 1.6670$, $n_Z = 1.6730$, $n_Z - n_X = 0.0108$. Colorless to white (pure); with some Fe it is yellow or light to dark green. PD 2.06, 3.04, 2.72; 5–0710. When heated to

[13a] Schaller: *Am. Min.* XVI, p. 114 (1931) and XVIII, p. 490 (1933).

[14] Nikolaev and Chelishcheva: *Dokl. Akad. Sci. U.S.S.R.* XVIII, p. 431 (1938). [*Min. Abst.* VIII, p. 114 and 257 (1941–43)].

[15] Gale, Foshag and Vonsen: *Am. Min.* XXIV, p. 48 (1939).

[16] Guppy: *Min. Mag.* XXVII, p. 51 (1944).

[17] Mallard: *Bull. Soc. Fr. Min.* VI, p. 129 (1883).

or above 265° C. it becomes isometric and isotropic with[17] $n = 1.6776$ (for $\lambda = 501.6$) at 290° and 1.6796 at 502°. PD 2.05, 3.01, 2.70; 3–1034.

$CaB_3O_4(OH)_3 \cdot H_2O$ **(Colemanite)** is monoclinic with $a = 8.72$, $b = 11.29$, $c = 6.06\ kX$, $\beta = 110°7'$. U.C. 2. Crystals equant with {110}, {001}, etc. Also massive. Perfect 010 and distinct 001 cleavages. H. 4.5. G. 2.42. $X = b$,[18] $Y \wedge c = -6°$. $(+)2V = 55°$, r > v weak. $n_X = 1.5863$, $n_Y = 1.5920$, $n_Z = 1.6140$, $n_Z - n_X = 0.0277$. Colorless, white or yellowish. PD 3.13, 5.64, 3.85; 6–0331. Made from solution at 70° C.

$CaMgB_6O_8(OH)_6 \cdot 3H_2O$ **(Hydroboracite)** is monoclinic with $a:b:c = 1.765:1:1.233$, $\beta = 102°39'$. Crystals {010} lamellar fibers along c. Perfect {010} and {100} cleavages. H. 2. G. 2.17. $X \wedge c = 33°$, $Y = b$. $(+)2V = 60°-66°$, r < v weak.[19] $n_X = 1.520-1.523$, $n_Y = 1.534-1.535$, $n_Z = 1.569-1.571$, $n_Z - n_X = 0.048-0.050$. Colorless to white. Made from a solution at 50° C.

$CaMgB_6O_8(OH)_6 \cdot 8H_2O$ **(Inderborite)** is monoclinic with $a:b:c = 1.635:1:1.317$, $\beta = 90°48'$. Good {100} cleavage. H. 3.5. G. 2.00. $X \wedge c = 2.5°$; $Z = b$;[20] $(-)2V = 77°$, $n_X = 1.483 \pm 0.002$, $n_Y = 1.512 \pm 0.002$, $n_Z = 1.530 \pm 0.002$, $n_Z - n_X = 0.047$. Again:[21] $(-)2V = 80°-86°$, $n_X = 1.496$, $n_Y = 1.521$, $n_Z = 1.54$, $n_Z - n_X = 0.044$. Also:[22] $n_X = 1.480$, $n_Y = 1.509$, $n_Z = 1.527$, $n_Z - n_X = 0.047$. Colorless.

$CaB_3O_4(OH)_3 \cdot 5H_2O$ **(Inyoite)** is monoclinic with $a:b:c = 0.883:1:0.695$, $\beta = 114°1'$. Crystals short prisms to basal tablets; also massive. Good {001} cleavage; also {010}. H. 2. G. 1.875. $X \wedge c = +37°$, $Y = b$.[23] $(-)2V = 70°$, r < v weak. $n_X = 1.495$, $n_Y = 1.51$, $n_Z = 1.520$, $n_Z - n_X = 0.025$. Again:[14] $n_X = 1.491$, $n_Y = 1.505$, $n_Z = 1.518$, $n_Z - n_X = 0.0027$. Colorless. PD 3.03, 7.59, 2.29; 6–0361.

$CaB_3O_4(OH)_3 \cdot 2H_2O$ **(Meyerhofferite)** is triclinic with $a = 6.60$, $b = 8.33$, $c = 6.48\ kX$, $\alpha = 91°$, $\beta = 101°31'$, $\gamma = 86°55'$. U.C. 1. Crystals {100} plates elongated along c. Perfect {010} cleavage. H. 2. G. 2.12. On {010} $X' \wedge c = 30°$; on {100} $Z' \wedge c = 25°$. $(-)2V = 78°$, n_X[23] = 1.500, $n_Y = 1.535$, $n_Z = 1.560$, $n_O - n_X = 0.060$. Colorless or white. PD 8.39, 6.51, 3.17; 6–0032.

$MgB_3O_4(OH)_3 \cdot 15H_2O$ **(Inderite)** is triclinic with $a = 8.14$, $b = 10.47$, $c = 6.33$ Å, $\alpha = 96°56'$, $\beta = 106°28'$, $\gamma = 106°3'$. U.C. 1. Tabular with perfect {010} and good {110} cleavages; also prismatic. H. 3. G. 1.86.

[18] Mülheims: *Zeit. Krist.* XIV, p. 230 (1888).

[19] Schaller: *Festschrift Goldschmidt*, p. 256 (1928); Nikolaiev and Selivanova: *Dokl. Akad. Sci. U.S.S.R.* XX, p. 29 (1938). [*Min. Abst.* VII, p. 476 (1940)].

[20] Ikornikova and Godlevsky: *Dokl. Akad. Sci. U.S.S.R.* XXXIII, p. 257 (1941).

[21] Gorshkov: *Dokl. Akad. Sci. U.S.S.R.* XXXIII, p. 254 (1941).

[22] Kurnakova: *Dokl. Akad. Sci. U.S.S.R.* L, p. 241 (1945) [*Chem. Abst.* XLIII, p. 2128 (1949)].

[23] Schaller: *U. S. Geol. Surv. Bull.* 610, p. 35 and 41 (1916).

X nearly $= b$;[24] $Z \wedge c^{14} = -22°$. $(-)2V = 63° \pm 3°$, r $>$ v weak, $n_X =$ 1.488 $\pm$ 0.002, $n_Y = 1.508 \pm 0.002$, $n_Z = 1.515 \pm 0.002$, $n_Z - n_X = 0.027$. Again: $Z \wedge c = 5°$, $(+)2V =$ large. $n = 1.488$ and 1.505. Colorless, white, or pink. PD 5.00, 7.36, 3.18; 8–164*. Made from solution at 35° C.

C. COMPOUND BORATES

5CaO·SiO₂·B₂O₃ [$= \mathbf{Ca_2SiO_4·Ca_3(BO_3)_2}$?] is biaxial.[25] Polysynthetic twinning is very common, suggesting monoclinic or triclinic symmetry. M.P. 1419° C. $(-)2V =$ moderate. $n_X = 1.666 \pm 0.003$, $n_Y = 1.682 \pm 0.003$, $n_Z = 1.690 \pm 0.003$, $n_Z - n_X = 0.024 \pm 0.006$. Colorless.

[24] Heinrich: *Am. Min.* XXXI, p. 71 (1946).
[25] Flint and Wells: *Nat. Bur. Stand. J. Res.* XVII, p. 727 (1936).

VII. Sulfates

Sulfates, chromates, selenates, and the related sulfites, thiosulfates, pyrosulfates, pyrosulfites, sulfamates, thionates, dichromates, etc., are included with sulfates. The classification is as follows:

A. ANHYDROUS SULFITES, SELENITES, THIOSULFATES, THIONATES, SULFAMATES, ETC.

Na_2SO_3 is hexagonal[1] in prisms and tablets. Uniaxial negative with $n_O = 1.565\pm$, $n_E = 1.515\pm$, $n_O - n_E = 0.050\pm$. Colorless. PD 2.58, 2.73, 3.75; 5–0653.

$NaHSO_3$ occurs in formless grains[1] with $(+)2V = 65°\pm$, $n_X = 1.474$, $n_Y = 1.526$, $n_Z = 1.685\pm$, $n_Z - n_X = 0.211\pm$. Colorless.

$Rb_2S_2O_3$ is hexagonal[2] (trigonal) with $a = 10.02$, $c = 6.35$ kX. U.C. 3. Uniaxial positive with $n_O = 1.46$ $ca.$, $n_E = 1.51$, $n_E - n_O = 0.0504$. Specific rotation about 2° per mm.

[1] H. E. Merwin: *pers. comm.* March 25, 1931.
[2] Barnes and Wendling: *Zeit. Krist.* XCIX, p. 153 (1938).

$Na_{10}Cu_2Ag_4(S_2O_3)_8 \cdot 6NH_3$ is tetragonal with $c/a = 0.84$. Crystals prismatic with poor $\{001\}$ cleavage. Uniaxial negative with $n_O = ?$, $n_E = 1.7\pm$. Color deep blue with X pale sapphire-blue, Z deep cobalt-blue.

$4(NH_4)_2S_2O_3 \cdot AgBr \cdot NH_4Br$ is tetragonal with $c/a = 0.63$. Uniaxial negative with $n_O = 1.6769$, $n_E = 1.6294$, $n_O - n_E = 0.0475$.

$K_2S_2O_6$ is hexagonal (trigonal) with $c/a = 0.647$. Crystals hexagonal prisms. G. 2.28. Uniaxial positive[2] with $n_O = 1.4532$ C, 1.4550 D, 1.4595 F, $n_E = 1.5119$ C, 1.5153 D, 1.5239 F, $n_E - n_O = 0.0603$ D.

$Rb_2S_2O_6$ is hexagonal (trigonal) with $c/a = 0.631$. Crystals hexagonal prisms. Uniaxial positive with[3] $n_O = 1.4544$ C, 1.4565 D, 1.4613 F, $n_E = 1.5034$ C, 1.5068 D, 1.5153 F, $n_E - n_O = 0.0503$ D.

$Cs_2S_2O_6$ is hexagonal (trigonal) with $c/a = 0.632$. Crystals prismatic. Uniaxial positive with[1] $n_O = 1.5207$ C, 1.5230 D, 1.5285 F, $n_E = 1.5405$ C, 1.5438 D, 1.5518 F, $n_E - n_O = 0.0208$ D.

$K_2S_3O_6$ is orthorhombic with $a:b:c = 0.717:1:0.409$. Crystals prismatic or tabular. No distinct cleavage. G. 2.34. X = c; Y = b. $(-)2V = 72°$ $(68°)$ Na. For[4] $\lambda = 691 : n_X = 1.4903$, $n_Y = 1.5591$, $n_Z = 1.596$, $n_Z - n_X = 0.1061$. For $\lambda = 589 : n_X = 1.4934$, $n_Y = 1.5641$, $n_Z = 1.602$, $n_Z - n_X = 0.1086$. For $\lambda = 436 : n_X = 1.5040$, $n_Y = 1.5805$, $n_Z = 1.621$, $n_Z - n_X = 0.117$.

$Rb_2S_3O_6$ is orthorhombic with $a:b:c = 0.706:1:0.418$. Crystals prismatic. G. 2.83. X = c, Y = b. $(-)2V = 62°33'$. $n_X = 1.4874$, $n_Y = 1.5580$, $n_Z = 1.5867$, $n_Z - n_X = 0.0993$.

HNH_2SO_3 is orthorhombic[5] with $a:b:c = 0.995:1:1.149$. Crystals $\{010\}$ tablets with $\{111\}$, $\{120\}$, $\{201\}$, etc. No cleavage seen. X = c; Y = b. $(-)2V = 63°$ or $64°$ with weak dispersion.[6] $n_X = 1.553$, $n_Y = 1.563$, $n_Z = 1.568$, all ±0.003 (for $\lambda = 546$), $n_Z - n_X = 0.015$. PD 3.37, 3.70, 4.01; 8–483.

$LiNH_2SO_3$[7] is probably orthorhombic. Crystals acicular. Deliquescent. $(-)2V = 48°$, r $\ll$ v. $n = 1.507$, $n_Z - n_X = 0.007$.

$NaNH_2SO_3$ forms prismatic needles[7] with octagonal cross-section. $(-)2V = 82°–84°$. $n_X = 1.494$, $n_Y = 1.498\pm$ calc., $n_Z = 1.501$, $n_Z - n_X = 0.007$.

KNH_2SO_3 forms rhombic tablets.[7] $(+)2V = 26°$. $n_X = 1.487$, $n_Y = 1.490\pm$ calc., $n_Z = 1.515$, $n_Z - n_X = 0.028$.

$NH_4NH_2SO_3$ forms needles[7] normal to X. $(-)2V = 84°$, r > v. $n_X = 1.526$, $n_Y = 1.532$, $n_Z = 1.538$, $n_Z - n_X = 0.012$. Again[6] $n_Y = 1.537$.

---

[3] Ehringhaus and Rose: *Zeit. Krist.* LVIII, p. 460 (1923); also LIX, p. 249 (1924).

[4] Merwin: *J. Wash. Acad. Sci.* IX, No. 15, p. 429 (1919).

[5] Fock: *Zeit. Krist.* XIV, p. 531 (1888); Jaeger: *Ver. Akad. Wet. Amsterdam* XXXV, p. 68 (1926). See also E. Mariani: *Ric. sci.* XX, p. 1285 (1950).

[6] Bryant: *J. Am. Chem. Soc.* LXI, p. 2551 (1939).

[7] Mariani: *Ric. sci.* XX, p. 1285 (1950).

RbNH₂SO₃ forms six-sided rhombic plates.[7] $(-)2V = 65°$, $r > v$. $n = 1.537$, $n_Z - n_X = 0.015$.

Be(NH₂SO₃)₂ forms tabular crystals.[7] Soluble in water. $(-)2V = 60°$, $n_X = 1.552$, $n_Y = 1.563$ calc., $n_Z = 1.567$, $n_Z - n_X = 0.015$.

Mg(NH₂SO₃)₂ forms very small crystals;[7] also cryptocrystalline. Soluble in water. $(+)2V = 68°–70°$, $r < v$. $n_X = 1.510$, $n_Y = 1.517$ calc., $n_Z = 1.535$, $n_Z - n_X = 0.025$.

Ba(NH₂SO₃)₂ forms long prismatic crystals.[7] $(-)2V = 48°–50°$, $r \gg v$. $n = 1.599$, $n_Z - n_X = 0.022$.

K₂S₄O₆ is monoclinic[8] with $a = 22.05$, $b = 7.99$, $c = 10.09$ kX. $\beta = 102°5'$. U.C. 8. Crystals tablets or prismatic. Perfect {100} cleavage. G. 2.30. $Y = b$; $Z \wedge c = 33°$ in obtuse angle β. $(+)2V = 66°$ C, $69°$ F, $r < v$. $n_X = 1.5896$, $n_Y = 1.6057$, $n_Z = 1.6435$ (all ± 0.0002), $n_Z - n_X = 0.0539$. Colorless. PD 3.37, 2.92, 3.17; 2–0441.

(NH₄)₂S₂O₈ is monoclinic[8a] with $a:b:c = 1.296:1:1.187$, $\beta = 103°48'$. Crystals basal tablets or elongated along b. Poor {001} cleavage. G. 1.98. $Y = b$; $Z \wedge c = +27°$. $(+)2V = 24°$, $r < v$ moderate. $n_X = 1.4981$, $n_Y = 1.5016$, $n_Z = 1.5866$, $n_Z - n_X = 0.0885$. Colorless. Made from aqueous solution.

Rb₂S₂O₈ is monoclinic with[8a] $a:b:c = 1.281:1:1.188$, $\beta = 103°28'$. Crystals basal tablets or elongated along b. No good cleavage. G. 3.13. $Y = b$; $Z \wedge c = +26.5°$. $(+)2V = 35°$, $r < v$ weak. $n_X = 1.4812$, $n_Y = 1.4888$, $n_Z = 1.5719$, $n_Z - n_X = 0.0907$. Made from warm solution.

(NH₄)₂Cr₂O₇ is monoclinic prismatic with $a:b:c = 1.0277:1:1.767$, $\beta = 93°42'$. Crystals basal or {101} plates or columns along b. Distinct {101} cleavage. G. 2.15. $Y = b$; $Z \wedge c = +35°$ (in obtuse angle β).[8b] $(+)2H = 104°$ red. $n_X = 1.725$, $n_Y = 1.80$ ca., $n_Z = 1.905$, $n_Z - n_X = 0.180$.

K₂S₂O₈ is triclinic with[8a] $a:b:c = 0.576:1:0.574$, $\alpha = 98°33'$, $\beta = 94°2'$, $\gamma = 88°39'$. Crystals {010} tablets. Twinning on {010}. Distinct {010} cleavage. G. 2.48. The optic axes are in the positive octant. $(+)2V = 29°32'$. $n_X = 1.4609$, $n_Y = 1.4669$, $n_Z = 1.5657$, $n_Z - n_X = 0.1048$. Made from solution at ordinary temperature.

K₂Cr₂O₇ is dimorphous. A metastable phase is monoclinic[9] with $a = 7.47$, $b = 7.35$, $c = 12.97$ Å. $\beta = 91°55'$. U.C. 4. Crystals basal plates with {111}, {101}, {110}, etc. G. 2.736. For $\lambda = 758$: $(+)2V = 64°14'$, $n_X = 1.715$, $n_Y = 1.762$, $n_Z = 1.892$, $n_Z - n_X = 0.177$. Pleochroic. A second (stable) phase **(Lopezite)** is triclinic pinacoidal with $a = 7.50$, $b = 7.37$, $c = 13.40$ Å. $\alpha = 82°0'$, $\beta = 90°51'$, $\gamma = 83°47'$. Crystals prismatic or

[8] Tunell, Merwin and Ksanda: *Am. J. Sci.* XXXV A, p. 361 (1938).

[8a] Groth in *Chemische Krystallographie*, II, p. 724–726 (1908).

[8b] Optic data from D. Davis, American Cyanamid Co. in 1940.

[9] Stedehouder and Terpstra: *Physica* X, p. 113 (1930).

{010} tablets. Twinning, as on {010}. Perfect {010}, distinct {100} and {001} cleavages. G. 2.69. The optic plane is nearly normal to (001) between (100) and (0$\bar{1}$0). X makes angles of 86°27', 68°6' and 13°43' with normals to {100}, {0$\bar{1}$0} and {00$\bar{1}$}; Z makes angles of 77°5', 23°5' and 76°21' with normals to {100}, {0$\bar{1}$0} and {00$\bar{1}$}. (+)2V = 52°24' Li, 51°53' Na; n_X = 1.7202, n_Y = 1.7380, n_Z = 1.8197, $n_Z - n_X$ = 0.0995. Color aurora red; pleochroic with X red, Z yellow. Made from warm solution.

CaS_4O_6 is biaxial with[1] (+)2V = 32°±, n_X = 1.535±, n_Y = 1.540±, n_Z = 1.675±, $n_Z - n_X$ = 0.140±. Colorless.

B. ANHYDROUS ACID SULFATES

$KHSO_4$ (Mercallite) is orthorhombic with $a:b:c$ = 0.861:1:1.934. Crystals basal tablets. No cleavage. G. 2.32. X = b, Y = c.[10] (+)2V = 56°, r < v weak. n_X = 1.445, n_Y = 1.460 calc., n_Z = 1.491, $n_Z - n_X$ = 0.046. Colorless when pure; also sky-blue (due to copper?). Easily made from water solution.

NH_4HSO_4 is orthorhombic with $a:b:c$ = 0.613:1:0.744. Crystals long prismatic or thick {010} tablets. Perfect {100} cleavage. G. 1.82. Y = b, Z = c. (+)2V = 60°±, with weak dispersion.[1] n_X = 1.463, n_Y = 1.473, n_Z = 1.510, $n_Z - n_X$ = 0.047. Colorless. PD 4.75, 3.69, 2.61; 1–0290.

$RbHSO_4$ is orthorhombic with $a:b:c$ = 0.75:1:0.60. X = c, Y = b. (+)2V = 55°52', r < v weak. n_Y = 1.473.

$K_8H_6(SO_4)_7$ (Misenite) is monoclinic with $a:b:c$ = 3.2196:1:2.1842, β = 102°5'. Occurs as fibrous masses or needles. Distinct {010} cleavage. G. 2.32. (+)2V = large.[11] X $\wedge$ c = +29°; Z = b. n_X = 1.475, n_Y = 1.480, n_Z = 1.487, $n_Z - n_X$ = 0.012. Colorless. PD 3.85, 3.40, 3.01; 1–0477.

$K_3H(SO_4)_2$ is monoclinic[12] with $a:b:c$ = 1.722:1:3.767, β = 90°11'. Crystals tabular or pyramidal. Twinning on {110}; or on {310} in pseudo-hexagonal trillings. Distinct {001} cleavage. G. 2.59. X $\wedge$ c = −35°; Z = b. (−)2V = 60°42'. n_X = 1.4793, n_Y = 1.4899, n_Z = 1.5259, $n_Z - n_X$ = 0.0466 Na. Colorless. Made from an aqueous solution of $KHSO_4$ from which K_2SO_4 was first separated.

$(NH_4)_3H(SO_4)_2$ (Letovicite) is monoclinic with[12] $a:b:c$ = 1.739:1:2.647, β = 102°6'. Crystals basal tablets. Twinning often on {110} or {310}. Distinct {001} cleavage. G. 1.83. X $\wedge$ c = 78°, Z = b. On artificial crystals[13] n_X = 1.499, n_Z = 1.526. Again:[13] (−)2V = 75°, n_X = 1.501, n_Y =

[10] Carobbi: *Acc. Linc. Rend.* XXI, p. 385 (1935). Lang: *Sitzb. Akad. Wiss. Wien* LI, p. 95 (1858).

[11] Larsen: *U. S. Geol. Surv. Bull.* 679 (1921).

[12] Fischer: *N. Jahrb. Min. Bl. Bd.* XXXII, p. 10 and p. 25 (1911).

[13] Sekanina: *Zeit. Krist.* LXXXIII, p. 117 (1932).

1.516, n_Z = 1.526, $n_Z - n_X$ = 0.024. Inverts to a uniaxial phase. Colorless. Made by cooling a solution of $(NH_4)_2SO_4$ and H_2SO_4.

C. ANHYDROUS NORMAL SULFATES, CHROMATES, AND SELENATES

1. Formula Type A$_2$XO$_4$

LiKSO$_4$ is hexagonal with c/a = 1.676. Crystals columnar prismatic, basal tablets or plainly hemimorphic. Twinning often obscures the hemimorphism. Poor basal cleavage. H. 3. G. 2.39. Uniaxial negative[14] with n_O = 1.4703 C, 1.4723 D, 1.4765 F, n_E = 1.4697 C, 1.4717 D, 1.4759 F, $n_O - n_E$ = 0.0006 D. Rotates the plane of polarization. Colorless. Formed from an acid solution. Inverts at about 435° C. PD 3.94, 3.09, 2.57; 1–0459.

LiNaSO$_4$ is hexagonal[15] with a = 7.64, c = 9.76 Å. G. 2.54. Uniaxial positive with n_O = 1.490, n_E = 1.495, $n_E - n_O$ = 0.005. Colorless. Made from water solution.

(K,Na)$_3$Na(SO$_4$)$_2$ (Aphthitalite) is hexagonal with a = 5.65, c = 7.29 kX. Crystals tabular with marked trigonal development; bladed aggregates, etc. Fair $\{10\bar{1}0\}$ and poor $\{0001\}$ cleavages. H. 3. G. 2.7. F. 1.5. Uniaxial positive with n_O = 1.491, n_E = 1.499, $n_E - n_O$ = 0.008 for[16] K:Na = 2.46:1; n_O = 1.487, n_E = 1.492, $n_E - n_O$ = 0.005 for K[17]:Na = 1:1.5. New data follow:

Na:K ratio	n_O	n_E	$n_E - n_O$	a	c	G
Na$_4$K	1.485	1.490	0.005	5.49	7.26	2.71
NaK	1.490	1.495	0.005	5.64	7.27	
NaK$_2$	1.491	1.4965	0.0055			
NaK$_3$	1.493	1.498	0.005	5.66	7.33	2.697
NaK$_4$	1.4935	1.500	0.0065	5.67	7.39	

It may have a small optic angle. Colorless unless stained by iron oxide. PD 2.81, 2.02, 2.92; 6–0461*. Easily made from dry fusions and also from aqueous solutions; the former have all ratios between K and Na; the latter are 71 to 75 mol. per cent K_2SO_4 at 25° C. The refringence[17] and birefringence increase a little with increase in the tenor of K. Continuity from $Na_2K_8(SO_4)_5$ to K_2SO_4 is improbable.[17a]

[14] Blittersdorf: *Zeit. Krist.* LXXI, p. 141 (1929).
[15] Hilmy: *Am. Min.* XXXVIII, p. 118 (1953).
[16] Bücking: *Zeit. Krist.* XV, p. 561 (1889).
[17] Washington and Merwin: *Am. Min.* VI, p. 121 (1921).
[17a] Carapezza: *Rend. Soc. Min. Ital.* XI, p. 47 (1955).

NaK₃(CrO₄)₂ is hexagonal with $c/a = 1.286$. Crystals basal tablets or rhombohedral. Distinct basal cleavage. G. 2.767. Uniaxial positive with $n_O = 1.7278$ Na, $n_E = 1.7361$, $n_E - n_O = 0.0083$. Strong dispersion giving an unusual interference figure. Also monoclinic, pseudo-hexagonal, biaxial positive. 2V small, Z nearly normal to (001); $Y = b$. Color in plates 1 mm. thick, X orange yellow, Z lemon yellow.

Na₂SO₄ (Thenardite) is orthorhombic with[18] $a = 9.75$, $b = 12.29$, $c = 5.85$ kX. U.C. 8. Crystals dipyramidal, short prismatic, or basal plates. Distinct basal cleavage. H. 2.5–3. G. 2.66. F. 1.5–2. $Y = c$; $Z = a$. $(+)2V = 83°35'$ Na, r > v weak. $n_X = 1.471$, $n_Y = 1.477$, $n_Z = 1.484$, $n_Z - n_X = 0.013$. Again:[18] $n_X = 1.4669$ Na, $n_Y = 1.4731$, $n_Z = 1.4809$, $n_Z - n_X = 0.014$. Colorless. PD 2.78, 4.66, 3.18; 5–0631*. Made from aqueous solution at about 50° C. NaSO₄ inverts[19] at about 160°–180° C. to a phase ("IV")

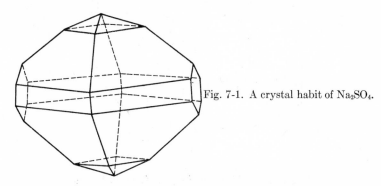

Fig. 7-1. A crystal habit of Na₂SO₄.

which is probably monoclinic with $n_X < 1.46$, $n_Y = ?$, $n_Z = 1.480$, $n_Z - n_X > 0.02$. It inverts again at about 185° C. to an orthorhombic phase ("III") thought to be isomorphous with K₂SO₄; it has G. 2.696, all indices between 1.480 and 1.485; very stable at ordinary temperature. PD 2.80, 3.91, 3.76; 8–31. Na₂SO₄ inverts finally at 241° C. to a hexagonal phase ("I") probably isomorphous with the high temperature phase of K₂SO₄; it is uniaxial negative with both indices below 1.475 and very weak birefringence; it was found at Mont Pelée by Lacroix and called *meta-thenardite*. These inversions occur very slowly, so that several phases may be found together after heating and cooling. On cooling, if the change at 241° C. is avoided, an irreversible inversion occurs at 236° C. to a phase ("II") with very strong birefringence, having n_X much less than 1.465, $n_Y = ?$, $n_Z = 1.480$; not stable at low pressure.

K₂SO₄ (Arcanite) is orthorhombic with $a = 5.731$, $b = 10.008$, $c =$

[18] Zachariasen and Ziegler: *Zeit. Krist.*, LXXXI, p. 92 (1932).

[19] Kracek: *J. Phys. Chem.* XXXIII, p. 1281 (1929) and Kracek and Gibson, *ibid.*, XXXIV, p. 188 (1930). See also reference 17

7.424 kX. Crystals nearly equant or {010} tablets. Often pseudo-hexagonal by twinning on {110}. Good {010} and {001} cleavages. G. 2.66. Soluble in water. Y = a, Z = c.[20] (+)2V = 67°20′ D, r > v very weak. n_X = 1.4916 C, 1.4935 D, 1.4982 F, n_Y = 1.4928 C, 1.4947 D, 1.4995 F, n_Z = 1.4954 C, 1.4973 D, 1.5023 F, $n_Z - n_X$ = 0.0038 D. Colorless. PD 2.90, 3.00, 2.89; 5–0613*. Inverts to a uniaxial negative phase at about 650° C. Miscible in all proportions with $(NH_4)_2SO_4$, KCr_2O_4 and probably with Rb_2SO_4 and Cs_2SO_4.

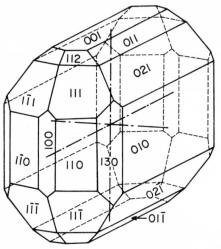

Fig. 7-2. A combination of crystal forms in K_2SO_4.

$(NH_4)_2SO_4$ (Mascagnite) is orthorhombic with a = 5.98, b = 10.62, c = 7.78 kX, U.C. 4. Crystals {010} tablets or nearly equant. Twinning on {110} often gives pseudo-hexagonal habit. Good {001} cleavage. H. 2. G. 1.77. F. 1. Volatile. Y = b, Z = a.[21] (+)2V = 52°12′ Na, r > v very weak. n_X = 1.5177 Li, 1.5209 Na, n_Y = 1.5199 Li, 1.5230 Na, n_Z = 1.5297 Li, 1.5330 Na, $n_Z - n_X$ = 0.0128 Na. PD 4.33, 4.39, 3.06; 10–343*. Colorless or stained gray to yellow. Made from aqueous solution. Miscible in all proportions with K_2SO_4, Rb_2SO_4, Tl_2SO_4 or Cs_2SO_4.

NH_4LiSO_4 is orthorhombic[22] with $a:b:c$ = [23] 0.595:1:0.583. Crystals {010} plates with horizontal striations on prism faces. Perfect {010} cleavage. G. 1.20. Y = a; Z = b. (+)2V = 36°32′ red, 49°4′ green. n_Y = 1.437 Li, $n_Z - n_X$ = very weak. Colorless. Made from cold water solution. A pseudo-hexagonal phase is also known with one perfect cleavage. G. 1.16. Common twinning. (+)2E = 63°30′ red, 61°32′ green. Made from hot water solution.

[20] Tutton: *Trans. Chem. Soc. London* LXV, p. 628 (1894).

Rb₂SO₄ is orthorhombic with[21] $a:b:c = 0.572:1:0.749$. Crystals varied, nearly equant or {100} tablets. Common pseudo-hexagonal forms from twinning on {110}. Distinct {010} and poor {001} cleavages. G. 3.61. $X = b$; $Y = c$. $(+)2V = 38°40'$ Li, $41°55'$ Na, $43°35'$ Tl (but variations are found). $n_X = 1.5108$ Li, 1.5131 Na, 1.5153 Tl, $n_Y = 1.5109$ Li, 1.5133 Na, 1.5155 Tl, $n_Z = 1.5120$ Li, 1.5144 Na, 1.5166 Tl, $n_Z - n_X = 0.0013$ Na at room temperature. At $180°$ C. $n_X = 1.5075$ Na, $n_Y = 1.5085$, $n_Z = 1.5096$, $n_Z - n_X = 0.0021$. The optic angle decreases with rising temperature, becoming $0°$ for Li light at $42°$, for Na at $48°$ and for F light at $58°$. At higher temperatures the optic plane is (010). Colorless. PD 3.12, 3.00, 2.98; 8–51. Made from water solution.

Ag₂SO₄ is orthorhombic with[23a] $a:b:c = 0.461:1:0.808$. Crystals pyramidal with distinct {010} and poor {111} cleavages. G. 5.363. $(+)2V = 73°$ calc.; $n_X = 1.7583$, $n_Y = 1.7748$, $n_Z = 1.7842$, $n_Z - n_X = 0.0269$. $n_X = 1.7524$ Li, 1.7627 (for $\lambda = 546$). PD 2.87, 2.64, 3.17; 7–203.

Cs₂SO₄ is orthorhombic with[21] $a:b:c = 0.571:1:0.753$. Crystals {001} or {010} tablets with all three pinacoids prominent. Distinct {010} and poor {001} cleavages. G. 4.24. $Y = b$; $X = c$. $(-)2V = 65°20'$ D, $r < v$ weak. $n_X = 1.5573$ C, 1.5598 D, 1.5660 F, $n_Y = 1.5619$ C, 1.5644 D, 1.5706 F, $n_Z = 1.5637$ C, 1.5662 D, 1.5725 F, $n_Z - n_X = 0.0064$. PD 3.29, 3.15, 3.13; 8–462. Made from aqueous solution. Probably miscible in all proportions with $(NH_4)_2SO_4$, K_2SO_4, Rb_2SO_4 and Tl_2SO_4.

Tl₂SO₄ is orthorhombic with[21] $a:b:c = 0.555:1:0.733$. Crystals {010} tablets often long parallel to a. Perfect {010} and very good {001} cleavages. G. 6.765. $Y = b$; $Z = a$. $(+)2V = 68°4'$ Na, $r > v$ very weak. $n_X = 1.8509$ C, 1.8600 D, 1.8859 F, $n_Y = 1.8579$ C, 1.8671 D, 1.8935 F, $n_Z = 1.8753$ C, 1.8853 D, 1.9126 F, $n_Z - n_X = 0.0253$ D. Colorless. PD 3.12, 3.05, 3.53; 7–188.

K₂CrO₄ (Tarapacaite) is orthorhombic with $a = 5.92$, $b = 10.40$, $c = 7.61$ kX. U.C. 4. Crystals often {001} tablets. Common pseudo-hexagonal forms from twinning on {110}. Distinct {010} and {001} cleavages. G. 2.74. $X = b$; $Y = a$. $(-)2V = 52°$, $r > v$ weak.[24] $n_X = 1.687$, $n_Y = 1.722$, $n_Z = 1.731$, $n_Z - n_X = 0.044$. Color bright yellow. PD 2.96, 4.28, 3.07; 1–0892. Made from aqueous solution. It has a reversible inversion at $666°$ C. Miscible in all proportions with K_2SO_4. With 19 per cent K_2SO_4, $n_X =$?, $n_Y = 1.6688$, $n_Z = 1.6727$. With 79.4 per cent K_2SO_4, $n_X = 1.5316$, $n_Y = 1.5378$, $n_Z = 1.5432$, $n_Z - n_X = 0.0115$.

[21] Tutton: *Zeit. Krist.* XXXVIII, p. 602 (1904). *Trans. Chem. Soc. London* LXXXIII, p. 1049 (1903).

[22] Wyrouboff: *Bull. Soc. Fr. Min.* III, p. 198 (1880).

[23] *abc* changed to *bac* to make $b > a > c$.

[23a] Herman and Ilge: *Zeit. Krist.* LXXX, p. 402 (1931).

[24] Larsen and Berman: *U. S. Geol. Surv. Bull.* 848, 1934.

Rb₂CrO₄ is orthorhombic with $a:b:c = 0.566:1:0.749$. Crystals long parallel with a. Good {001} cleavage. G. 3.52. X = c; Y = b. $(-)2H = 74°$, r < v. Bolland[25] gives for "rubidium chromate" (hydrated?): $n_1 = 1.71$, $n_2 = 1.72$; these are probably n_Y and n_Z. Color yellow. Made from aqueous solution.

K₂SeO₄ is orthorhombic with[26] $a:b:c = 0.573:1:0.732$. Crystals {010} tablets or prismatic needles vertically striated. Common three-part twins. Perfect {010} and distinct {001} cleavages. G. 3.067. Deliquescent. Y = a; Z = c. $(+)2V = 76°47'$ C, $76°53'$ D, $76°57'$ F, r < v. $n_X = 1.5325$ C, 1.5352 D, 1.5421 F, $n_Y = 1.5362$ C, 1.5390 D, 1.5460 F, $n_Z = 1.5418$ C, 1.5446 D, 1.5518 F, $n_Z - n_X = 0.0094$ D. Colorless. PD 3.00, 4.30, 3.08; 1–0857. Made from aqueous solution.

Rb₂SeO₄ is orthorhombic with[26] $a:b:c = 0.571:1:0.739$. Crystals brachydomatic columnar. Perfect {010} and distinct {001} cleavages. G. 3.902. Deliquescent. Y = a; Z = c. $(+)2V = 68°53'$ D, r > v very weak. $n_X = 1.5487$ C, 1.5515 D, 1.5586 F, $n_Y = 1.5509$ C, 1.5537 D, 1.5609 F, $n_Z = 1.5554$ C, 1.5582 D, 1.5655 F, $n_Z - n_X = 0.0067$ D. Colorless. Made from aqueous solution.

Cs₂SeO₄ is orthorhombic with[26] $a:b:c = 0.570:1:0.742$. Crystals thick basal tablets. Perfect {010} and distinct {001} cleavages. G. 4.456. Very deliquescent. X = b; Y = c. $(-)2V = 73°7'$ C, $71°49'$ Na, $68°58'$ F, r > v distinct. $n_X = 1.5955$ C, 1.5989 D, 1.6070 F, $n_Y = 1.5965$ C, 1.5999 D, 1.6080 F, $n_Z = 1.5969$ C, 1.6003 D, 1.6084 F, $n_Z - n_X = 0.0014$ D. The optic angle increases rapidly with heat becoming positive at about 60° C. and uniaxial at about 95° C.; at 150° C. it is again decidedly biaxial (positive) with Y = b; at 280° C. the optic angle about (Z = b) is much more than 90° and the sign is again negative (X = c). Made from aqueous solution.

Tl₂SeO₄ is orthorhombic[26] with $a:b:c = 0.555:1:0.724$. Crystals columnar brachydomatic or {010}, {001} or {011} tablets. {010} and {001} cleavages. G. 6.875. X = b; Y = c. $(-)2V = 72°58'$, r > v weak. $n_X = 1.9355$ C, 1.9493 D, 1.9840 F, $n_Y = 1.9450$ C, 1.9592 D, 1.9942 F, $n_Z = 1.9500$ C, 1.9640 D, 1.9987 F, $n_Z - n_X = 0.0147$ D. Made from a dilute acid solution.

(NH₄)₂SeO₄ is monoclinic[27] with $a:b:c = 1.890:1:1.199$, $\beta = 115°29'$. Crystals {100} or {001} tablets or columnar parallel to b. Twinning on {001} common. Perfect {100} and {001} and distinct {010} cleavages. G. 2.194. X = b; Z ∧ c = $+113°11'$. $(+)2V = 37°19'$ C, $37°54'$ D, $38°44'$ F, r < v weak. $n_X = 1.5571$ C, 1.5607 D, 1.5687 F, $n_Y = 1.5594$ C,

[25] Bolland: *Sitzb. Akad. Wiss. Wien* CXIX, p. 275 (1910).
[26] Tutton: *Trans. Chem. Soc. London* LXXI, p. 846 (1897).
[27] Tutton: *Trans. Chem. Soc. London* LXXXIX, p. 1059 (1906).

1.5630 D, 1.5713 F, $n_Z = 1.5806$ C, 1.5846 D, 1.5935 F, $n_Z - n_X = 0.0239$ D. Becomes uniaxial at 114° C. for D and at 119° C. for F. $(NH_4)_2SeO_4$ is also orthorhombic in isomorphous mix-crystals (and also alone?); it is then said to have $a:b:c = 0.534:1:0.75$, and G. 2.077. Crystals {010} tablets. $X = c$; $Y = b$. $(-)2V = 55°36'$ red, 58°54' blue. $n_Y = 1.56$. Colorless. Made from aqueous solution.

Li_2SO_4 is monoclinic with $a:b:c = 1.004:1:1.380$, $\beta = 92°8'$. Crystals pseudo-octahedral and pyramidal. Perfect {101}, {10$\bar{1}$} and {011} cleavages. G. 2.23. Unstable in air. $X \wedge c = -31°$; $Z = b$. $(-)2V = 72°58'$, r > v weak, $n_Y = 1.465$, $n_Z - n_X$ = rather weak. Colorless. Made from fusion. Two other phases are known; one is hexagonal and inverts at 500° C.; the other is isometric. PD 4.01, 3.16, 2.47; 1–0443 (which phase?).

2. Formula Type AXO₄

$CaSO_4$ (**Anhydrite**) is orthorhombic with $a = 6.94$, $b = 6.97$, $c = 6.20$ kX. U.C. 4. Crystals varied in habit; equant or {010}, {100} or {001} tablets; or elongated parallel to a or c. Perfect {010}, very good {100} and distinct {001} cleavages. H. 3–3.5. G. 2.98. Soluble in HCl. M.P. 1450° C. $X = b$; $Z = c$. $(+)2V = 43°$, r < v weak.[28] $n_X = 1.5698$, $n_Y = 1.5754$, $n_Z = 1.6136$ Na, $n_Z - n_X = 0.0438$. Colorless in transmitted light; thick crystals may be bluish or violet with X colorless to pale yellow or rose, Y pale violet or rose, Z violet. PD 3.50, 2.85, 2.33; 6–0226*. Made in several ways: for example by cooling a fusion of $CaSO_4$ with $CaCl_2$ or NaCl. $CaSO_4$ inverts at 1195° C. to the α-phase which is monoclinic[29] with lamellar twinning like plagioclase; it has[30] $n_X = 1.50$, $n_Y = ?$, $n_Z = 1.56$, $n_Z - n_X = 0.06$. Another phase (β-$CaSO_4$) is obtained by heating anhydrite above 170° C. It is stable to at least 500° C. It is probably orthorhombic and is pseudo-hexagonal. G. 2.85. $Z = c$. $(+)2E = 45°\pm$, $n_X = 1.562 \pm 0.003$, $n_Y = ?$, $n_Z = 1.595$, $n_Z - n_X = 0.013$. A third phase (γ-$CaSO_4$) has been called "soluble anhydrite" since it is much more soluble in water than ordinary anhydrite. It is made by dehydrating $CaSO_4 \cdot 0.5H_2O$ at about 30° C. Crystals are hexagonal basal plates. G. 2.61 (Gaubert[31]), 2.55 (Gaudefroy[30]). Uniaxial positive[31] with $n_O = 1.505$, $n_E = 1.548 \pm .003$, $n_E - n_O = 0.043$. Again:[30] $n_O = 1.56$, $n_E = 1.50$, $n_E - n_O = 0.06$. This phase takes up $0.5H_2O$ readily in contact with moist air. It varies markedly in properties with variation of temperature: for example[32] at

[28] Kolb: *Zeit. Krist.* XLIX, p. 14 and 24 (1911).

[29] Posnjak: *Am. J. Sci.* XXXV A, p. 247 (1938).

[30] Gaudefroy: *Bull. Soc. Fr. Min.* XLII, p. 298 (1919).

[31] Gaubert: *Bull. Soc. Fr. Min.* LVII, p. 252 (1934).

[32] Belyankin and Lapin: *Dokl. Akad. Sci. U.S.S.R.* LI, p. 535 (1946) [*Min. Abst.* X, p. 109 (1947)].

100° C. it has $n_X = 1.547$, $n_Z = 1.570$; at 150° C. it has $n_X = 1.499$, $n_Z = 1.544$; and at 450°–550° C. it is isotropic with $n = 1.500$. PD 6.05, 3.01, 2.80; 2–0134.

ZnSO₄ (Zinkosite?) is orthorhombic[33] with $a = 6.74$, $b = 8.58$, $c = 4.76$ kX. Crystals rectangular or rhombic {001} plates. G. 3.7. Alters on exposure to air. X = b; Z = c. (−)2V = small, $n_X = 1.658$, $n_Y = 1.669$, $n_Z = 1.670$, $n_Z - n_X = 0.012$. Colorless or white. PD 3.54, 4.17, 2.65; 8–491. Made by dissolving zinc in H_2SO_4 and drying. A natural substance called zinkosite is perhaps the same.

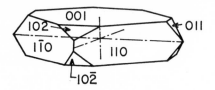

Fig. 7-3. A crystal habit of BaSO₄, barite.

CuSO₄ (Chalcocyanite) is orthorhombic with $a:b:c = 0.797:1:1.130$. Crystals tabular, pseudo-hexagonal.[34] Effloresces slowly in air, altering to chalcanthite. H. 3.5. G. 3.65. X = b; Z = c. (−)2V = large, r > v extreme. $n_X = 1.724$, $n_Y = 1.733$, $n_Z = 1.739$, $n_Z - n_X = 0.015$. Pure $CuSO_4$ crystals are colorless, but natural crystals are pale green, brownish, yellowish, sky-blue or violet with Z darkest. PD 2.62, 4.20, 3.55; 1–1081.

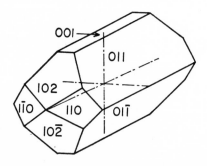

Fig. 7-4. A crystal habit of BaSO₄, barite.

BaSO₄ (Barite) is orthorhombic with $a = 8.85$, $b = 5.43$, $c = 7.13$ kX. U.C. 4. Crystals {001} tablets often bounded by {210}, or equant or columnar parallel to a or to b. Perfect {001} and {210} and poor {010} cleavages. H. 3–3.5. G. 4.50. M.P. 1580° C. Insoluble. Y = b, Z = a.[28] (+)2V =

[33] Schiff: *Zeit. Krist.* LXXXVII, p. 379 (1934). a and b interchanged to make $b > a > c$.

[34] Posnjak and Tunell: *Am. J. Sci.* CCXVIII, p. 1 (1929).

$36°37'$ C, $37°2'$ D, $37°45'$ F, r < v distinct. $n_X = 1.6336$ C, 1.6363 D, 1.6427 F, $n_Y = 1.6346$ C, 1.6373 D, 1.6440 F, $n_Z = 1.6456$ C, 1.6484 D, 1.6551 F, $n_Z - n_X = 0.0121$ D. PD 3.44, 3.10, 2.12; 5–0448. Colorless to white or (stained?) yellow, reddish brown, gray. Inverts to a monoclinic (?) phase at $1149°$ C. Made by fusion of $BaSO_4$ with $BaCl_2$ and in other ways. Forms a (probably) continuous series with $SrSO_4$; may contain Pb up to about Pb:Ba = 1:4.

$SrSO_4$ (Celestite) is orthorhombic with $a = 8.36$, $b = 5.36$, $c = 6.84 kX$. U.C. 4. Crystals resemble barite in form. Perfect {001}, good {210} and poor {010} cleavages. H. 3–3.5. G. 3.97. M.P. about $1605°$ C. X = c; Y = b.[28] (+)2V = $49°50'$ C, $50°25'$ D, $51°36'$ F; r < v distinct. $n_X = 1.6189$ C, 1.6215 D, 1.6273 F, $n_Y = 1.6207$ C, 1.6232 D, 1.6292 F, $n_Z = 1.6279$ C, 1.6305 D, 1.6367 F, $n_Z - n_X = 0.0092$ D. Colorless to pale blue; also white, reddish, greenish or brownish. PD 2.97, 3.30, 2.73; 5–0593. Inverts to a hexagonal phase at about $1152°$ C. Forms a series (probably complete) with $BaSO_4$.

$PbSO_4$ (Anglesite) is orthorhombic with $a = 8.45$, $b = 5.38$, $c = 6.93 kX$. U.C. 4. Crystals of varied habit—thick {001} tablets, pyramidal, prismatic along a, equant, etc. Good {001}, distinct {210} and poor {010} cleavages. H. 2.5–3. G. 6.38. Decomposes at $900°$–$1000°$ C. X = c; Y = b.[28] (+)2V = $68°7'$ B, $68°28'$ D, $68°42'$ F, r < v weak. $n_X = 1.8707$ C, 1.8781 D, 1.8965 F, $n_Y = 1.8761$ C, 1.8832 D, 1.9020 F, $n_Z = 1.8869$ C, 1.8947 D, 1.9137 F, $n_Z - n_X = 0.0166$ D. PD 3.00, 4.26, 3.33; 5–0577. Colorless to white or tinted gray, yellow, green or blue. Streak colorless. Made by slow precipitation of lead chloride dissolved in H_2SO_4 (with HCl). Inverts to a monoclinic phase at about $864°$ C.

$PbCrO_4$ (Crocoite) is monoclinic with $a = 7.10$, $b = 7.40$, $c = 6.80 kX$, $\beta = 102°27'$. U.C. 4. Crystals prismatic, equant, etc. Distinct {110} and poor {001} and {100} cleavages. H. 2.5–3. G. 6.1. Y = b; Z $\wedge$ c[35] = $+5.5°$. (+)2V = $57°$ Li, $54°3'$ Na, r > v very strong. $n_X = 2.29 \pm 0.02$ Li,[11] $n_Y = 2.36 \pm 0.02$, $n_Z = 2.66 \pm 0.02$ Li, $n_Z - n_X = 0.37\pm$. Inclined dispersion. Color hyacinth-red or orange or yellow. Pleochroic with X and Y orange-red, Z blood-red. PD 3.28, 3.03, 3.48; 8–209/10. Made by cooling a solution of $PbCrO_4$ in HCl or KNO_3. It can dissolve considerable $PbSO_4$ or $PbMoO_4$. Two other phases are known. One is tetragonal; it is stable only at high temperature or as mix-crystals with $PbMoO_4$. An unstable orthorhombic phase can form mix-crystals with $PbSO_4$; it is more orange in color.

3. Formula Type $A_2(XO_4)_3$

$Fe_2(SO_4)_3$ has at least two phases. One is hexagonal[24] with $c/a = 1.35$. Crystals flattened rhombohedrons with rhombohedral cleavage. Uniaxial

[35] Des Cloizeaux: *Bull. Soc. Fr. Min.* V, p. 103 (1882).

negative with $n_O = 1.756$ C, 1.770 D, 1.809 F, $n_E = 1.746$ C, 1.760 D, 1.798 F, $n_O - n_E = 0.010$ D. Colorless or grayish yellow. Made in a steel bomb at moderate temperature. A second phase is orthorhombic with[36] $a:b:c = 0.957:1:1.357$. Crystals basal tablets bounded by {010}, {110}, {111}, {101} and {100}. $(-)2V = 60°$, $n_X = 1.787$ C, 1.802 D, 1.844 F, $n_Y = 1.799$ C, 1.814 D, 1.857 F, $n_Z = 1.803$ C, 1.818 D, 1.861 F, $n_Z - n_X = 0.016$ D. Color grayish yellow. PD 3.59, 6.08, 4.40; 9–5. Made in a steel bomb at moderate temperature.

4. Formula Type $A_m B_n (XO_4)_p$

$K_2 Mg_2 (SO_4)_3$ **(Langbeinite)** is isometric with $a = 9.96 \, kX$. U.C. 4. Crystals rare; usually massive or granular. No cleavage. H. 3.5–4. G. 2.83. M.P. 930° C. Isotropic[37] with $n = 1.5323$ Li, 1.5347 Na, 1.5370 Tl. Again: 1.5281 Li, 1.5329 Na, 1.5344 Tl. PD 3.14, 2.67, 4.06; 3–0532. Colorless; rarely tinted (with stain?). Made by heating the mixed anhydrous sulfates[36] to 80° C.

$K_2 Mn_2 (SO_4)_3$ **(Manganolangbeinite)** is isometric with[38] $a = 10.014$ Å. U.C. 4. Crystals small tetrahedrons. G. 3.02. Isotropic with $n = 1.572$. Color rose-red. Made from fusion.

$(NH_4)_2 Ca_2 (SO_4)_3$ is isometric and pyritohedral. Isotropic with $n = 1.532$. Colorless.

$K_2 Al_2 (SO_4)_4$ is hexagonal. Crystals rhombohedral with prisms and base. Micaceous basal cleavage. Uniaxial negative with $n_O = 1.545\pm$, $n_E = 1.533\pm$, $n_O - n_E = 0.012\pm$. Colorless. PD 3.63, 2.86, 2.36; 3–0337.

$K_2 Pb (SO_4)_2$ **(Palmierite)** is hexagonal with $a = 5.58$, $c = 20.67 \, kX$. Crystals basal plates. G. 4.5. Uniaxial negative[39] with $n_O = 1.712$, $n_O - n_E = $ strong. Colorless. Made from fusion of components.

$Na_2 Ca (SO_4)_2$ **(Glauberite)** is monoclinic with $a = 9.99$, $b = 8.19$, $c = 8.41 \, kX$, $\beta = 112°11'$. U.C. 4. Crystals basal tablets, prismatic, or pyramidal. Perfect {001} and poor {110} cleavages. H. 2.5–3. G. 2.8. Y $\wedge$ c = $12°$, Z = b.[24] $(-)2V = 7°$, r > v strong; also inclined dispersion. $n_X = 1.515$, $n_Y = 1.535$, $n_Z = 1.536$, $n_Z - n_X = 0.021$. The optic properties vary markedly with change of temperature.[40] Color gray, yellowish or colorless or stained red with iron oxide. PD 3.13, 6.22, 2.66; 2–0556. Made from aqueous solutions of $Na_2 SO_4$ and $CaSO_4$ at about 35° C.

$Na_6 Mg (SO_4)_4$ **(Vanthoffite)** is biaxial (probably monoclinic). Known

[36] Posnjak and Merwin: *J. Am. Chem. Soc.* XLIV, p. 1965 (1922). Also Scharizer: *Zeit. Krist.* LXV, p. 335 (1927).

[37] Görgey: *Tsch. Min. Pet. Mitt.* XXVIII, p. 334 (1909).

[38] Bellanca: *Acc. Linc. Att. Cl. Sci.* II, p. 451 (1947).

[39] Zambonini: *N. Jahrb. Min. Monatshefte*, 1955, p. 209.

[40] Kraus: *Zeit. Krist.* LII, p. 321 (1913); Kraus and Peck: *Mich. Acad. Sci. Ann. Rept.* XIX, p. 95 (1917).

only in grains or masses. H. 3.5–4. G. 2.69. $(-)2V = 84°$, $r < v$ weak.[37] $n_X = 1.4855$, $n_Y = 1.4876$, $n_Z = 1.4893$, $n_Z - n_X = 0.0038$. Colorless. Made from a mixture of the two sulfates under pressure at 80° C.

D. HYDRATED SULFITES, SELENITES, THIOSULFATES, THIONATES, ETC.

$CaS_2O_6 \cdot 4H_2O$ is hexagonal rhombohedral with $c/a = 1.50$. Crystals six-sided basal plates. Poor {0001} cleavage. G. 2.18. Uniaxial negative with[40a] $n_O = 1.5456$ B, 1.5516 D, 1.5580 F, $n_E = 1.5369$ B, 1.5414 D, 1.5467 F, $n_O - n_E = 0.0102$ D. Colorless.

$SrS_2O_6 \cdot 4H_2O$ is hexagonal rhombohedral with $c/a = 1.502$. Crystals six-sided basal plates. Poor {0001} cleavage. G. 2.37. Uniaxial negative with[40a] $n_O = 1.5260$ (672), 1.5297 (579), 1.5357 (492), $n_E = 1.5232$ (672), 1.5262 (579), 1.5310 (492), $n_O - n_E = 0.0035$ D. Colorless.

$PbS_2O_6 \cdot 4H_2O$ is hexagonal rhombohedral with $c/a = 1.516$. Crystals six-sided basal plates. No cleavage. G. 3.25. Uniaxial positive with[40a] $n_O = 1.6303$ (672), 1.6366 (579), 1.6480 (492), $n_E = 1.6500$ (672), 1.6557 (579), 1.6672 (492), $n_E - n_O = 0.0191$ (579). May be slightly biaxial. Made from cold water solution. It forms a continuous series of mix-crystals with $SrS_2O_6 \cdot 4H_2O$, with linear variation of the refractive indices.

$Na_3Ir(SO_3)_3(NH_3)_3 \cdot 6H_2O$ is hexagonal[40b] with $c/a = 3.169$. Uniaxial negative with $n_O = 1.570$, $n_E = 1.546$, $n_O - n_E = 0.024$.

$K_3Rh(SO_3)_3(NH_3)_3 \cdot 6H_2O$ is hexagonal[40b] with $c/a = 3.184$. Uniaxial negative with $n_O = 1.597$, $n_E = 1.563$, $n_O - n_E = 0.034$.

$MgSO_3 \cdot 6H_2O$ is hexagonal (trigonal hemimorphic) with $a = 8.82$, $c = 9.04$ kX. Crystals trigonal pyramids above a basal pedion. G. 1.725. Star-shaped twinning. Colorless. Uniaxial negative with[41] $n_O = 1.511$, $n_E = 1.464$, $n_O - n_E = 0.047$ for yellow Hg light and $n_O = 1.524$, $n_E = 1.474$, $n_O - n_E = 0.050$ for blue Hg light. No rotary polarization. PD 3.87, 2.74, 4.10; 1–0473.

$CoSO_3 \cdot 6H_2O$ is trigonal hemimorphic[41] with $c/a = 1.004$. G. 2.01. Uniaxial negative with $n_O = 1.553$, $n_E = 1.506$, $n_O - n_E = 0.047$. Color ruby-red.

$NiSO_3 \cdot 6H_2O$ is trigonal hemimorphic[41] with $c/a = 1.012$. G. 2.027. Star-like twins common. Uniaxial negative with $n_O = 1.552$, $n_E = 1.509$, $n_O - n_E = 0.043$ (Hg-green). Color emerald-green.

[40a] Rose: N. Jahrb. Min. Bl. Bd. XXIX, p. 53 (1910).

[40b] Bokii and Burovaya: Trudy Inst. Krist., 1947, p. 47 [Chem. Abst. XLIV, p. 7704 (1950)].

[41] Klasens, Perdok and Terpstra: Rec. Trav. Chim. Pays-Bas LIV, p. 728 (1935) [Min. Abst. VI, p. 334 (1936)].

CuSeO$_3$·2H$_2$O (Chalcomenite) is orthorhombic with $a = 6.56$, $b = 9.10$, $c = 7.36$ kX. U.C. 4. Crystals acicular. No cleavage. H. 2–2.5. G. 3.35. X = a; Y = c. $(-)2V = 34°$ Li, r > v strong.[11] $n_X = 1.710$, $n_Y = 1.731$, $n_Z = 1.732$ all ±0.003, $n_Z - n_X = 0.022$. Color blue. Made by heating the precipitated salt with water in a closed tube.

Ca(NH$_2$SO$_3$)$_2$·3H$_2$O is biaxial;[7] micro- to cryptocrystalline. $(-)2V = 48°$, r > v. $n_X = 1.488$, $n_Y = 1.508$ calc., $n_Z = 1.512$, $n_Z - n_X = 0.029$.

Li$_2$S$_2$O$_6$·2H$_2$O is orthorhombic with $a:b:c = 0.966:1:0.578$. Crystals macrodomatic. Perfect {100} cleavage. G. 2.16.[42] Y = c; Z = a. $(+)2V^{42a} = 78°16'$, $n_X = 1.5462$ C, 1.5487 D, 1.5548 F, $n_Y = 1.5565$ C, 1.5602 D, 1.5680 F, $n_Z = 1.5763$ C, 1.5788 D, 1.5887 F, $n_Z - n_X = 0.0301$ D. Colorless.

Na$_2$S$_2$O$_6$·2H$_2$O is orthorhombic with $a:b:c = 0.992:1:0.598$. Crystals prismatic. Perfect {110} cleavage. G. 2.19.[42] Y = b; Z = a. $(+)2V = 73°26'$ Li, 75°14' Na, 76°28' green, r < v strong. $n_X = 1.4803$ Li, 1.4820 Na, 1.4838 green, $n_Y = 1.4927$ Li, 1.4953 Na, 1.4978 green, $n_Z = 1.5158$ Li, 1.5185 Na, 1.5212 green, $n_Z - n_X = 0.0365$ Na. Colorless. PD 3.82, 5.35, 4.87; 5–0357*.

Ag$_2$S$_2$O$_6$·2H$_2$O is orthorhombic with $a:b:c = 0.988:1:0.581$. Crystals prismatic. Perfect {110} cleavage. G. 3.61.[42] X = b; Y = c. $(-)2V^{42a} = 33°21'$ C, 28°6' F, r > v strong. $n_X = 1.6272$ C, 1.6404 F, $n_Y = 1.6573$ C, 1.6748 F, $n_Z = 1.6601$ C, 1.6770 F, $n_Z - n_X = 0.0329$ C, 0.0366 F. Isomorphous with Na$_2$S$_2$O$_6$·2H$_2$O. PD 3.82, 5.35, 4.87; 5–0357*.

3K$_2$S$_5$O$_6$·2H$_2$O is orthorhombic with $a:b:c = 0.456:1:0.305$. Crystals prismatic with {110}, {010}, {011}, etc., or thick {010} tablets terminated by {221}. No distinct cleavage. X = a; Y = b.[42b] Positive elongation. $(-)2V = 65°\pm$, r > v. $n_X = 1.570$, $n_Y = 1.63\pm$, $n_Z = 1.658$, $n_Z - n_X = 0.088$. Again:[1] $n_X = 1.565$, $n_Y = 1.63$, $n_Z = 1.655\pm$, $n_Z - n_X = 0.090$. Colorless. Made from water solution.

7BaS$_5$O$_6$·2H$_2$O? is orthorhombic in rectangular tablets flattened parallel with the optic plane. $(+)2V$ fairly large.[42b] $n_X = 1.620-$, $n_Y = 1.640-$, $n_Z = 1.670$, $n_Z - n_X = 0.050+$. Colorless. Made from water solution by addition of alcohol.

K$_2$Cr$_2$O$_7$·Hg(CN)$_2$·2H$_2$O is orthorhombic with $a:b:c = 0.794:1:1.495$. Crystals short prismatic with {110} cleavage. Y = a; Z = c. $(+)2V = 57°18'$ red, r > v strong. $n_Y = 1.591$ red. Made from solution.

NaAgS$_2$O$_3$·H$_2$O is monoclinic domatic[42c] with $a:b:c = 0.853:1:0.868$, $\beta = 97°32'$. Crystals {010} tablets or prismatic. Strongly piezoelectric.

[42] Topsøe: *Arch. Sci. Phys. Nat. Genève* XLV [2], p. 227 (1872).
[42a] Topsøe and Christiansen: *Ann. Chim. Phys.* I [5], p. 42 (1874).
[42b] C. W. Mason, *pers. comm.* Jan. 31, 1930.
[42c] Baines: *J. Chem. Soc. London*, 1929, p. 2763.

$X \wedge c = +12°; Z = b$. $2V =$ about $90°; n_X = 1.69, n_Y =$ about 1.715 calc., $n_Z = 1.74, n_Z - n_X = 0.05$.

$BaS_2O_6 \cdot 2H_2O$ is monoclinic with $a:b:c = 0.94:1:1.38$, $\beta = 111°21'$. Crystals varied; perfect $\{001\}$ cleavage. Twinning on $\{001\}$. G. 3.12. $Y = b$;[42d] $Z \wedge c = -13°$. $(+)2V = 83°6'-83°31'$ Li, $84°28'-84°38'$ Na, $87°18'-87°38'$ green, $r < v$ strong. $n_X = 1.5848$ Li, 1.5860 Na, 1.5881 green, $n_Y = 1.5935$ Li, 1.5951 Na, 1.5976 green, $n_Z = 1.6055$ Li, 1.6072 Na, 1.6090 green, $n_Z - n_X = 0.0212$ Na. Colorless.

$BaS_2O_6 \cdot 4H_2O$ is monoclinic with $a:b:c = 1.222:1:1.127$, $\beta = 94°16'$. $\{110\}$ cleavage. Pseudo-hexagonal by twinning on $\{110\}$. G. 3.1. $X \wedge c = -45°; Z = b$. $(+)2V = 87°20'$ red, $89°42'$ green, $r < v$ strong. $n_Y = 1.532$ red,[42e] $n_Z - n_X =$ strong. Colorless.

$CaS_2O_3 \cdot 6H_2O$ forms biaxial crystals[1] with oblique extinction. $(+)2V = 60°\pm$ calc., $n_X = 1.545\pm$, $n_Y = 1.560\pm$, $n_Z = 1.605\pm$, $n_Z - n_X = 0.060\pm$. Colorless.

$Na_2S_2O_3 \cdot 5H_2O$ is monoclinic with $a:b:c = 0.351:1:0.275$, $\beta = 103°58'$. Crystals prismatic or $\{010\}$ laths. G. $1.7\pm$. $X \wedge c = -41.5°$ Na, $-42°18'$ F; $Z = b$. $(+)2V = 80°40'$ Na, $r < v$. $n_X = 1.4849$ Li, 1.4886 Na, 1.4919 Tl, $n_Y = 1.5038$ Li, 1.5079 Na, 1.5117 Tl, $n_Z = 1.5311$ Li, 1.5360 Na, 1.5405 Tl, $n_Z - n_X = 0.0474$ Na. Colorless. PD 2.93, 5.4, 2.84; 1–0914. Made from water solution.

$Na_2Cr_2O_7 \cdot 2H_2O$ is monoclinic with[42f] $a:b:c = 0.57:1:1.182$, $\beta = 94°55'$. Crystals basal plates. No cleavage. Deliquescent. G. 2.53. $X = b; Z \wedge c = +13°$. $(+)2V = 83°42'$, $r < v$. $n_X = 1.6610$, $n_Y = 1.6994$, $n_Z = 1.7510$, $n_Z - n_X = 0.090$. PD 3.93, 5.4, 3.04; 1–0460. Made from solution.

$SrCr_2O_7 \cdot 3H_2O$ is monoclinic with $a:b:c = 0.602:1:0.546$, $\beta = 92°32'$. Crystals $\{100\}$ plates. $Y = b$; $Z \wedge c = +78°$. $(+)2V = 20°28'$, $r < v$. $n_X = 1.7146$, $n_Y = 1.7174$, $n_Z = 1.812$ calc., $n_Z - n_X = 0.0954$. Made from solution.

$Ce_2(S_2O_6) \cdot 15H_2O$ is triclinic pinacoidal with $a:b:c = 0.592:1:1.191$, $\alpha = 81°26'$, $\beta = 105°21'$, $\gamma = 86°38'$. Crystals thick $\{001\}$ tablets. Perfect $\{100\}$ cleavage. G. 2.29. Both optic axes visible through $\{001\}$ with the acute bisectrix inclined to the left and with unsymmetrical dispersion; the optic plane cuts the a axis at about $20°$. $(-)2V = 88°52'$, $r > v$ weak. $n_Y = 1.507$, $n_Z - n_X =$? Made from solution below $15°$ C.

[42d] Brio: *Sitzb. Akad. Wiss. Wien*, LV (II), p. 145 (1867).
[42e] Wyrouboff: *Bull. Soc. Fr. Min.* VIII, p. 78 (1885).
[42f] Wyrouboff: *Bull. Soc. Fr. Min.* XIV, p. 77 (1891).

E. HYDRATED ACID SULFATES

$(UO_2)_2H_2(SO_4)_3 \cdot 5H_2O$ is orthorhombic with[42g] $a = 12.86$, $b = 12.99$, $c = 11.57$ Å. G. 3.16. Z = c. $(-)2V$ near $0°$. $n_X = 1.555$, $n_Y = 1.586$, $n_Z = 1.586$, $n_Z - n_X = 0.031$. Pleochroic with X colorless, Y and Z pale yellow. PD 6.32, 3.19, 2.76; 8–152. Made from solution.

$FeH(SO_4)_2 \cdot 4H_2O$ **(Rhomboclase)** is orthorhombic with $a:b:c = 0.5577:1:0.9370$. Crystals basal plates. Perfect $\{001\}$ and good $\{110\}$ cleavages. H. 2. G. 2.23. X = c;[43] Y = a. $(+)2V = 27°$. $n_X = 1.533$, $n_Y = 1.550$, $n_Z = 1.635$, $n_Z - n_X = 0.102$. Colorless to white, gray or yellow. It is a stable phase in the system Fe_2O_3—SO_3—H_2O at temperatures up to $140°$ C.

$NaHSO_4 \cdot H_2O$ is monoclinic with $a:b:c = 0.997:1:1.048$, $\beta = 119°35'$. Crystals prismatic, often platy parallel (110) or ($1\bar{1}0$). Bolland[25] measured on "sodium bisulfate" (hydrated?): $n_X = 1.43$, $n_Y = 1.46$, $n_Z = 1.47$, $n_Z - n_X = 0.04$ ∴ $(-)2V$ = moderate. Colorless. PD 3.40, 2.98, 2.77; 1–0624. Made from a solution of Na_2SO_4 containing an excess of H_2SO_4.

F. HYDRATED NORMAL SULFATES, CHROMATES, AND SELENATES

1. Formula Type $A_2XO_4 \cdot qH_2O$

$Na(NH_4,K)SO_4 \cdot 2H_2O$ **(Lecontite)** is orthorhombic with $a:b:c = 0.785:1:1.532$. Crystals prismatic.[11] H. 2–2.5. $(-)2V = 40° \pm 1°$, $n_X = 1.440$, $n_Y = 1.452$, $n_Z = 1.453$ all ± 0.003, $n_Z - n_X = 0.013$–0.006. Colorless. PD 5.07, 4.64, 3.85; 2–0161*. $NaNH_4SO_4 \cdot 2H_2O$ crystallizes from a water solution of Na_2SO_4 with excess of $(NH_4)_2 \cdot SO_4$.

$Li_2SO_4 \cdot H_2O$ is monoclinic[44] with $a:b:c = 1.607:1:0.563$, $\beta = 92°5'$. Crystals $\{\bar{1}01\}$ plates long parallel with b. Twinning on $\{\bar{1}01\}$ common. Perfect $\{101\}$ distinct $\{100\}$ and poor $\{110\}$ cleavages. G. 2.06. X ∧ $c = -36°32'$; Z = b. $(-)2V = 78°24'$, r < v very weak. $n_X = 1.459$, $n_Y = 1.477$, $n_Z = 1.488$, $n_Z - n_X = 0.029$. Colorless. PD 4.12, 5.10, 3.54; 1–0425.

$Na_2SO_4 \cdot 10H_2O$ **(Mirabilite)** is monoclinic with $a:b:c = 1.110:1:1.239$, $\beta = 107°45'$. Crystals columnar parallel to b, $\{001\}$ tablets long parallel to b, or short prismatic. Perfect $\{100\}$ and poor $\{001\}$, $\{010\}$ and $\{011\}$ cleavages. Loses some water easily. H. 1.5–2. G. 1.49; also reported as

[42g] Traill: *Am. Min.* XXXVII, p. 394 (1952).

[43] Posnjak and Merwin: *J. Am. Chem. Soc.* XLIV, p. 1983 (1922).

[44] Johnsen: *N. Jahrb. Min. Bl. Bd.* XXXIX, p. 500 (1914). Scacchi in Dufet (*Rec. Don. Num.* 1900, p. 1238) gives $n_Y = 1.510$ D.

1.46–1.48. $X = b$; $Z \wedge c = +31°$ Li, 26.5° blue. $(-)2V = 76°$, $r > v$ weak with strong crossed dispersion.[11] $n_X = 1.394$, $n_Y = 1.396$, $n_Z = 1.398$ all ± 0.003, $n_Z - n_X = 0.004$. Again:[45] $n_X = 1.396$ Na, $n_Y = 1.4103$, $n_Z = 1.419$ calc., $n_Z - n_X = 0.023$. Sections or grains normal to X give abnormal interference colors; other sections give sharp extinction. Colorless. PD 5.50, 3.22, 3.10; 1–0207.

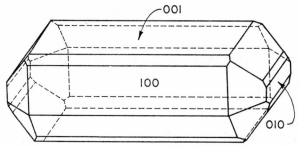

Fig. 7-5. A crystal habit of $Na_2SO_4 \cdot 10H_2O$.

$Na_2CrO_4 \cdot 4H_2O$ is monoclinic with $a:b:c = 1.112:1:1.062$, $\beta = 105°4'$. Crystals often elongated along a. No distinct cleavage. Twinning on $\{001\}$. Deliquescent. The optic plane is $\{010\}$ for light of wave-length less than 645 mμ and normal to $\{010\}$ for $\lambda = $ more than 645 mμ; it is uniaxial positive at $\lambda = 645$ mμ. $(+)2V = 31°$ to 12° for $\lambda = 450$–600 mμ. $Z \wedge c = 5°$ for $\lambda = 589$ mμ.

λ	472	535	573	589	625	645	650	670
n_X		1.342		1.321	1.308		1.291	1.221
n_Y		1.471		1.447	1.383		1.297	1.285
n_Z		1.576		1.561	1.551		1.545	1.536
$n_Z - n_X$		0.234		0.240	0.243		0.254	0.315
$Z \wedge c$	17°		5.5°				2.5°	
2V	35° ca.					0°	12°	

PD 4.50, 3.58, 3.20; 1–0334. Made from solution at 25°–29° C.

2. Formula Type $A_2B(XO_4)_2 \cdot qH_2O$

$Na_4Mg_2(SO_4)_4 \cdot 5H_2O$ **(Loeweite)** is tetragonal[46](?). Poor basal cleavage. H. 2.5–3. G. 2.37. F. 1.5. Soluble in water. Uniaxial negative with[47] $n_O = 1.490$, $n_E = 1.471$, $n_O - n_E = 0.019$. Colorless. Made from water solution. Also said to be trigonal[47] with c/a 0.702.

[45] Rosicky: *Zeit. Krist.* XLV, p. 473 (1908).
[46] Haidinger: *Abh. Bohm. Ges.* IV, p. 663 (1847).
[47] Görgey: *Tsch. Min. Petr. Mitt.* XXIX, p. 198 (1910).

$K_2Ca(SO_4)_2 \cdot H_2O$ (Syngenite) is monoclinic with $a = 9.70$, $b = 7.15$, $c = 6.20$ kX. $\beta = 104°5'$. U.C. 2. Crystals {100} tablets or prismatic. Common twinning on {100}. Perfect {110} and {100} and distinct {010} cleavages. H. 2.5. G. 2.6. X $\wedge$ $c^{48} = -2°17'$; Z $= b$. $(-)2V = 28°18'$ Na, r $<$ v very strong. $n_X = 1.5010$ Na, $n_Y = 1.5166$, $n_Z = 1.5176$, $n_Z - n_X = 0.0166$. When heated the optic angle becomes zero in yellow light at 158° and then opens out in the {010} plane. 2V is 0° at 127° in red light, at 172° in green light and at 177.5° in blue light. Colorless or white. Made from solutions rich in H_2SO_4 between 0° and 100° C.

$(NH_4)_2Ca(SO_4)_2 \cdot H_2O$ (Koktaite) is monoclinic.[49] Crystals acicular. No cleavage. Soluble in water. G. 2.09. Y $= b$; Z $\wedge$ c on (110) is 2°. $(-)2V = 72°$, r $<$ v. $n_X = 1.524$, $n_Y = 1.532$, $n_Z = 1.536$, $n_Z - n_X = 0.012$. Again:[50] $(-)2V = 50°$, $n_X = 1.521$, $n_Y = 1.527$, $n_Z = 1.529$, $n_Z - n_X = 0.007$. Colorless. PD 3.04, 3.19, 5.70; 2–0615.

$K_4Cd_2(SO_4)_4 \cdot 3H_2O$ is monoclinic with $a:b:c = 0.987:1:2.025$, $\beta = 104°42'$. Crystals prismatic with {010} cleavage. X $\wedge$ $c = -69°15'$; Z $= b$. $(-)2V = 63°33'$ Li, $64°16'$ Tl. $n_Y = 1.509$ Li, 1.511 Tl. $n_Z - n_X = ?$ Made from solution at room temperature.

$K_4Mn_2(SO_4)_4 \cdot 3H_2O$ is monoclinic with $a:b:c = 0.974:1:1.058$, $\beta = 104°$. Crystals prismatic with distinct basal cleavage. X $\wedge$ $c = +100°$; Z $= b$. $(+)2V = 61°48'$, r $<$ v. $n_Y = 1.512$ D, $n_Z - n_X = ?$ Made from water solution above 55° C.

$Na_2Cu(SO_4)_2 \cdot 2H_2O$ (Kröhnkite) is monoclinic with $a = 5.78$, $b = 12.58$, $c = 5.48$ kX, $\beta = 108°30'$. U.C. 2. Crystals short prismatic, octahedral, etc. Twinning on {101} common. Perfect {010} and poor {$\bar{1}$01} cleavages. H. 2.5–3. G. 2.90. X $\wedge$ $c = +48°$, Y $= b$.[51] $(-)2V = 78°36'$, r $<$ v weak; also inclined dispersion. $n_X = 1.544$, $n_Y = 1.578$, $n_Z = 1.601$, $n_Z - n_X = 0.057$ Na. Color sky-blue. Made from water solution above 17° C.

$Na_2Mg(SO_4)_2 \cdot 4H_2O$ (Bloedite) is monoclinic with $a = 11.04$, $b = 8.15$, $c = 5.49$ kX, $\beta = 100°41'$. U.C. 4. Crystals equant, short prismatic, often highly modified. H. 3. G. 2.25. X $\wedge$ $c = 37°$; Y $= b$.[52] $(-)2V = 70°5'$ red, $72°34'$ blue, $n_X = 1.4826$, $n_Y = 1.4855$, $n_Z = 1.4869$, $n_Z - n_X = 0.0041$ Na. Colorless or stained bluish green or reddish. PD 3.25, 4.53, 2.71; 4–0549. Made from a solution at 21°–71° C.

$Na_2Fe(SO_4)_2 \cdot 4H_2O$ is monoclinic with[53] $a:b:c = 1.356:1:0.671$, $\beta =$

[48] Schreiber: *N. Jahrb. Min. Bl. Bd.* XXXVII, p. 247 (1914).

[49] Sekanina: *Acta Ac. Sci. Nat. Moravo Siles.* XX, No. 1 (1948).

[50] Merz, Hardesty, and Hendricks: *J. Am. Chem. Soc.* LV, p. 3571 (1933).

[51] Merwin in Palache and Warren: *Am. J. Sci.* XXVI, p. 342 (1908).

[52] Laszkiewicz: *Arch. Min. Soc. Warsaw* V, p. 79 (1929); Schaller: *Am. Min.* XVII, p. 530 (1932).

[53] Boky: *N. Jahrb. Min.* I, p. 94 (1936).

100°34′. Crystals show {001}, {110} and {210}. $(-)2V = 60°$, $n_X = 1.493$, $n_Y = 1.500$ calc., $n_Z = 1.503$, $n_Z - n_X = 0.010$. Color green. Made from water solution.

K₂Mg(SO₄)₂·4H₂O (Leonite) is monoclinic with $a:b:c = 1.232:1:1.038$, $\beta = 95°9′$. Crystals {100} tablets long parallel to c. May show lamellar twinning. H. 2.5–3. G. 2.20. Y = b; Z $\wedge$ a small. $(+)2V$ large.[54] $n_X = 1.479$, $n_Y = 1.482$, $n_Z = 1.487$, $n_Z - n_X = 0.008$. Colorless or yellowish. Made from solution at 41°–89° C.

A₂B(XO₄)₂·6H₂O—Tutton's Salts

Nearly 80 monoclinic salts with this formula (in which A = K, NH₄, Rb, Cs, or Ti, B = Mg, Zn, Cd, Mn, Fe, Co, Ni, or Cu, and X = S, Se, or Cr) have been studied by Tutton. Another isostructural crystal is (NH₄)₂Ni(BeF₄)₂·6H₂O, and no doubt still others will be found.

Crystals of these salts are generally prismatic parallel to c or to a, or tabular parallel to {001}, or intermediate combinations. All show good cleavage parallel to {20$\bar{1}$}. A few have cleavage parallel to {010}, this being the better cleavage in (NH₄)₂Cu(SO₄)₂·6H₂O. The sulfates tend to be less strongly colored than the selenates; they are blue or greenish blue in the Cu salts, green or bluish green in the Ni and Fe salts, rose or pink in the Mn salts, ruby-red in the Co salts, and colorless or white in the Mg, Zn, and Cd salts. The chromates are yellow. All these colors are pale enough to be invisible in small microscopic grains. Solid solutions intermediate between these salts have not been studied, but presumably could be made.

The following tables show selected data for the known compositions; they are useful for comparisons and preliminary identification. Complete data are given in the descriptions of the individual compounds. The tables indicate the degree to which refringence and birefringence tend to increase as the element A ranges through the series K, Rb, NH₄, Cs, Tl, and as the element B ranges through the series Mg, Mn, Cd, Fe, Zn, Cu, Co, and Ni. Most of the exceptions to these rules are compounds containing Cu. The crystallographic ratios $a:b:c$, and β are remarkably constant, as would be expected in an isostructural group of substances. The optic orientation X $\wedge$ c varies from 0° to 93° as shown in Fig. 7-6; extinction angles X $\wedge$ {20$\bar{1}$} cleavage correspondingly range from about $-40°$ through zero to $+52°$. However, the sign is rarely determinable without special techniques. Measurements of $2V_Z$ are useful in distinguishing various members of this family because that angle varies from about zero to somewhat over 90°. The optic sign is mostly $(+)$ but in about 20 instances it is $(-)$. The

[54] Schaller and Henderson: *U. S. Geol. Surv. Bull.* 833 (1932).

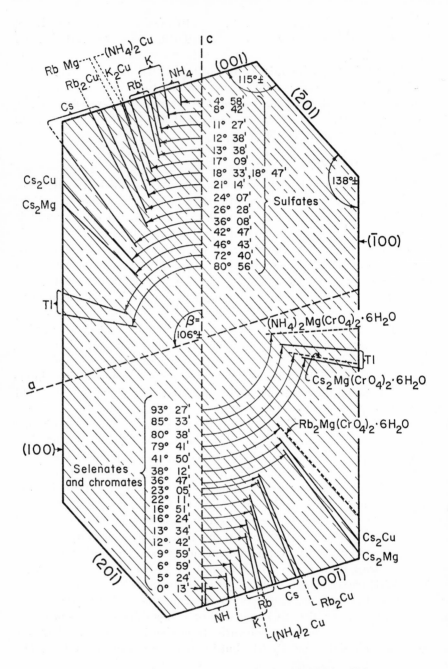

Fig. 7-6. Optic orientation of Tutton's salts $A_2B(XO_4)_2 \cdot 6H_2O$.

three chromates of Mg and NH_4, Rb, or Cs fit the patterns indicated in the table, but have distinctly higher refringences.

Refractive index n_X in Tutton's salts, $A_2B(XO_4)_2 \cdot 6H_2O$

a. Sulfates, X = S

Element	B = Mg	Zn	Cd	Mn	Fe	Co	Ni	Cu
A = K	1.4607	1.4775			1.4759	1.4807	1.4836	1.4836
NH$_4$	1.4716	1.4888	1.4847	1.4801	1.4870	1.4902	1.4949	1.4910
Rb	1.4672	1.4833	1.4798	1.4767	1.4815	1.4859	1.4895	1.4886
Cs	1.4857	1.5022	1.4975	1.4946	1.5003	1.5057	1.5087	1.5048
Tl	1.5705	1.5931		1.5861	1.5929	1.6009	1.6024	1.5996

b. Selenates, X = Se

	B = Mg	Zn	Cd	Mn	Fe	Co	Ni	Cu
A = K	1.4969	1.5121			1.5095	1.5158	1.5181	1.5101
NH$_4$	1.5070	1.5240	1.5206	1.5160	1.5216	1.5361	1.5285	1.5201
Rb	1.5011	1.5162		1.5094	1.5133	1.5199	1.5198	1.5153
Cs	1.5178	1.5326		1.5250	1.5306	1.5354	1.5395	1.5282
Tl	1.6250	1.6414		1.6276	1.6352	1.6442	1.6378	

Birefringence $n_Z - n_X$ in Tutton's salts

a. Sulfates, X = S

	B = Mg	Zn	Cd	Mn	Fe	Co	Ni	Cu
A = K	.0148	.0194			.0210	.0197	.0215	.0184
NH$_4$	.0070	.0106	.0112	.0112	.0119	.0130	.0132	.0144
Rb	.0107	.0124	.0150	.0140	.0162	.0155	.0157	.0150
Cs	.0059	.0071	.0087	.0079	.0091	.0075	.0075	.0105
Tl	.0244	.0237		.0223	.0233	.0229	.0200	.0194

b. Selenates, X = Se

	B = Mg	Zn	Cd	Mn	Fe	Co	Ni	Cu
A = K	.0170	.0214			.0250	.0222	.0246	.0248
NH$_4$	.0099	.0145	.0146	.0128	.0165	.0156	.0185	.0186
Rb	.0124	.0169		.0164	.0195	.0170	.0192	.0165
Cs	.0058	.0086		.0088	.0108	.0099	.0094	.0112
Tl	.0154	.0201		.0255	.0237	.0148	.0182	.0324

Optic axial angle, $2V_z$ ($>90°$ if optically negative)

a. Sulfates, X = S

	B = Mg	Zn	Cd	Mn	Fe	Co	Ni	Cu
A = K	47°54′	68°14′			67°07′	68°41′	75°16′	46°32′
NH$_4$	51 11	79 00	72°51′	69°46′	76 25	82 09	86 33	111 57
Rb	48 46	73 33	72 26	67 05	73 21	75 11	82 00	44 42
Cs	16 25	74 11	67 53	59 57	74 51	81 34	92 39	43 24
Tl	105 03	110 36		108 34	111 00	113 21	118 23	94 44

b. Selenates, X = Se

	B = Mg	Zn	Cd	Mn	Fe	Co	Ni	Cu
A = K	39°38′	66°15′			64°18′	62°19′	72°48′	91°33′
NH$_4$	54 47	82 07	76°31′	70°23′	77 44	82 14	86 21	124 53
Rb	47 03	75 08		66 02	73 32	73 37	82 13	126 49
Cs	18 35	83 06		68 49	82 47	86 48	96 52	131 34
Tl	102 27	111 26		107 33	110 24	113 18	121 01	

$A_2B(SO_4)_2 \cdot 6H_2O$ Salts (Sulfates) of Tutton

$K_2Mg(SO_4)_2 \cdot 6H_2O$ (Picromerite) is monoclinic with $a = 9.04$, $b = 12.24$, $c = 6.095$ kX, $\beta = 104°48'$. Crystals nearly equant and short prismatic. Perfect $\{20\bar{1}\}$ cleavage. H. 2.5. G. 2.03. $X \wedge c^{55} = +13°38'$; $X \wedge \{20\bar{1}\}$ cleavage $= 27°50'$ D; $Y = b$. $(+)2V = 47°54'$ D, $r > v$ very

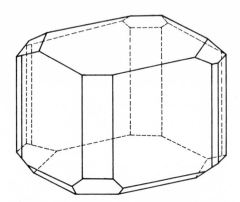

Fig. 7-7. A crystal habit of $K_2Mg(SO_4)_2 \cdot 6H_2O$.

weak.[56] $n_X = 1.4585$ C, 1.4607 D, 1.4658 F, $n_Y = 1.4607$ C, 1.4629 D, 1.4678 F, $n_Z = 1.4731$ C, 1.4755 D, 1.4810 F, $n_Z - n_X = 0.0148$ D. Colorless, white or stained. Made from water solution between $-5°$ and $47.5°$ C.

$(NH_4)_2Mg(SO_4)_2 \cdot 6H_2O$ (Boussingaultite) is monoclinic with $a = 9.28$, $b = 12.57$, $c = 6.20$ kX, $\beta = 107°6'$. Crystals short prismatic. Perfect $\{20\bar{1}\}$ and distinct $\{010\}$ cleavages. H. 2. G. 1.72. $X \wedge c = 4°58'$; $X \wedge \{20\bar{1}\} = 37°53'$; $Y = b$.[56] $(+)2V = 51°11'$, $r > v$ very weak. $n_X = 1.4689$ C, 1.4716 D, 1.4771 F, $n_Y = 1.4705$ C, 1.4730 D, 1.4786 F, $n_Z = 1.4760$ C, 1.4786 D, 1.4842 F, $n_Z - n_X = 0.007$ D. Colorless. Made from water solution between $0°$ and $100°$ C. (or more?).

$Rb_2Mg(SO_4)_2 \cdot 6H_2O$ is monoclinic with[57] $a:b:c = 0.740:1:0.498$, $\beta = 105°59'$. Crystals thick basal tablets to short prismatic. Distinct $\{20\bar{1}\}$ cleavage. G. 2.38. $X \wedge c = +21°14'$; $X \wedge \{20\bar{1}\}$ cleavage $= 20°31'$; $Y = b$. $(+)2V = 49°2'$ C, $48°46'$ D, $48°10'$ F, $r > v$ distinct. $n_X = 1.4650$ C, 1.4672 Na, 1.4724 F, $n_Y = 1.4668$ C, 1.4689 D, 1.4743 F, $n_Z = 1.4759$ C, 1.4779 D, 1.4835 F, $n_Z - n_X = 0.0107$ Na. Colorless. Made from water solution.

[55] The positive sign of the extinction angle signifies that it lies in the obtuse angle between the crystal axes a and c.

[56] Tutton: *Trans. Chem. Soc. London* LXXXVII, p. 1123 (1905). *Zeit. Krist.* XXVII, p. 113 (1897).

[57] Tutton: *Trans. Chem. Soc. London* LXIII, p. 337 (1893) and LXIX, p. 344 (1896).

$Cs_2Mg(SO_4)_2 \cdot 6H_2O$ is monoclinic with[57] $a:b:c = 0.728:1:0.495$, $\beta = 107°6'$. Crystals short prismatic parallel to a. Perfect $\{20\bar{1}\}$ cleavage. G. 2.67. X $\wedge$ $c = +46°43'$; X $\wedge$ $\{20\bar{1}\}$ = 4°47'; the optic plane is (010) for wave-lengths greater than 450 mμ (including daylight) and normal to (010) for shorter wave-lengths (blue and violet). $(+)2V = 18°0'$ C, 16°25' D, 11°15' F, 8° (450 mμ), 7°0' G. $n_X = 1.4832$ C, 1.4857 D, 1.4912 F, $n_Y = 1.4834$ C, 1.4858 D, 1.4912 F, $n_Z = 1.4892$ C, 1.4916 D, 1.4970 F, $n_Z - n_X = 0.0059$ D. Colorless. Made from water solution.

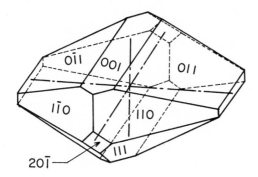

Fig. 7-8. A common crystal habit of $Cs_2Mg(SO_4)_2 \cdot 6H_2O$.

$Tl_2Mg(SO_4)_2 \cdot 6H_2O$ is monoclinic with[58] $a:b:c = 0.744:1:0.500$; $\beta = 106°30'$. Crystals nearly equant with $\{110\}$, $\{011\}$, $\{010\}$, $\{20\bar{1}\}$, etc. Distinct $\{20\bar{1}\}$ cleavage. G. 3.57. X $\wedge$ $c = +80°56'$; X $\wedge$ $\{20\bar{1}\}$ cleavage = 38°49'; Y = b. $(-)2V = 74°42'$ C, 74°57' D, 75°34' F. $n_X = 1.5665$ C, 1.5705 D, 1.5808 F, $n_Y = 1.5841$ C, 1.5884 D, 1.5993 F, $n_Z = 1.5905$ C, 1.5949 D, 1.6063 F, $n_Z - n_X = 0.0244$ D. Colorless. Made from water solution.

$K_2Zn(SO_4)_2 \cdot 6H_2O$ is monoclinic with[57] $a:b:c = 0.741:1:0.504$, $\beta = 104°48'$. Crystals nearly equant, with $\{001\}$, $\{110\}$, etc. Perfect $\{20\bar{1}\}$ cleavage. G. 2.24. X $\wedge$ $c = +10°18'$; X $\wedge$ $\{20\bar{1}\}$ cleavage = 30°52'; Y = b.[56] $(+)2V = 68°16'$ C, 68°14' Na, 68°9' F, r > v very weak. $n_X = 1.4752$ C, 1.4775 D, 1.4826 F, $n_Y = 1.4809$ C, 1.4833 D, 1.4889 F, $n_Z = 1.4942$ C, 1.4969 D, 1.5027 F, $n_Z - n_X = 0.0194$ D. Colorless. PD 4.14, 3.68, 2.37; 1–0421.

$(NH_4)_2Zn(SO_4)_2 \cdot 6H_2O$ is monoclinic[56] with $a:b:c = 0.737:1:0.4997$, $\beta = 106°52'$. Crystals short prismatic to thick basal tablets. Good $\{20\bar{1}\}$ cleavage. H. 2. G. 1.93. X $\wedge$ $c = +7°$; X $\wedge$ $\{20\bar{1}\}$ cleavage = 34°56'; Y = b. $(+)2V = 78°58'$ C, 79° D, 79°3' F, r > v very weak. $n_X = 1.4862$ C, 1.4888 D, 1.4947 F, $n_Y = 1.4904$ C, 1.4930 D, 1.4990 F, $n_Z = 1.4967$ C,

[58] Tutton: *Proc. Roy. Soc. London* A CXVIII, p. 367 (1928).

1.4994 D, 1.5056 F, $n_Z - n_X = 0.0106$ D. Colorless. PD 4.20, 3.78, 3.03; 1–0408.

Rb$_2$Zn(SO$_4$)$_2$·6H$_2$O is monoclinic with[57] $a:b:c = 0.737:1:0.501$, $\beta = 105°53'$. Crystals thick basal tablets with {110}, etc. Distinct {20$\bar{1}$} cleavage. G. 2.58. X $\wedge$ $c = 16°43'$; X $\wedge$ {20$\bar{1}$} cleavage $= 24°50'$; Y $= b$. (+)2V $= 73°40'$ C, 73°33' D, 73°18' F, r > v very weak. $n_X = 1.4811$ C, 1.4833 D, 1.4886 F, $n_Y = 1.4860$ C, 1.4884 D, 1.4938 F, $n_Z = 1.4951$ C, 1.4975 D, 1.5033 F, $n_Z - n_X = 0.0124$ D. Colorless.

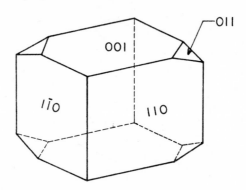

Fig. 7-9. A crystal habit of K$_2$Zn(SO$_4$)$_2$·6H$_2$O.

Cs$_2$Zn(SO$_4$)$_2$·6H$_2$O is monoclinic with[57] $a:b:c = 0.727:1:0.496$, $\beta = 107°1'$. Crystals short prismatic parallel to a, with {011}, {001}, {110}, etc. Distinct {20$\bar{1}$} cleavage. G. 2.87. X $\wedge$ $c = +30°16'$; X $\wedge$ {20$\bar{1}$} cleavage $= 11°30'$; Y $= b$. (+)2V $= 74°27'$ C, 74°11' D, 73°31' F, r > v weak. $n_X = 1.4998$ C, 1.5022 D, 1.5079 F, $n_Y = 1.5024$ C, 1.5048 D, 1.5104 F, $n_Z = 1.5068$ C, 1.5093 D, 1.5152 F, $n_Z - n_X = 0.0071$ D. Colorless.

Tl$_2$Zn(SO$_4$)$_2$·6H$_2$O is monoclinic with[59] $a:b:c = 0.741:1:0.501$, $\beta = 106°16'$. Crystals basal tablets to short prisms. Perfect {20$\bar{1}$} cleavage. G. 3.72. X $\wedge$ $c = +76°31'$; X $\wedge$ {20$\bar{1}$} cleavage $= 55°26'$; Y $= b$. (−)2V $= 69°12'$ C; 69°24' D, 69°55' F, r < v weak. $n_X = 1.5887$ C, 1.5931 D, 1.6033 F, $n_Y = 1.6046$ C, 1.6093 D, 1.6203 F, $n_Z = 1.6119$ C, 1.6168 D, 1.6281 F, $n_Z - n_X = 0.0237$ D. Colorless.

(NH$_4$)$_2$Cd(SO$_4$)$_2$·6H$_2$O is monoclinic with[56] $a:b:c = 0.736:1:0.493$, $\beta = 106°41'$. Crystals short prismatic parallel to a or to c. Distinct {20$\bar{1}$} cleavage. G. 2.06. X $\wedge$ $c = +11°27'$; X $\wedge$ {20$\bar{1}$} cleavage $= 30°56'$; Y $= b$. (+)2V $= 72°46'$ C, 72°51' D, 73°1' F, r < v very weak. $n_X = 1.4821$ C, 1.4847 D, 1.4907 F, $n_Y = 1.4860$ C, 1.4887 D, 1.4947 F, $n_Z = 1.4932$ C, 1.4959 D, 1.5019 F, $n_Z - n_X = 0.0112$ D. Colorless.

[59] Tutton: *Proc. Roy. Soc. London* A LXXXIII, p. 211 (1910).

$Rb_2Cd(SO_4)_2 \cdot 6H_2O$ is monoclinic with[60] $a:b:c = 0.735:1:0.493$, $\beta = 105°53'$. Crystals thick {001} or {20$\bar{1}$} tablets, or short prismatic. G. 2.67. Effloresces easily. Perfect {20$\bar{1}$} cleavage. X $\wedge$ $c = +15°53'$; X $\wedge$ {20$\bar{1}$} cleavage $= 26°4'$; Y $= b$.[56] $(+)2V = 72°21'$ C, $72°26'$ D, $72°37'$ F, r $<$ v very weak, $n_X = 1.4777$ C, 1.4798 D, 1.4856 F, $n_Y = 1.4324$ C, 1.4848 D, 1.4905 F, $n_Z = 1.4923$ C, 1.4948 D, 1.5007 F, $n_Z - n_X = 0.0150$. Colorless.

$Cs_2Cd(SO_4)_2 \cdot 6H_2O$ is monoclinic with[60] $a:b:c = 0.726:1:0.491$, $\beta = 107°11'$. Crystals short prismatic parallel to a or to b. Distinct {20$\bar{1}$} cleavage. Effloresces slowly. G. 2.96. X $\wedge$ $c = +26°56'$; X $\wedge$ {20$\bar{1}$} cleavage $= 15°10'$. Y $= b$. $(+)2V = 68°2'$ C, $67°53'$ D, $67°28'$ F, r $>$ v weak. $n_X = 1.4951$ C, 1.4975 D, 1.5033 F, $n_Y = 1.4976$ C, 1.5000 D, 1.5058 F, $n_Z = 1.5038$ C, 1.5062 D, 1.5023 F, $n_Z - n_X = 0.0087$ D. Colorless.

$(NH_4)_2Mn(SO_4)_2 \cdot 6H_2O$ is monoclinic[61] with $a:b:c = 0.740:1:0.493$, $\beta = 106°51'$. Crystals prismatic. Perfect {20$\bar{1}$} and distinct {001} cleavages. G. 1.83. X $\wedge$ $c = +7°47'$; X $\wedge$ {20$\bar{1}$} cleavage $= 34°56'$; Y $= b$. $(+)2V = 69°46'$ C, $69°49'$ D, $70°2'$ F, r $<$ v very weak. $n_X = 1.4775$ C, 1.4801 D, 1.4858 F, $n_Y = 1.4815$ C, 1.4840 D, 1.4897 F, $n_Z = 1.4887$ C, 1.4913 D, 1.4971 F, $n_Z - n_X = 0.0112$ D. Color pale pink.

$Rb_2Mn(SO_4)_2 \cdot 6H_2O$ is monoclinic[62] with $a:b:c = 0.738:1:0.495$, $\beta = 105°57'$. Crystals basal tablets or short prismatic. Perfect {20$\bar{1}$} cleavage. Unstable. G. 2.46. X $\wedge$ $c = +16°57'$; X $\wedge$ {20$\bar{1}$} cleavage $= 25°2'$; Y $= b$. $(+)2V = 67°8'$ C, $67°5'$ D, $66°55'$ F, r $>$ v very weak. $n_X = 1.4745$ C, 1.4767 D, 1.4821 F, $n_Y = 1.4785$ C, 1.4807 D, 1.4860 F, $n_Z = 1.4884$ C, 1.4907 D, 1.4965 F, $n_Z - n_X = 0.0140$ D. Color rose-red.

$Cs_2Mn(SO_4)_2 \cdot 6H_2O$ is monoclinic[62] with $a:b:c = 0.727:1:0.491$, $\beta = 107°7'$. Crystals short prismatic parallel to a. Perfect {20$\bar{1}$} cleavage. G. 2.74. X $\wedge$ $c = +25°27'$; X $\wedge$ {20$\bar{1}$} cleavage $= 16°45'$; Y $= b$. $(+)2V = 60°7'$ C, $59°57'$ D, $59°28'$ F, r $>$ v very weak. $n_X = 1.4922$ C, 1.4946 D, 1.5003 F, $n_Y = 1.4940$ C, 1.4966 D, 1.5022 F, $n_Z = 1.4999$ C, 1.5025 D, 1.5083 F, $n_Z - n_X = 0.0079$ D. Color rose-red.

$Tl_2Mn(SO_4)_2 \cdot 6H_2O$ is monoclinic with[58] $a:b:c = 0.745:1:0.496$, $\beta = 106°22'$. Crystals basal tablets with large {20$\bar{1}$} faces. Perfect {20$\bar{1}$} cleavage. G. 3.685. X $\wedge$ $c = +75°45'$; X $\wedge$ {20$\bar{1}$} cleavage $= 33°21'$. Y $= b$. $(-)2V = 71°16'$ C, $71°26'$ D, $71°59'$ F, r $<$ v very weak. $n_X = 1.5826$ C, 1.5861 D, 1.5959 F, $n_Y = 1.5960$ C, 1.5996 D, 1.6096 F, $n_Z = 1.6047$ C, 1.6084 D, 1.6186 F, $n_Z - n_X = 0.0223$ D. Color pink.

---

[60] Tutton: *Trans. Roy. Soc. London* A CCXVI, p. 1 (1916); *Trans. Chem. Soc. London* LXIII, p. 337 (1893) and LXIX, p. 344 (1896).
[61] Tutton: *Trans. Roy. Soc. London* A CCXVI, p. 1 (1916); *Trans. Chem. Soc. London* LXXXVII, p. 1123 (1905).
[62] Tutton: *Trans. Roy. Soc. London* A CCXVI, p. 1 (1916); *Trans. Chem. Soc. London* LXIII, p. 337 (1893).

K$_2$Fe(SO$_4$)$_2$·6H$_2$O is monoclinic with[57] $a:b:c = 0.738:1:0.502$, $\beta = 104°32'$. Crystals thick basal tablets. Distinct $\{20\bar{1}\}$ cleavage. Effloresces easily. G. 2.17. X $\wedge$ c = +11°57'; X $\wedge$ $\{20\bar{1}\}$ cleavage = 29°14'; Y = b. (+)2V = 67°2' C, 67°7' D, 67°19' F, r < v very weak. n_X = 1.4735 C, 1.4759 D, 1.4811 F, n_Y = 1.4799 C, 1.4821 D, 1.4877 F, n_Z = 1.4945 C, 1.4969 D, 1.5028 F, $n_Z - n_X$ = 0.0210 D. Color pale green.

(NH$_4$)$_2$Fe(SO$_4$)$_2$·6H$_2$O is monoclinic[63] with $a:b:c = 0.738:1:0.496$, $\beta = 106°50'$. Crystals thick basal tablets or short prisms. Distinct $\{20\bar{1}\}$ cleavage. G. 1.86. X $\wedge$ c = +8°42'; X $\wedge$ $\{20\bar{1}\}$ cleavage = 33°32'; Y = b. (+)2V = 76°18' C, 76°25' D, 76°33' F, r > v very weak. n_X = 1.4844 C, 1.4870 D, 1.4926 F, n_Y = 1.4890 C, 1.4915 D, 1.4972 F, n_Z = 1.4962 C, 1.4989 D, 1.5047 F, $n_Z - n_X$ = 0.0119 D. Color pale bluish green. PD 4.20, 3.80, 3.03; 1–0405.

Rb$_2$Fe(SO$_4$)$_2$·6H$_2$O is monoclinic with[57] $a:b:c = 0.738:1:0.5004$, $\beta = 105°44'$. Crystals clinodomatic to $\{001\}$ tablets. Distinct $\{20\bar{1}\}$ cleavage. G. 2.52. X $\wedge$ c = +17°9', X $\wedge$ $\{20\bar{1}\}$ cleavage = 24°27'. Y = b. (+)2V = 73°23' C, 73°21' D, 73°13' F, r > v very weak. n_X = 1.4793 C, 1.4815 D, 1.4870 F, n_Y = 1.4851 C, 1.4874 D, 1.4929 F, n_Z = 1.4953 C, 1.4977 D, 1.5034 F, $n_Z - n_X$ = 0.0162 D. Color pale green.

Cs$_2$Fe(SO$_4$)$_2$·6H$_2$O is monoclinic with[57] $a:b:c = 0.726:1:0.495$, $\beta = 106°52'$. Crystals short clinodomatic. Distinct $\{20\bar{1}\}$ cleavage. G. 2.80. X $\wedge$ c = +28°17', X $\wedge$ $\{20\bar{1}\}$ cleavage = 13°27'; Y = b. (+)2V = 75°0' C, 74°51' D, 74°31' F, r > v very weak. n_X = 1.4980 C, 1.5003 D, 1.5061 F, n_Y = 1.5011 C, 1.5035 D, 1.5093 F, n_Z = 1.5069 C, 1.5094 D, 1.5153 F, $n_Z - n_X$ = 0.0091 D. Color pale green.

Tl$_2$Fe(SO$_4$)$_2$·6H$_2$O is monoclinic with[58] $a:b:c = 0.743:1:0.4999$, $\beta = 106°16'$. Crystals $\{20\bar{1}\}$ tablets. Distinct $\{20\bar{1}\}$ cleavage. G. 3.65. X $\wedge$ c = +73°45'; X $\wedge$ $\{20\bar{1}\}$ cleavage = 31°42'; Y = b. (−)2V = 68°46' C, 69°0' D, 69°59' F, r < v weak. n_X = 1.5886 C, 1.5929 D, 1.6040 F, n_Y = 1.6048 C, 1.6093 D, 1.6209 F, n_Z = 1.6117 C, 1.6162 D, 1.6292 F, $n_Z - n_X$ = 0.0233 D. Color pale green.

K$_2$Co(SO$_4$)$_2$·6H$_2$O is monoclinic with[57] $a:b:c = 0.740:1:0.504$, $\beta = 104°55'$. Crystals short prismatic basal tablets as in Fig. 7-10. Distinct $\{20\bar{1}\}$ cleavage. G. 2.21. X $\wedge$ c = +10°5'; X $\wedge$ $\{20\bar{1}\}$ cleavage = 31°12'; Y = b. (+)2V = 68°39' C, 68°41' D, 68°48' F, r < v very weak. n_X = 1.4784 C, 1.4807 D, 1.4861 F, n_Y = 1.4842 C, 1.4865 D, 1.4919 F, n_Z = 1.4977 C, 1.5004 D, 1.5059 F, $n_Z - n_X$ = 0.0197 D. Color ruby-red and pleochroic with X violet-red, Y yellow, Z yellowish pink.

(NH$_4$)$_2$Co(SO$_4$)$_2$·6H$_2$O) is monoclinic with[61] $a:b:c = 0.739:1:0.498$, $\beta = 107°2'$. Crystals short prismatic or basal tablets. Distinct $\{20\bar{1}\}$ cleavage. G. 1.90. X $\wedge$ c = +6°19'; X $\wedge$ $\{20\bar{1}\}$ cleavage = 35°57'; Y = b.

[63] Tutton: *Proc. Roy. Soc. London* A LXXXVIII, p. 361 (1913).

$(+)2V = 82°2'$ C, $82°9'$ D, $82°27'$ F, r < v very weak. $n_X = 1.4876$ C, 1.4902 D, 1.4964 F, $n_Y = 1.4927$ C, 1.4953 D, 1.5014 F, $n_Z = 1.5006$ C, 1.5032 D, 1.5094 F, $n_Z - n_X = 0.0130$ D. Color ruby-red. PD 4.20, 3.79, 5.4; 1–0407.

$Rb_2Co(SO_4)_2 \cdot 6H_2O$ is monoclinic with[57] $a:b:c = 0.739:1:0.501$, $\beta = 106°1'$. Crystals short prismatic to thick basal tablets. Perfect $\{20\bar{1}\}$ cleavage. G. 2.56. X $\wedge$ $c = +16°1'$; X $\wedge$ $\{20\bar{1}\}$ cleavage $= 25°36'$; Y $= b$. $(+)2V = 75°14'$ C, $75°11'$ D, $75°3'$ F, r > v very weak. $n_X = 1.4837$ C, 1.4859 D, 1.4910 F, $n_Y = 1.4893$ C, 1.4916 D, 1.4968 F, $n_Z = 1.4989$ C, 1.5014 D, 1.5068 F, $n_Z - n_X = 0.0155$ D. Color ruby-red.

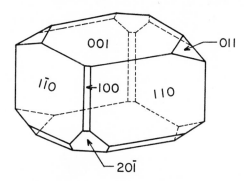

Fig. 7-10. A crystal habit of $K_2Co(SO_4)_2 \cdot 6H_2O$.

$Cs_2Co(SO_4)_2 \cdot 6H_2O$ is monoclinic with[57] $a:b:c = 0.727:1:0.497$. $\beta = 107°8'$. Crystals clinodomatic. Distinct $\{20\bar{1}\}$ cleavage. G. 2.84. X $\wedge$ $c = +36°8'$; X $\wedge$ $\{20\bar{1}\}$ cleavage $= 15°36'$; Y $= b$. $(+)2V = 81°40'$ C, $81°34'$ D, $81°22$ F, r > v very weak. $n_X = 1.5032$ C, 1.5057 D, 1.5112 F, $n_Y = 1.5061$ C, 1.5085 D, 1.5142 F, $n_Z = 1.5106$ C, 1.5132 D, 1.5187 F, $n_Z - n_X = 0.0075$ D. Color brownish red.

$Tl_2Co(SO_4)_2 \cdot 6H_2O$ is monoclinic with[64] $a:b:c = 0.741:1:0.4995$, $\beta = 106°25'$. Crystals short prismatic or basal tablets. Distinct $\{20\bar{1}\}$ and poor $\{010\}$ cleavages. G. 3.78. X $\wedge$ $c = +74°20'$; X $\wedge$ $\{20\bar{1}\}$ cleavage $= 32°22'$; Y $= b$. $(-)2V = 66°7'$ C, $66°39'$ D, $67°8'$ Tl, r < v distinct with weak inclined dispersion. $n_X = 1.5965$ C, 1.6009 D, 1.6121 F, $n_Y = 1.6128$ C, 1.6176 D, 1.6293 F, $n_Z = 1.6188$ C, 1.6238 D, 1.6359 F, $n_Z - n_X = 0.0229$ D. Color ruby-red. Difficultly made from water solution.

$K_2Ni(SO_4)_2 \cdot 6H_2O$ is monoclinic with[57] $a:b:c = 0.738:1:0.502$, $\beta = 105°0'$. Crystals short prismatic to thick basal tablets. Perfect $\{20\bar{1}\}$ cleavage. G. 2.23. X $\wedge$ $c = +8°42'$; X $\wedge$ $\{20\bar{1}\}$ cleavage $= 32°34'$; Y $= b$. $(+)2V = 75°19'$ C, $75°16'$ D, $75°9'$ F, r > v very weak. $n_X = 1.4813$ C,

[64] Tutton: *Proc. Roy. Soc. London* A CVIII, p. 240 (1925).

1.4836 D, 1.4889 F, $n_Y = 1.4893$ C, 1.4916 D, 1.4972 F, $n_Z = 1.5026$ C, 1.5051 D, 1.5109 F, $n_Z - n_X = 0.0215$. Color bright green.

$(NH_4)_2Ni(SO_4)_2 \cdot 6H_2O$ is monoclinic with[61] $a:b:c = 0.737:1:0.500$, $\beta = 106°57'$. Crystals short prisms or basal tablets. Distinct $\{20\bar{1}\}$ and $\{010\}$ cleavages. G. 1.92. $X \wedge c = +5°12'$; $X \wedge \{20\bar{1}\}$ cleavage $= 36°40'$; $Y = b$. $(+)2V = 86°33'$, r < v very weak. $n_X = 1.4921$ C, 1.4949 D, 1.5007 F, $n_Y = 1.4980$ C, 1.5007 D, 1.5069 F, $n_Z = 1.5051$ C, 1.5081 D, 1.5142 F, $n_Z - n_X = 0.0132$ D. Color deep bluish green. PD 4.16, 3.76, 5.4; 1–0419.

$Rb_2Ni(SO_4)_2 \cdot 6H_2O$ is monoclinic with[57] $a:b:c = 0.735:1:0.502$, $\beta = 106°3'$. Crystals short prismatic to basal tablets. Good $\{20\bar{1}\}$ cleavage. G. 2.58. $X \wedge c = +12°38'$; $X \wedge \{20\bar{1}\}$ cleavage $= 28°49'$; $Y = b$. $(+)2V = 82°4'$ C, 82°0' D, 81°48' F, r > v very weak. $n_X = 1.4872$ C, 1.4895 D, 1.4949 F, $n_Y = 1.4937$ C, 1.4961 D, 1.5017 F, $n_Z = 1.5027$ C, 1.5052 D, 1.5110 F, $n_Z - n_X = 0.0157$ D. Color deep green.

$Cs_2Ni(SO_4)_2 \cdot 6H_2O$ is monoclinic with[57] $a:b:c = 0.727:1:0.498$, $\beta = 107°2'$. Crystals clinodomatic. Distinct $\{20\bar{1}\}$ cleavage. G. 2.87. $X \wedge c = +24°7'$; $X \wedge \{20\bar{1}\}$ cleavage $= 17°27'$; $Y = b$.[56] $(-)2V = 87°17'$ C, 87°21' D, 87°40' F, r < v very weak. $n_X = 1.5065$ C, 1.5087 D, 1.5146 F, $n_Y = 1.5104$ C, 1.5129 D, 1.5187 F, $n_Z = 1.5137$ C, 1.5162 D, 1.5221 F, $n_Z - n_X = 0.0075$ D. Color bright green.

$Tl_2Ni(SO_4)_2 \cdot 6H_2O$ is monoclinic with[64] $a:b:c = 0.740:1:0.4997$, $\beta = 106°23'$. Crystals short clinodomatic. Distinct $\{20\bar{1}\}$ cleavage. G. 3.77. $X \wedge c = +75°20'$; $X \wedge \{20\bar{1}\}$ cleavage $= 33°23'$; $Y = b$. $(-)2V = 60°58'$ C, 61°37' D, 63°11' F, r < v strong. $n_X = 1.5990$ C, 1.6024 D, 1.6115 F, $n_Y = 1.6150$ C, 1.6183 D, 1.6280 F, $n_Z = 1.6190$ C, 1.6224 D, 1.6324 F, $n_Z - n_X = 0.0200$ D. Again:[65] $n_X = 1.6025$ D, $n_Y = 1.6184$, $n_Z = 1.6252$, $n_Z - n_X = 0.0227$ D. Color green. Difficultly made from water solution.

$K_2Cu(SO_4)_2 \cdot 6H_2O$ (Cyanochroite) is monoclinic with[61] $a:b:c = 0.749:1:0.5088$, $\beta = 104°28'$. Crystals thick basal tablets. Perfect $\{20\bar{1}\}$ cleavage. G. 2.23. $X \wedge c = +18°33'$; $X \wedge \{20\bar{1}\}$ cleavage $= 22°36'$; $Y = b$. $(+)2V = 46°6'$ C, 46°32' D, 47°33' F, r < v distinct. $n_X = 1.4811$ C, 1.4836 D, 1.4893 F, $n_Y = 1.4838$ C, 1.4864 D, 1.4922 F, $n_Z = 1.4994$ C, 1.5020 D, 1.5081 F, $n_Z - n_X = 0.0184$ D. Color greenish blue. PD 3.68, 4.21, 2.37; 1–0507.

$(NH_4)_2Cu(SO_4)_2 \cdot 6H_2O$ is monoclinic with[61] $a:b:c = 0.746:1:0.507$, $\beta = 106°9'$. Crystals short prisms or thick basal tablets. Perfect $\{010\}$ and distinct $\{20\bar{1}\}$ cleavages. G. 1.93. $X \wedge c = +18°47'$; $X \wedge \{20\bar{1}\}$ cleavage $= 22°49'$; $Y = b$. $(-)2V = 68°57'$ C, 68°31' D, 66°55' F, r > v distinct. $n_X = 1.4883$ C, 1.4910 D, 1.4971 F, $n_Y = 1.4977$ C, 1.5007 D,

[65] Merwin: *Int. Crit. Tables*, VII, p. 31 (1930).

1.5067 F, n_Z = 1.5025 C, 1.5054 D, 1.5116 F, $n_Z - n_X$ = 0.0144 D. Color pale blue. PD 4.19, 3.74, 5.4; 1–0410.

$Rb_2Cu(SO_4)_2 \cdot 6H_2O$ is monoclinic with[62] $a:b:c$ = 0.749:1:0.503, β = 105°18′. Crystals basal tablets or short prisms. Good $\{20\bar{1}\}$ cleavage. G. 2.57. X $\wedge$ c = +26°28′; X $\wedge$ $\{20\bar{1}\}$ cleavage = 15°20′; Y = b. (+)2V = 44°29′ C, 44°42′ D, 45°15′ F, r > v very weak. n_X = 1.4862 C, 1.4886 D, 1.4943 F, n_Y = 1.4882 C, 1.4906 D, 1.4966 F, n_Z = 1.5011 C, 1.5036 D, 1.5098 F, $n_Z - n_X$ = 0.0150 D. Color pale greenish blue.

$Cs_2Cu(SO_4)_2 \cdot 6H_2O$ is monoclinic with[65] $a:b:c$ = 0.743:1:0.495, β = 106°10′. Crystals clinodomatic to short prismatic. Distinct $\{20\bar{1}\}$ cleavage. G. 2.86. X $\wedge$ c = +42°47′; X $\wedge$ $\{20\bar{1}\}$ cleavage = 0°37′. (+)2V = 43°9′ C, 43°24′ D, 44°3′ F, r < v weak. n_X = 1.5021 C, 1.5048 D, 1.5108 F, n_Y = 1.5036 C, 1.5061 D, 1.5123 F, n_Z = 1.5126 C, 1.5153 D, 1.5216 F, $n_Z - n_X$ = 0.0105 D. Color pale greenish blue.

$Tl_2Cu(SO_4)_2 \cdot 6H_2O$ is monoclinic with[58] $a:b:c$ = 0.750:1:0.503, β = 105°33′. Crystals equant to basal tablets with $\{110\}$, $\{011\}$, and $\{20\bar{1}\}$ prominent. Distinct $\{20\bar{1}\}$ cleavage. G. 3.73. X $\wedge$ c = −72°40′; X $\wedge$ $\{20\bar{1}\}$ cleavage = 30°29′; Y = b. (−)2V = 85°21′ C, 85°16′ D, 85°2′ F, r > v very weak. n_X = 1.5950 C, 1.5996 D, 1.6120 F, n_Y = 1.6050 C, 1.6096 D, 1.6222 F, n_Z = 1.6144 C, 1.6190 D, 1.6318 F, $n_Z - n_X$ = 0.0194 D. Color bright blue.

$A_2B(SeO_4)_2 \cdot 6H_2O$ SALTS (SELENATES) OF TUTTON

$K_2Mg(SeO_4)_2 \cdot 6H_2O$ is monoclinic with[66] $a:b:c$ = 0.749:1:0.503, β = 104°18′. Crystals short prismatic to basal tablets. Distinct $\{20\bar{1}\}$ cleavage. G. 2.36. X $\wedge$ c = +11°18′; X $\wedge$ $\{20\bar{1}\}$ cleavage = 30°7′; Y = b. (+)2V = 39°42′ C, 39°38′ D, 39°25′ F, r > v very weak. n_X = 1.4941 C, 1.4969 D, 1.5035 F, n_Y = 1.4963 C, 1.4991 D, 1.5058 F, n_Z = 1.5108 C, 1.5139 D, 1.5210 F, $n_Z - n_X$ = 0.0170 D. Colorless.

$(NH_4)_2Mg(SeO_4)_2 \cdot 6H_2O$ is monoclinic[61] with $a:b:c$ = 0.742:1:0.497. β = 106°27′. Crystals short prisms or thick basal tablets. Perfect $\{20\bar{1}\}$ cleavage. G. 2.06. X $\wedge$ c = +0°13′; X $\wedge$ $\{20\bar{1}\}$ cleavage = 31°59′; Y = b. (+)2V = 54°55′ C, 54°47′ D, 54°4′ F, r > v very weak. n_X = 1.5038 C, 1.5070 D, 1.5144 F, n_Y = 1.5060 C, 1.5093 D, 1.5166 F, n_Z = 1.5136 C, 1.5169 D, 1.5242 F, $n_Z - n_X$ = 0.0099 D. Colorless.

$Rb_2Mg(SeO_4)_2 \cdot 6H_2O$ is monoclinic with[66] $a:b:c$ = 0.742:1:0.501, β = 105°14′. Crystals thick basal tablets to short prisms. Distinct $\{20\bar{1}\}$ cleavage. G. 2.68. X $\wedge$ c = +16°24′; X $\wedge$ $\{20\bar{1}\}$ cleavage = 25°13′; Y = b. (+)2V = 47°24′ C, 47°3′ D, 46°6′ F, r > v weak. n_X = 1.4983 C, 1.5011 D, 1.5077 F, n_Y = 1.5002 C, 1.5031 D, 1.5098 F, n_Z = 1.5105 C, 1.5135 D, 1.5205 F, $n_Z - n_X$ = 0.0124 D. Colorless.

[66] Tutton: *Trans. Roy. Soc. London* A CXCVII, p. 255 (1901).

Cs₂Mg(SeO₄)₂·6H₂O is monoclinic with[66] $a:b:c = 0.731:1:0.496$, $\beta = 106°17'$. Crystals prismatic parallel to a. Distinct {20$\bar{1}$} cleavage. G. 2.94. $X \wedge c = +36°47'$; $X \wedge$ {20$\bar{1}$} cleavage $= 4°59'$. The optic plane is (010) for wave-lengths greater than 466 mμ and normal thereto for shorter wave-lengths (blue). $(+)2V = 20°34'$ C, $18°35'$ D, $10°30'$ F, $0°$ (466 mμ), $12°49'$ G. At 78° C. it is uniaxial for Na light. $n_X = 1.5148$ C, 1.5178 D, 1.5248 F, $n_Y = 1.5150$ C, 1.5179 D, 1.5248 F, $n_Z = 1.5206$ C, 1.5236 D, 1.5308 F, $n_Z - n_X = 0.0058$ D. Colorless.

Tl₂Mg(SeO₄)₂·6H₂O is monoclinic with[58] $a:b:c = 0.749:1:0.499$, $\beta = 105°36'$. Crystals basal tablets with {001}, {110}, {011}, etc. Distinct {20$\bar{1}$} cleavage. G. 3.72. $X \wedge c = +85°33'$; $X \wedge$ {20$\bar{1}$} cleavage $= 43°27'$; $Y = b$. $(-)2V = 77°20'$ C, $77°33'$ D, $78°10'$ F, $r < v$ weak. $n_X = 1.6210$ C, 1.6250 D, 1.6363 F, $n_Y = 1.6297$ C, 1.6337 D, 1.6452 F, $n_Z = 1.6364$ C, 1.6404 D, 1.6521 F, $n_Z - n_X = 0.0154$ D. Colorless. Made from water solution containing an excess of magnesium selenate.

K₂Zn(SeO₄)₂·6H₂O is monoclinic with[67] $a:b:c = 0.746:1:0.507$. $\beta = 104°12'$. Crystals short prisms to thick basal tablets. Distinct {20$\bar{1}$} cleavage. G. 2.55. $X \wedge c = +9°9'$; $X \wedge$ {20$\bar{1}$} cleavage $= 31°51'$; $Y = b$. $(+)2V = 66°13'$ C, $66°15'$ D, $66°20'$ F, $r < v$ very weak. $n_X = 1.5092$ C, 1.5121 D, 1.5189 F, $n_Y = 1.5151$ C, 1.5181 D, 1.5252 F, $n_Z = 1.5302$ C, 1.5335 D, 1.5410 F, $n_Z - n_X = 0.0214$ D. Colorless.

(NH₄)₂Zn(SeO₄)₂·6H₂O is monoclinic with[61] $a:b:c = 0.741:1:0.504$, $\beta = 106°14'$. Crystals short prisms or thick {001} tablets. Perfect {20$\bar{1}$} cleavage. G. 2.26. $X \wedge c = +3°24'$; $X \wedge$ {20$\bar{1}$} cleavage $= 38°14'$; $Y = b$. $(+)2V = 82°5'$ C, $82°7'$ D, $82°10'$ F, $r < v$ very weak. $n_X = 1.5206$ C, 1.5240 D, 1.5316 F, $n_Y = 1.5265$ C, 1.5300 D, 1.5378 F, $n_Z = 1.5349$ C, 1.5385 D, 1.5463 F, $n_Z - n_X = 0.0145$ D. Colorless.

Rb₂Zn(SeO₄)₂·6H₂O is monoclinic with[67] $a:b:c = 0.743:1:0.502$, $\beta = 105°16'$. Crystals thick basal tablets or short prisms. Perfect {20$\bar{1}$} cleavage. G. 2.86. $X \wedge c = +13°13'$; $X \wedge$ {20$\bar{1}$} cleavage $= 28°21'$; $Y = b$. $(+)2V = 75°14'$ C, $75°8'$ D, $74°55'$ F, $r > v$ very weak. $n_X = 1.5134$ C, 1.5162 D, 1.5233 F, $n_Y = 1.5193$ C, 1.5222 D, 1.5293 F, $n_Z = 1.5299$ C, 1.5331 D, 1.5405 F, $n_Z - n_X = 0.0169$ D. Colorless.

Cs₂Zn(SeO₄)₂·6H₂O is monoclinic with[67] $a:b:c = 0.731:1:0.497$, $\beta = 106°11'$. Crystals prismatic parallel to a. Perfect {20$\bar{1}$} cleavage. G. 3.12. $X \wedge c = +21°57'$; $X \wedge$ {20$\bar{1}$} cleavage $= 19°48'$; $Y = b$. $(+)2V = 83°30'$ C, $83°6'$ D, $82°14'$ F, $r > v$ weak. $n_X = 1.5295$ C, 1.5326 D, 1.5399 F, $n_Y = 1.5331$ C, 1.5362 D, 1.5435 F, $n_Z = 1.5380$ C, 1.5412 D, 1.5488 F, $n_Z - n_X = 0.0086$. Colorless.

Tl₂Zn(SeO₄)₂·6H₂O is monoclinic with[58] $a:b:c = 0.748:1:0.502$, $\beta = $

---

[67] Tutton: *Proc. Roy. Soc. London* A LXVII, p. 58 (1900); *Zeit. Krist.* XXXIII, p. 1 (1900).

$105°54'$. Crystals basal tablets with $\{110\}$, $\{100\}$ and $\{010\}$ or $\{20\bar{1}\}$, $\{110\}$ and $\{011\}$. Distinct $\{20\bar{1}\}$ cleavage. G. 3.96. X $\wedge$ $c = +83°14'$; X $\wedge$ $\{20\bar{1}\}$ cleavage $= 41°14'$; Y $= b$. $(-)2V = 68°15'$ C, $68°34'$ D, $69°30'$ F, r $<$ v weak. $n_X = 1.6358$ C, 1.6414 D, 1.6576 F, $n_Y = 1.6481$ C, 1.6539 D, 1.6706 F, $n_Z = 1.6555$ C, 1.6615 D, 1.6793 F, $n_Z - n_X = 0.0201$ D. Colorless.

$(NH_4)_2Cd(SeO_4)_2 \cdot 6H_2O$ is monoclinic with[68] $a:b:c = 0.742:1:0.503$, $\beta = 106°1'$. Crystals $\{001\}$ or $\{20\bar{1}\}$ tablets or varied. Distinct $\{20\bar{1}\}$ cleavage. G. 2.45. X $\wedge$ $c = 6°0'$; X $\wedge$ $\{20\bar{1}\}$ cleavage $= 35°44'$; Y $= b$. $(+)2V = 76°11'$ C, $76°31'$ D, $77°13'$ F, r $<$ v weak. $n_X = 1.5172$ C, 1.5206 D, 1.5283 F, $n_Y = 1.5227$ C, 1.5260 D, 1.5338 F, $n_Z = 1.5317$ C, 1.5352 D, 1.5427 F, $n_Z - n_X = 0.0146$ D. Colorless. Made from water solution at about $0°$ C.

$(NH_4)_2Mn(SeO_4)_2 \cdot 6H_2O$ is monoclinic with[69] $a:b:c = 0.743:1:0.499$, $\beta = 106°16'$. Crystals basal tablets, prisms or varied. Perfect $\{010\}$ and distinct $\{20\bar{1}\}$ cleavages. G. 2.16. X $\wedge$ $c = +3°22'$; X $\wedge$ $\{20\bar{1}\}$ cleavage $= 38°42'$; Y $= b$. $(+)2V = 70°18'$ C, $70°23'$ D, $70°34'$ F, r $<$ v very weak. $n_X = 1.5129$ C, 1.5160 D, 1.5235 F, $n_Y = 1.5169$ C, 1.5202 D, 1.5276 F, $n_Z = 1.5255$ C, 1.5288 D, 1.5364 F, $n_Z - n_X = 0.0128$ D. Color pink.

$Rb_2Mn(SeO_4)_2 \cdot 6H_2O$ is monoclinic with[69] $a:b:c = 0.742:1:0.501$, $\beta = 105°9'$. Crystals basal tablets or short prisms. Good $\{20\bar{1}\}$ cleavage. G. 2.76. X $\wedge$ $c = +13°7'$; X $\wedge$ $\{20\bar{1}\}$ cleavage $= 28°27'$; Y $= b$. $(+)2V = 66°5'$ C, $66°2'$ D, $65°52'$ F, r $<$ v very weak. $n_X = 1.5064$ C, 1.5094 D, 1.5163 F, $n_Y = 1.5110$ C, 1.5140 D, 1.5210 F, $n_Z = 1.5226$ C, 1.5258 D, 1.5332 F, $n_Z - n_X = 0.0164$ D. Color pale pink.

$Cs_2Mn(SeO_4)_2 \cdot 6H_2O$ is monoclinic with[69] $a:b:c = 0.732:1:0.496$, $\beta = 106°22'$. Crystals short prismatic parallel to a or to c. Perfect $\{20\bar{1}\}$ cleavage. G. 3.01. X $\wedge$ $c = +22°11'$; X $\wedge$ $\{20\bar{1}\}$ cleavage $= 19°36'$; Y $= b$. $(+)2V = 69°1'$ C, $68°49'$ D, $68°5'$ F, r $>$ v weak. $n_X = 1.5220$ C, 1.5250 D, 1.5323 F, $n_Y = 1.5248$ C, 1.5279 D, 1.5350 F, $n_Z = 1.5306$ C, 1.5338 D, 1.5415 F, $n_Z - n_X = 0.0088$ D. Color pink.

$Tl_2Mn(SeO_4)_2 \cdot 6H_2O$ is monoclinic with[58] $a:b:c = 0.746:1:0.499$, $\beta = 105°29'$. Crystals $\{001\}$ tablets with $\{110\}$. Distinct $\{20\bar{1}\}$ cleavage. G. 3.83. X $\wedge$ $c = +81°39'$; X $\wedge$ $\{20\bar{1}\}$ cleavage $= 39°43'$; Y $= b$. $(-)2V = 72°4'$ C, $72°27'$ D, $73°32'$ F, $n_X = 1.6219$ C, 1.6276 D, 1.6422 F, $n_Y = 1.6370$ C, 1.6429 D, 1.6579 F, $n_Z = 1.6470$ C, 1.6531 D, 1.6685 F, $n_O - n_X = 0.0255$ D. Color pink. Made from water solution with an excess of manganese selenate.

[68] Tutton: *Proc. Roy. Soc. London* A CI, p. 245 (1922).
[69] Tutton: *Proc. Roy. Soc. London* A CI, p. 225 (1922).

$K_2Fe(SeO_4)_2 \cdot 6H_2O$ is monoclinic with[70] $a:b:c = 0.749:1:0.504$, $\beta = 103°50'$. Crystals thick basal tablets or short prisms. Good $\{20\bar{1}\}$ cleavage. G. 2.49. $X \wedge c = +10°27'$; $X \wedge \{20\bar{1}\}$ cleavage $= 30°45'$; $Y = b$. $(+)2V = 64°12'$ C, $64°18'$ D, $64°36'$ F, $r < v$ very weak. $n_X = 1.5064$ C, 1.5095 D, 1.5164 F, $n_Y = 1.5149$ C, 1.5182 D, 1.5253 F, $n_Z = 1.5311$ C, 1.5345 D, 1.5421 F, $n_Z - n_X = 0.0250$ D. Color pale green. Made from water solution at $0°$ C. Dehydrates quickly at ordinary temperature.

$(NH_4)_2Fe(SeO_4)_2 \cdot 6H_2O$ is monoclinic with[70] $a:b:c = 0.743:1:0.502$, $\beta = 106°9'$. Crystals thick basal tablets or short prisms. Good $\{20\bar{1}\}$ cleavage. G. 2.19. $X \wedge c = +5°24'$; $X \wedge \{20\bar{1}\}$ cleavage $= 36°28'$; $Y = b$. $(+)2V = 77°37'$ C, $77°44'$ D, $77°54'$ F, $r < v$ very weak. $n_X = 1.5182$ C, 1.5216 D, 1.5291 F, $n_Y = 1.5246$ C, 1.5280 D, 1.5354 F, $n_Z = 1.5348$ C, 1.5381 D, 1.5457 F, $n_Z - n_X = 0.0165$ D. Color very pale yellowish green. Made from water solution at $0°$ C.

$Rb_2Fe(SeO_4)_2 \cdot 6H_2O$ is monoclinic with[70] $a:b:c = 0.742:1:0.500$, $\beta = 104°57'$. Crystals clinodomatic to basal tablets. Distinct $\{20\bar{1}\}$ cleavage. G. 2.80. $X \wedge c = +13°37'$; $X \wedge \{20\bar{1}\}$ cleavage $= 27°56'$; $Y = b$. $(+)2V = 73°34'$ C, $73°32'$ D, $73°26$ F, $r > v$ very weak. $n_X = 1.5104$ C, 1.5133 D, 1.5202 F, $n_Y = 1.5170$ C, 1.5200 D, 1.5272 F, $n_Z = 1.5295$ C, 1.5328 D, 1.5404 F. $n_Z - n_X = 0.0195$ D. Color pale bluish green. Made from water solution at about $0°$ C.

$Cs_2Fe(SeO_4)_2 \cdot 6H_2O$ is monoclinic with[70] $a:b:c = 0.731:1:0.498$, $\beta = 106°2'$. Crystals clinodomatic. Perfect $\{20\bar{1}\}$ cleavage. G. 3.05. $X \wedge c = +21°4'$; $X \wedge \{20\bar{1}\}$ cleavage $= 20°27'$; $Y = b$. $(+)2V = 82°56'$ C, $82°47'$ D, $82°20'$ F, $r > v$ very weak. $n_X = 1.5274$ C, 1.5306 D, 1.5379 F, $n_Y = 1.5322$ C, 1.5352 D, 1.5425 F, $n_Z = 1.5384$ C, 1.5414 D, 1.5491 F, $n_Z - n_X = 0.0108$ D. Color very pale bluish green. Made from water solution at $0°$ C.

$Tl_2Fe(SeO_4)_2 \cdot 6H_2O$ is monoclinic with[58] $a:b:c = 0.745:1:0.501$, $\beta = 105°27'$. Crystals thick $\{001\}$ tablets with $\{110\}$, $\{011\}$, $\{100\}$, $\{20\bar{1}\}$, etc. Distinct $\{20\bar{1}\}$ cleavage. G. 3.94. $X \wedge c = +80°51'$; $X \wedge \{20\bar{1}\}$ cleavage $= 39°2'$; $Y = b$. $(-)2V = 69°5'$ C, $69°36'$ D, $70°45'$ F, $r < v$ weak. $n_X = 1.6297$ C, 1.6352 D, 1.6496 F, $n_Y = 1.6459$ C, 1.6514 D, 1.6662 F, $n_Z = 1.6533$ C, 1.6589 D, 1.6743 F, $n_Z - n_X = 0.0237$ D. Color of fresh crystals very pale green, slowly becoming yellowish green. Made from water solution with an excess of iron selenate.

$K_2Co(SeO_4)_2 \cdot 6H_2O$ is monoclinic[71] with $a:b:c = 0.752:1:0.506$, $\beta = 104°17'$. Crystals short prismatic to basal tablets. Perfect $\{20\bar{1}\}$ cleavage. G. 2.53. $X \wedge c = +8°54'$; $X \wedge \{20\bar{1}\}$ cleavage $= 32°25'$; $Y = b$. $(+)2V$

[70] Tutton: *Trans. Roy. Soc. London* A CCXVII, p. 395 (1919); *Proc. Roy. Soc. London* A XCIV, p. 352 (1918).
[71] Tutton: *Proc. Roy. Soc. London* A XCVI, p. 156 (1920).

$= 62°13'$ C, $62°19'$ D, $62°27'$ F, r $<$ v very weak. $n_X = 1.5127$ C, 1.5158 D, 1.5231 F, $n_Y = 1.5186$ C, 1.5218 D, 1.5291 F, $n_Z = 1.5347$ C, 1.5380 D, 1.5456 F, $n_Z - n_X = 0.0222$ D. Color ruby-red.

$(NH_4)_2Co(SeO_4)_2 \cdot 6H_2O$ is monoclinic with[71] $a:b:c = 0.745:1:0.503$, $\beta = 106°23'$. Crystals $\{001\}$ tablets with $\{110\}$ and $\{011\}$. Perfect $\{20\bar{1}\}$ and poor $\{010\}$ cleavages. G. 2.23. X $\wedge$ $c = +2°23'$; X $\wedge$ $\{20\bar{1}\}$ cleavage $= 39°30'$; Y $= b$. $(+)2V = 82°6'$ C, $82°14'$ D, $82°28'$ F, r $<$ v very weak. $n_X = 1.5228$ C, 1.5261 D, 1.5335 F, $n_Y = 1.5292$ C, 1.5327 D, 1.5401 F, $n_Z = 1.5382$ C, 1.5417 D, 1.5496 F, $n_Z - n_X = 0.0156$ D. Color ruby-red.

$Rb_2Co(SeO_4)_2 \cdot 6H_2O$ is monoclinic with[71] $a:b:c = 0.743:1:0.502$, $\beta = 105°14'$. Crystals basal tablets to short prisms. Perfect $\{20\bar{1}\}$ cleavage. G. 2.84. X $\wedge$ $c = +12°50'$; X $\wedge$ $\{20\bar{1}\}$ cleavage $= 28°41'$; Y $= b$. $(+)2V = 73°41'$ C, $73°37'$ D, $73°33'$ F, r $<$ v very weak. $n_X = 1.5163$ C, 1.5199 D, 1.5273 F, $n_Y = 1.5225$ C, 1.5256 D, 1.5332 F, $n_Z = 1.5334$ C, 1.5369 D, 1.5446 F, $n_Z - n_X = 0.0170$ D. Color ruby-red.

$Cs_2Co(SeO_4)_2 \cdot 6H_2O$ is monoclinic with[71] $a:b:c = 0.731:1:0.499$, $\beta = 106°18'$. Crystals clinodomatic. Perfect $\{20\bar{1}\}$ cleavage. G. 3.09. X $\wedge$ $c = +19°23'$; X $\wedge$ $\{20\bar{1}\}$ cleavage $= 22°9'$; Y $= b$. $(+)2V = 87°8'$ C, $86°48'$ D, $86°32'$ F, r $>$ v very weak. $n_X = 1.5321$ C, 1.5354 D, 1.5430 F, $n_Y = 1.5365$ C, 1.5399 D, 1.5475 F, $n_Z = 1.5418$ C, 1.5453 D, 1.5531 F, $n_Z - n_X = 0.0099$ D. Color ruby-red.

$Tl_2Co(SeO_4)_2 \cdot 6H_2O$ is monoclinic with[58] $a:b:c = 0.746:1:0.502$, $\beta = 105°40'$. Crystals thick $\{001\}$ tablets with $\{110\}$ prominent. Distinct $\{20\bar{1}\}$ cleavage. G. 4.00. X $\wedge$ $c = +81°38'$; X $\wedge$ $\{20\bar{1}\}$ cleavage $= 39°45'$; Y $= b$. $(-)2V = 66°15'$ C, $66°42'$ D, $67°36'$ F, r $<$ v very weak. $n_X = 1.6402$ C, 1.6442 D, 1.6552 F, $n_Y = 1.6495$ C, 1.6535 D, 1.6646 F, $n_Z = 1.6550$ C, 1.6590 D, 1.6706 F, $n_Z - n_X = 0.0148$ D. Color ruby-red. Made from water solution with excess of cobalt selenate.

$K_2Ni(SeO_4)_2 \cdot 6H_2O$ is monoclinic with[72] $a:b:c = 0.747:1:0.506$, $\beta = 104°27'$. Crystals basal tablets to short prisms. Distinct $\{20\bar{1}\}$ cleavage. G. 2.56. X $\wedge$ $c = +6°59'$; X $\wedge$ $\{20\bar{1}\}$ cleavage $= 34°15'$; Y $= b$. $(+)2V = 72°45'$ C, $72°48'$ D, $72°56'$ F, r $<$ v very weak. $n_X = 1.5147$ C, 1.5181 D, 1.5251 F, $n_Y = 1.5237$ C, 1.5272 D, 1.5344 F, $n_Z = 1.5392$ C, 1.5427 D, 1.5507 F, $n_Z - n_X = 0.0246$ D. Color bright green.

$(NH_4)_2Ni(SeO_4)_2 \cdot 6H_2O$ is monoclinic with[72] $a:b:c = 0.740:1:0.505$, $\beta = 106°17'$. Crystals thick basal tablets. Perfect $\{20\bar{1}\}$ and poor $\{010\}$ cleavages. G. 2.24. X $\wedge$ $c = +2°0'$; X $\wedge$ $\{20\bar{1}\}$ cleavage $= 39°31'$; Y $= b$. $(+)2V = 86°19'$ C, $86°21'$ D, $86°29'$ F. r $<$ v very weak. $n_X = 1.5251$ C, 1.5285 D, 1.5360 F, $n_Y = 1.5337$ C, 1.5370 D, 1.5447 F, $n_Z = 1.5424$ C, 1.5460 D, 1.5539 F, $n_Z - n_X = 0.0185$ D. Color bright green.

$Rb_2Ni(SeO_4)_2 \cdot 6H_2O$ is monoclinic with[72] $a:b:c = 0.740:1:0.503$, $\beta =$

[72] Tutton: *Trans. Roy. Soc. London* A CCXVII, p. 199 (1918).

105°20′. Crystals basal tablets to short prisms. Distinct $\{20\bar{1}\}$ cleavage. G. 2.86. $X \wedge c = +9°59′$; $X \wedge \{20\bar{1}\}$ cleavage $= 31°23′$; $Y = b$. $(+)2V = 82°22′$ C, $82°13′$ D, $81°58′$ F, $r > v$ very weak. $n_X = 1.5166$ C, 1.5189 D, 1.5268 F, $n_Y = 1.5258$ C, 1.5291 D, 1.5362 F, $n_Z = 1.5356$ C, 1.5390 D, 1.5466 F, $n_Z - n_X = 0.0192$ D. Color bright green.

$Cs_2Ni(SeO_4)_2 \cdot 6H_2O$ is monoclinic with[72] $a:b:c = 0.729:1:0.499$, $\beta = 106°11′$. Crystals prismatic parallel to a or basal tablets. Distinct $\{20\bar{1}\}$ cleavage. G. 3.11. $X \wedge c = +16°51′$; $X \wedge \{20\bar{1}\}$ cleavage $= 24°26′$; $Y = b$. $(-)2V = 82°43′$ C, $83°8′$ D, $83°43′$ F, $r < v$ weak. $n_X = 1.5363$ C, 1.5395 D, 1.5467 F, $n_Y = 1.5417$ C, 1.5450 D, 1.5525 F, $n_Z = 1.5456$ C, 1.5489 D, 1.5568 F, $n_Z - n_X = 0.0094$ D. Color deep green.

$Tl_2Ni(SeO_4)_2 \cdot 6H_2O$ is monoclinic with[58] $a:b:c = 0.746:1:0.502$, $\beta = 105°36′$. Crystals nearly equant with $\{110\}$, $\{001\}$ and $\{011\}$ prominent. Distinct $\{20\bar{1}\}$ cleavage. G. 3.99. $X \wedge c = +79°41′$; $X \wedge \{20\bar{1}\}$ cleavage $= 38°0′$; $Y = b$. $(-)2V = 58°10′$ C, $58°59′$ D, $60°53′$ F, $r < v$. $n_X = 1.6339$ C, 1.6378 D, 1.6523 F, $n_Y = 1.6459$ C, 1.6498 D, 1.6643 F, $n_Z = 1.6517$ C, 1.6560 D, 1.6709 F, $n_Z - n_X = 0.0182$ D. Color bright green. Made from water solution with an excess of nickel selenate.

$K_2Cu(SeO_4)_2 \cdot 6H_2O$ is monoclinic with[73] $a:b:c = 0.751:1:0.514$, $\beta = 103°25′$. Crystals short prismatic or basal tablets. Perfect $\{20\bar{1}\}$ and distinct $\{010\}$ cleavages. G. 2.54. $X \wedge c = +13°34′$; $X \wedge \{20\bar{1}\}$ cleavage $= 26°56′$; $Y = b$. $(-)2V = 88°46′$ C, $88°27′$ D, $87°36′$ F, $r > v$ weak. $n_X = 1.5068$ C, 1.5101 D, 1.5171 F, $n_Y = 1.5195$ C, 1.5228 D, 1.5308 F, $n_Z = 1.5317$ C, 1.5349 D, 1.5428 F, $n_Z - n_X = 0.0248$ D. Color pale blue.

$(NH_4)_2Cu(SeO_4)_2 \cdot 6H_2O$ is monoclinic with[73] $a:b:c = 0.748:1:0.515$, $\beta = 105°30′$. Crystals short prismatic. Perfect $\{20\bar{1}\}$ and $\{010\}$ cleavages. G. 2.22. $X \wedge c = +12°42′$; $X \wedge \{20\bar{1}\}$ cleavage $= 28°42′$; $Y = b$. $(-)2V = 55°42′$ C, $55°7′$ D, $53°48′$ F, $r > v$ weak. $n_X = 1.5166$ C, 1.5201 D, 1.5278 F, $n_Y = 1.5309$ C, 1.5344 D, 1.5424 F, $n_Z = 1.5352$ C, 1.5387 D, 1.5469 F, $n_Z - n_X = 0.0186$ D. Color pale blue.

$Rb_2Cu(SeO_4)_2 \cdot 6H_2O$ is monoclinic with[73] $a:b:c = 0.750:1:0.507$, $\beta = 104°44′$. Crystals basal tablets. Perfect $\{20\bar{1}\}$ and distinct $\{010\}$ cleavages. G. 2.84. $X \wedge c = +23°5′$; $X \wedge \{20\bar{1}\}$ cleavage $= 18°14′$; $Y = b$. $(+)2V = 52°58′$ C, $53°11′$ D, $53°43′$ F, $r < v$ weak. $n_X = 1.5122$ C, 1.5153 D, 1.5225 F, $n_Y = 1.5152$ C, 1.5183 D, 1.5257 F, $n_Z = 1.5286$ C, 1.5318 D, 1.5396 F, $n_Z - n_X = 0.0165$ D. Color pale blue.

$Cs_2Cu(SeO_4)_2 \cdot 6H_2O$ is monoclinic with[73] $a:b:c = 0.740:1:0.498$, $\beta = 105°42′$. Crystals clinodomatic. Perfect $\{20\bar{1}\}$ and distinct $\{010\}$ cleavages. G. 3.07. $X \wedge c = +38°12′$; $X \wedge \{20\bar{1}\}$ cleavage $= 40°53′$; $Y = b$. $(+)2V = 48°20′$ C, $48°26′$ D, $48°42′$ F, $r < v$ very weak. $n_X = 1.5248$ C,

[73] Tutton: *Proc. Roy. Soc. London* A XCVIII, p. 67 (1921).

1.5282 D, 1.5355 F, n_Y = 1.5264 C, 1.5298 D, 1.5372 F, n_Z = 1.5360 C, 1.5394 D, 1.5467 F, $n_Z - n_X$ = 0.0112 D. Color pale blue.

$Tl_2Cu(SeO_4)_2 \cdot 6H_2O$ is monoclinic with[58] $a:b:c$ = 0.753:1:0.505, β = 104°59'. Crystals short prismatic to basal tablets. Perfect {20$\bar{1}$} cleavage. G. 3.94. X ∧ c = +75°35'; X ∧ {20$\bar{1}$} cleavage = 33°53'; Y = b. (−)2V = 85°13' C, 85°9' D, 84°56' F, r > v very weak. n_X = 1.6345 C, 1.6396 D, 1.6537 F, n_Y = 1.6511 C, 1.6565 D, 1.6709 F, n_Z = 1.6662 C, 1.6720 D, 1.6867 F, $n_Z - n_X$ = 0.0324 D. Color bright blue. Made from water solution with an excess of copper selenate.

$A_2B(CrO_4)_2 \cdot 6H_2O$ SALTS (CHROMATES) OF TUTTON

$(NH_4)_2Mg(CrO_4)_2 \cdot 6H_2O$ is monoclinic with[74] $a:b:c$ = 0.752:1:0.492, β = 106°7'. Crystals short prismatic parallel to c and also to a as in Fig. 7-11, or basal tablets. Perfect {20$\bar{1}$} cleavage. G. 1.83. The optic plane

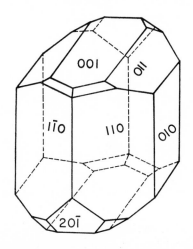

Fig. 7-11. A crystal habit of $(NH_4)_2Mg(CrO_4)_2 \cdot 6H_2O$.

is {010} for wave-lengths less than 664 mμ and normal to {010} for wave-lengths greater than 664 mμ (red). X ∧ c = +93°27'; X ∧ {20$\bar{1}$} cleavage = 52°31'. (+)2V = 10°47' (684 mμ), 0° (664 mμ), 26°53' (589 mμ = Na), 38°57' Tl, 44°37' Cd. n_X = 1.6248 Li, 1.6363 Na, 1.6489 Tl, 1.6571 Cd, n_Y = 1.6250 Li, 1.6371 Na, 1.6509 Tl, 1.6602 Cd, n_Z = 1.6390 Li, 1.6531 Na, 1.6687 Tl, 1.6799 Cd, $n_Z - n_X$ = 0.0168 Na. Color yellow. $(NH_4)_2Mg(CrO_4)_2 \cdot 6H_2O$ is said to be miscible in all proportions with[75] $(NH_4)_2Mg(SO_4)_2 \cdot 6H_2O$, but crystals are not homogeneous (suggesting imperfect miscibility) and very accurate measures are impossible; with 11.6 molecular per cent of the sulfate n_X = 1.627, n_Y = 1.627, n_Z = 1.641;

---

[74] Tutton and Porter: *Min. Mag.* XVI, p. 169 (1912).
[75] Porter: *Proc. Roy. Soc. London* A CIX, p. 78 (1925).

with 37.2 per cent: $n_X = 1.589$, $n_Y = 1.590$, $n_Z = 1.598$; with 56.2 per cent: $n_X = 1.554$, $n_Y = 1.557$, $n_Z = 1.560$; with 73.8 per cent: $n_X = 1.520$, $n_Y = 1.525$, $n_Z = 1.528$; with 90.0 per cent: $n_X = 1.491$, $n_Y = 1.493$, $n_Z = 1.495$. $(NH_4)_2Mg(CrO_4)_2 \cdot 6H_2O$ is miscible in all proportions with[75] $Rb_2Mg(CrO_4)_2 \cdot 6H_2O$. In such mix-crystals the refractive index for light vibrating along b is directly proportional to the volume (sensibly = the molecular) composition, while the other indices are curvilinear functions of the composition. These variations are shown in Fig. 7-12.

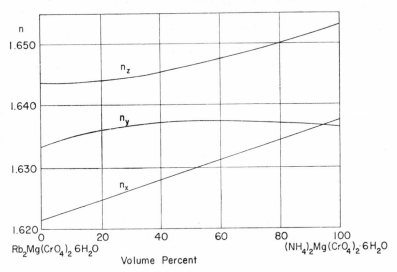

Fig. 7-12. Variations in composition and in optic properties in the $Rb_2Mg(CrO_4)_2 \cdot 6H_2O$ —$(NH_4)_2Mg(CrO_4)_2 \cdot 6H_2O$ series.

$Rb_2Mg(CrO_4)_2 \cdot 6H_2O$ is monoclinic with[74] $a:b:c = 0.753:1:0.495$, $\beta = 104°49'$. Crystals short prismatic or basal tablets. Good $\{20\bar{1}\}$ cleavage. G. 2.47. $X \wedge c = +41°50'$ (5° less for green than for red light). $X \wedge \{20\bar{1}\}$ cleavage = $0°35'$ and Z is nearly normal to the cleavage. $(-)2V = 88°4'$ C, $86°32'$ D, $84°31'$ Tl, $83°15'$ Cd, $r > v$ strong. $n_X = 1.6105$ Li, 1.6217 Na, 1.6342 Tl, 1.6426 Cd, $n_Y = 1.6208$ Li, 1.6330 Na, 1.6466 Tl, 1.6561 Cd, $n_Z = 1.6310$ Li, 1.6435 Na, 1.6577 Tl, 1.6672 Cd, $n_Z - n_X = 0.0218$ Na. Color yellow. Miscible in all proportions with $(NH_4)_2Mg(CrO_4)_2 \cdot 6H_2O$ as described above.

$Cs_2Mg(CrO_4)_2 \cdot 6H_2O$ is monoclinic with[74] $a:b:c = 0.743:1:0.489$, $\beta = 106°4'$. Crystals prismatic parallel to a or to c. Good $\{20\bar{1}\}$ cleavage. G. 2.75. $X \wedge c = +80°38'$; $X \wedge \{20\bar{1}\}$ cleavage = $37°44'$; $Y = b$. $(+)2V = 67°7'$ C, $67°3'$ D, $66°33'$ Tl, $65°57'$ Cd, $r > v$ distinct. $n_X = 1.6257$ Li, 1.6369 Na, 1.6493 Tl, 1.6578 Cd, $n_Y = 1.6310$ Li, 1.6425 Na, 1.6552 Tl,

1.6640 Cd, $n_Z = 1.6424$ Li, 1.6547 Na, 1.6683 Tl, 1.6778 Cd, $n_Z - n_X = 0.0178$ Na. Color bright yellow.

3. Formula Type $A_m B_n (XO_4)_p \cdot q H_2O$ with $(m + n):p < 3:2$ and $> 1:1$

$Na_3Fe(SO_4)_3 \cdot 3H_2O$ **(Ferrinatrite)** is hexagonal with[76] $c/a = 0.556$. Crystals short prismatic; also stellate groups of fibrous masses. Perfect $\{10\bar{1}0\}$ and good $\{11\bar{2}0\}$ cleavages. H. 2.5. G. 2.6 ca. Uniaxial positive with $n_O = 1.558$, $n_E = 1.614$, $n_E - n_O = 0.055$. Colorless. Made by the action of H_2SO_4 on $Na_2Fe(SO_4)_2(OH) \cdot 3H_2O$.

$Na_4Ca(SO_4)_3 \cdot 2H_2O$ forms long needles[77] which are labile. In the long direction $n_Z = 1.510 \pm 0.003$. Colorless.

$K_2Ca_5(SO_4)_6 \cdot H_2O$ **(Görgeyite)** is monoclinic. Crystals prismatic.[78] No cleavage. G. 2.897. $Y = b$; $Z \wedge c = 11°$. $(+)2V = 85°\pm$, $n_X = 1.550$, $n_Y = 1.565$, $n_Z = 1.583$, $n_Z - n_X = 0.033$. Again:[78a] $n_X = 1.560$, $n_Y = 1.569$, $n_Z = 1.584$, $Z \wedge c = +17°$. Colorless. PD 3.14, 2.98, 2.83; 2–0551.

$(NH_4)_2Ca_5(SO_4)_6 \cdot H_2O$ is monoclinic. $\beta = 122°$. Crystals prismatic with base and pyramids. $Y = b$; $Z \wedge c = 8°$. $(+)2V = 86°$, r $<$ v. $n_X = 1.567$, $n_Y = 1.580$, $n_Z = 1.595$, all ± 0.003, $n_Z - n_X = 0.028$. Colorless.

$Na_2Ca_5(SO_4)_6 \cdot 3H_2O$ is probably monoclinic.[77] Crystals acicular ended by pyramid faces. $Z \wedge c = 11° \pm 2°$. $n_X = 1.5557 \pm 0.003$, $n_Y = ?$, $n_Z = 1.567$, $n_Z - n_X = 0.0113$. Colorless. Made from water solution at 60°–70° C.

$K_2Ca_2Mg(SO_4)_4 \cdot 2H_2O$ **(Polyhalite)** is triclinic with $a:b:c = 0.7176:1:0.4657$, $\alpha = 91°39'$, $\beta = 89°50.5'$, $\gamma = 88°6.5'$. Crystals rare; tabular on $\{010\}$ or vertically elongated. Twinning common and often complicated. Perfect $\{10\bar{1}\}$ cleavage. H. 3.5. G. 2.78. $(-)2V = 62°$. $n_X{}^{24} = 1.547$, $n_Y = 1.560$, $n_Z = 1.567$, $n_Z - n_X = 0.020$. Colorless or stained pink to red by iron oxide inclusions. The easy cleavage lamellæ show one optic axis just outside the field of view. PD 2.90, 3.17, 3.39; 10–355.

4. Formula Type $A_m B_n (XO_4)_p \cdot q H_2O$ with $(m + n):p \approx 1:1$

$KFe''Fe'''(SO_4)_3 \cdot 4H_2O(?)$ **(Voltaite)** is isometric with $a = 27.33$ kX. Crystals cubic, octahedral, or, rarely, dodecahedral. No cleavage. H. 3. G. 2.7 $\pm$ 0.1. Isotropic with[11] $n = 1.593^{79} - 1.608$,[80] the variation being probably due to variation in composition (Mg may replace some Fe'' and

---

[76] Gordon: *Not. Nat. Acad. Sci. Philadelphia*, No. 103 (1942).

[77] Hill and Wills: *J. Am. Chem. Soc.* LX, p. 1647 (1938).

[78] Krüll and Vetter: *Zeit. Krist.* LXXXVI, p. 389 (1933).

[78a] Mayrhofer: *N. Jahrb. Min., Monatsh. for 1953*, p. 35, on natural material from Ischl, Austria.

[79] Mélon and Donnay: *Bull. Soc. Géol. Belg.* LIX, p. B 162 (1936).

[80] Bandy: *Am. Min.* XXIII, p. 669 (1938).

Al may replace some Fe'''). Often weakly birefringent in sectors, due probably to strain from variations in composition or pressure. Color greenish black or oil-green; translucent on edges or splinters and greenish. Made from water solution. Similar salts have been synthesized, including $KMgFe'''$, $KMnFe'''$, $KCoFe'''$, $TlFe''Fe'''$, $TlMgFe'''$, $TlCdFe'''$, $RbCdFe'''$, NH_4MgFe''', $KZnFe'''$ and others, but indices are not known.

$NaAl(SO_4)_2 \cdot 12H_2O$ (Soda alum) is isometric diploidal with $a = 12.19$ kX. U.C. 4. Crystals octahedral. H. $3\pm$. G. 1.67. Isotropic[81] with $n = 1.4365$ C, 1.4388 D, 1.4441 F. Colorless. Made (not easily) from water solution. Not isostructural with potash alum. $NaAl(SO_4)_2 \cdot 12H_2O$ (or only $11H_2O$?) has also a monoclinic phase (known in nature as mendozite) with $a:b:c = 2.506:1:0.9125$. $\beta = 109°1'$. Crystals prismatic or pseudo-rhombohedral. Good $\{100\}$ and poor $\{001\}$ and $\{010\}$ cleavages. H. $3\pm$. G. 1.76. $X = b$; $Y \wedge c = 30°$. $(-)2V = 56°$ with distinct crossed dispersion. $n_X = 1.449$,[11] $n_Y = 1.461$, $n_Z = 1.463$, $n_Z - n_X = 0.014$. Colorless. PD 4.23, 3.65, 3.98; 1–0397. Made from water solution above 20° C.

$KAl(SO_4)_2 \cdot 12H_2O$ (Potash alum) is isometric diploidal with $a = 12.133$ kX. U.C. 4. Crystals octahedral or cubic. H. 2. G. 1.757. No cleavage. Isotropic with[81] $n = 1.4540$ C, 1.4565 D, 1.4600 F. Colorless. PD 4.30, 3.25, 4.05; 7–17. $KAl(SO_4)_2 \cdot 12H_2O$ is alum in the narrowest sense. It intercrystallizes freely with $NH_4Al(SO_4)_2 \cdot 12H_2O$ and rather freely also with NH_4Cr, NH_4Fe, KFe, KCr-alums. Such intergrowths are often birefringent, perhaps due to lamellar intercrystallization, and can be either positive or negative. $KAl(SO_4)_2 \cdot 12H_2O$ seems to have another phase, known as kalinite, which is probably hexagonal; it is uniaxial negative[11] with $n_O = 1.456$, $n_E = 1.429$, $n_O - n_E = 0.027$. Colorless. A third phase is probably monoclinic; it is platy and fibrous. Z is normal to the plates[11] and $Y \wedge c$ (= elongation) = 13°. $(-)2V = 52°$ with slight dispersion, $n_X = 1.430$, $n_Y = 1.452$, $n_Z = 1.458$, $n_Z - n_X = 0.028$. Colorless.

$NH_4Al(SO_4)_2 \cdot 12H_2O$ (Ammonia alum) is isometric diploidal with $a = 12.215$ kX. U.C. 4. Isostructural with potash alum but not with soda alum. Crystals octahedral. H. 1.5. G. 1.645. Isotropic with[82] $n = 1.4569$ C, 1.4594 D, 1.4648 F. Optic anomalies (birefringence, etc.) easily produced in it by pressure; they are not rare in nature. PD 4.33, 4.08, 3.27; 7–22. There is a complete series of artificial mix-crystals with $KAl(SO_4)_2 \cdot 12H_2O$. Similar (complete?) mix-crystals are known with KCr, NH_4Cr, NH_4Fe-alums. These often show anomalous birefringence, either positive or negative.

The following salts also belong to the alum group.[82]

---

[81] Soret: *Arch. Sc. Phys. Nat. Genève* XIII, p. 9 (1885).

[82] For other measures of some alums (similar to those given) see Widmer: *Zeit. Krist.* LX, p. 195 and 206 (1924) and Wendekamm: *Zeit. Krist.* LXXXV, p. 35 and 169 (1933).

| | | Sulfates | | | | |
Salt	G	n (C)	n (D)	n (F)	Notes	PD
$RbAl(SO_4)_2 \cdot 12H_2O$	1.89	1.4542	1.4566	1.4619	$a = 12.220$ Colorless	4.33 2.81 3.27; 7–16
$CsAl(SO_4)_2 \cdot 12H_2O$	1.97	1.4562	1.4586	1.4639	$a = 12.333$ Colorless	4.37 2.84 2.76; 7–4
$TlAl(SO_4)_2 \cdot 12H_2O$	2.33	1.4944	1.4975	1.5046	$a = 12.206$ Also biref.	4.32 2.81 7.06; 7–20
$NH_4V(SO_4)_2 \cdot 12H_2O$	1.69		1.475		violet	
$RbV(SO_4)_2 \cdot 12H_2O$	1.915		1.469		violet	
$CsV(SO_4)_2 \cdot 12H_2O$	2.03		1.478		violet	
$TlV(SO_4)_2 \cdot 12H_2O$	2.34		1.514		violet	
$KCr(SO_4)_2 \cdot 12H_2O$	1.85	1.4787	1.4814	1.4875	$a = 12.175$ No cleavage	4.31 3.26 4.06; 7–14
$NH_4Cr(SO_4)_2 \cdot 12H_2O$	1.73	1.4813	1.4842	1.4904	$a = 12.251$ No cleavage	4.34 3.28 7.08; 7–3
$RbCr(SO_4)_2 \cdot 12H_2O$	1.97	1.4787	1.4815	1.4878	$a = 12.256$ Dark red	4.34 3.28 2.82; 7–21
$CsCr(SO_4)_2 \cdot 12H_2O$	2.04	1.4784	1.4810	1.4872	$a = 12.378$ Dark red	4.39 2.84 2.77; 8–59
$TlCr(SO_4)_2 \cdot 12H_2O$	2.39	1.5192	1.5228	1.5308	$a = 12.238$ Octahedrons	4.34 2.81 2.74; 7–15
$CsMn(SO_4)_2 \cdot 12H_2O$		1.483 Li			No cleavage	
$KFe(SO_4)_2 \cdot 12H_2O$	1.83	1.4783	1.4817	1.4893	Darkens slowly	
$NH_4Fe(SO_4)_2 \cdot 12H_2O$	1.72	1.4815	1.4848	1.4929	$a = 12.14$ Opt. anom.	4.34 3.29 4.10; 7–5
$RbFe(SO_4)_2 \cdot 12H_2O$	1.92	1.4789	1.4825	1.4900	Octahedrons	
$CsFe(SO_4)_2 \cdot 12H_2O$	2.06	1.4804	1.4838	1.4914	Colorless or violet	4.39 2.85 2.78; 7–1
$TlFe(SO_4)_2 \cdot 12H_2O$	2.38	1.5194	1.5237	1.5328	Octahedrons	
$RbTi(SO_4)_2 \cdot 12H_2O$		1.465 Li			Color red	
$CsTi(SO_4)_2 \cdot 12H_2O$		1.472 Li	1.4736	1.476	Violet-red	
$KGa(SO_4)_2 \cdot 12H_2O$	1.90	1.4630	1.4653	1.4709	$a = 12.223$ Colorless	
$NH_4Ga(SO_4)_2 \cdot 12H_2O$	1.78	1.4658	1.4684	1.4741	$a = 12.268$ Colorless	4.34 7.08 3.70; 7–18
$RbGa(SO_4)_2 \cdot 12H_2O$	1.96	1.4633	1.4658	1.4713	$a = 12.270$ Colorless	
$CsGa(SO_4)_2 \cdot 12H_2O$	2.11	1.4624	1.4650	1.4703	$a = 12.402$ Colorless	4.39 2.77 6.21; 8–58
$TlGa(SO_4)_2 \cdot 12H_2O$	2.48	1.5035	1.5067	1.5139	$a = 12.258$ Colorless	4.34 6.12 2.74; 7–19
$NH_4In(SO_4)_2 \cdot 12H_2O$	2.01	1.4635	1.4664	1.4723	Unstable Colorless	
$RbIn(SO_4)_2 \cdot 12H_2O$	2.06	1.4613	1.4638	1.4696	Unstable Colorless	
$CsIn(SO_4)_2 \cdot 12H_2O$	2.24	1.4628	1.4652	1.4711	Colorless	
$NH_4Rh(SO_4)_2 \cdot 12H_2O$		1.5073 Li	1.5103	1.5150 gr.	Orange yellow	
$RbRh(SO_4)_2 \cdot 12H_2O$		1.498 ± Li	1.501 ±	1.504 ± gr.	Yellow Octah.	
$CsRh(SO_4)_2 \cdot 12H_2O$		1.5063 Li	1.5077	1.5112 gr.	Honey-yellow	
$TlRh(SO_4)_2 \cdot 12H_2O$		1.546 Li	1.548	1.549 ± gr.	Honey-yellow	
$NH_3CH_3Al(SO_4)_2 \cdot 12H_2O$	1.595	1.4506	1.4531	1.4584	$a = 12.479$ Colorless	
$NH_2(OH)HAl(SO_4)_2 \cdot 12H_2O$	1.672	1.4617	1.4642	1.4698	Colorless	
$NH_2(CH_3)_2Al(SO_4)_2 \cdot 12H_2O$	1.591	1.4500	1.4525	1.4578	Colorless	
$N(CH_3)_4Al(SO_4)_2 \cdot 12H_2O$	1.66	1.4559	1.4592	1.4651	Colorless	
$NH_3C_2H_5Al(SO_4)_2 \cdot 12H_2O$	1.64		1.459		Colorless	
$NH_2(C_2H_5)_2Al(SO_4)_2 \cdot 12H_2O$	1.648	1.4562	1.4592	1.4654	Colorless	
$NH(C_2H_5)_3Al(SO_4)_2 \cdot 12H_2O$	1.655		1.4594		Colorless	
$N(C_2H_5)_4Al(SO_4)_2 \cdot 12H_2O$	1.650		1.4595		Colorless	
$NH_3C_3H_7Al(SO_4)_2 \cdot 12H_2O$	1.650	1.4568	1.4602	1.4652	Colorless	
$NH_3C_4H_9Al(SO_4)_2 \cdot 12H_2O$		1.4567	1.4598	1.4660	Colorless	
$NH_3C_5H_{11}Al(SO_4)_2 \cdot 12H_2O$		1.4578	1.4602	1.4672	Colorless	

Salt	G	n (C)	n (D)	n (F)	Notes
$NH_3(OH)Cr(SO_4)_2 \cdot 12H_2O$	1.750		1.4863		Violet-red
$NH_3CH_3Cr(SO_4)_2 \cdot 12H_2O$	1.662		1.4745		Violet-red
			Selenates		
$NH_3CH_3Al(SeO_4)_2 \cdot 12H_2O$	1.833		1.4780		Very dark
$KAl(SeO_4)_2 \cdot 12H_2O$	1.991	1.4773	1.4801	1.4868	Opt. anom.
$NH_4Al(SeO_4)_2 \cdot 12H_2O$	1.891		1.4856		Very dark
$RbAl(SeO_4)_2 \cdot 12H_2O$	2.123		1.4810		Very dark
$CsAl(SeO_4)_2 \cdot 12H_2O$	2.232		1.4865		Very dark
$TlAl(SeO_4)_2 \cdot 12H_2O$	2.531		1.522		Very dark
$RbFe(SeO_4)_2 \cdot 12H_2O$	2.13	1.5047 Li	1.5070	1.5119 gr.	Very dark
$CsFe(SeO_4)_2 \cdot 12H_2O$	3.62	1.5088 Li	1.5116	1.5162 gr.	Very dark

The color of the alum salts seems to depend chiefly upon the trivalent base; thus, the aluminum salts are all colorless (unless stained by impurities); vanadium alums are all violet; chromium alums are violet to dark red; the manganese alum is garnet red; the iron alums are colorless when pure and freshly prepared, but usually violet; gallium and indium alums are all colorless; titanium alums are reddish violet; rhodium alums are yellow to orange; the selenate alums are nearly black, but not opaque in thin splinters.

$NaAl(SO_4)_2 \cdot 6H_2O$ **(Tamarugite)** is monoclinic prismatic with $a:b:c = 0.292:1:0.242$, $\beta = 94°49.5'$. Crystals {010} tablets or short prisms. Perfect {010} cleavage. Multiple twinning may occur. H. 3 $ca.$ G. 2.07. Soluble in water. X $\wedge$ $c = +4°$ to 5°; Y = b. $(+)2V^{83} = 60°$ $ca.$ $n_X = 1.488$, $n_Y = 1.491$, $n_Z = 1.500$, all ± 0.001, $n_Z - n_X = 0.013$. Again:[80] $n_X = 1.490$, $n_Y = 1.492$, $n_Z = 1.504$, $n_Z - n_X = 0.014$. Colorless. Made by partial dehydration of soda alum or mendozite.

5. Formula Type $AXO_4 \cdot qH_2O$

$BeSO_4 \cdot 4H_2O$ is tetragonal with $c/a = 0.946$. Crystals pyramidal. No distinct cleavage. Cruciform or lamellar twinning on {101} common. G. 1.73. Uniaxial negative with $n_O = 1.4691$ C, 1.4720 D, 1.4779 F, $n_E = 1.4374$ C, 1.4395 D, 1.4450 F, $n_O - n_E = 0.0325$ D. Again[84] $n_O - n_E = 0.0392$ Na. Colorless. PD 3.91, 2.53, 3.21; 1–0469. May take $BeSeO_4 \cdot 4H_2O$ in crystal solution with little effect on the optic properties.

$NiSO_4 \cdot 6H_2O$ **(Retgersite)** is tetragonal with $a = 6.776$, $c = 18.249\,kX$. U.C. 4. Crystals thick {001} tablets to short prismatic. Perfect {001} cleavage. H. 2.5. G. 2.07. Uniaxial negative with[85] $n_O = 1.5078$ C, 1.5109 D, 1.5173 F, $n_E = 1.4844$ C, 1.4873 D, 1.4930 F, $n_O - n_E = 0.0236$ D. Color emerald green (bluish). Made from water solution at about 35° C. Crystallizing from solution at about 60° C. the crystals are monoclinic with

[83] Gordon: *Not. Nat. Acad. Sci. Philadelphia*, No. 57 (1940).

[84] Wulff: *Zeit. Krist.* XVII, p. 592 (1890).

[85] Topsøe and Christiansen: *Ann. Chim. Phys.* I [5], p. 39 (1874).

$a:b:c = 1.372:1:1.676$, $\beta = 98°17'$. Crystals basal tablets with no cleavage. $X \wedge c = 26°17'$; $Y = b$. $(-)2H = 19°25'$, $r > v$. Color emerald green. PD 4.25, 4.57, 2.96; 8–470.

$NiSeO_4 \cdot 6H_2O$ is tetragonal with $c/a = 1.836$. Crystals from cold solutions are basal tablets and from hot solutions are acute pyramidal. Perfect basal cleavage. G. 2.31. Uniaxial negative with $n_O = 1.5357$ C, 1.5393 D, 1.5473 F, $n_E = 1.5089$ C, 1.5125 D, 1.5196 F, $n_O - n_E = 0.0268$ D. Made from water solution.

$CoSO_4 \cdot 6H_2O$ is probably tetragonal being uniaxial[86] negative with $n_O = 1.495$, $n_E = 1.460$, $n_O - n_E = 0.035$. Blue in mass; faintly pleochroic in pink. Also monoclinic when crystallized at about 45° C. Crystals prismatic with $\{001\}$. G. 2.0. X nearly normal to $\{\bar{1}02\}$; $Y = b$. $(-)2H = 8°$, $r > v$ with weak inclined dispersion.

$ZnSeO_4 \cdot 6H_2O$ is tetragonal with $c/a = 1.895$. Crystals basal tablets or pyramidal. Perfect basal cleavage. G. 2.33. Uniaxial negative with $n_O = 1.5255$ C, 1.5291 D, 1.5367 F, $n_E = 1.5004$ C, 1.5039 D, 1.5108 F, $n_O - n_E = 0.0183$ D. Colorless. Made from water solution at about 15° C.

$2CaSO_4 \cdot H_2O$ (Bassanite?) is hexagonal with[87] $a = 6.82$, $c = 6.24$ kX. Crystals six-sided prisms. G. 2.7. Uniaxial positive with $n_O = 1.558$, $n_E = 1.586$, $n_E - n_O = 0.028$. The water is zeolitic and is held in channels in the crystal structure; it is nearly or entirely lost at about 130° C. Colorless. PD 2.98, 2.78, 5.98; 2–0675. Made by partial dehydration of gypsum at about 120° C.; it is then acicular with a silken luster. Commercially it is *plaster of Paris*. $2CaSO_4 \cdot H_2O$ (another phase?) is also reported to be monoclinic with[88] $a:b:c = 1.744:1:1.852$, $\beta = 90°36'$. Crystals pseudo-hexagonal with common twinning on $\{100\}$. $(+)2V = 14°$, $n_X = 1.559$, $n_Y = 1.5595$, $n_Z = 1.5836$, $n_Z - n_X = 0.0246$. Again:[89] fibers have parallel extinction and positive elongation. $n_X = 1.55$, $n_Z = 1.57$, $n_Z - n_X = 0.02$. Also:[90] $n_X = 1.550$, $n_Z = 1.556$, $n_Z - n_X = 0.006$. Once more[91] $2CaSO_4 \cdot H_2O$ is said to be rhombohedral above 45° C., and orthorhombic below 45° C. with $2V = 10°$–15° and $n_Z = 1.584$.

$BeSeO_4 \cdot 4H_2O$ is orthorhombic with $a:b:c = 0.960:1:0.903$. Crystals macrodomatic columnar. No good cleavage. Cruciform twinning on $\{110\}$. G. 2.03. $X = c$; $Y = a$. $(-)2V = 26°43'$, $n_X = 1.4637$ C, 1.4664 D, 1.4725 F, $n_Y = 1.4973$ C, 1.5007 D, 1.5084 F, $n_Z = 1.4992$ C, 1.5027 D, 1.5101 F, $n_Z - n_X = 0.0363$ D. Colorless. Made from water solution. May

[86] Larsen and Glenn: *Am. J. Sci.* CC, p. 225 (1920).

[87] Caspari: *Proc. Roy. Soc. London*, CLV A, p. 41 (1936).

[88] Gallitelli: *Period. Min.* IV, p. 132 (1933); *N. Jahrb. Min.* 1933, I, p. 472.

[89] Milton: *Am. Min.* XXVII, p. 517 (1942).

[90] Berg and Sveshnikova: *Acad. Sci. U.S.S.R. Cl. Sci. Chim.* No. 1, p. 19 (1946) [*Min. Abst.* X, p. 464 (1949)].

[91] Flörke: *N. Jahrb. Min. Abh.* LXXXIV, p. 189 (1952) [*Min. Abst.* XII, p. 94 (1953)].

take BeSO$_4$·4H$_2$O in crystal solution to at least 60 per cent with little change in the optic properties.

MgSO$_4$·7H$_2$O (Epsomite) is orthorhombic with $a = 11.94$, $b = 12.03$, $c = 6.865$ kX. U.C. 4. Crystals usually prismatic terminated by one (or

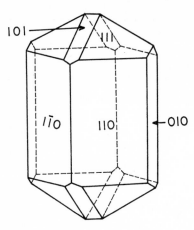

Fig. 7-13. Crystal habit of MgSO$_4$·7H$_2$O.

more) sphenoids; often fibrous. See Figs. 7-13, 7-14. H. 2.5. G. 1.677. Distinct {010} and poor {101} cleavages. Soluble in water. X = b; Y = c. $(-)2V = 51°25'$ D, r > v weak. $n_X = 1.4305$ C, 1.4325 D, 1.4374 F, $n_Y = 1.4530$ C, 1.4554 D, 1.4607 F, $n_Z = 1.4583$ C, 1.4608 D, 1.4657 F,

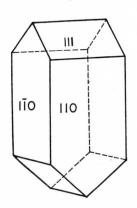

Fig. 7-14. Crystal habit of MgSO$_4$·7H$_2$O.

$n_Z - n_X = 0.0283$ D. Colorless. PD 4.21, 5.35, 2.68; 8–467. Made from water solution at temperatures below about 50° C. It rotates the plane of polarization 1.98° per mm. (of thickness) for $\lambda = 579$. Epsomite is miscible in all proportions with[92] NiSO$_4$·7H$_2$O or ZnSO$_4$·7H$_2$O with linear variation

[92] Porter: *Zeit. Krist.* LXXV, p. 288 (1930). Hutton: *Am. Min.* XXXII, p. 553 (1947).

of the refractive indices. Also miscible to some extent with Mn, Fe, Cu or Co sulfates. A second phase of $MgSO_4 \cdot 7H_2O$ is monoclinic with $a:b:c =$ 1.22:1:1.58, $\beta = 104°24'$. Crystals pseudo-rhombohedral and isomorphous with $FeSO_4 \cdot 7H_2O$ with which it is miscible to at least 40 per cent; likewise miscible with $CuSO_4 \cdot 7H_2O$, but optic data are lacking.

$NiSO_4 \cdot 7H_2O$ (Morenosite) is orthorhombic with $a = 11.8$, $b = 12.0$, $c = 6.80$ kX. U.C. 4. Crystals short prismatic or fibrous. Perfect {010} cleavage. H. 2–2.5. G. 1.95. F. 7. X = b; Y = c. $(-)2V = 41°45'$, r > v weak.[93] $n_X = 1.4693$, $n_Y = 1.4893$, $n_Z = 1.4923$, $n_Z - n_X = 0.023$ D. Color apple-green. PD 4.20, 5.30, 2.85; 1–0403. Miscible in all proportions with $MgSO_4 \cdot 7H_2O$.

$ZnSO_4 \cdot 7H_2O$ (Goslarite) is orthorhombic with $a = 11.85$, $b = 12.00$, $c = 6.83$ kX. U.C. 4. Crystals stout prismatic to acicular. Perfect {010} cleavage. H. 2–2.5. G. 1.98. Dehydrates in dry air. X = b; Y = c.[92] $(-)2V = 46°14'$ r > v weak. $n_X = 1.4544$ C, 1.4568 D, 1.4620 F, $n_Y =$ 1.4776 C, 1.4801 D, 1.4860 F, $n_Z = 1.4812$ C, 1.4836 D, 1.4897 F, $n_Z -$ $n_X = 0.0268$. Colorless. PD 4.21, 5.36, 4.18; 9–395. Made from water solution. Miscible in all proportions with $MgSO_4 \cdot 7H_2O$ and at least to some extent with Cu, Fe or Mn sulfates. With Fe:Zn = 1:2 it has[94] $(+)2V = 78°48'$, $n_X = 1.4709$, $n_Y = 1.4785$, $n_Z = 1.4867$, $n_Z - n_X =$ 0.0158. Color green to brown.

$MgCrO_4 \cdot 7H_2O$ is orthorhombic sphenoidal with $a:b:c = 0.990:1:0.574$. Crystals columnar prismatic. Perfect {010} cleavage. G. 1.69. X = b; Y = c. $(-)2V = 75°28'$, r < v. $n_X = 1.5131$ C, 1.5211 D, $n_Y = 1.5415$ C, 1.5500 D, $n_Z = 1.5633$ C, 1.5680 D, $n_Z - n_X = 0.0469$ D. PD 5.00, 3.77, 6.00; 1–0243. Made from water solution.

$MgSO_4 \cdot H_2O$ (Kieserite) is monoclinic prismatic with $a = 6.89$, $b =$ 7.69, $c = 7.52$ kX, $\beta = 116°5'$. U.C. 4. Crystals bipyramidal. Perfect {110} and {111} and poor {$\bar{1}$11}, {$\bar{1}$01} and {011} cleavages. H. 3.5. G. 2.57. Slowly soluble in water. Y = b; Z $\wedge$ c = $-76.5°$. $(+)2V = 57°$, r > v distinct.[95] $n_X = 1.523$, $n_Y = 1.525$, $n_Z = 1.596$, $n_Z - n_X = 0.063$. Colorless. PD 3.38, 4.82, 2.55; 1–0638. Made from water solution above 67° C.

$FeSO_4 \cdot H_2O$ (Szomolnokite) is monoclinic with $a:b:c = 0.934:1:1.008$, $\beta = 116°14'$. Crystals bipyramidal. Common twinning. H. 2.5. G. 3.05. X $\wedge$ c = $-26°$; Y = b.[80] $(+)2V = 80°$, r > v strong. $n_X = 1.591$, $n_Y =$ 1.623, $n_Z = 1.663$, $n_Z - n_X = 0.072$. Color yellow to brown; also blue or colorless. PD 3.42, 4.85, 3.13; 1–0612. Made by dehydrating $FeSO_4 \cdot ?H_2O$ at 100° C.

$MnSO_4 \cdot H_2O$ (Szmikite) is probably monoclinic. H. 1.5. G. 3.15. F. 7.

[93] Dufet: *Bull. Soc. Fr. Min.* I, p. 58 (1878).
[94] Andreatta: *Atti R. Accad. Lincei, Cl. Sci.* 6, XI, p. 760 (1930).
[95] Blasdale and Robson: *J. Am. Chem. Soc.* L, p. 35 (1928).

One perfect cleavage. Y $\wedge$ c = large; Z = b. $(+)2V^{86}$ = nearly 90°. n_X = 1.562, n_Y = 1.595, n_Z = 1.632, $n_Z - n_X$ = 0.070. Color dirty white to rose-red. PD 3.51, 3.15, 2.59; 1–0565. Made by dehydration of any higher hydrate at 100° C.

CoSO$_4$·H$_2$O is probably monoclinic since it has inclined extinction. $(-)2V$ = nearly[96] 90°, n_X = 1.603, n_Y = 1.639, n_Z = 1.683, $n_Z - n_X$ = 0.080 as formed in a desiccator from CoSO$_4$·6H$_2$O. The monohydrate formed by evaporation on a steam bath has n_X = 1.600, n_Y = ?, n_Z = 1.645, $n_Z - n_X$ = 0.045, and negative elongation. PD 3.40, 4.82, 3.08; 1–0619.

CuSO$_4$·H$_2$O is biaxial,[34] but of unknown symmetry. $(-)2V$ = 75° calc., r < v. n_X = 1.626, n_Y = 1.671, n_Z = 1.699, $n_Z - n_X$ = 0.073. Bluish white in mass; colorless in section. PD 3.40, 4.81, 2.47; 1–0620.

4MgSO$_4$·5H$_2$O is probably monoclinic[97] in twinned diamond-shaped crystals with n_X = 1.512, n_Y = 1.530, n_Z = ? Colorless.

MgSO$_4$·2H$_2$O forms fine radiated masses[97] with n_Y = 1.493. A substance given as MgSO$_4$·3H$_2$O (?) is perhaps the same. It is biaxial negative with[98] n_Y = 1.490±. Colorless.

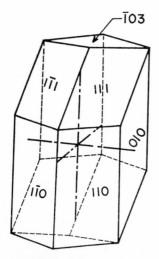

Fig. 7-15. A crystal habit of CaSO$_4$·2H$_2$O.

CaSO$_4$·2H$_2$O (Gypsum) is monoclinic with a = 5.67, b = 15.15, c = 6.28 kX, β = 113°50'. Crystals usually simple in habit, often tabular parallel to {010} as in Fig. 7-15, or prismatic to acicular along c. Perfect {010} and poor {100} and {$\bar{1}$11} cleavages. Twinning on {100} common in

[96] The indices require a *positive* sign.
[97] Robson: *J. Am. Chem. Soc.* XLIX, p. 2772 (1927).
[98] Shannon: *Proc. U. S. Nat. Mus.* LXXIV, Art. 13 (1929).

arrow-head forms, as in Fig. 7-16. H. 2. G. 2.32. F. 2.5–3. Soluble in HCl. $Y = b$; $Z \wedge c = +52°$. At room temperature $(+)2V = 58°$ Na, $r > v$ with strong inclined dispersion, $n_X = 1.5205$ Na, $n_Y = 1.5226$, $n_Z = 1.5296$, $n_Z - n_X = 0.0091$. At 105° C.[99] $n_X = 1.5184$, $n_Y = 1.5188$, $n_Z = 1.5274$,

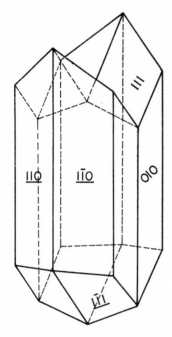

Fig. 7-16. Gypsum crystal twinned on (100).

$n_Z - n_X = 0.0090$ Na. The optic angle varies rapidly with change of temperature from $2E$ = about 95° at 20° C. to 0° at about 91° C. The optic angle then opens in a plane normal to (010) (X and Y changing places) at temperatures above 91° C. At the same time the dispersion becomes $r < v$ and horizontal (for example, at 120° C.). PD 7.56, 3.06, 4.27; 6–0046/7. Gypsum loses three-fourths of its water at about 120° C. (becoming *plaster of Paris*) and the rest of the water at 163° C.: when heated above this temperature it is "dead burned" and has $n_O = 1.50$ and $n_E = 1.56$. Made by reaction of soluble calcium salts with sulfates.

3CdSO$_4$·8H$_2$O(?) is monoclinic with $a:b:c = 0.799:1:0.690$, $\beta = 117°58'$. Crystals basal plates. Perfect {010} cleavage. G. 3.05. X = b; $Z \wedge c = +76°14'$ red, 77°3' blue. $(-)2V = 87°57'$ red, 88°9' Na, 88°23' blue, $r > v$ weak. $n_Y = 1.563$ red, 1.565 Na, 1.576 blue, $n_Z - n_X = ?$. Made from water solution.

[99] Tutton: *Zeit. Krist.* XLVI, p. 135 (1909); Hutchinson and Tutton: *Zeit. Krist.* LII, p. 223 (1913).

CuSO₄·3H₂O is monoclinic with[99a] $a:b:c = 0.432:1:0.552$, $\beta = 96°25'$. Crystals short prismatic; twinning common on {100}. Distinct {010} cleavage. (+)2V = 75° calc. $n_X = 1.554$, $n_Y = 1.577$, $n_Z = 1.618$, $n_Z - n_X = 0.064$. Blue; colorless in section. PD 4.45, 3.65, 5.15; 3–0194.

MgSO₄·4H₂O is monoclinic with $a:b:c = 0.45:1:?$, $\beta = 90°11'$. Crystals short prismatic. Good {100} and {010} cleavages.[97] X $\wedge$ $c = +81°$, Z = b. (+)2V = 50°, r > v with strong horizontal dispersion. $n_X = 1.490$, $n_Y = 1.491$, $n_Z = 1.497$, $n_Z - n_X = 0.007$. The prism angle, (110) $\wedge$ (1$\bar{1}$0), (= 48°40') is often seen. Colorless. PD 4.48, 2.95, 5.50; 1–0341.

FeSO₄·4H₂O is monoclinic[100] with $a:b:c = 0.438:1:0.587$, $\beta = 90°31'$. Crystals short prismatic. Good {010} cleavage. Striations on {001} and {011}. G. 2.28. Z = b. (−)2V = very large. Horizontal dispersion. $n_X = 1.533$, $n_Y = 1.535$, $n_Z = 1.537$ (from n_X, n_Y and 2V), $n_Z - n_X = 0.004$. Color pale green. PD 5.50, 4.49, 3.99; 1–0201. Made from water solution at about 80° C.

MnSO₄·4H₂O is monoclinic with $a:b:c = 0.432:1:0.582$, $\beta = 90°53'$. Crystals short prismatic or basal plates along parallel to a. Perfect {010} cleavage. G. 2.26. Y = b; Z $\wedge$ c = 85°48' Li, 84°8' blue. (−)2V = 63°, r > v weak.[24] $n_X = 1.508$, $n_Y = 1.518$, $n_Z = 1.522$, $n_Z - n_X = 0.014$. Color pink. PD 4.48, 5.56, 3.96; 3–0185. Made from water solution at about 45° C.

MgSO₄·6H₂O (Hexahydrite) is monoclinic with $a = 10.04$, $b = 7.15$, $c = 24.34$ kX, $\beta = 98°14'$. Crystals thick basal tablets or prismatic. Perfect {100} cleavage. H. 2. G. 1.75. F. 7, but exfoliates. X $\wedge$ $c = -25°$; X is nearly normal[101] to {$\bar{1}$02}; Y = b. (−)2V = 38°, r > v. $n_X = 1.426$, $n_Y = 1.453$, $n_Z = 1.456$, $n_Z - n_X = 0.030$. Colorless, white or rarely pale green. PD 4.40, 2.92, 4.04; 1–0354. Made from water solution between 48° and 69°.

ZnSO₄·6H₂O (Bianchite) is monoclinic with $a:b:c = 1.385:1:3.352$, $\beta = 98°12'$. Crystals basal tablets with {110} and {112}, etc. H. 2.5 ca. G. 2.03. Often contains some Fe in place of Zn. With Zn:Fe = 2:1 it has[102] X $\wedge$ c = −26°; Y = b. (−)2V = 10°. $n_X = 1.465$, $n_Y = 1.494$, $n_Z = 1.495$, $n_Z - n_X = 0.030$. With no Fe: (−)2V = 15°–16°, $n_X = 1.462$, $n_Y = 1.4895$, $n_Z = 1.490$, $n_Z - n_X = 0.028$. Color white, becoming yellowish as iron oxidizes. PD 4.40, 4.05, 2.92; 1–0352.

MgSeO₄·6H₂O is monoclinic with $a:b:c = 1.385:1:1.685$, $\beta = 98°32'$. Crystals thick basal tablets with perfect {10$\bar{1}$} cleavage. G. 1.93. X $\wedge$ $c = -27°$; Y = b. (−)2V = 28°12', r > v strong. $n_X = 1.4856$ D, $n_Y =$

[99a] Posnjak and Tunell: *Am. J. Sci.* CCXVIII, p. 1 (1929).
[100] Scharizer: *N. Jahrb. Min.* I, p. 302 (1928); *Fest. Goldschmidt*, 1928, p. 263.
[101] Dolivo-Dobrovolsky: *Mém. Soc. Russe Min.* LVIII, p. 3 (1929).
[102] Andreatta: *Rend. Acad. Lincei* [6], XVI, p. 62 (1932).

1.4864 C, 1.4892 D, 1.4965 F, n_Z = 1.4911 D, $n_Z - n_X$ = 0.0055. Colorless. Made from water solution at ordinary temperature.

CoSeO$_4$·6H$_2$O is monoclinic with $a:b:c$ = 1.371:1:1.682, β = 98°14′. Crystals thick basal tablets or short prismatic with perfect $\{10\bar{1}\}$ cleavage. G. 2.18. X $\wedge$ c = −34°42′; Y = b. (−)2V = 7°13′, r > v. n_X = 1.47 calc., n_Y = 1.5183 Li, 1.5225 Na, n_Z = 1.5227 Na, $n_Z - n_X$ = 0.05 calc. Made from water solution above 15° C.

FeSO$_4$·7H$_2$O (Melanterite) is monoclinic with a = 15.34, b = 12.98, c = 20.02 kX, β = 104°16′. U.C. 16. Crystals nearly equant as in Fig. 7-17

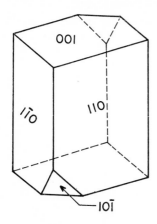

Fig. 7-17. A crystal habit of FeSO$_4$·7H$_2$O.

or varied. Perfect $\{001\}$ and distinct $\{110\}$ cleavages. H. 2. G. 1.90. F. easy. Dehydrates in dry air. Y = b; Z $\wedge$ c = −62°. (+)2V = 85°27′, r > v weak with weak inclined dispersion.[103] n_X = 1.4681 Li, 1.4713 Na, n_Y = 1.4748 Li, 1.4782 Na, 1.4861 blue, n_Z = 1.4824 Li, 1.4856 Na, $n_Z - n_X$ = 0.0143 Na. Color green to nearly white; becomes yellow by alteration. PD 4.90, 3.78, 3.23; 1–0255. Made from water solution at temperatures up to 56° C. When dehydrated to about 5H$_2$O (as found in some drugs) it has:[104] n_X = 1.525, n_Y = ?, n_Z = 1.539, $n_Z - n_X$ = 0.014. The iron of melanterite may be replaced in part (or even wholly in some cases) by Mg, Cu, Zn, Co, Ni, or Mn (or 2 or more of these). With some Cu (in nature called *pisanite*) the optic properties remain nearly the same, with Y = b, Z $\wedge$ c = −68°, (+)2V = very large. n_X = 1.472, n_Y = 1.479, n_Z = 1.487, $n_Z - n_X$ = 0.015. Color pale blue. PD 4.86, 3.77, 5.37; 7–392. With some Zn (and Cu)—called *calingastite*—it has (+)2V = large, n_X = 1.479, n_Y = 1.483, n_Z = 1.488, $n_Z - n_X$ = 0.009. Color blue-green.

CuSO$_4$·7H$_2$O (Boothite) is monoclinic with $a:b:c$ = 1.162:1:1.500,

[103] Erofejeff: *Sitzb. Akad. Wiss. Wien* LVI, p. 63 (1867).
[104] Keenan and Eisenberg: *J. Ass. Off. Agric. Chem.* XXVI, p. 256 (1943).

$\beta = 105°36'$. Crystals fibrous. Poor basal cleavage. H. 2–2.5. G. about 2. X near c; Y $= b$. $(-?)2V =$ large,[24] $n_X = 1.47$, $n_Y = 1.48$, $n_Z = 1.49$, $n_Z - n_X = 0.02$. Color pale blue. Made from water solution by seeding with $FeSO_4 \cdot 7H_2O$.

$CoSO_4 \cdot 7H_2O$ (Bieberite) is monoclinic with $a = 15.45$, $b = 13.08$, $c = 20.04$ kX, $\beta = 104°40'$. U.C. 16. Crystals complex $\{10\bar{1}\}$ tablets. Perfect $\{001\}$ and distinct $\{110\}$ cleavages. H. 2. G. 1.96. F. easy. Dehydrates in dry air. The optic plane is (010); $(-)2V = 88°$, r < v weak.[105] $n_X = 1.4748$, $n_Y = 1.4820$, $n_Z = 1.4885$, $n_Z - n_X = 0.0137$. Color carmine; slightly pleochroic in pink tints. Made from water solution at 23° C.

$MgSO_4 \cdot 5H_2O$ (Pentahydrite) is triclinic with[106] $a:b:c = 0.602:1:0.560$, $\alpha = 81°30'$, $\beta = 109°0'$, $\gamma = 104°55'$. Crystals vertically elongated with $\{100\}$ and $\{11\bar{1}\}$ prominent. No cleavage. G. 1.718. Unstable in air.

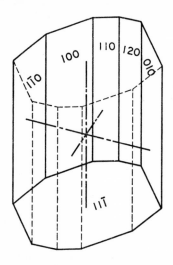

Fig. 7-18. A crystal habit of $CuSO_4 \cdot 5H_2O$.

X nearly normal to[97] (010). $(-)2V = 45°8'$, r < v. $n_X = 1.482$, $n_Y = 1.492$, $n_Z = 1.493$, $n_Z - n_X = 0.011$. Colorless. Made from water solution.

$FeSO_4 \cdot 5H_2O$ (Siderotil) is triclinic[106a] with $a:b:c = 0.596:1:0.577$, $\alpha = 81°23'$, $\beta = 110°28'$, $\gamma = 105°33'$. Crystals short prismatic to acicular. H. 2–3. G. 2.2. F. 3. $(-)2V =$ moderate, r > v weak. $n_X = 1.526$, $n_Y = 1.536$, $n_Z = 1.542$, $n_Z - n_X = 0.016$. Again:[11] $n_X = 1.528$, $n_Y = 1.537$, $n_Z = 1.545$, $n_Z - n_X = 0.017$. Color white to yellowish or pale green. Not certainly produced artificially.

[105] Porter: *Festsch. V. Goldschmidt*, 1928, p. 210.
[106] Wyrouboff: *Bull. Soc. Fr. Min.* XII, p. 371 (1889).
[106a] Larsen and Glenn: *Am. J. Sci.* CC, p. 225 (1920).

CuSO₄·5H₂O (Chalcanthite) is triclinic[107] with $a = 6.104$, $b = 10.72$, $c = 5.949$ Å, $\alpha = 97°34'$, $\beta = 107°17'$, $\gamma = 77°26'$, U.C. 2. Crystals short prismatic, almost equant. Poor {110} and {1$\bar{1}$0} cleavages. H. 2.5. G. 2.28. F. 3. X $\wedge$ $c = 76°$ in a plane[107] at 79° with (010); Z $\wedge$ $c = 18°$ in a plane

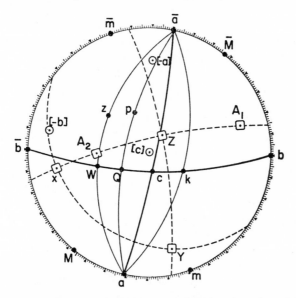

Fig. 7-19. Stereogram showing common forms and optic orientation of CuSO₄·5H₂O.

at 35° with (010). Angular coordinates of common faces and of optical directions and crystal axes follow:[107]

Form	φ	ρ	Form	φ	ρ
c(001)	76°22'	17°45½'	p($\bar{1}\bar{1}1$)	−112°38'	37°44'
b(010)	0 00	90 00	z($\bar{1}\bar{2}1$)	−140 33	48 20
a(100)	100 52	90 00	X*	168 47	75 53
m(110)	70 00	90 00	Y*	75 25	76 51
M($1\bar{1}0$)	126 48	90 00	Z*	−55 03	19 29
q(011)	25 44	35 37	$[c]$†	——	0 00
Q($0\bar{1}1$)	147 50	30 18	$[-b]$†	−169 08	82 26
W($0\bar{2}1$)	163 43	47 59	$[-a]$†	−90 00	72 43

* Axis of indicatrix.   † Crystallographic axis.

Crystals formed on a glass slide by evaporation of an aqueous solution all lie on the face $M(1\bar{1}0)$ or $-M(\bar{1}10)$, which is only 15° from normal to

[107] Fisher: *Am. Min.* XXXVII, p. 95 (1952); also Barth and Tunell: *ibid.* XVIII 187 (1933).

the optic symmetry plane containing X and Y. Such a face is usually an almost equilateral parallelogram with angles of 57° and 123°, and the optic symmetry plane XY intersects one of these sides at about 75° in the obtuse angle of the parallelogram. $(-)2V = 56°02'$, r < v weak[108] with components of crossed and strongly inclined dispersion. $n_X = 1.5141$ Na, $n_Y = 1.5368$, $n_Z = 1.5435$, $n_Z - n_X = 0.0294$. Color blue; nearly colorless in section. PD 4.70, 5.45, 3.97; 8–89. Made from water solution. It may contain Mg, Fe, Mn, or Zn replacing some Cu.

(Zn,Cu)SO$_4$·5H$_2$O is similar.[106a] G. 2.1. $(-)2V$ = moderate. $n_X = 1.513$, $n_Y = 1.533$, $n_Z = 1.540$, $n_Z - n_X = 0.027$. Color pale blue; nearly colorless in section.

CoSO$_4$·5H$_2$O is similar.[106a] H. 2–3. G. 2.2. F. 3. $(-)2V$ = moderate, dispersion not strong. $n_X = 1.530$, $n_Y = 1.548$, $n_Z = 1.550$. $n_Z - n_X = 0.020$. Color rose-pink. Made from water solution.

MnSO$_4$·5H$_2$O is triclinic[106a] with $a:b:c = 0.589:1:0.569$, $\alpha = 81°37'$, $\beta = 100°5'$, $\gamma = 104°59'$. Crystals nearly equant, acicular parallel to c, or lamellar parallel to (100). Poor {011} cleavage. H. 2–3. G. 2.1. F. 3. Y nearly normal to plates in which extinction is at 15° to length. $(-)2V$ = rather large, with r > v. $n_X = 1.495$, $n_Y = 1.508$, $n_Z = 1.514$, $n_Z - n_X = 0.019$. Color pale pink. Made from water solution in a desiccator under reduced pressure.

CuSeO$_4$·5H$_2$O is triclinic with $a:b:c = 0.568:1:0.555$, $a = 98°2'$, $\beta = 106°54'$, $\gamma = 103°11'$. Crystals short prismatic, vertically striated like CuSO$_4$·5H$_2$O. G. 2.56. Bolland[25] measured on "copper selenate" of unknown formula: $n_1 = 1.565$, $n_2 = 1.56$; sign $-$, and extinction angle of 34°. Color red. Made from water solution.

6. Formula Type AB$_2$(XO$_4$)$_4$·qH$_2$O

MgAl$_2$(SO$_4$)$_4$·22H$_2$O (Pickeringite) is monoclinic with $a = 20.8$, $b = 24.2$, $c = 6.17$ kX, $\beta = 95°$ ca. U.C. 4. Crystals acicular. Poor {010} cleavage. H. 1.5. G. 1.73–1.79. Y = b; Z $\wedge$ $c = 36°$. $(-)2V^{11} = 60°$; $n_X = 1.476$, $n_Y = 1.480$, $n_Z = 1.483$, $n_Z - n_X = 0.008$. Colorless or tinted yellowish or reddish probably due to some Fe in place of Mg. A complete replacement is possible leading to halotrichite. It may also have some Mn in place of Mg. Seems to have been made from a dilute H$_2$SO$_4$ solution of Mg and Al sulfates.

FeAl$_2$(SO$_4$)$_4$·22H$_2$O (Halotrichite) is monoclinic with $a = 20.47$, $b = 24.2$, $c = 6.17$ kX, $\beta = 101°$ ca. U.C. 4. Crystals acicular. Poor {010} cleavage. H. 1.5. G. 1.89. Y = b; Z $\wedge$ $c = 38°$. $(-)2V = 35°$; $n_X = 1.480$, $n_Y = 1.486$, $n_Z = 1.490$, $n_Z - n_X = 0.010$ Na. Colorless or pale yellow or green. Made from water solution.

---

[108] Lavenir: *Bull. Soc. Fr. Min.* XIV, p. 116 (1891).

(Zn,Fe,Mn)Al$_2$(SO$_4$)$_4$·22H$_2$O (Dietrichite) is monoclinic. Fibrous aggregates. H. 2. X = b; Z $\wedge$ c = 29° *ca.* (+)2V = large.[11] n_X = 1.475, n_Y = 1.480, n_Z = 1.488, all ±0.003, n_Z − n_X = 0.013. Color dirty white to brownish yellow. Said to have been made from water solution.

7. Formula Type A$_2$(XO$_4$)$_3$·qH$_2$O

Cr$_2$(SO$_4$)$_3$·18H$_2$O as obtained commercially is granular and amorphous with[109] n = 1.564 ± .003 Na. Color dark green. No crystals form; no X-ray pattern is obtained; it is isotropic.

La$_2$(SO$_4$)$_3$·9H$_2$O is hexagonal with c/a = 0.736. Crystals long prismatic; no cleavage. G. 2.82. Uniaxial positive with n_O = 1.564, n_E = 1.569, n_E − n_O = 0.005. Made from water solution.

Fe$_2$(SO$_4$)$_3$·9H$_2$O (Coquimbite) is hexagonal with a = 10.85, c = 17.03 kX. U.C. 4. Crystals short prismatic or pyramidal. Poor {10$\bar{1}$1} cleavage. H. 2.5. G. 2.11. Uniaxial positive with[110] n_O = 1.536, n_E = 1.572, n_E − n_O = 0.036. Color pale violet to amethystine; also yellowish or greenish. PD 8.26, 2.76, 5.45; 6–0040. Made from water solution containing an excess of H$_2$SO$_4$.

Fe$_2$(SO$_4$)$_3$·6H$_2$O (Lausenite) is monoclinic.[36] Crystals {010} laths long parallel to c. X $\wedge$ c = 22° red, 26° blue; Y = b. (−)2V = large, n_X = 1.598 C, 1.605 D, 1.624 F, n_Y = 1.627 C, 1.635 D, 1.656 F, n_Z = 1.648 C, 1.657 D, 1.681 F, n_Z − n_X = 0.052 D. Again: X $\wedge$ c = 27°, n_X = 1.598, n_Y = 1.628, n_Z = 1.654, n_Z − n_X = 0.056. Colorless. Made from water solution; stable from 50° to about 150° C.

Fe$_2$(SO$_4$)$_3$·7H$_2$O (Kornelite) is monoclinic[36] with $a:b:c$ = 0.707:1:0.542, β = 97°5'. Crystals laths or needles or fibers with {010} cleavage. G. 2.31. X $\wedge$ c = 20° ± 2°; Z = b. (+)2V = 49°–62°, r > v. n_X = 1.572, n_Y = 1.586, n_Z = 1.640, all ±0.003, n_Z − n_X = 0.068 Na. Color pale rose-pink to violet. Made from Fe$_2$O$_3$·SO$_3$·H$_2$O below 80° C.

Y$_2$(SO$_4$)$_3$·8H$_2$O is monoclinic with $a:b:c$ = 3.028:1:2.009, β = 118°25'. Crystals equant to columnar by elongation parallel to {11$\bar{1}$}. Twinning on {100}. Perfect {001} and distinct {101} cleavages. G. 2.56. X nearly normal to {001}; Y = b.[111] (+)2V = 50°43', r < v. n_X = 1.5433, n_Y = 1.549, n_Z = 1.5755, n_Z − n_X = 0.0322. Made from solution.

Pr$_2$(SO$_4$)$_3$·8H$_2$O is monoclinic with $a:b:c$ = 2.986:1:2.00, β = 118°. Crystals basal tablets or nearly equant with {001}, {11$\bar{1}$}, {100}, etc. Perfect {001} and distinct {10$\bar{1}$} cleavages. G. 2.82. X nearly normal to (001); Z = b.[111] (+)2V = 84°51' Li, 85°27' Na, 84°52' Tl; (abnormal

[109] V. A. Vigfusson: *pers. comm.* Dec. 18, 1930.

[110] Lausen: *Am. Min.* XIII, p. 203 (1928).

[111] Kraus: *Zeit. Krist.* XXXIV, p. 411 (1900); Dufet: *Bull. Soc. Fr. Min.* XXIV, p. 378 (1901).

variations in 2V between $\lambda = 580$ and 600 (an absorption band). $n_X = 1.5366$ Li, 1.5399 Na, 1.5430 Tl, $n_Y = 1.5459$ Li, 1.5494 Na, 1.5525 Tl, $n_Z = 1.5573$ Li, 1.5607 Na, 1.5641 Tl, $n_Z - n_X = 0.0208$ Na. Color dark green. Made from solution.

$Nd_2(SO_4)_3 \cdot 8H_2O$ is monoclinic with $a:b:c = 2.984:1:1.997$, $\beta = 118°$ ca. Crystals of varied habit. Perfect basal cleavage. G. 2.85. X nearly normal to $\{001\}$;[111] $Z = b$. $(+)2V = 83°49'$ Li, $83°57'$ Na, $83°48'$ Tl. $n_X = 1.5379$ Li, 1.5413 Na, 1.5441 Tl, $n_Y = 1.5469$ Li, 1.5505 Na, 1.5534 Tl, $n_Z = 1.5583$ Li, 1.5621 Na, 1.5652 Tl, $n_Z - n_X = 0.0092$ Na. Color light red with weak pleochroism and X and $Y > Z$. Made from solution. The same compound with Pr replacing some Nd has G. 2.83, $X \wedge c = 26°$ ca., $Z = b$. $(+)2V = 84°10'$. $n_X = 1.5392$, $n_Y = 1.5479$, $n_Z = 1.5592$, $n_Z - n_X = 0.020$. Color light red (to green).

$Sm_2(SO_4)_3 \cdot 8H_2O$ is monoclinic with $a:b:c = 3.003:1:2.002$, $\beta = 118°16'$. Crystals basal tablets, etc. Perfect $\{001\}$ cleavage. Twinning common on $\{001\}$. X nearly normal to $\{001\}$;[111] $Z = b$. $(+)2V = $ large. $n_X = 1.5395$ Li, 1.5427 Na, 1.5458 Tl, $n_Y = 1.5486$ Li, 1.5519 Na, 1.5551 Tl, $n_Z = 1.5594$ Li, 1.5629 Na, 1.5663 Tl, $n_Z - n_X = 0.0202$ Na. Made from solution.

$Al_2(SO_4)_3 \cdot 18H_2O$ **(Alunogen)** is triclinic with[112] $a:b:c = 0.836:1:0.675$, $\alpha = 89°58'$, $\beta = 97°26'$, $\gamma = 91°52'$. Crystals rare, prismatic; usually fibrous. Perfect $\{010\}$ cleavage; also (?) $\{100\}$ and $\{\bar{3}13\}$. H. 1.5–2. G. 1.78. X nearly $= b$; $Z \wedge c = 41°$. $(+)2V = 31°$, $n_X = 1.460$, $n_Y = 1.461$, $n_Z = 1.470$, $n_Z - n_X = 0.010$. Colorless. PD 4.42, 3.95, 2.48; 1–0348. The water content of alunogen varies easily; the indices depend on the water content. Indices given are for a sample with 15.5 H_2O. On heating to 75° C. the content was about 12.5 and the indices were $n_X = 1.483$, $n_Y = 1.484$, $n_Z = 1.496$. Over about 90° C. the material becomes isotropic with n about 1.50; at 290° C. the index is 1.54. The substance does not rehydrate easily on exposure. Made from solution in HCl.

8. Formula Type $A(XO_4)_2 \cdot qH_2O$

$Th(SO_4)_2 \cdot 8H_2O$ is monoclinic with $a:b:c = 0.754:1:0.557$, $\beta = 93°$. Crystals prismatic, striated parallel with $\{001\}$. $Y = b$; $Z \wedge c = +65°$. $(+)2V = 76°20'$, $r < v$ weak. $n_Y = 1.5168$, $n_Z - n_X = $ very weak. Made from solution at about 30° C.

G. SULFITES, ETC., CONTAINING HALOGEN OR HYDROXYL

$CsSO_3F$ is tetragonal[113] with $a = 5.61$, $c = 14.13$ Å. U.C. 4. Crystals basal plates. G. > 3.38. Good basal cleavage. Uniaxial negative with $n_O = $

---

[112] Larsen and Steiger: *Am. J. Sci.* XV, p. 1 (1928).
[113] Seifert: *Zeit. Krist.* CIV, p. 385 (1942).

1.4755, $n_E = 1.4645$, $n_O - n_E = 0.011$. Also slightly biaxial. Colorless. PD 3.48, 2.21, 1.73; 3–0371.

$(NH_4)_3PdSO_3Cl_3 \cdot H_2O$ is hexagonal rhombohedral with $c/a = 0.892$. Distinct prismatic cleavage. Uniaxial positive with $n_O = 1.643$, $n_E - n_O =$ strong. Color deep red with O carmine and E reddish yellow. Made from water solution.

H. SULFATES, ETC., CONTAINING HALOGEN, HYDROXYL, OR EXTRA OXYGEN

1. Formula Type $A_m(XO_4)_p Z_q$ with $m{:}p > 2{:}1$

$Na_3SO_4(F,Cl)$ **(Schairerite)** is hexagonal with $a = 12.12$, $c = 19.19\,kX$. Crystals basal tablets or rhombohedral. Distinct {0001} cleavage. H. 3.5. G. 2.612. Uniaxial positive with[114] $n_O = 1.436$, $n_E = 1.439$, $n_E - n_O = 0.003$ Na for the pure artificial F salt. With F:Cl $= 4{:}1$ $n_O = 1.440$, $n_E = 1.445$, $n_E - n_O = 0.005$; no cleavage. With F:Cl $= 1{:}1$ the compound is isometric. Colorless. PD 2.99, 2.69, 1.74; 2–0668. Made from water solution.

$Cu_3SO_4(OH)_4$ **(Antlerite)** is orthorhombic dipyramidal with $a = 8.22$, $b = 11.97$, $c = 6.02\,kX$. U.C. 4. Crystals often {010} tablets or equant or short prismatic. Perfect {010} and poor {100} cleavages. H. 3.5. G. 3.88. $X = b$; $Y = a$.[34] $(+)2V = 53°$, $n_X = 1.726$, $n_Y = 1.738$, $n_Z = 1.789$, $n_Z - n_X = 0.051$. Color green; pleochroic with X yellow-green, Y blue-green, Z green. PD 4.86, 2.57, 3.60; 7–407/8. Made from water solution.

$Cu_4SO_4(OH)_6$ **(Brochantite)** is monoclinic[114a] with $a = 13.05$, $b = 9.83$, $c = 5.85\,kX$, $\beta = 103°22'$. Crystals prismatic; twinning on {100} common. Perfect {100} cleavage. H. 3.5–4. G. 3.97. $X \wedge a = 13°$; $Y = b$; Z very near c. $(-)2V = 77° \pm 2°$, r < v medium.[34] $n_X = 1.728$, $n_Y = 1.771$, $n_Z = 1.800$, $n_Z - n_X = 0.072$. Color emerald green. PD 3.91, 6.5, 2.53; 3–0282. Made from water solution.

2. Formula Type $A_m(XO_4)_p Z_q$ with $m{:}p \approx 2{:}1$

$Pb_2SO_4(OH)_2$ is isometric[115] and isotropic with $n = 1.93$.

$KAl_3(SO_4)_2(OH)_6$ **(Alunite)** is hexagonal with $a = 6.96$, $c = 17.35\,kX$. Crystals rare, may be pseudo-cubic. Distinct {0001} cleavage. H. 3.5–4. G. 2.75. F. 7. Uniaxial positive with[116] $n_O = 1.572$, $n_E = 1.592$, $n_E - n_O = 0.020$. Colorless. PD 1.90, 1.75, 3.00; 4–0865*. Made by heating a solution of alum and aluminum sulfate in a sealed tube at 230° C.

[114] Foote and Schairer: *J. Am. Chem. Soc.* LII, p. 4202 (1930).
[114a] Palache: *Am. Min.* XXIV, p. 463 (1939).
[115] Merwin: *Proc. Am. Soc. Test. Mat.* XVII [2], p. 496 (1917).
[116] Michel-Lévy and Lacroix: *Les Minéraux des Roches*, p. 140 (1888).

KFe$_3$(SO$_4$)$_2$(OH)$_6$ (Jarosite) is hexagonal, ditrigonal-pyramidal, with $a = 7.20$, $c = 17.00$ kX. Crystals pseudo-cubic rhombohedrons. Distinct {0001} cleavage. H. 2.5–3.5. G. 2.9–3.2. Uniaxial negative[11] with $n_O = 1.820$, $n_E = 1.715$, $n_O - n_E = 0.105$. Also anomalously biaxial[117] with $(-)2V$ very small. $n_X = 1.715 \pm .003$, $n_Y = 1.817$, $n_Z = 1.820$, $n_Z - n_X = 0.105$. Color brown with O brown, E colorless. PD 3.08, 3.11, 2.29; 10–443. Made at 110° C. from a water solution.

NH$_4$Fe$_3$(SO$_4$)$_2$(OH)$_6$ (Ammoniojarosite) is hexagonal, ditrigonal-pyramidal with $a = 7.20$, $c = 17.00$ kX. Small grains may have hexagonal outline. G. 3.1 calc. Uniaxial negative with[118] $n_O = 1.800 \pm 0.005$, $n_E = 1.750 \pm 0.005$, $n_O - n_E = 0.05$. Again:[119] $n_O = 1.83$, $n_E = 1.745$, $n_O - n_E = 0.085$. Colorless.

RbFe$_3$(SO$_4$)$_2$(OH)$_6$ is hexagonal rhombohedral. Basal cleavage. Uniaxial negative. $n_O = 1.805$, $n_E = 1.720$, $n_O - n_E = 0.085$. Color brown. Easily formed in a pyrex tube at 110° C.

AgFe$_3$(SO$_4$)$_2$(OH)$_6$ (Argentojarosite) is hexagonal rhombohedral, with $a = 7.22$, $c = 16.40$ kX. Crystals {0001} scales. Basal cleavage. G. 3.66. Uniaxial negative with[24] $n_O = 1.882$, $n_E = 1.785$, $n_O - n_E = 0.097$. Color yellow to brown; pleochroic with O yellow, E pale yellow. Made from an acid solution at 110° C.

PbFe$_6$(SO$_4$)$_4$(OH)$_{12}$ (Plumbojarosite) is hexagonal scalenohedral with $a = 7.20$, $c = 33.60$ kX. Fair {10$\bar{1}$4} cleavage. H. 1 ca. G. 3.665. Uniaxial negative[120] with $n_O = 1.870$, $n_E = 1.783$, $n_O - n_E = 0.087$. Again:[11] $n_O = 1.875$, $n_E = 1.786$, $n_O - n_E = 0.089$ (with a little Na, K, Cu, Ca). Color brown; pleochroic with O yellow-brown, E nearly colorless. PD 2.78, 1.72, 3.57; 5–0635.

(H$_2$O)Fe$_3$(SO$_4$)$_2$[(OH)$_5$H$_2$O] (Carphosiderite) is hexagonal, ditrigonal pyramidal with $a = 7.16$, $c = 16.70$ kX. Crystals hexagonal plates or rhombohedrons. H. 4–4.5. G. 2.9(?). Uniaxial negative with[36] $n_O = 1.816$, $n_E = 1.728$, $n_O - n_E = 0.088$. Color yellow with O deep yellow, E pale yellow. PD 3.06, 4.9, 1.97; 2–0597. Made from acid solutions[36] of ferric sulfate up to 170° C.

Pb$_2$SO$_4$O (Lanarkite) is monoclinic prismatic with $a = 13.73$, $b = 5.68$, $c = 7.07$ kX, $\beta = 116°13'$. Crystals long parallel to b. Perfect {$\bar{2}$01} and poor {$\bar{4}$01} and {201} cleavages. H. 2–2.5. G. 6.92. Y = b;[121] Z $\wedge$ c = 30°. $(-)2V = 60° \pm 2°$, r > v strong, with inclined dispersion. $n_X = 1.928$,

[117] Schaller: *U. S. Geol. Surv. Bull.* 610, p. 137 (1916).
[118] Shannon: *Am. Min.* XII, p. 424 (1927).
[119] Ulrich: *Mém. Soc. Sci. Bohème* XXXVI, p. 34 (1931).
[120] Fairchild: *Am. Min.* XVIII, p. 543 (1933).
[121] Richmond and Wolfe: *Am. Min.* XXIII, p. 799 (1938).

$n_Y = 2.007$, $n_Z = 2.036$, all ± 0.003, $n_Z - n_X = 0.108$. Colorless or nearly so. PD 3.33, 2.95, 3.67; 6–0276. Made by fusing PbO with PbSO$_4$.

Cu$_2$SO$_4$O (Dolerophanite) is monoclinic prismatic with $a = 9.39$, $b = 6.30$, $c = 7.62$ kX, $\beta = 127°41'$. Crystals long parallel to b. Perfect $\{\bar{1}01\}$ cleavage. H. 3. G. 4.17. $Y = b^{121a}$; $Z \wedge c = +10°$. $(+)2V = 85°$, r > v strong with crossed dispersion. $n_X = 1.715$, $n_Y = 1.820$, $n_Z = 1.880$, $n_Z - n_X = 0.165$. Color brown; pleochroic with X deep brown, Y brownish yellow, Z lemon yellow. Made by ignition of CuSO$_4$ at 650° C.

CuPb(SO$_4$)(OH)$_2$ (Linarite) is monoclinic with $a:b:c = 1.716:1:0.8296$, $\beta = 102°37'$. Crystals prismatic along b. Distinct $\{100\}$ and poor $\{001\}$ cleavages. G. 5.3–5.4. X $\wedge$ $c = -14°$, $Z = b$.[122] $(-)2V = 79°59'$, r < v. $n_X = 1.8090$, $n_Y = 1.8380$, $n_Z = 1.8593$, $n_Z - n_X = 0.0503$. Color blue with weak pleochroism. PD 3.12, 3.53, 1.79; 4–0598. Found in many old furnace slags.

3. Formula Type A$_m$(XO$_4$)$_p$Z$_q\cdot$xH$_2$O

Ca$_4$Al$_2$SO$_4$(OH)$_{12}\cdot$6H$_2$O is hexagonal.[123] Crystals basal plates. G. 1.95. Positive elongation. Uniaxial negative with[11] $n_O = 1.504$, $n_E = 1.488$, $n_O - n_E = 0.016$. Again: $n_O = 1.517$, $n_E = 1.499$, $n_O - n_E = 0.018$. Partial dehydration (to 4H$_2$O?) leads to[124] $n_O = 1.519$, $n_E = 1.506$, $n_O - n_E = 0.013$. Dehydration at 110° C. to about 3H$_2$O leads to variable results, as $n_O = 1.529$–1.535, $n_E = 1.519$–1.527, $n_O - n_E = 0.010$–0.008. Not as stable as Ca$_6$Al$_2$(SO$_4$)$_3$(OH)$_{12}\cdot$26H$_2$O. Colorless. Produced by reaction of sulfate water on Portland cement; also from water solution at high temperature.

Cu$_4$SO$_4$(OH)$_6\cdot$H$_2$O(?) (Langite) is orthorhombic with $a:b:c = 0.5347:1:0.6346$. Crystals equant or lamellar. $\{001\}$ and $\{010\}$ cleavages. H. 2.5–3. G. 3.48–3.50. X = c; Y = b.[125] $(-)2V = 37°$–66°, $n_X = 1.654$, $n_Y = 1.713$, $n_Z = 1.722$, $n_Z - n_X = 0.068$ Na. Color blue or greenish. Pleochroic with X light yellow-green, Y blue-green, Z sky-blue. Made by treating Cu$_2$SO$_5$ with cold water. PD 3.91, 6.50, 2.53; 3–0282(?).

Al$_4$SO$_4$(OH)$_{10}\cdot$10H$_2$O (Paraluminite) is orthorhombic(?). X parallel with elongation.[125a] $(-)2V = $ small, $n_X = 1.463 \pm .003$, $n_Y = 1.471$, $n_Z = 1.471$, $n_Z - n_X = 0.008$. Color white to pale yellow. Found in concrete.

[121a] Richmond and Wolfe: *Am. Min.* XXV, p. 606 (1940); the usual meaning of "crossed dispersion" cannot apply if Y = b.

[122] Brugnatelli: *Zeit. Krist.* XXVIII, p. 307 (1897).

[123] Lerch, Ashton and Bogue: *J. Res. Nat. Bur. Stand.* II, p. 715 (1929).

[124] Mylius: *Acta Acad. Abo Math. Phys.* VII, No. 3 (1933).

[125] Meixner: *Zent. Min.* p. 11 (1941); Koritnig: *Zent. Min.* p. 154 (1941).

[125a] Hutton: *New Zealand J. Sci. Tech.* XXVI, 242 (1945).

$Ca_6Fe_2(SO_4)_3(OH)_{12} \cdot 26H_2O$ is hexagonal. Crystals prismatic with positive elongation. Uniaxial positive[126] with $n_O = 1.486$, $n_E = 1.492$, $n_O - n_E = 0.006$.

$Ca_6Al_2(SO_4)_3(OH)_{12} \cdot 26H_2O$ **(Ettringite)** is hexagonal with $a = 11.24$, $c = 21.45$ kX. U.C. 2. Crystals small prismatic. Perfect $\{10\bar{1}0\}$ cleavage. H. 2–2.5. G. 1.77. Uniaxial negative with $n_O = 1.464$, $n_E = 1.458$, $n_O - n_E = 0.006$. During dehydration the indices increase, n_E more rapidly than n_O, and the sign becomes positive.[127] Colorless. PD 9.73, 5.61, 3.88; 9–414. Made from solution at moderate temperature.

$KMgSO_4Cl \cdot 3H_2O$ **(Kainite)** is monoclinic with[127] $a = 19.05$, $b = 16.24$, $c = 9.86$ Å, $\beta = 94°55'$. Crystals nearly equant often with many faces. Perfect $\{001\}$ cleavage. H. 2.5–3. G. 2.15. $Y = b$; $Z \wedge c = 13°$. $(-)2V = 85°$ $ca.$, r > v very weak. $n_X = 1.494$, $n_Y = 1.505$, $n_Z = 1.516$, $n_Z - n_X = 0.022$. Colorless or may be stained blue, violet, gray, yellowish or reddish; blue or violet samples may be pleochroic with X violet, Y blue and Z yellowish. Made from water solutions[12⁻a] (rich in $MgCl_2$) between 13° C. and 95° C.

$Na_4Fe_2(SO_4)_4(OH)_2 \cdot 3H_2O$ **(Metasideronatrite)** is orthorhombic with $a:b:c = 0.4571:1:0.1187$. Crystals prismatic, rare. Perfect $\{100\}$ and $\{010\}$, and good $\{001\}$ cleavages. H. 2.5. G. 2.46. $X = a$; $Y = b$. $(+)2V = 60°$, r > v strong.[80] $n_X = 1.543$, $n_Y = 1.575$, $n_Z = 1.634$, $n_Z - n_X = 0.091$. Color yellow; pleochroic with X colorless, Y light yellow, Z brownish yellow. Made by dehydration of sideronatrite over sulfuric acid.

$Na_2Fe(SO_4)_2(OH) \cdot 3H_2O$ **(Sideronatrite)** is orthorhombic(?). Crystals acicular along c. Perfect $\{100\}$ cleavage. H. 1.5–2.5. G. 2.15–2.35. $X = a$; $Y = b$.[11] $(+)2V = 58° \pm 5°$ calc., r > v strong. $n_X = 1.508$, $n_Y = 1.525$, $n_Z = 1.586$, all ± 0.003, $n_Z - n_X = 0.078$. Color yellow of various shades. Pleochroic with X nearly colorless, Y very pale amber yellow, Z pale amber yellow. Made from water solution.

$K_2(UO_2)(SO_4)_2 \cdot 2H_2O$ is orthorhombic with[128] $a = 11.55$, $b = 13.78$, $c = 7.28$ Å. U.C. 4. Crystals basal tablets or pyramidal. Distinct $\{001\}$ cleavage. G. 3.33. $X = c$; $Y = a$. $(+)2V = 60°$ calc.; for[128] $\lambda = 720$ mμ: $n_X = 1.510$, $n_Y = 1.522$, $n_Z = 1.563$, $n_Z - n_X = 0.054$; for $\lambda = 580$ mμ: $n_X = 1.5144$, $n_Y = 1.5266$, $n_Z = 1.5705$, $n_Z - n_X = 0.0561$; for $\lambda = 500$ mμ: $n_X = 1.520$, $n_Y = 1.535$, $n_Z = 1.585$, $n_Z - n_X = 0.065$. Again:[129] $n_X = ?$, $n_Y = 1.529$, $n_Z = 1.575$. Not pleochroic. PD 6.81, 5.54, 3.65; 8–128. Made from water solution with NH_4OH added at 25° C.

[126] Bogue: *Chemistry of Portland Cement*, 1947, p. 424.

[127] Evans in *Dana's System of Mineralogy* II, p. 539 and 594 (1951).

[127a] Linstedt: *N. Jahrb. Miner. Monat.* 1955, p. 157.

[128] Nichols and Howes: *Carn. Inst. Publ.* 298, p. 220 (1919).

[129] Traill: *Am. Min.* XXXVII, p. 394 (1952).

$H_2(UO_2)(SO_4)_2 \cdot 5H_2O$ is orthorhombic[129] with $a = 12.86$, $b = 12.99$, $c = 11.57$ Å. U.C. 4. G. 3.16. Z = c. $(-)2V$ = very small, $n_X = 1.555$, $n_Y = 1.586$, $n_Z = 1.586$, $n_Z - n_X = 0.031$. Pleochroic with X colorless, Y and Z pale yellow. Made from water solution.

$(UO_2)_3(SO_4)_2(OH)_2 \cdot 8H_2O$ **(Zippeite)** is monoclinic with[129] $a = 8.81$, $b = 14.13$, $c = 8.85$ Å, $\beta = 104°15'$. U.C. 2. Crystals tiny {010} plates. Twinning on {001} very common. H. 3. G. 3.66. X = b; Z $\wedge$ c = 3°. $(-)2V = 83°$ calc. $n_X = 1.655$, $n_Y = 1.717$, $n_Z = 1.765$, $n_Z - n_X = 0.110$. Again:[11] $n_X = 1.64$, $n_Y = 1.718$, $n_Z = 1.766$, $n_Z - n_X = 0.126$. Color orange yellow with X colorless, Y pale yellow, Z yellow. PD 7.31, 3.66, 3.15; 8–402*. Made from water solution.

$(NH_4)_2UO_2(SO_4)_2 \cdot 2H_2O$ is monoclinic with[129] $a = 20.53$, $b = 7.30$, $c = 7.74$, $\beta = 99°25'$. U.C. 4. G. 3.07. $n_X = ?$, $n_Y = 1.555$, $n_Z = 1.600$. Pleochroic with X and Y colorless, Z pale green. PD 6.7, 3.38, 5.38; 8–182.

$(UO_2)_6(OH)_{10}SO_4 \cdot 12H_2O$ **(Uranopilite)**[129a] is probably monoclinic.[129] Crystals needles or laths. Perfect {010} cleavage. G. 3.7–4.0. Loses H_2O easily down to $5H_2O$. X = b; Y $\wedge$ c = 16°–18°. $(+)2V$ = moderate, r < v extreme. $n_X = 1.620$, $n_Y = 1.624$, $n_Z = 1.630$, $n_Z - n_X = 0.010$. Color yellow, not pleochroic. PD 7.12, 9.18, 4.28; 8–443.

$Be_2(C_2H_5)_2(SO_4)_2O \cdot 4H_2O$ is tetragonal with[130] $c/a = 0.671$. Crystals show {001}, {111}, {100}. No good cleavage. G. 1.857. Uniaxial negative with $n_O = 1.473$, $n_E = 1.435$, $n_O - n_E = 0.038$.

$(K,Na)_2Fe'''_3(SO_4)_6(OH) \cdot 9H_2O(?)$ **(Metavoltine)** is hexagonal with $a = 19.43$, $c = 18.60$ kX. U.C. 8. (It may contain some Fe''.) Crystals basal tablets. Perfect {0001} cleavage. H. 2.5. G. 2.396. Uniaxial negative with[80] $n_O = 1.589$–1.590, $n_E = 1.572$–1.574, $n_O - n_E = 0.017$–0.016. Color yellowish to greenish brown with O dark yellow to lemon, E light yellow (greenish).

$(UO_2)(SO_4) \cdot 3H_2O$ is orthorhombic with[129] $a = 12.58$, $b = 17.00$, $c = 6.73$ kX. U.C. 8. G. 3.84. Z = c. $(-)2V = 54°$ calc. $n_X = 1.574$, $n_Y = 1.589$, $n_Z = 1.593$, $n_Z - n_X = 0.019$. Pleochroic with X colorless, Y pale green, Z grayish green. PD 5.0, 3.99, 2.50; 8–191. Made from water solution.

$Fe(SO_4)(OH) \cdot 2H_2O$ **(Butlerite)** is monoclinic(?) with $a:b:c = 0.8752:1:0.7897$, $\beta = 108°35'$. Crystals {001} or {100} tablets or octahedral. Perfect {100} cleavage. H. 2.5. G. 2.55. X $\wedge$ c = 19°; Z = b.[36] $(-)2V$ = large, $n_X = 1.588$, $n_Y = 1.678$, $n_Z = 1.749$, $n_Z - n_X = 0.161$. Color deep orange; pleochroic with X colorless, Y faint yellow, Z light yellow. Made from water solution.

$Fe(SO_4)(OH) \cdot 3H_2O$ **(Amarantite)** is triclinic pinacoidal with $a:b:c =$

[129a] Bignand: *Bull. Soc. Fr. Min. Crist.* LXXVIII, p. 1 (1955).
[130] Jaeger: *Rec. Trav. Chim. Pays-Bas* III, p. 343 (1914).

0.769:1:0.574, $\alpha = 95°38.5'$, $\beta = 90°23.5'$ $\gamma = 97°13'$. Crystals long parallel c and nearly square in cross section. Perfect {010} and {100} cleavages. H. 2.5. G. 2.19; again: G. 2.286. Optical orientation: for X, $\phi = 82°$, $\rho = 72°$; for Y, $\phi = 178°$, $\rho = 68°$; for Z, $\phi = -44°$, $\rho = 29°$. $(-)2V = 30°$, r < v, with horizontal dispersion. $n_X{}^{80} = 1.516$, $n_Y = 1.598$, $n_Z = 1.621$, $n_Z - n_X = 0.105$ Na. Color red; pleochroic with X colorless, Y pale yellow, Z reddish brown. Made from water solution.

Fe″Fe₄‴(SO₄)₆(OH)₂·20H₂O (Copiapite) is triclinic pinacoidal with $a = 7.33$, $b = 18.15$, $c = 7.27$ kX, $\alpha = 93°51'$, $\beta = 101°30'$, $\gamma = 99°23'$. U.C. 1. Crystals {010} tablets, etc.; often twin scales. Perfect {010} and poor {$\bar{1}$01} cleavages. H. 2.5–3. G. 2.08–2.17. X nearly normal to {010}; Y and Z nearly parallel with the diagonals of [$\bar{1}$01] and [101]. $(+)2V^{36} = 52°$, r > v strong. $n_X = 1.531$, $n_Y = 1.546$, $n_Z = 1.597$, $n_Z - n_X = 0.066$. Color yellow; pleochroic with X (greenish) yellow, Y yellow to colorless, Z sulfur yellow to yellowish green. Made from water solution. A complete series of mix-crystals from Fe to Mg and probably also to Cu and Zn.

MgFe₄‴(SO₄)₆(OH)₂·20H₂O (Magnesiocopiapite) is triclinic and miscible in all proportions with copiapite. Properties very similar but $(+)2V = $ moderate,[11] $n_X = 1.510$, $n_Y = 1.535$, $n_Z = 1.575$, $n_Z - n_X = 0.065$.

CuFe₄‴(SO₄)₆(OH)₂·20H₂O (Cuprocopiapite) is triclinic and probably miscible in all proportions with copiapite. Properties very similar but[131] $(+)2V = 63°$, $n_X = 1.558$, $n_Y = 1.575$, $n_Z = 1.620$, $n_Z - n_X = 0.062$. Color green. Made from water solution.

I. COMPOUND SULFATES

Na₂₂K(CO₃)₂(SO₄)₉Cl (Hanksite) is hexagonal dipyramidal with $a = 10.46$, $c = 21.18$ kX. U.C. 2. Crystals short prismatic or basal tablets. Good {0001} cleavage. H. 3–3.5. G. 2.56. Uniaxial negative[132] with $n_O = 1.481$, $n_E = 1.461$, $n_O - n_E = 0.020$. Colorless or stained. PD 3.78, 2.78, 2.61; 4–0414. Made from water solution.

Na₆(CO₃)(SO₄)₂ (Burkeite) is orthorhombic with $a:b:c = 0.574:1:1.213$. Crystals {100} tablets; twinning on {110} common. H. 3.5. G. 2.57. X = c; Y = a. $(-)2V = 34°$, r > v distinct. $n_X = 1.450$, $n_Y = 1.490$, $n_Z = 1.492$, $n_Z - n_X = 0.042$. Color white, pale buff or grayish. PD 2.78, 3.78, 2.58; 2–0840. Made from water solution. It can take[133] either $3Na_2CO_3$ or $3Na_2SO_4$ in crystal solution. With maximum tenor (about 40 per cent) of $3Na_2CO_3$: $n_X = 1.445$, $n_Y = 1.495$, $n_Z = 1.497$, $n_Z - n_X = 0.052$. With

131 Berry: *Univ. Toronto Stud. Geol. Ser.* No. 51, p. 21 (1947).

132 Pabst in *Dana's System of Mineralogy*, II, p. 628 (1951).

133 Schroeder, Berk and Gabriel: *J. Am. Chem. Soc.* LVIII, p. 843 (1936).

maximum tenor (about 50 per cent) of $3Na_2SO_4$: $n_X = 1.465$, $n_Y = 1.486$, $n_Z = 1.488$, $n_Z - n_X = 0.023$.

$(NH_4)_4(NO_3)_2SO_4$ is orthorhombic with[134] $a:b:c = 1.106:1:3.804$. Crystals {001} hemimorphic tablets and similar to $(NH_4)_2SO_4$ in crystal habit with {001} cleavage and pseudo-hexagonal twinning on {110}. X = c; Y = b (or a). $(-)2V = 64°$, $n_X = 1.521$, $n_Y = 1.531$, $n_Z = 1.536$, $n_Z - n_X = 0.015$. Colorless. Made from water solution. Another sample of the same composition resembled NH_4NO_3 in crystal habit and had cleavages normal to X and to Y with $n_X = 1.469$, $n_Y = 1.528$, $n_Z = 1.543$, $n_Z - n_X = 0.074$, so $(-)2V = 55°$ calc.

$NaCa_3(UO_2)(CO_3)_3(SO_4)F \cdot 10H_2O$ (Schroeckingerite) is orthorhombic[135] with $a = 9.69$, $b = 16.83$, $c = 14.26$ Å. U.C. 4. Crystals often thin six-sided basal plates. G. 2.55. X = c; Y = b. $(-)2V = 16°$,[136] $n_X = 1.495$, $n_Y = 1.543$, $n_Z = 1.544$, $n_Z - n_X = 0.049$. Again: $(-)2V = 5°$, $n_X = 1.489$, $n_Y = 1.542$, $n_Z = 1.542$, $n_Z - n_X = 0.053$. Color yellow-green and pleochroic with X very pale yellow, Y and Z yellowish green. PD 7.26, 4.80, 8.48; 8–397. Made by mixing three solutions.[136]

$NaCa_3(UO_2)(CO_3)_3(SO_4)F \cdot 4H_2O$ is hexagonal with $a = 9.72$, $c = 11.03$ Å. U.C. 2. Crystals hexagonal basal plates. G. 2.86. Uniaxial negative with[135] $n_O = 1.581$, $n_E = 1.532$, $n_O - n_E = 0.049$. Color yellow with O pale yellow and E colorless. Made by dehydrating schroeckingerite.[135]

$Co(CO_3)(SO_4) \cdot 4NH_3 \cdot 3H_2O$ is monoclinic with[137] $a = 11.80$, $b = 10.60$, $c = 7.42$ kX, $\beta = 98°39'$. Crystals hemihedral or pseudo-orthorhombic by twinning on {100}. Perfect {100} and distinct {010} and {102} cleavages. G. 1.88. X $\wedge$ $c = 5°$; Z = b. $(-)2V = 24°$, $n_X = 1.595$, $n_Y = 1.631$, $n_Z = 1.632$, $n_Z - n_X = 0.037$ Na. Color ruby-red and strongly pleochroic.

$(NH_4)_5(NO_3)_3(SO_4)$ is monoclinic prismatic with[138] $a:b:c = 1.041:1:0.834$, $\beta = 92°42'$. $(-)2V = 50°$, $n_X = 1.488$, $n_Y = 1.540$ calc., $n_Z = 1.552$, $n_Z - n_X = 0.064$.

$4Co(NH_2)_2 \cdot CaSO_4$ is triclinic pinacoidal with[139] $a = 14.74$, $b = 14.95$, $c = 5.47$ kX, $\alpha = 92°6'$, $\beta = 90°22'$, $\gamma = 86°50'$. U.C. 4. Crystals equant with {110}, {1$\bar{1}$0}, {001}, {100}, {010}, etc. No cleavage. G. 1.80. X nearly parallel with c; Z nearly normal to (110). $(-)2V = 70°$, $n_X = 1.523$, $n_Y = 1.583$, $n_Z = 1.615$ D, $n_Z - n_X = 0.092$. Colorless.

[134] Thomas and Hallimond: *Trans. Faraday Soc.* XX, p. 56 (1924); Jänecke *et al.* *Zeit. anorg. Chem.* CLX, p. 171 (1927).

[135] Hurlbut: *Am. Min.* XXXIX, p. 901 (1954).

[136] Ross: *Am. Min.* XL, p. 515 (1955); Jaffe, Sherwood, and Peterson: *Am. Min.* XXXIII, p. 152 (1948).

[137] Strock: *Zeit. Krist.* LXXXVI, p. 42 (1933).

[138] Boky and Burovaya: *Mém. Soc. Russe Min.* LXVI, p. 45 (1937).

[139] Hendricks: *J. Phys. Chem.* XXXVII, p. 1109 (1933).

VIII. Molybdates and Tungstates

The molybdates and tungstates are classified as A. anhydrous, B. hydrated, C. compound. The anhydrous have three types of formula: AXO_4, $A_2(XO_4)_3$ and $AB(XO_4)_2$.

A. ANHYDROUS

1. Formula Type AXO_4

CaWO₄ (Scheelite) is tetragonal dipyramidal with $a = 5.246$, $c = 11.349$ kX. U.C. 4. Crystals pyramidal or tabular with distinct {101} cleavage. H. 4.5–5. G. 6.10. M.P. 1570° C. Decomposed by HCl. Uniaxial positive with[1] $n_O = 1.9124$ C, 1.9200 D, 1.9298 E, 1.9344 (475), $n_E = 1.9281$ C, 1.9365 D, 1.9468 E, 1.9525 (475), $n_E - n_O = 0.0165$ D. Color white. Made from fusion and in other ways. $CaWO_4$ with 10.3 per cent of $Ce_2(WO_4)_3$ is nearly the same, with $n_O = 1.9197$ C, 1.9266 D, 1.9365 E, $n_E = 1.9331$ C, 1.9412 D, 1.9517 E, $n_E - n_O = 0.0146$ D. Color yellow. PD 3.11, 1.60, 1.94; 8–145*.

CaMoO₄ (Powellite) is tetragonal dipyramidal with $a = 5.23$, $c = 11.44$ kX. U.C. 4. Crystals pyramidal; rarely thin basal plates. Poor {101} cleavage; also {112} and {001}. H. 3.5–4. G. 4.2. F. 4. Decomposed by HCl. Uniaxial positive with[2] $n_O = 1.959$, $n_E = 1.967$ for 667 mμ; $n_O = 1.974$, $n_E = 1.984$, $n_E - n_O = 0.010$ for 570 mμ; $n_O = 1.982$, $n_E = 1.993$ for 533 mμ. Color yellow, brown, greenish blue, etc. Made from fusion. $CaMoO_4$ with 10.28 per cent of WO_3 has[3] $n_O = 1.967 \pm 0.005$, $n_E = 1.978 \pm 0.005$, $n_E - n_O = 0.013$. $CaMoO_4$ with[1] 39 per cent of $(Nd,Pr)_2(MoO_4)_3$ is uniaxial positive[4] with $n_O = 2.007$, $n_E = 2.001$, $n_O - n_E = 0.006$. Color violet. $CaMoO_4$ with[1] 4.7 per cent of $Y_2(MoO_4)_3$ has $n_O = 1.978$, $n_E = 1.986$ for 667 mμ; $n_O = 1.993$, $n_E = 2.002$, $n_E - n_O = 0.009$ for 570 mμ; $n_O = 2.003$, $n_E = 2.012$ for 533 mμ. Color white. $CaMoO_4$ with[1] 21 per cent of

[1] Zambonini: *Bull. Soc. Fr. Min.* XXXVIII, p. 206 (1915).
[2] Zambonini: *Zeit. Krist.* LVIII, p. 248 (1923).
[3] Larsen: *U. S. Geol. Surv. Bull.* 679 (1921).
[4] Described as positive, but the indices make it negative.

$Ce_2(MoO_4)_3$ and 24.3 per cent of $Y_2(MoO_4)_3$ has $n_O = 1.9905$ C, 2.0004 D, 2.0163 E, $n_E = 1.9939$ C, 2.0049 D, 2.0208 E, $n_E - n_O = 0.0045$ D. Color orange red. PD 3.10, 1.93, 4.76; 7–212*.

SrMoO$_4$ is tetragonal[1] with $c/a = 1.574$. Crystals pyramidal. G. 4.15. Uniaxial positive. With 2.4 per cent of $Ce_2(MoO_4)_3$: $n_O = 1.9088$, $n_E = 1.9127$ for 667 $m\mu$; $n_O = 1.9210$, $n_E = 1.9258$, $n_E - n_O = 0.0048$ for 570 $m\mu$; $n_O = 1.9290$, $n_E = 1.9350$ for 533 $m\mu$. With 39.7 per cent of $Ce_2(MoO_4')_3$: $n_O = 1.937$, $n_E = 1.940$ for 667 $m\mu$; $n_O = 1.952$, $n_E = 1.956$, $n_E - n_O = 0.004$ for 570 $m\mu$; $n_O = 1.958$, $n_E = 1.963$ for 533 $m\mu$. Color yellow. Made from fusion with NaCl at 1200° C. PD 3.22, 2.01, 1.64; 8–482.

PbMoO$_4$ (Wulfenite) is tetragonal with $a = 5.401$, $c = 12.079\ kX$. U.C. 4. Crystals basal tablets or, rarely, pyramidal. Distinct {011} cleavage. H. 3. G. 6.5–7.0. M.P. 1065° C. Uniaxial negative with[5] $n_O = 2.3620$, $n_E = 2.2558$ for 687 $m\mu$, $n_O = 2.4053$, $n_E = 2.2826$, $n_O - n_E = 0.1227$ for 589 $m\mu$; $n_O = 2.4542$, $n_E = 2.3131$ for 527 $m\mu$. Color yellow; also gray, green, brown, red. Made by fusion. May contain some W for Mo and (or) Ca for Pb. PD 3.24, 2.02, 1.65; 8–475*.

PbWO$_4$ (Stolzite) is tetragonal with $a = 5.452$, $c = 12.031\ kX$. U.C. 4. Crystals often pyramidal. Poor {001} cleavage. H. 2.5–3. G. 7.9–8.3. M.P. 1123° C. Uniaxial negative with[3] $n_O = 2.27 \pm 0.01$, $n_E = 2.19 \pm 0.01$, $n_O - n_E = 0.08$. Color brown or yellow; rarely green or red. Made by sublimation or fusion. PD 3.24, 1.66, 2.02; 8–108*.

MnWO$_4$ (Huebnerite) is monoclinic prismatic with $a = 4.84$, $b = 5.76$, $c = 4.97\ kX$, $\beta = 90°53'$. Crystals usually prismatic. Perfect {010} cleavage. H. 4. G. 7.1. $X = b$; $Z \wedge c = 17°$ in acute β. $(+)2V = 75°$. $n_X = 2.150$, $n_Y = 2.195$, $n_Z = 2.283$, $n_Z - n_X = 0.133$. Color yellowish to reddish brown with varying pleochroism, for example: X green or yellow or red, Y yellowish brown or greenish yellow or red, Z olive green or red. Made by fusion.[6] PD 3.00, 2.96, 3.78; 10–477. MnWO$_4$ forms a complete series of mix-crystals (wolframite) with FeWO$_4$ (ferberite).

FeWO$_4$ (Ferberite) is monoclinic with $a = 4.70$, $b = 5.69$, $c = 4.93\ kX$, $\beta = 90°0'$. Crystals often long parallel with b; rarely prismatic. Perfect {010} cleavage. H. 4.5. G. 7.5. $X = b$; $Z \wedge c = 30°\ ca.$ (less with some Mn) in acute β. $(+)2V = 68°$, $n_X = 2.255$, $n_Y = 2.305$, $n_Z = 2.414$, $n_Z - n_X = 0.159$. Color black. Opaque even in thin flakes. Optic properties determined in infrared light.[7] Made by fusion.[6] PD 2.94, 1.71, 2.47; 10–449. FeWO$_4$ forms a complete series of mix-crystals (wolframite) with MnWO$_4$ (huebnerite).

[5] Ehringhaus: *N. Jahrb. Min. Bl. Bd.* XLIII, p. 566 (1920).

[6] Michel, *Bull. Soc. Min. France*, II, p. 142 (1879).

[7] Bailly: *Am. Min.* XXXIII, p. 519 (1948).

MgWO$_4$ is monoclinic[8] and isomorphous with wolframite with $a = 4.67$, $b = 5.66$, $c = 4.92$ Å., $\beta = 90°25'$. G. 5.66. Y $= b$ and extinction on {010} is at 4.5°. 2V $=$ large. Refringence very high and birefringence extreme. PD 2.93, 3.70, 4.68; 7–190.

PbWO$_4$ (Raspite) is monoclinic prismatic with $a:b:c = 1.345:1:1.115$, $\beta = 107°37'$. Crystals usually {100} tablets with {001}, {011}, {010}, etc. Perfect {100} cleavage. H. 2.5–3. G. 8.46. Y $= b$,[3] Z $\wedge c \approx 30°$. (+)2V $=$ very small. n_X and $n_Y = 2.27 \pm 0.02$, $n_Z = 2.30 \pm 0.02$, $n_Z - n_X = 0.03$. Color brown, yellow, gray. Two phases of PbWO$_4$ have been made; they are probably stolzite and raspite. PD 3.25, 2.02, 1.66; 8–476 (raspite?); 3.24, 1.66, 2.02; 8–108 (stolzite).

2. Formula Type AB(XO$_4$)$_2$

NaAl(WO$_4$)$_2$ is orthorhombic.[8a] Crystals acicular. $n_X = 1.658$, $n_Y = ?$, $n_Z = 1.702$, $n_Z - n_X = 0.044$. Color white. Made from fusion.

3. Formula Type A$_2$(XO$_4$)$_3$

Y$_2$(MoO$_4$)$_3$ is tetragonal with $c/a = 1.542$. Crystals pyramidal with {001}. Distinct basal cleavage. G. 4.79. M.P. 1347° C. Uniaxial positive with $n_E = 2.013$ for 667 $m\mu$, 2.031 for 570 $m\mu$, and 2.043 for 533 $m\mu$. $n_E - n_O =$ very weak. Also slightly biaxial with 2E $= 10°$ or less. Also orthorhombic with perfect {001} and distinct {110} cleavages. Color white or yellowish. Made from fusion.

Ce$_2$(MoO$_4$)$_3$ is tetragonal[1] (above 900° C.) with $c/a = 1.562$. Uniaxial negative with $n_O = 2.0185$, $n_E = 2.0067$ for 667 $m\mu$; $n_O = 2.0403$, $n_E = 2.0277$, $n_O - n_E = 0.0126$ for 570 $m\mu$; $n_O = 2.0512$, $n_E = 2.0375$ for 533 $m\mu$. Color orange to red; yellow in powder. Made by heating to about 900° C. Metastable at 0° C., the stable form being orthorhombic and dark green, not measured optically.

Pr$_2$(MoO$_4$)$_3$ is tetragonal[1] with $c/a = 1.544$. Crystals pyramidal. G. 4.84. M.P. 1030° C. Uniaxial negative with $n_E = 1.990$ for 667 $m\mu$, 2.007 for 570 $m\mu$ and 2.016 for 533 $m\mu$. $n_O - n_E =$ weak: Color grass-green. Made from fusion.

(Nd,Pr)$_2$(MoO$_4$)$_3$ is tetragonal[1] with $c/a = 1.549$. Crystals pyramidal or {001} tablets. G. 4.96. M.P. 1125–1144° C. Uniaxial negative with $n =$ 2.012 C, 2.026 D, 2.054 F, $n_O - n_E =$ weak. Made from fusion.

Nd$_2$(MoO$_4$)$_3$ is tetragonal[1] with $c/a = 1.548$. Crystals pyramidal. G. 5.14. M.P. 1176° C. Uniaxial negative with $n_O = 2.0052$, $n_E = 2.0038$ for 667 $m\mu$; $n_O = 2.0239$, $n_E = 2.0218$, $n_O - n_E = 0.0021$ for 570 $m\mu$; $n_O = 2.0313$, $n_E = 2.0293$ for 533 $m\mu$. Color violet. Made from fusion.

[8] Machatschki: *Zeit. Krist.* LXVII, p. 163 (1928).
[8a] Saalfeld: *N. Jahrb. Min. Monatshefte*, 1955, p. 207.

B. HYDRATED

$Na_2WO_4 \cdot 2H_2O$ is orthorhombic with $a:b:c = 0.800:1:0.647$. Crystals basal tablets with good basal cleavage. G. 3.25. $X = b$; $Y = a$,[9] $(+)2V = 25°$ D, $2V_F - 2V_C = 9°$. $n_X = 1.5526$, $n_Y = 1.5533$, $n_Z = 1.5695$, $n_Z - n_X = 0.0169$. Dispersion (F—C) for n_X, 0.0123; for n_Y, 0.0130; for n_Z, 0.0138. PD 6.9, 4.22, 3.17; 1–0107.

$(NH_4)_3H_6Al(MoO_4)_6 \cdot 7H_2O$ is probably orthorhombic[10] in rhombs (assumed to be basal plates) with $(110) \wedge (1\bar{1}0) = 86°$ and symmetrical extinction with the fast ray parallel to b. Parallel extinction when placed on edge. $n_1 (=n_X$ or $n_Y) = 1.700$, $n_2 (=n_Y$ or $n_Z) = 1.741$, $n_2 - n_1 = 0.041$. Colorless. Made from water solution.

$Fe_2(MoO_4)_3 \cdot 8H_2O$? (Ferrimolybdite) is probably orthorhombic. Massive or fibrous. Soft. G. 2.99. Z parallel fibers.[11] $(+)2V =$ small to $28°$, $r < v$ marked. $n_X = 1.78$, $n_Y = 1.79$, $n_Z = 2.04$, $n_Z - n_X = 0.26$. Again: $n_X = 1.74$, $n_Y = 1.75$, $n_Z = 1.95$, $n_Z - n_X = 0.21$. Also: $n_X = 1.720$, $n_Y = 1.733$, $n_Z = 1.935$, $n_Z - n_X = 0.215$. This variation in indices seems probably due to variation in water content, which occurs easily. Color yellow; pleochroic with X and Y clear and nearly colorless, Z dirty gray to canary yellow.

$H_6Mg(WO_4)_4 \cdot 5H_2O$ is monoclinic with $a:b:c = 0.676:1:0.779$, $\beta = 106°43'$. Crystals basal plates. $X \wedge c = -66°$; $Z = b$. $(+)2V = 77°50'$, $r < v$ weak. $n_Y = 1.74$, $n_Z - n_X = ?$. Made from barium metatungstate and magnesium sulfate.

$H_8Na_6(MoO_4)_7 \cdot 18H_2O$ is monoclinic with $a:b:c = 2.092:1:2.024$, $\beta = 103°25'$. Crystals short columnar {100} and {010}, twinned on {100}, with poor {100} cleavage. $X = b$; $Z \wedge c = -85°$ red, $-84°30'$ Na, $-83°$ blue. $(+)2V = 84°16'$ red, $84°6'$ Na, $83°$ blue, $r > v$ weak. $n_Y = 1.627$, $n_Z - n_X =$ strong. Made from HNO_3 solution of sodium molybdate.

C. COMPOUND MOLYBDATES AND TUNGSTATES

$Li_6Te(MoO_4)_6 \cdot 13H_2O$ is hexagonal with[9] $c/a = 1.915$. Crystals often flattened on a rhombohedral face. Doubtful basal cleavage. H. 2.5. G. 2.2. Uniaxial negative with $n_O = 1.703$, $n_E = 1.612$, $n_O - n_E = 0.091$. Colorless to very pale pink. Made from water solution.

$K_6Te(MoO_4)_6 \cdot 8H_2O$ is orthorhombic and pseudo-tetragonal[11a] with

[9] H. E. Merwin: *pers. comm.* March 25, 1931.
[10] Staples: *Am. Min.* XXI, p. 613 (1936).
[11] Larsen and Berman: *U. S. Geol. Surv. Bull.* 848 (1934).
[11a] Donnay and Mélon: *Proc. Nat. Acad. Sci.* XX, p. 327 (1934).

$a:b:c = 1:1:1.052$. Crystals equant or tabular on $\{010\}$ or $\{100\}$. H. 2.5. G. 3.25. Y = a; Z = b. $(+)2V = 81°$, $n_X = 1.66$, $n_Y = 1.70$, $n_Z = 1.76$, $n_Z - n_X = 0.10$. Colorless.

$Na_6P_2Mo_5O_{23} \cdot 14H_2O$ is orthorhombic with $a:b:c = 0.797:1:1.073$. Crystals prismatic. Perfect $\{102\}$ cleavage. X = b; Y = a. $(-)2V = 51°18'$ Na, r < v weak. $n_X = 1.5906$ Li, 1.5962 Na, 1.6017 Tl, $n_Y = 1.6328$ Li, 1.6411 Na, 1.6494 Tl, $n_Z = 1.6430$ Li, 1.6520 Na, 1.6610 Tl, $n_Z - n_X = 0.0558$ Na. Colorless.

$Sr_2SiW_{12}O_{40} \cdot 16H_2O$ is monoclinic with $a:b:c = 1.845:1:1.570$, $\beta = 104°36'$. Crystals prismatic with $\{110\}$, $\{100\}$, $\{10\bar{1}\}$, $\{001\}$, $\{011\}$, etc. X = b; Z $\wedge$ c = $-17°$. $(+)2V = 86°50'$ Na, r < v strong. $n_Y = 1.749$, $n_Z - n_X$ = rather strong. Made from water solution above 50° C.

$Be_2SiW_{12}O_{40} \cdot 16H_2O$ is monoclinic with $a:b:c = 1.799:1:1.544$, $\beta = 103°53'$. Crystals short prismatic with $\{110\}$, $\{100\}$, $\{10\bar{1}\}$ and $\{011\}$. X = b; Z $\wedge$ c = $-14°$. $(-)2V = 78°44'$ Na, r > v very strong. $n_Y = 1.816$, $n_Z - n_Y$ = rather strong. Made from solution above 30° C.

$(NH_4)_6Te_2(OH)_6(MoO_4)_6 \cdot 7H_2O$ is monoclinic with[12] $a:b:c = 1.891:1:1.073$, $\beta = 115°38'$. Crystals basal tablets with distinct $\{100\}$ cleavage. H. 2.5. G. 2.22. X = b; Z $\wedge$ c = $-58.5°$. $(-)2V = 58°$ calc. $n_X = 1.684$, $n_Y = 1.727$, $n_Z = 1.741$, $n_Z - n_X = 0.057$. Made from water solution.

$Cs_6Te(MoO_4)_6 \cdot 7H_2O$ is triclinic with[13] $a:b:c = 0.950:1:0.606$, $\alpha = 96°41'$, $\beta = 102°1'$, $\gamma = 101°31'$. Crystals of varied habit. No cleavage or twinning seen. $(+)2V = 34°$, r < v weak. $n_X = 1.709$, $n_Y = 1.716$, $n_Z = 1.797$, $n_Z - n_X = 0.088$. Colorless. Another caesium telluro-molybdate is also triclinic with[13] $a:b:c = 0.937:1:0.799$, $\alpha = 93°45'$, $\beta = 94°8'$, $\gamma = 88°21'$. Crystals $\{1\bar{1}0\}$ tablets. No cleavage or twinning seen. $(-)2V = 30°$, r > v strong. $n_X = 1.669$, $n_Y = 1.734$, $n_Z = 1.738$, $n_Z - n_X = 0.069$. Colorless. Made from water solution. Unstable in air.

$Na_6Te(MoO_4)_6 \cdot 22H_2O$ is triclinic with[14] $a:b:c = 0.955:1:0.934$, $\alpha = 115°22'$, $\beta = 105°14'$, $\gamma = 89°54'$. Crystals often $\{100\}$ or $\{010\}$ tablets. No cleavage or twinning seen. H. 2.5. G. 2.58. X makes angles of 102.5°, 58.5°, and 29.5° with the normals to (100), (010), and (001); Y makes angles of 42°, 110°, and 63°, and Z makes angles of 129°, 140°, and 102.5° with the same normals. The extinction angle to the edge (100):(010) is 34° on (100) and 17° on (010). $(-)2V = 51°$, r > v. $n_X = 1.577$, $n_Y = 1.662$, $n_Z = 1.683$, all ± 0.003, $n_Z - n_X = 0.106$. Colorless. Alters slowly in dry air.

[12] Donnay and Mélon: *Am. Min.* XXI, p. 250 (1936).
[13] Donnay and Mélon: *Am. Min.* XXI, p. 299 (1936).
[14] Donnay and Mélon: *Am. Min.* XVIII, p. 225 (1933).

4Na₂O·P₂O₅·24WO₃·nH₂O is triclinic with[15] $a:b:c = 1.112:1:1.065$, $\alpha = 91°2'$, $\beta = 94°13'$, $\gamma = 83°46'$. Crystals equant. $(+)2V = 69°$, $n_X = 1.766$, $n_Y = 1.776$, $n_Z = 1.789$, $n_Z - n_X = 0.023$. Readily attacked in the air.

[15] Bokii: *Trudy Inst. Krist. Nauk. U.S.S.R.* 1947, No. 3. [*Chem. Abstr.* XLII, p. 3764 (1950)].

IX. Phosphates, etc.

The phosphates, vanadates, arsenates and antimonates are included in this division. The arrangement begins with anhydrous salts which are followed by hydrated salts, and then salts containing halogen, hydroxyl or extra oxygen. Phosphites, metaphosphates, hypophosphates and pyrophosphates are then considered, and finally come some compound phosphates. An outline follows:

A. ANHYDROUS ACID PHOSPHATES, ETC.

1. Formula Type AH_2XO_4 (or A_2HXO_4)

$KH_2(PO_4)$ is tetragonal scalenohedral with $c/a = 0.939$. Crystals simple prisms terminated by a simple pyramid. No distinct cleavage. G. 2.34.

Uniaxial negative[1] with $n_O = 1.5064$ C, 1.5095 D, 1.5154 F, $n_E = 1.4664$ C, 1.4684 D, 1.4734 F, $n_O - n_E = 0.0411$ D. Colorless. Made from cold solution.

$KH_2(AsO_4)$ is tetragonal scalenohedral with $c/a = 0.938$. Crystals simple prisms terminated by a simple pyramid. G. 2.88. Uniaxial negative with[1,2] $n_O = 1.5632$ C, 1.5674 D, 1.5762 F, $n_E = 1.5146$ C, 1.5179 D, 1.5252 F, $n_O - n_E = 0.0495$ D. Colorless.

$NH_4H_2(PO_4)$ is tetragonal scalenohedral with $c/a = 1.0076$. Crystals prismatic terminated by a pyramid. G. 1.80. Uniaxial negative[1] with $n_O = 1.5212$ C, 1.5246 D, 1.5314 F, $n_E = 1.4768$ C, 1.4792 D, 1.4847 F, $n_O - n_E = 0.0454$ D. Colorless. PD 5.32, 3.08, 3.07; 6–0125.

$NH_4H_2(AsO_4)$ is tetragonal scalenohedral with $c/a = 1.0035$. Crystals prismatic or pyramidal. No distinct cleavage. G. 2.32. Uniaxial negative[1] with $n_O = 1.5721$ C, 1.5766 D, 1.5859 F, $n_E = 1.5186$ C, 1.5217 D, 1.5296 F, $n_O - n_E = 0.0549$ D. Colorless.

$Ag_2H(PO_4)$ is hexagonal (trigonal) with $c/a = 0.7297$. Crystals prisms or basal tablets. Very unstable in light or moisture. Uniaxial negative with[3] $n_O = 1.8036$ Na, $n_E = 1.7983$, $n_O - n_E = 0.0053$.

$NaH_2(PO_4)$ is biaxial with[4] $(-)2V = 64°$, $n_X = 1.481$, $n_Y = 1.507$, $n_Z = 1.517$, $n_Z - n_X = 0.036$. Colorless.

$Na_2H(PO_4)$ is biaxial with[4] $(+)2V = 78°$, $n_X = 1.483$, $n_Y = 1.499$, $n_Z = 1.525$, $n_Z - n_X = 0.042$. Formed by evaporation at 105° C.

$(NH_4)_2H(PO_4)$ is monoclinic prismatic with $a{:}b{:}c = 1.198{:}1{:}1.655$, $\beta = 113°14'$. Crystals equant with[5] $\{110\}$, $\{001\}$, $\{10\bar{1}\}$, etc., or long parallel with b. $(-)2V = 28°$, $n_X = 1.468$, $n_Y = 1.570$, $n_Z = 1.582$, $n_Z - n_X = 0.114$. PD 5.05, 3.24, 3.21; 8–33.

2. Formula Type $AHXO_4$

$SrH(PO_4)$ is orthorhombic with $a{:}b{:}c = 0.648{:}1{:}0.858$. Crystals thin $\{100\}$ plates. G. 3.54. $Y = a$.[6] $n_X = 1.608$, $n_Y = ?$, $n_Z = 1.625$, $n_Z - n_X = 0.017$. Colorless. Made from solution above 150° C.

$BaH(PO_4)$ is orthorhombic with $a{:}b{:}c = 0.713{:}1{:}0.812$. Crystals short prisms. G. 4.16. $Y = a$.[6] $n_X = 1.617$, $n_Y = ?$, $n_Z = 1.635$, $n_Z - n_X = 0.018$. Colorless. Made from solution. PD 3.59, 2.52, 3.53; 9–113.

$PbH(AsO_4)$ (Schultenite) is monoclinic with $a{:}b{:}c = 0.865{:}1{:}0.720$, $\beta = 95°24'$. Crystals $\{010\}$ plates. Distinct $\{010\}$ cleavage. H. 2.5. G. 5.94.

[1] Topsøe and Christiansen: *Ann. Chim. Phys.* I, p. 33 (1874).
[2] Topsøe: *Sitz. Akad. Wiss. Wien* LXVI (II), p. 32 (1872).
[3] Dufet: *Bull. Soc. Fr. Min.* IX, p. 36 (1886).
[4] Ingerson and Morey: *Am. Min.* XXVIII, p. 448 (1943).
[5] Data from A. F. Kirkpatrick of the American Cyanamid Co.
[6] Gaubert: *Bull. Soc. Fr. Min.* L, p. 504 (1927).

$X = b$; $Y \wedge c^7 = -24°$, $Z \wedge c = +66°$; $(+)2V = 58°$, $n_X = 1.8903$ (calc.), $n_Y = 1.9097$, $n_Z = 1.9765$ Na, $n_Z - n_X = 0.0862$. Colorless. Made by cooling a boiling solution of the salt in dilute HNO_3. Used as an insecticide. PD 3.39, 3.17, 2.93; 1–0635.

CaH(PO$_4$) (Monetite) is triclinic pinacoidal[7a] with $a = 6.91$, $b = 6.66$, $c = 7.02$ Å, $\alpha = 96°7'$, $\beta = 103°53'$, $\gamma = 89°11'$. Crystals thin {010} plates; often in crusts or stalactites. H. 3.5. G. 2.93. F. 3. Soluble in acid. X nearly normal to {11$\bar{1}$} and at 52° to the normal to {010}. On (010) an extinction is at 15° with (101) and at 38° with (01$\bar{1}$); on (001) an extinction is at 30° with (010). $(-)2V = $ large,[8] $r > v$ weak. $n_X = 1.587$, $n_Y \approx 1.615$, $n_Z = 1.640$, $n_Z - n_X = 0.053$. Colorless. Made from solution above 50° C. PD 2.96, 3.35, 3.37; 9–80.

SrH(AsO$_4$) is triclinic with $a:b:c = 0.647:1:0.835$, $\alpha = 86°32'$, $\beta = 90°46'$, $\gamma = 92°4'$. Crystals long parallel b. G. 4.03. On (100) an extinction at 14° to b^6 in obtuse angle α. $n_X = 1.65$, $n_Y = ?$, $n_Z = 1.67$, $n_Z - n_X = 0.02$. Colorless. Made from solution.

CaH(AsO$_4$) is triclinic(?). G. 3.47. Crystals long plates with inclined extinction[9] and two "true" indices—1.625 and 1.655. Again:[10] $n_X = 1.635$, $n_Y = 1.650$, $n_Z = 1.653$, $n_Z - n_Y = 0.018$. $\therefore (-)2V = 50°$ ca.

3. Formula Type AH$_4$(XO$_4$)$_2$ or ABH$_2$(XO$_4$)$_2$

CaH$_4$(PO$_4$)$_2$[11] is triclinic with[7a] $a = 5.55$, $b = 7.60$, $c = 9.07$ Å. $\alpha = 121°54'$, $\beta = 108°48'$, $\gamma = 87°28'$. Crystals rods parallel with a, or {010} or {01$\bar{1}$} tablets. No cleavage seen. G. 2.546. It decomposes at 268° C. The XY plane is normal to {010} and nearly parallel with a, Y inclined 15° to {010} in obtuse angle γ. $(+)2V = 85°14'$ calc., $r < v$ very weak. For $\lambda = 425 \, m\mu$ $n_X = 1.543$, $n_Y = 1.567$, $n_Z = 1.596$, $n_Z - n_X = 0.053$. For $\lambda = 610 \, m\mu$ $n_X = 1.548$, $n_Y = 1.572$, $n_Z = 1.602$, $n_Z - n_X = 0.054$. Colorless. Made from water solution at 130° C. PD 3.63, 3.61, 3.49; 9–390.

PbH$_4$(AsO$_4$)$_2$ is triclinic.[12] Crystals rhomboidal plates with an angle of 68°. G. 4.46. $(-?)2V = ?$, $n_X = 1.74$, $n_Y = 1.82$, $n_Z = ?$, $n_Z - n_X > 0.08$. Extinction at 8° to a long edge.

KFeH$_2$(PO$_4$)$_2$ is triclinic[13] with $\alpha = 106°$, $\beta = 109°$, $\gamma = 99°$. Crystals {010} tablets. Twinning common on {110}. G. 2.90. Optic plane nearly

[7] Spencer: *Min. Mag.* XXI, p. 149 (1926).

[7a] Smith, Lehr and Brown: *Am. Min.* XL, p. 893 (1955).

[8] Hill and Hendricks: *Ind. Eng. Chem.* XXVIII, p. 440 (1936).

[9] Nelson and Haring: *J. Am. Chem. Soc.* LIX, p. 2216 (1937).

[10] Guerin: *Ann. Chim. Paris*, XVI p. 101 (1941).

[11] Bale, Bonner, Hodge, Adler, Wreath and Bell: *Ind. Eng. Chem. Anal. Ed.* XVII, p. 491 (1945).

[12] McDonnell and Smith: *J. Am. Chem. Soc.* XXXVIII, p. 2027 (1916).

[13] Haseman, Lehr and Smith: *Proc. Soil Sci. Soc. Am.* XV, p. 76 (1950).

normal to $\{010\}$. X nearly normal to $\{001\}$, $(-)2V = 66°$, r < v. $n_X = 1.631$, $n_Y = 1.665$, $n_Z = 1.680$, $n_Z - n_X = 0.049$. Color lavender.

$NH_4FeH_2(PO_4)_2$ is columnar[14] in spherulites. n_1 (parallel width) $= ca.$ 1.67; n_2 (parallel length) $= ca.$ 1.66, $n_2 - n_1 = 0.01$.

B. ANHYDROUS NORMAL PHOSPHATES, ETC.

1. Formula Type A_3XO_4

H_3PO_4 is monoclinic with[14a] $a = 5.80$, $b = 4.85$, $c = 11.62$ Å, $\beta = 95°30'$. Crystals prismatic parallel b. No cleavage seen. Y $= b$; Z $\wedge$ $c = 28°$ in acute β. $(-)2V = 12°16'$, r < v weak. $n_X = 1.455$, $n_Y = 1.504$, $n_Z = 1.505$, $n_Z - n_X = 0.050$ for $\lambda = 425$ mμ. Colorless.

Na_3PO_4 is monoclinic.[15] Crystals equant with $\{100\}$, $\{110\}$, $\{001\}$, etc. Common twinning on $\{100\}$. Y $\wedge$ $c = 10°$ $ca.$; Z $= b$. $(+)2V = 76°$ calc., r > v distinct. $n_X = 1.493$, $n_Y = 1.499$, $n_Z = 1.508$, $n_Z - n_X = 0.015$. Colorless. PD 2.55, 4.25, 2.70; 1–1103.

2. Formula Type $A_3(XO_4)_2$

$Ca_3(PO_4)_2$ **(Whitlockite)** is hexagonal with $a = 10.32$, $c = 36.9$ kX. Crystals rhombohedral; rarely basal tablets. No cleavage. H. 5. G. 3.12. Inverts at 1350° C. Uniaxial negative with[16] $n_O = 1.629$, $n_E = 1.626$, $n_O - n_E = 0.003$. Again:[11] $n_O = 1.622$, $n_E = 1.620$, $n_O - n_E = 0.002$. With some CO_3 (in place of PO_4) the indices are notably lower—$n_O = 1.607$, $n_E = 1.604$. Mg, Fe and Mn may replace some Ca. Colorless, gray or yellowish. Found in some slags. Another phase of $Ca_3(PO_4)_2$ (stable above about 1200° C.) is monoclinic[17] with $a = 12.86$, $b = 9.11$, $c = 15.23$ Å. $\beta = 125°20'$. U.C. 8. G. 2.814. M.P. 1720° C. It has two sets of polysynthetic twinning nearly at right angles with extinction nearly parallel to the twinning. $(+)2V = 75°$,[18] $n_X = 1.588$, $n_Y = 1.5891$ calc., $n_Z = 1.591$, $n_Z - n_X = 0.003$. Colorless. Found in some slags. PD 2.91, 2.62, 3.88; 9–348 (α-); 2.88, 2.61, 3.21; 9–169 (β-).

$Pb_3(PO_4)_2$ is hexagonal.[19] Crystals prismatic. M.P. 1015° C. Uniaxial negative with $n_O = 1.9588$ C, 1.9702 D, 1.9994 F, $n_Z = 1.9261$ C, 1.9364 D, 1.9618 F, $n_O - n_E = 0.0338$ D. Colorless. Made from fusion. It may take some Ce in place of Pb. With 3 per cent of $CePO_4$ crystals are golden yellow

[14] Data from T. G. Rochow of the American Cyanamid Co.

[14a] Smith, Brown and Lehr: *J. Am. Chem. Soc.* LXXVII, p. 2728 (1955).

[15] Schroeder, Berk and Gabriel: *J. Am. Chem. Soc.* LIX, p. 1783 (1937).

[16] Agrell: *J. Iron Steel Inst. London* CLII, p. 19 (1945).

[17] MacKay: *Acta Cryst.* VI, p. 743 (1953).

[18] Hill, Hendricks, Jefferson and Reynolds: *Ind. Eng. Chem.* XXIX, p. 1299 (1937).

[19] Zambonini: *Bull. Soc. Fr. Min.* XXXVIII, p. 206 (1915).

with O canary yellow and E colorless; then $n_O = 1.9586$ C, 1.9697 D, 1.9995 F, $n_E = 1.9221$ C, 1.9326 D, 1.9591 F, $n_O - n_E = 0.0371$ D. PD 2.88, 2.79, 3.99; 6–0431*.

3. Formula Type AXO$_4$

BPO$_4$ is tetragonal[20] pyramidal with $a = 4.332$, $c = 6.640$ kX. Crystals sphenoidal with a structure related to that of cristobalite. G. 2.76. Uniaxial positive with[20] $n_O = 1.5947$, $n_E = 1.6013$, $n_E - n_O = 0.0066$ D. Colorless. PD 3.62, 2.25, 1.87; 1–0519.

BAsO$_4$ is tetragonal[20] pyramidal with $a = 4.458$, $c = 6.796$ kX. Crystals pyramidal with a structure related to that of cristobalite. G. 3.64. Uniaxial positive with[20] $n_O = 1.681$, $n_E = 1.690$, $n_E - n_O = 0.009$ D. Colorless. PD 3.74, 2.32, 1.50; 3–0314.

YPO$_4$ (Xenotime) is tetragonal with $a = 6.88$, $c = 6.03$ kX. U.C. 4. Isostructural with zircon (ZrSiO$_4$). Crystals prismatic or pyramidal. Good {100} cleavage. H. 4–5. G. 4.4 ca. Uniaxial positive with $n_O = 1.7207$, $n_E = 1.8155$, $n_E - n_O = 0.0948$. Again:[21] $n_O = 1.720$, $n_E = 1.827$, $n_E - n_O = 0.107$. Color brown, red, yellow, gray; it may also show O pink, yellow or brownish, E brownish yellow, grayish brown or greenish. Made by fusion of yttrium oxide with potassium pyrophosphate. PD 3.44, 2.56, 1.76; 9–377.

AlPO$_4$ (Berlinite) is hexagonal with $a = 4.93$, $c = 10.94$ kX. U.C. 3. Crystals structurally like quartz, and forms are similar. No cleavage. H. 6.5 ca. G. 2.6. M.P. 1460° C. Uniaxial positive[22] with $n_O = 1.5235$, $n_E = 1.529$, $n_E - n_O = 0.0055$. Again:[13] $n_O = 1.523$, $n_E = 1.530$, $n_E - n_O = 0.007$. Colorless or nearly so. Made from solution in phosphoric acid. AlPO$_4$ is also orthorhombic in plates with $(+)2V = 50°$ calc., $n_X = 1.546$, $n_Y = 1.556$, $n_Z = 1.578$, $n_Z - n_X = 0.032$. PD 3.37, 4.28, 1.84; 10–423.

BiVO$_4$ (Pucherite) is orthorhombic with[23] $a = 5.38$, $b = 11.98$, $c = 5.04$ kX. U.C. 4. Crystals {010} tablets or acicular. Perfect basal cleavage. H. 4. G. 6.57 calc. X $= b$; Y $= a$. $(-)2V = 19°±5°$, r $<$ v extreme.[24] $n_X = 2.41$, $n_Y = 2.50$, $n_Z = 2.51$, all $±.02$, $n_Z - n_X = 0.10$. Color reddish to yellowish brown. Made from a solution of bismuth nitrate and vanadium chloride.

FeAsO$_4$ is monoclinic with $a:b:c = 0.616:1:0.322$, $\beta = 102°52'$. Crystals prismatic, vertically striated, with distinct {001} cleavage. H. 5. G. 4.32. F. easy. Slowly soluble in acid. Extinction on (010) at $+53°$ to c. $n = 1.78$.

---

[20] Schulze: *Zeit. Phys. Chem.* B-XXIV, p. 215 (1934).
[21] Hutton: *Am. Min.* XXXII, p. 141 (1947).
[22] Strunz: *Zeit. Krist.* CIII, p. 228 (1941).
[23] *abc* changed to *acb* to make $b > a > c$.
[24] Larsen: *U. S. Geol. Surv. Bull.* 679 (1921).

Color black to brown; strongly pleochroic with a greenish yellow, b dark brownish yellow as seen in (001) and olive brown to clear yellowish brown as seen in (010).

(Ce,La)PO₄ (Monazite) is monoclinic prismatic with $a = 6.782$, $b = 6.993$, $c = 6.445$ kX, $\beta = 103°38'$. U.C. 4. Crystals varied with {100}, {110}, {010}, {$\bar{1}$11}, etc. Twinning common on {100}. Distinct {100} cleavage. H. 5–5.5. G. 5.1 ca. X = b; Z $\wedge$ $c = 2°$–6°. (+)2V $\approx$ 11°–15°, usually r < v with weak horizontal dispersion.[21] $n_X = 1.787$–1.800, $n_Y = 1.788$–1.801, $n_Z = 1.837$–1.849, $n_Z - n_X = 0.045$–0.055. Notable variation of indices undoubtedly due to variation in composition; not only can the Ce–La ratio vary, but Th can replace them up to about 30 per cent of ThO₂ and Y earths and less Ca, Mg, Fe, etc., may be present. With no ThO₂[25] $n_X = 1.785$, $n_Y = 1.787$, $n_Z = 1.840$, $n_Z - n_X = 0.055$. Color yellow to brown with little or no pleochroism. Made by fusion of phosphate and chloride of cerium. PD 3.09, 3.31, 2.88; 4–0612.

BiAsO₄ (Rooseveltite) is monoclinic and isostructural with monazite. H. 4–4.5. G. 6.68. (+)2V = 50° calc.[26] $n_X = 2.14$, $n_Y = 2.15$, $n_Z = 2.18$, $n_Z - n_X = 0.04$. PD 3.28, 3.20, 3.11; 7–387*. On cooling it slowly inverts to a tetragonal phase with[27] $a = 5.08$, $c = 11.70$ Å. ($\pm$.02). Indices not known. PD 3.05, 1.91, 2.53; 5–0573.

4. Formula Type ABXO₄

LiMnPO₄ (Lithiophilite) is orthorhombic dipyramidal with $a:b:c = 0.5823:1:0.4541$. U.C. 4. Crystals rare; usually massive. Good {100} and poor {010} cleavages. H. 4–5. G. 3.34. X = c; Y = a. (+)2V = 65° ca. r < v strong. $n_X = 1.663$, $n_Y = 1.666$, $n_Z = 1.673$, $n_Z - n_X = 0.010$. Color brown to yellow or salmon; colorless or pleochroic in section with X deep pink, Y pale greenish yellow, Z pale pink. Made by fusion of LiCl, Li₃PO₄ and Mn₃(PO₄)₂. There is a complete series of mix-crystals from LiMnPO₄ to LiFePO₄. In this series the index of refraction for light vibrating along a is least (n_X) at the Mn end and greatest (n_Z) at the Fe end, the optic angle passing through zero twice, and the optic sign being negative at the Fe end with $n_X = 1.696$, $n_Y = 1.700$, $n_Z = 1.702$, $n_Z - n_X = 0.006$ for about 81 per cent LiFePO₄ (called triphylite). Some Mg is often present[28] in this series, lowering the indices.

NaBePO₄ (Beryllonite) is monoclinic[29] with $a = 8.13$, $b = 7.76$, $c = 14.17$ kX, $\beta = 90°0'$. U.C. 12. *Very* nearly orthorhombic. Perfect {010},

[25] Gordon: *Acad. Sci. Philadelphia, Not. Nat.* No. 2, 1939.

[26] *Hdb. Chem. Phys.* 1954, p. 482.

[27] Mooney, *Acta Cryst.* I, p. 163 (1948).

[28] Chapman: *Am. Min.* XXVIII, p. 90 (1943).

[29] Dana and Wells: *Am. J. Sci.* XXXVII, p. 23 (1889).

and good {100} cleavages. H. 5.5–6. G. 2.81. X = b; Y = a. $(-)2V =$ 67°51′ Li, 67°56′ Na, 67°57′ Tl, r < v. n_X = 1.5492 Li, 1.5520 Na, 1.5544 Tl, n_Y = 1.5550 Li, 1.5579 Na, 1.5604 Tl, n_Z = 1.560 Li, 1.561 Na, 1.564 Tl, $n_Z - n_X$ = 0.009. Colorless, white or pale yellow. Made from a fusion of BeO in sodium metaphosphate. PD 2.84, 3.65, 2.28; 6–0443.

C. HYDRATED ACID PHOSPHATES, ETC.

1. Formula Type A₂HXO₄·xH₂O

Na₂HPO₄·2H₂O is orthorhombic disphenoidal with G. 2.066. $(+)2V =$ 80° ca.,[4] n_X = 1.450, n_Y = 1.461, n_Z = 1.477, $n_Z - n_X$ = 0.027. Colorless. Made by evaporating a solution at 60°. PD 3.36, 4.64, 5.28; 10–190.

Na₂HPO₄·7H₂O is monoclinic prismatic with $a:b:c$ = 1.205:1:1.327, β = 96°57′. Crystals thick prismatic basal tablets. G. 1.68. X = b; Z $\wedge$ c^{30} = $-72°$. $(+)2V$ = 39°33′ Li, 38°50′ Na, 37°59′ Tl, r > v. n_X = 1.4382 Li, 1.4412 Na, 1.4437 Tl, n_Y = 1.4395 Li, 1.4424 Na, 1.4449 Tl, n_Z = 1.4497 Li, 1.4526 Na, 1.4552 Tl, $n_Z - n_X$ = 0.0114 Na. Colorless. Made from water solution above 30° C. PD 2.82, 4.25, 2.92; 10–191*.

Na₂HAsO₄·7H₂O is monoclinic with $a:b:c$ = 1.229:1:1.353, β = 97°14′. Crystals thick basal plates or prismatic. Good {100} cleavage. G. 1.88. X = b; Z $\wedge$ c = $-65°$. $(+)2V$ = 57°32′ Li, 57°7′ Na, 56°43′ Tl, r > v weak.[30] n_X = 1.4587 Li, 1.4622 Na, 1.4654 Tl, n_Y = 1.4623 Li, 1.4658 Na, 1.4689 Tl, n_Z = 1.4746 Li, 1.4782 Na, 1.4814 Tl, $n_Z - n_X$ = 0.016 Na. Colorless. Made from water solution above 20° C. PD 5.26, 3.93, 2.98; 3–0118.

Na₂HPO₄·12H₂O is monoclinic with $a:b:c$ = 1.732:1:1.416, β = 121°24′. Crystals prismatic, with {110}, {001}, {$\bar{1}$11}, {100}, {$\bar{1}$01}, {010}. G. 1.53. X $\wedge$ c = $-31°$, distinct dispersion;[30] Y = b. $(-)2V$ = 54°38′ Li, 56°43′ Na, 58°9′ Tl, r < v marked. n_X = 1.4290 Li, 1.4321 Na, 1.4348 Tl, n_Y = 1.4330 Li, 1.4361 Na, 1.4389 Tl, n_Z = 1.4341 Li, 1.4373 Na, 1.4402 Tl, $n_Z - n_X$ = 0.0052 Na. Colorless. Another phase is orthorhombic. PD 5.40, 2.94, 2.71; 1–0223.

Na₂HAsO₄·12H₂O is monoclinic with $a:b:c$ = 1.75:1:1.412, β = 131°49′. Crystals prismatic. G. 1.67. X $\wedge$ c^4 = 1°; Z = b. $(-)2V$ = 65°13′. n_X = 1.4420 Li, 1.4453 Na, 1.4482 Tl, n_Y = 1.4462 Li, 1.4496 Na, 1.4527 Tl. n_Z = 1.4480 Li, 1.4513 Na, 1.4545 Tl. $n_Z - n_X$ = 0.0060 Na. Colorless.

2. Formula Type ABHXO₄·xH₂O

(NH₄)NaH(AsO₄)·4H₂O is monoclinic with[31] $a:b:c$ = 2.8723:1:1.8589, β = 98°59′. Crystals short prismatic. No cleavage. H. 2. G. 1.845. Y = b;

---

[30] Dufet: *Bull. Soc. Fr. Min.* X, p. 77 (1887).
[31] Schaschek: *Tsch. Min. Pet. Mitt.* XXXII, p. 402 (1914).

$Z \wedge c = +18°$. $(+)2V = 38°$, $n_X = 1.4649$, $n_Y = 1.4663$, $n_Z = 1.4791$ Na, $n_Z - n_X = 0.0142$. Colorless.

$(NH_4)NaH(PO_4) \cdot 4H_2O$ **(Stercorite)** is triclinic and pseudo-monoclinic with $a:b:c = 2.908:1:1.859$, $\beta = 98°30'$. Crystals short prismatic with $\{110\}$ modified by $\{001\}$, $\{100\}$, $\{\bar{1}01\}$, and other $\{h0l\}$. Apparently monoclinic due to multiple twinning on $\{010\}$. No cleavage. H. 2. G. 1.57. M.P. 79° C. The optic plane is (nearly) normal[31] to $\{010\}$; on (001), $X' \wedge (100) = 9°35'$; on (100), $X' \wedge (001) = 1°20'$ with strong dispersion; Z is nearly normal to $\{001\}$. $(+)2V = 35°34'$; $r > v$ rather strong. $n_X = 1.439$, $n_Y = 1.442$, $n_Z = 1.469$, $n_Z - n_X = 0.030$. A section parallel to (010) shows two sets of lamellar twinning at about 90°. Colorless. Made from water solution. It is often called *microcosmic salt*. It loses NH_3 and H_2O between 96° and 200° C., changing to $NaPO_3$. PD 6.60, 2.89, 4.60; 1–0127.

3. Formula Type $AH_2XO_4 \cdot xH_2O$

$NaH_2(PO_4) \cdot H_2O$ is orthorhombic with $a:b:c = 0.934:1:0.962$. Crystals short prisms with $\{001\}$, etc. G. 2.06. $X = a$;[30] $Y = b$. $(-)2V = 29°0'$ Li, $29°22'$ Na, $29°48'$ Tl, $r < v$ weak. $n_X = 1.4527$ Li, 1.4557 Na, 1.4583 Tl, $n_Y = 1.4821$ Li, 1.4852 Na, 1.4881 Tl, $n_Z = 1.4841$ Li, 1.4873 Na, 1.4902 Tl, $n_Z - n_X = 0.0316$ Na. Colorless. Made from the syrupy water solution. A second phase is known to be orthorhombic with $a:b:c = 0.817:1:0.500$.

$NaH_2(AsO_4) \cdot H_2O$ is orthorhombic with $a:b:c = 0.8171:1:0.498$. Crystals prismatic with $\{110\}$, $\{111\}$, etc. G. 2.67. $X = c$;[31] $Y = b$. $(-)2V = 67°15'$ Li, $67°57'$ Na, $68°33'$ Tl, $r < v$. $n_X = 1.5341$ Li, 1.5382 Na, 1.5418 Tl, $n_Y = 1.5494$ Li, 1.5535 Na, 1.5573 Tl, $n_Z = 1.5563$ Li, 1.5607 Na, 1.5647 Tl, $n_Z - n_X = 0.0225$ Na. Colorless. Made from water solution. A second phase is monoclinic with $a:b:c = 1.1087:1:1.1588$, $\beta = 92°22'$.

$NaH_2(PO_4) \cdot 2H_2O$ is orthorhombic with $a:b:c = 0.915:1:1.569$. Crystals pyramidal or brachydomatic. G. 1.92. $X = c$; $Y = b$. $(-)2V = 82°50'$; $n_X = 1.4376$ Li, 1.4401 Na, 1.4423 Tl, $n_Y = 1.4600$ Li, 1.4629 Na, 1.4655 Tl, $n_X = 1.4782$ Li, 1.4815 Na, 1.4843 Tl, $n_Z - n_X = 0.0414$ Na. Colorless. Made from water solution. PD 3.70, 3.06, 5.71; 10–198.

$NaH_2(AsO_4) \cdot 2H_2O$ is orthorhombic with $a:b:c = 0.918:1:1.604$. Crystals pseudo-octahedral with $\{010\}$, $\{011\}$, etc. G. 2.31. $Y = b$;[31] $Z = c$. $(+)2V = 88°50'$, $r < v$. $n_X = 1.4794$ Na, $n_Y = 1.5021$, $n_Z = 1.5265$, $n_Z - n_X = 0.0471$ Na. Colorless.

4. Formula Type $AHXO_4 \cdot xH_2O$

$MgH(PO_4) \cdot 3H_2O$ **(Newberyite)** is orthorhombic dipyramidal with $a:b:c = 0.955:1:0.936$. Crystals equant or short prismatic or tabular. Perfect $\{010\}$ and poor $\{001\}$ cleavages. H. 3–3.5. G. 2.12. $X = a$; $Y = b$.

$(+)2V = 44°46'$, $r < v$ perceptible. $n_X = 1.514$, $n_Y = 1.517$, $n_Z = 1.533$, $n_Z - n_X = 0.019$.[24] Colorless. Made from a solution of magnesium phosphate in acetic acid. PD 3.45, 3.05, 5.9; 1–0597.

CaH(AsO$_4$)·H$_2$O (Haidingerite) is orthorhombic dipyramidal with $a:b:c = 0.839:1:0.499$. Crystals equant or short prismatic. Perfect {010} cleavage. H. 2–2.5. G. 2.96. X = b; Y = a. $(+)2V = 58° \pm 3°$, $r > v$ weak.[24] $n_X = 1.590$, $n_Y = 1.602$, $n_Z = 1.638$, all $\pm.003$, $n_Z - n_X = 0.048$. Colorless. Forms in the system CaO—As$_2$O$_3$—H$_2$O at temperatures of 60° C. or higher.

CaH(AsO$_4$)·3H$_2$O is orthorhombic.[10] G. 2.347. $(-)2V =$ large, $n_X = 1.513$, $n_Y = 1.523$–1.525, $n_Z = 1.532$, $n_Z - n_X = 0.019$. Colorless.

MgH(PO$_4$)·7H$_2$O (Phosphorroesslerite) is monoclinic prismatic with $a = 11.35$, $b = 25.36$, $c = 6.60$ kX, $\beta = 95°$. U.C. 8. Crystals equant or short prismatic. H. 2.5. G. 1.728. X = b; Z $\wedge$ $c^{32} = +6.5°$. $(-)2V = 38°10'$, $r > v$. $n_X = 1.477$, $n_Y = 1.485$, $n_Z = 1.486$, $n_Z - n_X = 0.009$. Again:[33] $n_X = 1.470$, $n_Y = 1.483$, $n_Z = 1.485$, $n_Z - n_X = 0.015$. Colorless. Made when a magnesium sulfate solution is precipitated by phosphate ions at room temperature.

MgH(AsO$_4$)·7H$_2$O (Roesslerite) is monoclinic prismatic with $a:b:c = 0.4473:1:0.2598$, $\beta = 94°26'$. Crystals {010} tablets; often in crusts or fibers. Poor {111} cleavage. H. 2–3. G. 1.94. X $\wedge$ $c = 14°$; Z = b. $(+)2V =$ small;[24] $n_X = 1.525 \pm .005$, $n_Y = 1.53 \pm .01$, $n_Z = 1.550 \pm .005$, $n_Z - n_X = 0.025$. Colorless. Made from an acid solution of disodium arsenate and ammonium sulfate by adding a solution of magnesium sulfate.

CaH(PO$_4$)·2H$_2$O (Brushite) is monoclinic sphenoidal with $a = 5.88$, $b = 15.15$, $c = 6.37$ kX, $\beta = 117°28'$. Crystals acicular or tabular, in some cases resembling gypsum. Perfect {010} and {001} cleavages. H. 2.5. G. 2.32. X $\wedge$ $c = -30°$; Z = b. $(+)2V = 86°$, $r > v$, with crossed dispersion. $n_X = 1.539$, $n_Y = 1.545$, $n_Z = 1.551$, $n_Z - n_X = 0.012$. Also[33a] X $\wedge$ $c = -13°$, Y $\wedge$ $a = +18°$, $(+)2V = 87°$, $n_X = 1.5412$, $n_Y = 1.5458$, $n_Z = 1.553$. Again:[33b] Y $\wedge$ $a = +18°$, $n_X = 1.543$, $n_Y = 1.548$, $n_Z = 1.554$. Colorless (or pale yellow). Made by adding sodium acid phosphat to a calcium chloride solution. PD 2.60, 4.20, 3.02; 4–0740.

CaH(AsO$_4$)·2H$_2$O (Pharmacolite) is monoclinic with $a = 6.00$, $b = 15.40$, $c = 6.29$ kX, $\beta = 114°32'$. U.C. 4. Crystals acicular; perfect {010} cleavage. H. 2–2.5. G. 2.71. X $\wedge$ $c = -29°$; Z = b.[34] $(-)2V = 79°24'$,

[32] Friedrich and Robitsch: *Cent. Min.* 1939A, p. 142.

[33] Alcock, Clark and Thurston: *J. Soc. Chem. Ind.* LXIII, p. 292 (1944).

[33a] Mélon and Dallemagne: *Bull. Soc. Géol. Belg.* LXIX, p. B19 (1946) [*Min. Abst.* X, p. 110].

[33b] Van Tassel: *Bull. Mus. Hist. Nat. Belg.* XXII No. 17 (1944) [*Min. Abst.* IX, p. 255].

[34] Dufet: *Bull. Soc. Fr. Min.* XI, p. 187 (1888).

r > v. $n_X = 1.583$, $n_Y = 1.589$, $n_Z = 1.594$, $n_Z - n_X = 0.011$. Colorless, white or gray. Made by adding sodium acid arsenate to a solution of calcium chloride having an excess of HCl.

5. Formula Type $A_5H_2(XO_4)_4 \cdot xH_2O$ or $AH_4(XO_4)_2 \cdot xH_2O$

$Mn_5H_2(PO_4)_4 \cdot 4H_2O$ (Hureaulite) is monoclinic prismatic with $a = 17.42$, $b = 9.12$, $c = 9.50$ kX, $\beta = 96°40'$. U.C. 4. Crystals short prismatic on {110}, also {100} tablets or equant. Good {100} cleavage. H. 3.5. G. 3.19. F. 3. Soluble in acid. X = b; Z $\wedge$ $c = -75°$. $(-)2V = 75°$, r < v very strong with strong crossed dispersion. $n_X^{35} = 1.647$, $n_Y = 1.654$, $n_Z = 1.660$, $n_Z - n_X = 0.013$. (With 4.56 per cent FeO.) The optic angle decreases 6.5° on heating from 41° to 121° C. Color orange-red, rose-violet, pink, grayish. The orange-red type is pleochroic with X colorless, Y clear yellow to pale rose, Z reddish yellow to reddish brown. Made by adding ammonia to a solution of manganese phosphate. Fe may replace Mn probably in any proportion.

$Ca_5H_2(AsO_4)_4 \cdot 5H_2O$ is monoclinic.[10] G. 3.08. Z $\wedge$ elongation = ?, $n_X = 1.613$, $n_Y = ?$, $n_Z = 1.615$, $n_Z - n_X = 0.002$. Again (for $6H_2O$?):[9] $n_X = 1.60$, $n_Y = ?$, $n_Z = 1.64$. Colorless.

$Ca_5H_2(AsO_4)_4 \cdot 9H_2O$ is monoclinic (or triclinic?).[10] G. 2.78. X $\wedge$ elongation = 24°. $n_X = 1.568$, $n_Y = ?$, $n_Z = 1.577$, $n_Z - n_X = 0.009$. Colorless.

6. Formula Type $A_mB_nH_p(XO_4)_q \cdot xH_2O$

$(NH_4)_2Fe_2H_4(PO_4)_4 \cdot H_2O$ is monoclinic[13] in {010} plates with $\beta = 109°-110°$. G. 2.65. X $\wedge$ $c = 50°$; Z = b. $(+)2V = 57°$, $n_X = 1.655$, $n_Y = 1.680$, $n_Z = 1.715$, $n_Z - n_X = 0.060$. Colorless.

$KFeH_2(PO_4)_2 \cdot H_2O$ is monoclinic.[13] Crystals basal plates. G. 2.63. X (nearly) = c; Y = b. $(-)2V = 79°$, $n_X = 1.592$, $n_Y = 1.614$, $n_Z = 1.630$, $n_Z - n_X = 0.038$.

$KAlH_2(PO_4)_2 \cdot H_2O$ is monoclinic.[13] Crystals prismatic or tabular. G. 2.52. Y = b; Z $\wedge$ $c = 7°$. $(-)2V = 50°$; $n_X = 1.522$, $n_Y = 1.536$, $n_Z = 1.539$, $n_Z - n_X = 0.017$. Colorless.

$(NH_4)_2Al_2H_4(PO_4)_4 \cdot H_2O$ is triclinic[13] in thin plates. G. 2.47. The optic plane makes an angle of 16° with a normal to the plate. Z $\wedge$ plate = 45°±. $(-)2V = 71°-73°$. $n_X = 1.565$, $n_Y = 1.586$, $n_Z = 1.597$, $n_Z - n_X = 0.032$. Color pale green.

$K_2Al_3H_4(PO_4)_5 \cdot 11H_2O$ is orthorhombic (or monoclinic?).[13] Crystals platy. G. 2.24. Z normal to plates. $(+)2V$ = small. $n_X = 1.510$, $n_Y = 1.510$–1.511, $n_Z = 1.515$, $n_Z - n_X = 0.005$. Colorless. Made by partial dehydration of $K_2Al_6H_{10}(PO_4)_{10} \cdot 15H_2O$.

$(NH_4)Fe_3H_8(PO_4)_6 \cdot 6H_2O$ is hexagonal.[13] Crystals thin basal plates. G.

[35] Larsen and Berman: *U. S. Geol. Surv. Bull.* 848, 1934.

2.29. Uniaxial positive with $n_O = 1.580$, $n_E = 1.591$, $n_E - n_O = 0.011$. Color pale lavender.

$KFe_3H_8(PO_4)_6 \cdot 6H_2O$ is hexagonal.[13] Crystals prismatic. G. 2.43. Uniaxial positive with $n_O = 1.595$, $n_E = 1.601$, $n_E - n_O = 0.006$. Color pale lavender.

$K_2Al_6H_{10}(PO_4)_{10} \cdot 15H_2O$ is monoclinic.[13] Crystals platy. G. 2.09. X normal to plates. $(-)2V = $ small. $n_X = 1.495$, $n_Y = 1.503$–1.504, $n_Z = 1.505$, $n_Z - n_X = 0.010$. Colorless.

$CaH_4(PO_4)_2 \cdot H_2O$ is triclinic with $a = 5.67$, $b = 11.92$, $c = 6.51$ Å, $\alpha = 99°50'$, $\beta = 118°31'$, $\gamma = 83°9'$. U.C. 2. Crystals {010} plates elongated along c; polysynthetic twinning on {010} common. Poor {100} and {001} cleavages. G. 2.22. Loses water at 109° C. and decomposes at 153° C. Z (nearly) parallel with (010) and $Z \wedge a = 2°40'$ in acute β. X inclined to (010) at 37° in obtuse α. $(-)2V = 81°30'$, r > v very weak.[36] For $\lambda = 425$ mμ: $n_X = 1.492$, $n_Y = 1.512$, $n_Z = 1.526$, $n_Z - n_X = 0.034$. For $\lambda = 610$ mμ: $n_X = 1.496$, $n_Y = 1.515$, $n_Z = 1.529$, $n_Z - n_X = 0.033$. Again:[36a] $(-)2V = 70°$, $n_X = 1.4932$, $n_Y = 1.5176$, $n_Z = 1.5292$, $n_Z - n_X = 0.036$. PD 3.88, 3.69, 11.7; 9–347.

D. HYDRATED NORMAL PHOSPHATES, ETC.

1. Formula Type $A_3XO_4 \cdot xH_2O$

$Na_3(VO_4) \cdot 10H_2O$ is isometric.[37] Crystals dodecahedral. Isotropic with $n = 1.5244$ Li, 1.5305 Na, 1.5366 Tl. Another phase is hexagonal, in basal plates. Uniaxial positive with $n_O = 1.5332$ Li, 1.5398 Na, 1.5460 Tl, $n_E = 1.5408$ Li, 1.5475 Na, 1.5537 Tl, $n_E - n_O = 0.0077$ Na.

$Na_3(VO_4) \cdot 12H_2O$ is hexagonal[37] (trigonal). Crystals resemble rhombohedrons. Uniaxial positive with $n_O = 1.5040$ Li, 1.5095 Na, 1.5150 Tl. $n_E = 1.5173$ Li, 1.5232 Na, 1.5293 Tl, $n_E - n_O = 0.0137$ Na.

$Na_3(AsO_4) \cdot 12H_2O$ is hexagonal (trigonal).[37] Crystals prismatic with {0001}. G. 1.76 (1.80). Uniaxial positive with $n_O = 1.4553$ Li, 1.4589 Na, 1.4624 Tl, $n_E = 1.4630$ Li, 1.4669 Na, 1.4704 Tl, $n_E - n_O = 0.008$ Na.

$Na_3(PO_4) \cdot 12H_2O$ is hexagonal (trigonal).[20] Crystals long prismatic with {0001}. M.P. 70–75° C. G. 1.645. Uniaxial positive with $n_O = 1.4458$, $n_E = 1.4524$, $n_E - n_O = 0.0066$. Again:[37] $n_O = 1.4486$, $n_E = 1.4539$, $n_O - n_E = 0.0053$. It contains some NaOH if formed from water solution and is actually $5(Na_3PO_4 \cdot 12H_2O) \cdot NaOH$ according to Bell.[38] PD 4.34, 10.3, 2.61; 10–189.

[36] Smith, Lehr and Brown: *Am. Min.* XL, p. 893 (1955).
[36a] Measures by Garth Volk at Univ. Wis. in 1935.
[37] Baker: *J. Chem. Soc. London* XLVII, p. 353 (1885).
[38] Bell: *Ind. Eng. Chem.* XLI, p. 2901 (1949).

$Na_3(PO_4) \cdot H_2O$ is uniaxial positive with[4] $n_O = 1.497$, $n_E = 1.522$, $n_E - n_O = 0.025$. Effloresces at 180° C. Apparently the water content may vary from about 0.5 to about 1.5. With[38] $0.5H_2O$ $n_O = 1.499$, $n_E = 1.525$, $n_E - n_O = 0.026$. Made by evaporating a solution (at 86° C.) containing some NaOH.

$Na_3(PO_4) \cdot 7H_2O$ melts at 110° C. It is biaxial with[4] $(+)2V = 85°$, $n_X = 1.462$, $n_Y = 1.470$, $n_Z = 1.478$, $n_Z - n_X = 0.016$. Made by evaporating a water solution at 83° C. Apparently the water content may vary from about 6 to 7 H_2O. With 6 H_2O: $(-)2V = 60°$ calc., $n_X = 1.462$, $n_Y = 1.473$, $n_Z = 1.477$, $n_Z - n_X = 0.015$.

$Na_3(PO_4) \cdot 8H_2O$ is monoclinic.[38] It effloresces at 86° C. The extinction angle $(X \wedge \text{elongation})$ is 22°. $(-)2V = 58°$ calc. $n_X = 1.458$, $n_Y = 1.468$, $n_Z = 1.471$, $n_Z - n_X = 0.013$. Colorless. Made from water solution.

$H_3PO_4 \cdot \frac{1}{2}H_2O$ is monoclinic with[14a] $a = 7.94$, $b = 12.94$, $c = 7.38$ Å, $\beta = 109°25'$. Crystals tabular {001}, rod-like along a. Poor {010} cleavage. M.P. 29° C. $Y = b$; $Z \wedge a = 20°$ in acute β. $(+)2V = 56°$, r > v very weak. $n_X = 1.485$, $n_Y = 1.492$, $n_Z = 1.519$, $n_Z - n_X = 0.034$. Colorless.

2. Formula Type $A_3(XO_4)_2 \cdot xH_2O$ (also $ABXO_4 \cdot xH_2O$)

$(NH_4)Mg(PO_4) \cdot 6H_2O$ (Struvite) is orthorhombic pyramidal with $a = 6.09$, $b = 6.97$, $c = 11.18$ kX. U.C. 2. Crystals varied: equant, wedge-shaped, prismatic or tabular. Good {001} and poor {100} cleavages. H. 2. G. 1.71. $X = b$; $Y = c$. $(+)2V = 37°22'$, r < v strong.[39] $n_X = 1.495$, $n_Y = 1.496$, $n_Z = 1.504$ Na, $n_Z - n_X = 0.009$. Colorless or stained. Made by reaction of magnesium sulphate and acid ammonium phosphate solutions. PD 4.28, 2.93, 2.69; 5–0316.

$Zn_3(PO_4)_2 \cdot 4H_2O$ (Hopeite) is orthorhombic with $a = 10.64$, $b = 18.32$, $c = 5.03$ kX. U.C. 6. Crystals {010} tablets or prismatic. Perfect {010}, good {100} and poor {001} cleavages. H. 3–3.5. G. 3.05. $X = a$;[40] $Y = c$. $(-)2V = 37°$, r < v. $n_X = 1.589$, $n_Y = 1.598$, $n_Z = 1.599$, $n_Z - n_X = 0.010$. Again:[24] $n_X = 1.574$, $n_Y = 1.582$, $n_Z = 1.582$, $n_Z - n_X = 0.008$. Colorless. Made from a solution of zinc phosphate in acetic acid. Hopeite crystals may show zonal growths, adjacent zones differing some in properties although apparently of the same composition. One zone has[41] a higher specific gravity and birefringence and optic angle than the next. PD 9.04, 4.57, 2.86; 9–497*. Another phase of $Zn_3(PO_4)_2 \cdot 4H_2O$ is triclinic—see beyond.

$Mg_3(PO_4)_2 \cdot 8H_2O$ (Bobierrite) is monoclinic with $a = 9.946$, $b = 27.654$, $c = 4.639$ kX, $\beta = 104°1'$. Crystals acicular. Perfect {010} cleavage.

[39] Bøggild: *Medd. Dansk. Geol. For.* III, p. 25 (1907).
[40] Wolfe: *Am. Min.* XXV, p. 787 (1940).
[41] Spencer: *Min. Mag.* XV, p. 1 (1908).

H. 2–2.5. G. 2.19. $Y = b;$[42] $Z \wedge c = 29°$. $(+)2V = 71° \pm 3°$, r < v. $n_X = 1.510$, $n_Y = 1.520$, $n_Z = 1.543$, $n_Z - n_X = 0.033$. Colorless. Made by slow precipitation of $MgSO_4$ solution by a solution of Na_2HPO_4 and $NaHCO_3$. Fe may replace some Mg; with 15 per cent FeO the optic properties[43] are: $(+)2V = 57° \pm 3°$, $n_X = 1.5468$, $n_Y = 1.5533$, $n_Z = 1.5820$, $n_Z - n_X = 0.0352$. PD 6.70, 2.94, 2.69; 1–0122.

$Mg_3(PO_4)_2 \cdot 22H_2O$ forms crystals which are biaxial[33] with large optic angle and $n_X = 1.461$, $n_Y = 1.465$, $n_Z = 1.469$ (all ± 0.002), $n_Z - n_X = 0.008$. Colorless. Made from water solution.

$Mg_3(PO_4)_2 \cdot 3–5H_2O$ forms acicular crystals[33] in coarse spherulites. n_Y is about 1.535, $n_Z - n_X = $ about 0.006. Colorless. Made by partial dehydration of $Mg_3(PO_4)_2 \cdot 22H_2O$. PD (?) 4.10, 5.2, 3.23; 1–0428.

$Mg_3(AsO_4)_2 \cdot 8H_2O$ **(Hoernesite)** is monoclinic prismatic with $a:b:c = 0.7676:1:0.3591$, $\beta = 104°25'$. Crystals prismatic. Perfect $\{010\}$ and poor $\{100\}$ cleavages. H. 1. G. 2.61. $X = b;$[24] $Z \wedge c = 31°$. $(+)2V = 60°$, $n_X = 1.563$, $n_Y = 1.571$, $n_Z = 1.596$, $n_Z - n_X = 0.033$. Colorless. Again:[44] $Z \wedge c = 45°$, $n_Y = 1.570$, $n_Z = 1.594$.

$Fe_3(PO_4)_2 \cdot 8H_2O$ **(Vivianite)** is monoclinic prismatic with $a = 10.039$, $b = 13.388$, $c = 4.687$ kX, $\beta = 104°18'$. U.C. 2. Crystals prismatic or equant or $\{010\}$ tablets; often earthy. Perfect $\{010\}$ cleavage. H. 1.5–2. G. 2.68. $X = b;$[45] $Z \wedge c = +28.5°$. $(+)2V = 83.5°$, r < v weak. $n_X = 1.5788$, $n_Y = 1.6024$, $n_Z = 1.6294$, $n_Z - n_X = 0.0506$. Colorless when fresh and unaltered, but rapidly becomes blue or greenish blue (or even black) due to oxidation of the iron; a little oxidation leads to pleochroism with X blue, Y and Z pale yellowish green; with more oxidation a sample may become black and then flakes are pleochroic with X indigo, Y green-yellow and Z yellow-olive; then, also, $(+)2V = 63.5°$, $n_X = 1.616$, $n_Y = 1.656$, $n_Z = 1.675$, $n_Z - n_X = 0.059$. Made by heating ferrous phosphate in a solution of sodium phosphate. PD 6.80, 2.97, 2.71; 3–0070.

$Co_3(AsO_4)_2 \cdot 8H_2O$ **(Erythrite)** is monoclinic prismatic with $a = 10.184$, $b = 13.34$, $c = 4.73$ kX, $\beta = 105°1'$. U.C. 2. Crystals prismatic to acicular; also earthy. Perfect $\{010\}$ and poor $\{100\}$ and $\{\bar{1}02\}$ cleavages. H. 2. G. 3.18. $X = b$; $Z \wedge c^{35} = +31°$. $(\pm)2V = $ approximately $90°$, r > v. $n_X = 1.626$, $n_Y = 1.661$, $n_Z = 1.699$, $n_Z - n_X = 0.073$. Color red; pleochroic with X pale pinkish or rose, Y very pale violet or rose, Z red or deep rose. Made by slow precipitation of a $CoSO_4$ solution with

[42] Gruner and Stauffer: *Am. Min.* XXVIII, p. 339 (1943).

[43] Hutton: *N. Zealand J. Sci. Tech.* Sec. B. XXIII, p. 9 (1941). *Dana's System of Mineralogy* II, p. 754 (1951).

[44] Barth: *Am. Min.* XXII, p. 325 (1937).

[45] Ulrich: *Rozpr. Česk̄é. Ak.* XXXIII, No. 33 (1924); Zieleniewski: *Arch. Min. Soc. Warsaw* XV, p. 51 (1945).

Na_2HAsO_4. $Co_3(AsO_4)_2 \cdot 8H_2O$ forms a complete series of mix-crystals with $Ni_3(AsO_4)_2 \cdot 8H_2O$. Minor amounts of Ca, Mg, Fe, Zn may be present. PD 6.69, 3.21, 2.99; 10–480.

$Ni_3(AsO_4)_2 \cdot 8H_2O$ **(Annabergite)** is monoclinic prismatic with $a = 10.122$, $b = 13.284$, $c = 4.698$ kX, $\beta = 104°45'$. U.C. 2. Usually in crystalline coatings. Perfect {010} cleavage. H. 2.5. G. 3. X $= b$;[35] Z $\wedge$ c = $+36°$. $(+)2V = 84°$, r > v rather strong. $n_X = 1.622$, $n_Y = 1.658$, $n_Z = 1.687$, $n_Z - n_X = 0.065$. Color apple green. Colorless or weakly pleochroic in flakes. Made by slow precipitation of a $NiSO_4$ solution with Na_2HAsO_4. Forms a complete series of mix-crystals with $Co_3(AsO_4)_2 \cdot 8H_2O$. It may contain some Mg or Zn.

$Zn_3(AsO_4)_2 \cdot 8H_2O$ **(Koettigite)** is monoclinic with $a = 10.11$, $b = 13.31$, $c = 4.70$ kX, $\beta = 104°30'$. Crystals prismatic, {010} plates with perfect {010} cleavage. H. 2.5–3. G. 3.33. X $= b$;[40] Z $\wedge$ c = 37°. $(-)2V = 74°$, r < v weak. $n_X = 1.622$, $n_Y = 1.638$, $n_Z = 1.671$, $n_Z - n_X = 0.049$. Color carmine or brownish. Made by aging the gelatinous precipitate from mixed solutions of $ZnSO_4$ and Na_2HAsO_4. It may contain some Co. PD 3.20, 3.00, 2.72; 1–0744*.

$Fe(AsO_4)_2 \cdot 8H_2O$ **(Symplesite)** is triclinic[40] with $a = 7.85$, $b = 9.39$, $c = 4.71$ kX, $\alpha = 99°55'$, $\beta = 97°57'$, $\gamma = 105°57'$. Crystals coarse fibers radially arranged. Perfect {1$\bar{1}$0} cleavage. H. 2.5. G. 3.01. X normal to cleavage. Z $\wedge$ c = 31°30'. $(-)2V = 86°30'$, r > v strong. $n_X = 1.635 \pm .005$, $n_Y = 1.668 \pm .005$, $n_Z = 1.702 \pm .005$, $n_Z - n_X = 0.067$. Color green, becoming greenish black or indigo-blue on oxidation. Pleochroic with X deep blue, Y nearly colorless, Z yellowish. Made hydrothermally.[45a] PD 6.79, 7.50, 8.97; 8–172.

$Zn_3(PO_4)_2 \cdot 4H_2O$ **(Parahopeite)** is triclinic pinacoidal with $a = 5.755$, $b = 7.535$, $c = 5.292$ kX, $\alpha = 93°17'$, $\beta = 91°55'$, $\gamma = 91°19'$. U.C. 1. Crystals long parallel with c and tabular {100}. Common polysynthetic twinning on {100}. Perfect {010} cleavage. H. 3.5–4. G. 3.31. X near a; Y' $\wedge$ c on {100} = 30°. $(+)2V$ near 90°, r < v perceptible. $n_X{}^{24} = 1.614$, $n_Y = 1.625$, $n_Z = 1.637$, $n_Z - n_X = 0.023$. Colorless. Stable to 163° C. Made by reaction of hot solution of $ZnCl_2$ and sodium ammonium phosphate. PD 7.56, 2.99, 4.48; 9–491*.

3. Formula Type $AXO_4 \cdot xH_2O$

$2CrPO_4 \cdot H_2O$ is formed between 300° C. and 900° C. by heating the hexahydrate under 2000 pounds per square inch of water-vapor pressure, or by heating it dry between 200° and 850° C, or by heating either α-$CrPO_4$ or β-$CrPO_4$ hydrothermally at 300° to 900° C. It is[45b] olive-green and

[45a] Pulow: *C. R. Acad. Sci. Paris* CCXL, p. 2333 (1955).
[45b] Shafer and Roy: *J. Am. Chem. Soc.* LXXVIII, p. 1087 (1956).

strongly birefringent, with $n \approx 1.810 \pm .006$. The strongest X-ray powder lines are at d = 3.278, 3.171, 1.582, 2.024, and 1.636.

$AlPO_4 \cdot 2H_2O$ (Variscite) is orthorhombic with[46] $a = 9.55$, $b = 9.85$, $c = 8.50$ kX. U.C. 8. Crystals pyramidal with {111} and {001}. Good {100} and poor {001} cleavages. H. 4–4.5. G. 2.57. X = b; Y = c. $(-)2V =$ moderate,[47] r < v perceptible. $n_X = 1.565$, $n_Y = 1.588$, $n_Z = 1.593$, $n_Z - n_X = 0.028$. Indices vary notably perhaps due to variation in water content. For example: $n_X = 1.550$, $n_Y = 1.565$, $n_Z = 1.570$, $n_Z - n_X = 0.020$. Color pale green, bluish green, colorless. Made by adding NaOH solution to acid solution of $AlCl_3$ and dihydrogen phosphate. It forms a complete series with $FePO_4 \cdot 2H_2O$. PD 5.31, 4.26, 3.05; 8–157.

$FePO_4 \cdot 2H_2O$ (Strengite) is orthorhombic[47] with $a = 9.80$, $b = 10.05$, $c = 8.65$ kX. U.C. 8. Crystals varied in habit; often in aggregates. Good {100} and poor {001} cleavages. H. 3.5–4. G. 2.90. X = b; Y = c. $(+)2V =$ small, r < v very strong.[24] $n_X = 1.730$, $n_Y = 1.732$, $n_Z = 1.762$, $n_Z - n_X = 0.032$. Colorless or pink with X and Y colorless, Z pale pink. Made by adding NaOH solution to acid solution of $FeCl_3$ and dihydrogen phosphate. It forms a complete series with $AlPO_4 \cdot 2H_2O$. PD 3.30, 3.65, 4.20; 3–0452*.

$FeAsO_4 \cdot 2H_2O$ (Scorodite) is orthorhombic dipyramidal with[46] $a = 10.01$, $b = 10.30$, $c = 8.90$ kX. U.C. 8. Crystals pyramidal or basal tablets or prismatic. Poor cleavage. H. 3.5–4. G. 3.28. X = b; Y = c. $(+)2V = 75°$ ca.,[48] r > v strong. $n_X = 1.784$, $n_Y = 1.795$, $n_Z = 1.814$, $n_Z - n_X = 0.030$. Color pale green to brown (or bluish or yellow), faintly pleochroic with Z > X, Y. Made by heating iron with H_2O and As_2O_5 in a closed tube up to 150° C. A complete series probably extends to **$AlAsO_4 \cdot 2H_2O$ (Mansfieldite)** which has $(+)2V = 30°$ ca., $n_X = 1.622$, $n_Y = 1.624$, $n_Z = 1.642$, $n_Z - n_X = 0.020$. Color white to gray. PD 5.56, 4.44, 3.16; 5–0216.

$YPO_4 \cdot 2H_2O$ (Weinschenkite) is monoclinic prismatic with $a = 6.48$, $b = 15.12$, $c = 6.28$ kX, $\beta = 129°24'$. U.C. 4. Crystals lath-like; usually in crusts or spherulites. {001} and {$\bar{1}01$} cleavages. G. 3.17. X = b; Z $\wedge$ $c = 35°$ ca. $(+)2V = 30°$ ca.[25] $n_X = 1.600$, $n_Y = 1.608$, $n_Z = 1.645$, $n_Z - n_X = 0.045$. Again: $n_X = 1.605$, $n_Y = 1.612$, $n_Z = 1.645$, $n_Z - n_X = 0.040$.[48a] Colorless or white. Made by reaction of yttrium nitrate and tribasic sodium phosphate solutions. Often contains minor amounts of Er, Yb, Ce, etc., replacing some Y.

$CePO_4 \cdot 2H_2O$ (Churchite) is probably monoclinic. Crystals minute

---

[46] $a\,b\,c$ changed to $b\,a\,c$ to make $b > a > c$.

[47] Schaller: *U. S. Geol. Surv. Bull.* 610 (1916).

[48] Allen and Fahey: *Am. Min.* XXXIII, p. 122 (1948).

[48a] Milton, Murata and Knechtel: *Am. Min.* XXIX, p. 92 (1944).

columnar. One perfect cleavage. H. 3. G. 3.14. $(+)2V^{24} =$ near $0°$, $n_X =$ 1.620 $\pm$ .003, $n_Y = 1.620$, $n_Z = 1.654$, $n_Z - n_X = 0.034$. Color gray, slightly reddish. Made from a cerium nitrate solution by adding sodium phosphate. PD 4.21, 7.50, 3.02; 8–167.

CrPO$_4$·6H$_2$O is triclinic. Crystals prismatic. G. 2.121. $(-)2V = 13°$, $n_X^{49} = 1.568$, $n_Y = 1.591$, $n_Z = 1.599$, $n_Z - n_X = 0.031$.

Al(VO$_4$)·3(or 3.5)H$_2$O (Steigerite) is amorphous[49a] (or nearly so). It forms pulverulent coatings or gum-like waxy masses. $n = 1.710 \pm .005$. Color canary yellow. Made from water solution of aluminum sulfate and calcium vanadate.

E. ANHYDROUS PHOSPHATES, ETC., CONTAINING HYDROXYL OR HALOGEN OR EXTRA OXYGEN

1. Formula Type A$_2$XO$_4$Z or ABXO$_4$Z

Mg$_2$(PO$_4$)(OH) forms needles[33] with parallel extinction and positive elongation, often in fan-like clusters. $(+)2V =$ small, $n_X = 1.533$, $n_Y =$ very near n_X, $n_Z = 1.552$ (both $\pm$.003), $n_Z - n_X = 0.019$. Colorless. Made from a water solution of Mg$_3$(PO$_4$)$_2$·22H$_2$O (with some NaOH) heated to $200°$ C.

Ca$_2$(PO$_4$)Cl (Chlor-spodiosite) is orthorhombic with[50] $a = 6.17$, $b = 6.89$, $c = 10.74$ Å. U.C. 4. Crystals oblong plates with good {001} cleavage. G. 3.04. Y $= b$; Z $= c$. $(-)2V =$ large, $n_X = 1.649$, $n_Y = 1.665$, $n_Z = 1.670$, $n_Z - n_X = 0.021$. Again:[51] $n_Y = 1.658$. Also:[52] $(-)2V = 75°$, $n_X = 1.650$, $n_Y = 1.663$, $n_Z = 1.670$, $n_Z - n_X = 0.020$. Colorless.

Zn$_2$(PO$_4$)(OH) is orthorhombic(?). X $= a$;[53] Y $= b$. $(-)2V =$ large. $n_X = 1.608$, $n_Y = 1.624$, $n_Z = 1.629$, $n_Z - n_X = 0.021$. Colorless to pale brown. Made by dehydration of spencerite. PD 6.1, 3.65, 2.76; 8–158.

Cu$_2$(PO$_4$)(OH) (Libethenite) is orthorhombic dipyramidal with $a = 8.08$, $b = 8.43$, $c = 5.90$ kX. U.C. 4. Crystals short prismatic or brachydomatic or equant. Poor {100} and {010} cleavages. H. 4. G. 3.97. X $= b$;[24] Y $= c$. $(-)2V =$ near $90°$, r $>$ v strong. $n_X = 1.701$, $n_Y = 1.743$, $n_Z = 1.787$ (all $\pm$.003), $n_Z - n_X = 0.086$. Again:[54] $(-)2V = 81°38'$ Li,

[49] Sullivan and McMurdie: *Nat. Bur. Stand. J. Res.* XLVIII, p. 159 (1952). *Chem. Abst.* XLVI, p. 7839 (1952).

[49a] Henderson: *Am. Min.* XX, p. 769 (1935).

[50] Cameron and McCaughey: *J. Phys. Chem.* XV, p. 463 (1911).

[51] Nacken: *Cent. Min.* 1912, p. 545.

[52] Mackay: *Min. Mag.* XXX, p. 166 (1955).

[53] Walker and Parsons: *Univ. Toronto Stud., Geol. Ser.* No. 12, p. 58 (1921).

[54] Des Cloizeaux: *Ann. Mines* XIV, p. 343 (1858).

81°8′ Na, 80°20′ blue. Color light to dark green. Made from cupric phosphate and phosphoric acid in water heated to about 200° C. PD 4.81, 2.63, 2.91; 1–0274.

$Zn_2(AsO_4)(OH)$ **(Adamite)** is orthorhombic dipyramidal with $a = 8.30$, $b = 8.51$, $c = 6.04$ Å. Crystals macrodomatic, equant or varied. Good {101} and poor {010} cleavages. H. 3.5. G. 4.43. X $= a$;[55] Y $= c$. $(+)2V = 87°$–$90°$, r $<$ v strong (in some cases negative), $n_X = 1.722$, $n_Y = 1.742$, $n_Z = 1.761$, $n_Z - n_X = 0.039$. Again:[24] $(-)2V = 87°$, $n_X = 1.708$, $n_Y = 1.734$, $n_Z = 1.758$, $n_Z - n_X = 0.050$. Color pale yellow, green or white; with some cobalt it is red; with some copper, green. Optic properties vary considerably; for example, with Cu: $(-)2V = 23°$ ca., $n_X = 1.742$, $n_Y = 1.768$, $n_Z = 1.773$, $n_Z - n_X = 0.031$. Made from hot solutions of zinc sulphate and disodium acid arsenate. PD 2.45, 4.90, 2.97; 6–0536.

$Zn_4(PO_4)_2O$ is orthorhombic(?). X $= a$;[53] Z $= b$. $(-)2V = 30°$ ca. $n_X = 1.630$ (calc. for $2V = 30°$), $n_Y = 1.656$, $n_Z = 1.660$, $n_Z - n_X = 0.030$. Color brown. Produced by dehydration of spencerite.

$Mg_2(PO_4)F$ **(Wagnerite)** is monoclinic prismatic with $a = 11.90$, $b = 12.51$, $c = 9.63$ kX, $\beta = 108°17′$. U.C. 16. Crystals prismatic or varied. Good {100} cleavage. H. 5–5.50. G. 3.15. Y $= b$;[56] Z $\wedge$ c $= -21.5°$. $(+)2V = 28°24′$, r $>$ v weak with inclined dispersion, $n_X = 1.5678$, $n_Y = 1.5719$, $n_Z = 1.5824$, $n_Z - n_X = 0.0146$ Na. Color yellow; rarely red or greenish. Colorless in flakes. Made by fusion of MgF_2 with ammonium phosphate.

$Ca_4(PO_4)_2O$ **(Hilgenstockite)** is monoclinic with $a:b:c = 0.577:1:1.255$, $\beta = 90°\pm$. Crystals {010} tablets with poor {010}, {100} and {001} cleavages. G. 3.06. Lamellar twinning on {001} and {100}. Y $= b$; Z near c. $(+)2V = 20°$ (red), $40°$ (blue), $n_Y = 1.64$. Again:[57] $(+)2V = 80°$, $n_X = 1.643$, $n_Y = ?$, $n_Z = 1.647$, $n_Z - n_X = 0.004$. Also:[16] $(+)2V = 30°$, $n_X = 1.650$, $n_Y = 1.651$, $n_Z = 1.656$, $n_Z - n_X = 0.006$. Colorless. Found in some slags.

$NaAl(AsO_4)F$ **(Durangite)** is monoclinic prismatic with $a = 6.53$, $b = 8.46$, $c = 7.00$ kX. $\beta = 115°46′$. Crystals prismatic or pyramidal. Distinct {110} cleavage. H. 5. G. 3.94–4.07, higher with some Fe‴. X $\wedge$ c $= -25°$, Z $= b$.[24] $(-)2V = 45°$, r $>$ v with horizontal dispersion. $n_X = 1.634$, $n_Y = 1.673$, $n_Z = 1.685$, $n_Z - n_X = 0.051$. Color green or orange-red. Pleochroic with X orange-yellow, Y pale orange-yellow, Z nearly colorless. Made from powdered cryolite and thick arsenic acid in a closed tube at 200° C.

[55] Mrose: *Am. Min.* XXXIII, p. 449 (1948).
[56] Hegemann and Steinmetz: *Cent. Min.* 1927A, p. 45.
[57] S. Zerfoss: *pers. comm.* Jan. 20, 1943.

2. Formula Type $AB_2(XO_4)_2Z$

$Fe''Fe_2'''(PO_4)_2(OH)_2$ **(Barbosalite)**[57a] is monoclinic(?)[58] at room temperature. It has been called ferrous ferric lazulite. G. 3.60. It has an extinction angle of $45°$; $(+?)2V$ = large, $n_X = 1.77$, $n_Y > 1.79$ (but near it), $n_Z = 1.835$, $n_Z - n_X = 0.065$. It is black and opaque except on the thin edges which are dark green; pleochroic with X and Y dark blue green and Z dark olive green. It changes to a tetragonal substance, called **lipscombite**, at about $110°$ C. The unit cell is body centered with $a = 5.37$ and $c = 12.81$ Å. This change is probably accompanied by oxidation of the ferrous iron and leads to the formula $Fe'''_8(PO_4)_6$ when completed. This compound forms small rectangular crystals with indices above 1.83. With crossed nicols the crystals show beautiful abnormal interference colors and no extinction.

3. Formula Type $A_5(XO_4)_3Z$

$Ca_5(PO_4)_3F$ **(Fluorapatite)** is hexagonal dipyramidal with $a = 9.36$, $c = 6.88 \, kX$. U.C. 2. Crystals prismatic, long to short. Poor basal cleavage. H. 5. G. 3.18. F. 5. Soluble in HCl or HNO_3. Uniaxial negative with[51] $n_O = 1.6325$, $n_E = 1.630$, $n_O - n_E = 0.0025$ Na. Colorless. Made from fusion. In apatite F may be replaced in part or wholly by (OH) or Cl or perhaps O; also the Ca may be replaced in part by Mn or Sr or Pb or in small part by Na, K, Mg, Fe (or even C?). Again the P may be replaced in any amount by As; finally there are more complicated substitutions such as SiS for PP, $Cr^3 + 2Cr^6$ for $3P^5$, etc. With[59] 4.23 per cent CrO_3 and 0.79 per cent Cr_2O_3 $n_O = 1.710$, $n_E = 1.707$, $n_O - n_E = 0.003$; pleochroic with O dark blue, E bright yellowish green. PD 2.81, 2.71, 1.84; 3–0736.

$Ca_5(PO_4)_3Cl$ **(Chlorapatite)** is hexagonal dipyramidal with $a = 9.52$, $c = 6.85 \, kX$. U.C. 2. Crystals prismatic. H. 5. G. 3.17. Soluble in HCl or HNO_3. Uniaxial negative with[60] $n_O = 1.6684$, $n_E = 1.6675$, $n_O - n_E = 0.0009$. Colorless. Made from fusion. Miscible with $Ca_5(PO_4)_3F$ and also with $Ca_5(PO_4)_3OH$. It may contain some Mn or Sr or CO_3. PD 2.77, 2.85, 1.95; 2–0851.

$Ca_5(PO_4)_3(OH)$ **(Hydroxylapatite)** is hexagonal dipyramidal with $a = 9.40$, $c = 6.93 \, kX$. U.C. 2. Crystals prismatic. H. 5. G. 3 ca. M.P. $1540°$ C. Soluble in HCl or HNO_3. Uniaxial negative with[61] $n_O = 1.651$, $n_E = 1.644$, $n_O - n_E = 0.007$. Colorless. Made from solutions of calcium salts by am-

[57a] Lindberg and Pecora: *Am. Min.* XL, p. 952 (1955).
[58] Gheith: *Am. Min.* XXXVIII, p. 612 (1953).
[59] Minguzzi: *Periodico Min. Roma* XII, p. 343 (1941). [*Min. Abst.* IX, p. 283 (1946)].
[60] Borgström: *Finska Kem. Medd.* No. 2, p. 51 (1952).
[61] Mitchell, Faust, Hendricks and Reynolds: *Am. Min.* XXVIII, p. 356 (1943).

moniacal solutions of phosphates. PD 2.79, 2.72, 2.63; 3–0747. It may contain Mn or Sr or CO_3.

$Ca_{10}(PO_4)_6(CO_3) \cdot H_2O$ (Carbonate-apatite) is hexagonal dipyramidal with $a = 9.41$, $c = 6.88$ kX. U.C. 1. H. 5. G. 2.9 ca. Soluble in HCl or HNO_3. Uniaxial negative with[62] $n_O = 1.628$, $n_E = 1.619$, $n_O - n_E = 0.009$. Again:[63] $n_O = 1.603$, $n_E = 1.598$, $n_O - n_E = 0.005$. The indices are much lower and the birefringence is greater than those of other apatites. Colorless. PD 2.82, 2.71, 3.44; 4–0697.

$Sr_5(PO_4)_3F$ is hexagonal with[64] M.P. 1685° C. Uniaxial negative with $n_O = 1.621$, $n_E = 1.619$, $n_O - n_E = 0.002$. Colorless.

$Sr_5(PO_4)_3Cl$ is hexagonal with[64] G. 4.87. M.P. 1625° C. Uniaxial positive with $n_O = 1.650$, $n_E = 1.655$, $n_E - n_O = 0.005$. Again:[5] $n_O = 1.658$, $n_E = 1.664$, $n_E - n_O = 0.006$. Colorless.

$Sr_{10}(PO_4)_6(CO_3)$ is hexagonal. Uniaxial negative with[64a] $n_O = 1.644$, $n_E = 1.638$, $n_O - n_E = 0.006$. Colorless.

$Ba_5(PO_4)_3F$ is hexagonal with[64] M.P. 1670° C. Uniaxial negative with $n_O = 1.669$, $n_E = 1.665$, $n_O - n_E = 0.004$. Colorless.

$Ba_5(PO_4)_3Cl$ is hexagonal with[64] G. 5.95. M.P. 1584° C. Uniaxial negative with $n_O = 1.701$, $n_E = 1.699$, $n_O - n_E = 0.002$. Colorless.

$Ba_{10}(PO_4)_6(CO_3)$ is hexagonal. Uniaxial negative with[64a] $n_O = 1.691$, $n_E = 1.683$, $n_O - n_E = 0.008$ Na. Colorless.

$Pb_5(PO_4)_3Cl$ (Pyromorphite) is hexagonal dipyramidal with $a = 9.95$, $c = 7.31$ kX. U.C. 2. Crystals prismatic with $\{10\bar{1}0\}$ and $\{0001\}$; also equant or pyramidal. Traces of $\{10\bar{1}1\}$ cleavage. H. 3.5–4. G. 7.04. Uniaxial negative with[65] $n_O = 2.144$ (λ 405), 2.058 Na, 2.041 (λ 691), $n_E = 2.131$ (λ 405), 2.048 Na, 2.030 (λ 691), $n_O - n_E = 0.011$ Na. Color green, yellow, brown, in section colorless or tinted with absorption O < E. Made from a fusion of lead phosphate with excess lead chloride. Cl may be replaced by OH. Miscible in all proportions with $Pb_5(AsO_4)_3Cl$. PD 2.97, 2.87, 3.38; 6–0389.

$Pb_5(AsO_4)_3Cl$ (Mimetite) is hexagonal dipyramidal with $a = 10.27$, $c = 7.43$ kX. U.C. 2. Crystals prismatic or acicular. Very poor prismatic cleavage. H. 3.5–4. G. 7.24. F. 1. Uniaxial negative with[65] $n_O = 2.263$ (λ 405), 2.147 Na, 2.124 (λ 691), $n_E = 2.239$ (λ 405), 2.128 Na, 2.106 (λ 691), $n_O - n_E = 0.019$ Na. Color pale yellow to yellowish brown, white or colorless. Colorless in section. Made from fusion of lead arsenate

[62] McConnell: *Am. J. Sci.* XXXVI, p. 296 (1938).

[63] Merwin in Washington: *Am. Min.* XIV, p. 369 (1929).

[64] Winter: *Inaug. Diss. Leipzig*, 1913, *Tables Ann. Int. Const.* IV, p. 1063, 1067 (1922).

[64a] Eitel: *Zeit. Krist.* LXI, p. 596 (1925).

[65] Lietz: *Zeit. Krist.* LXXVII, p. 437 (1931).

with excess lead chloride. Miscible in all proportions with $Pb_5(PO_4)_3Cl$. PD 3.05, 2.99, 2.10; 2–0609.

$Pb_5(VO_4)_3Cl$ (Vanadinite) is hexagonal dipyramidal with $a = 10.31$, $c = 7.34$ kX. U.C. 2. Crystals prismatic. H. 3. G. 6.88. Uniaxial negative with[65] $n_O = 2.628$ (λ 436), 2.416 Na, 2.370 (λ 691), $n_E = 2.505$ (λ 436), 2.350 Na, 2.313 (λ 691), $n_O - n_E = 0.066$ Na. Color red, brown, yellow. In section colorless or tinted with absorption O > E. Made from fusion of lead vanadate with lead chloride. It may contain some P and As replacing V; then the indices are lower.

F. HYDRATED PHOSPHATES, ETC., CONTAINING HYDROXYL OR HALOGEN OR EXTRA OXYGEN

1. Formula Type $A_m(XO_4)_pZ \cdot xH_2O$ with $m{:}p > 3{:}2$ or $A_mB_n(XO_4)_pZ \cdot xH_2O$ with $(m + n){:}p > 3{:}2$

$Na_7(PO_4)_2F \cdot 19H_2O$ is isometric; crystals octahedral. G. 2.22. Isotropic with[37] $n = 1.4489$ Li, 1.4519 Na, 1.4545 Tl. Colorless. Made from a solution of sodium phosphate, soda and sodium fluoride.

$Na_7(AsO_4)_2F \cdot 19H_2O$ is isometric; crystals octahedral. Isotropic with[37] $n = 1.4657$ Li, 1.4693 Na, 1.4726 Tl. Colorless. Made from a solution of sodium arsenate, sodium hydroxide and sodium fluoride.

$Na_7(VO_4)_2F \cdot 19H_2O$ is isometric; crystals octahedral. Isotropic with[37] $n = 1.5171$ Li, 1.5230 Na, 1.5284 Tl. Colorless. Made from fusion followed by crystallization in warm water.

$5(Na_3PO_4 \cdot 12H_2O) \cdot NaOH$ is uniaxial positive with[8] $n_O = 1.447$, $n_E = 1.452$, $n_E - n_O = 0.005$. Made from water solution.

$5(Na_3PO_4 \cdot 11H_2O) \cdot NaCl$ is uniaxial positive with[38] $n_O = 1.447$, $n_E = 1.453$, $n_E - n_O = 0.006$. Made from water solution.

$4(Na_3PO_4 \cdot 11H_2O) \cdot NaOCl$ is uniaxial positive with[38] $n_O = 1.450$, $n_E = 1.455$, $n_E - n_O = 0.005$. Made from water solution.

$H_2(UO_2)_2(PO_4)_2 \cdot 8H_2O$ (Hydrogen-autunite) is tetragonal with $a = 7.02$, $c = 9.04$ Å. Crystals square or octagonal plates. G. 3.3. Uniaxial negative with[66] $n_O = 1.579$, $n_E = 1.568$, $n_O - n_E = 0.011$. Color lemon-yellow. Made from autunite. PD 9.03, 3.80, 3.27; 8–296.

$H_2(UO_2)_2(AsO_4)_2 \cdot 8H_2O$ (Hydrogen-uranospinite) is tetragonal with[66a] $a = 7.16$, $c = 8.80 \pm .02$ Å., U.C. 1. Crystals are basal tablets bounded by {100}. Perfect basal cleavage. G. 3.55. Uniaxial negative with $n_O = 1.612$, $n_E = 1.584 \pm .003$, $n_O - n_E = 0.028$. Lemon-yellow in masses; O pale lemon-yellow, E nearly colorless. Made by reaction of uranyl nitrate

[66] Ross: *Am. Min.* XL, p. 917 (1955).
[66a] Mrose: *Am. Min.* XXXVIII, p. 1159 (1953).

and arsenic acid in hot water solution. The natural mineral **"troegerite"** is supposed[66b] to be $(UO_2)_3(AsO_4)_2 \cdot 12H_2O$; but this may be the same[66a] as hydrogen-uranospinite. Its properties were reported[66b] as follows: tetragonal, $a:c = 1:2.16$, in thin square tablets. Micaceous cleavage {001}, good cleavage {100}. Uniaxial negative, or biaxial with $(-)2V$ very small, $n_O = 1.630$ (also reported as 1.624), $n_E = 1.585$ (also 1.580), but modern chemical and physical data have not been determined on thoroughly authenticated material. PD 8.59, 3.79, 3.30; 8–326.

$Na_2(UO_2)_2(AsO_4)_2 \cdot 8H_2O$ is tetragonal with[66a] $a = 7.12$, $c = 8.70$ Å. Crystals basal tablets with {100}. G. 3.80. Basal cleavage. Uniaxial negative with $n_O = 1.617$, $n_E = 1.586$, both ± 0.003, $n_O - n_E = 0.031$. Color yellow with O pale lemon yellow, E colorless. Made by base exchange with $H_2(UO_2)_2(AsO_4)_2 \cdot 8H_2O$. It has been called sodium uranospinite. PD 8.42, 3.63, 3.27; 8–446.

$(NH_4)_2(UO_2)_2(AsO_4)_2 \cdot 8H_2O$ is tetragonal with[66a] $a = 7.21$, $c = 8.85$ Å. Crystals basal tablets. G. 3.60. Basal cleavage. Uniaxial negative with $n_O = 1.611$, $n_E = 1.601$ both ± 0.003, $n_O - n_E = 0.010$. Color yellow with O pale lemon yellow, E colorless. Made by base-exchange with $H_2(UO_2)_2(AsO_4)_2 \cdot 8H_2O$. It has been called ammonium-uranospinite. PD 9.26, 3.86, 3.36; 8–441.

$NaH(UO_2)_2(PO_4)_2 \cdot 7$–$8H_2O$ is uniaxial negative with[67] $n_O = 1.580$, $n_E = $?, $n_O - n_E = $ moderate. It may show abnormally $(-)2V = $ small. Made from autunite.

$Na_2(UO_2)_2(PO_4)_2 \cdot 6\frac{1}{2}H_2O$ is uniaxial negative with[67] $n_O = 1.582$, $n_E = 1.562$, $n_O - n_E = 0.020$. It may be abnormally biaxial with $(-)2V = $ small. Made from autunite.

$K_2(UO_2)_2(PO_4)_2 \cdot nH_2O$ is optically negative; the crystals are not rectangular in outline, but have an angle of 82° instead of 90°. They show fine rectangular lamellar twinning like microcline. Uniaxial or biaxial[67] with a small optic angle. $n_X = 1.553$, n_Y nearly $= n_Z = 1.575$, $n_Z - n_X = 0.022$. Made from autunite. (Apparently these crystals were produced by solution and redeposition rather than by base-exchange.—A.N.W.)

$K_2(UO_2)_2(VO_4)_2 \cdot 3H_2O$ **(Carnotite)** is orthorhombic or monoclinic(?). Crystals basal plates or laths; often a powder. Perfect basal cleavage. $X = c$;[24] $Y = b$. $(-)2V = 40°$ ca. $n_X = 1.750$, $n_Y = 1.925$, $n_Z = 1.950$, $n_Z - n_X = 0.200$ (with nearly $3H_2O$?). Again:[68] $n_X = 1.89 \pm$ calc., $n_Y = 2.06$, $n_Z = 2.08$ Na, $n_Z - n_X = 0.18$ (with 1.35 per cent H_2O). Color yellow with X nearly colorless, Y and Z canary yellow. The anhydrous compound has been made by fusion of potassium metavanadate and ammonium

---

[66b] Palache *et al.*: *Dana's System of Mineralogy*, II, p. 966 (1951).

[67] Fairchild (and Schaller): *Am. Min.* XIV, p. 265 (1929).

[68] Hess and Foshag: *Proc. U. S. Nat. Mus.* LXXII, Art. 12 (1927).

pyrouranate. The hydrous compound has been made by treating $Ca(UO_2)_2(VO_4)_2 \cdot nH_2O$ with potassium mercuric iodide solution. PD 6.56, 3.12, 3.53; 8–317.

$Ca_2(AsO_4)(OH) \cdot 2H_2O$ has oblique extinction.[10] G. 2.695. $n_X = 1.585$, $n_Y = ?$, $n_Z = 1.590$, $n_Z - n_X = 0.005$.

$CuAl_6(PO_4)_4(OH)_8 \cdot 4H_2O$ (Turquois) is triclinic pinacoidal with $a = 7.47$, $b = 9.93$, $c = 7.67$ kX, $\alpha = 111°39'$, $\beta = 115°23'$, $\gamma = 69°26'$. U.C. 1. Crystals rare, prismatic; usually massive. Perfect {001} and good {010} cleavages. H. 5–6. G. 2.84. For X,[69] $\phi = -30°$ and $\rho = 60°$; for Y, $\phi = 63°$ and $\rho = 83°$. $(+)2V = 40° \pm 2$, r < v very strong with crossed dispersion.[24] $n_X = 1.61$, $n_Y = 1.62$, $n_Z = 1.65$, $n_Z - n_X = 0.04$. Color of massive turquois sky-blue, bluish green to apple-green or greenish gray; crystals bright blue; weakly pleochroic in thick grains with X colorless and Z pale blue or pale green. Made by heating malachite, hydrous aluminum oxide and phosphoric acid to 100° C. PD 3.68, 2.91, 6.17; 6–0214/5.

2. Formula Type $A_mB_n(XO_4)_pZ \cdot xH_2O$ with $(m + n):p = 3:2$

$Ca(UO_2)_2(AsO_4)_2 \cdot 8H_2O$ (Uranospinite) is tetragonal with[66a] $a = 7.10$, $c = 8.81$ Å. Crystals thin basal plates. Perfect {001} and good {100} cleavages. H. 2–3. G. 3.65. Uniaxial negative with[24] $n_O = 1.586$, $n_E = 1.56$, $n_O - n_E = 0.026$. May be biaxial (due to strain?) with X = c and $(-)2V = 46°$. r > v moderate. $n_X = 1.560$, $n_Y = 1.582$, $n_Z = 1.587$, $n_Z - n_X = 0.027$. A single crystal may be biaxial with a uniaxial border.[66a] Again: $(-)2V = 62°$, $n_X = 1.55$, $n_Y = 1.567$, $n_Z = 1.572$, $n_Z - n_X = 0.022$. Color lemon-yellow to siskin-green with O pale yellow and E nearly colorless. Made by adding a solution of uranyl nitrate to one of lime in arsenic acid. Air-dried at room temperature it may have[66a] $n_X = 1.591$, $n_Y = 1.619$, $n_Z = 1.621$, $n_Z - n_X = 0.030$. Hydrated in water for one week: $n_O = 1.589$, $n_E = 1.562$, $n_O - n_E = 0.027$. Heated to 110°C.: $n_O = 1.637$, $n_E = 1.615$, $n_O - n_E = 0.022$. Heated to 1000° C.: $n_O = 1.778$, $n_E = 1.765$, $n_O - n_E = 0.013$. PD 8.85, 3.59, 3.34; 8–319*.

$Ca(UO_2)_2(PO_4)_2 \cdot 10$–$12H_2O$ (Autunite) is tetragonal with[70] $a = 6.989$, $c = 20.63$ kX. U.C. 2. Crystals basal plates. Perfect {001} and poor {100} cleavages. H. 2–2.5. G. 3.1. Uniaxial negative[71] with $n_O = 1.59$–1.60, $n_E = 1.58$–1.59, $n_O - n_E = 0.01$. Often abnormally biaxial with $(-)2V =$ about 10°–30° (up to 53° also) with r > v strong and X = c,[72] $n_X = 1.555$, $n_Y = 1.575$, $n_Z = 1.578$, $n_Z - n_X = 0.023$. The optic angle decreases and indices increase with decreasing water content. Color yellow with O (or

[69] Graham: *U. Toronto Stud., Geol. Ser.* No. 52, p. 39 (1947).
[70] Beintema: *Rec. Trav. Chim. Pays-Bas* LVII, p. 155 (1938).
[71] Meixner: *Chem. Erde* XII, p. 433 (1940).
[72] Shannon: *Am. Min.* XI, p. 35 (1926).

Y and Z) yellow, E (or X) colorless or nearly so. Made from solutions of monocalcium phosphate and uranyl nitrate at low temperature. On drying or slight heating it passes to meta-autunite I with about 5–8 H_2O and at about 80° C. this changes irreversibly to meta-autunite II with about 0–6 H_2O. The tenor of water in autunite changes very easily like that in zeolites, and, as in zeolites, base exchange occurs very easily—in fact, the Ca of autunite can be wholly (or partly) replaced[67] by H_2, Na_2, Ba, Mn, Cu, Ni, Co, Pb, or Mg. These changes have been made especially in meta-autunite I. PD 10.3, 4.96, 3.59; 8–314*.

$Ca(UO_2)_2(PO_4)_2 \cdot 3$–$8H_2O$ **(Meta-autunite I)** is tetragonal with $a = 6.98$, $c = 8.42$ kX. Lamellar twinning may occur on $\{100\}$. Uniaxial negative with[67] $n_O = 1.600$, $n_E = 1.590$, $n_O - n_E = 0.010$. Again:[67] $n_O = 1.598$, $n_E = 1.586$, $n_O - n_E = 0.012$ (the variation probably due to variations in H_2O). Colorless. Made from water solution. PD 8.51, 3.50, 3.63; 8–359.

$Mg(UO_2)_2(PO_4)_2 \cdot 8H_2O$ **(Mg-Autunite)** is tetragonal(?); basal plates isotropic or nearly so. Nearly colorless. Possibly this is **saléeite** which is ditetragonal dipyramidal(?) with $a = 6.980$, $c = 19.813$ Å, and has $10H_2O$. Uniaxial negative with[72a] $n_O = 1.574 \pm .002$, $n_E = 1.559 \pm .002$, $n_O - n_E = 0.016$. Again:[67] $n_O = 1.58$. Also, may be biaxial. Color yellow with O pale greenish yellow, E colorless. PD 9.85, 3.49, 4.95; 8–313.

$Mn(UO_2)_2(PO_4)_2 \cdot 7.6H_2O$ **(Mn-Autunite)** is tetragonal or pseudo-tetragonal. Lamellar twinning on $\{110\}$. Uniaxial negative with[67] $n_O = 1.598$–1.601, $n_O - n_E = $ weak to moderate. Made from autunite.

$Cu(UO_2)_2(PO_4)_2 \cdot 12H_2O$ **(Torbernite)** is tetragonal with $a = 7.05$, $c = 20.5$ kX. U.C. 2. Perfect $\{001\}$ and poor $\{100\}$ cleavages. H. 2–2.5. G. 3.22. F. 2.5. Soluble in HNO_3. Uniaxial negative with[24] $n_O = 1.592$, $n_E = 1.582$, $n_O - n_E = 0.010$. Again:[67] $n_O = 1.608$. Also may be biaxial with small 2V (due to strain?). Color various shades of green with O sky-blue or pale green, E green or greenish yellow. Made from water solution up to about 75° C.; at higher temperatures metatorbernite is formed. PD 10.3, 4.94, 3.58; 8–360.

$Cu(UO_2)_2(PO_4)_2 \cdot 8H_2O$ **(Metatorbernite)** is tetragonal with $a = 6.95$, $c = 8.60$ kX. U.C. 1. Crystals basal tablets often in aggregates. Perfect $\{001\}$ cleavage. H. 2.5. G. 3.7. Uniaxial positive with[73] $n_O = 1.610$–1.628, $n_O - n_E = $ about 0.002 for λ 575 and 0.004 for λ 640. Uniaxial negative for $\lambda < 516$. Color green with O sky-blue and E green. It may be biaxial (due to strain?). Made by partial dehydration of torbernite. On further dehydration the crystals show twinning on $\{110\}$ and turn brown. PD 3.69, 8.66, 3.24; 8–309.

[72a] Mrose: *Am. Min.* XXXV, p. 525 (1950).
[73] Bowen: *Am. J. Sci.* XLVIII, p. 195 (1919).

$Cu(UO_2)_2(AsO_4)_2 \cdot 10\text{--}16H_2O$ **(Zeunerite)** is tetragonal. Crystals basal tablets. H. 2–2.5. G. 3.2. Uniaxial negative with $n_O = 1.602$ (with $16H_2O$); 1.610 (with $10H_2O$), $n_E = ?$. Color green. Made from copper carbonate dissolved in excess arsenic acid to which uranium nitrate was added. PD 3.60, 10.3, 5.07; 8–400*.

$Cu(UO_2)_2(AsO_4)_2 \cdot 5\text{--}8H_2O$ **(Metazeunerite)** is tetragonal with $a = 7.13$, $c = 8.83$ Å. U.C. 1. Crystals basal tablets. H. 2.5. G. 3.64. Perfect basal cleavage. Uniaxial negative with[74] $n_O = 1.647$, $n_E = 1.630$, $n_O - n_E = 0.017$. Again:[24] $n_O = 1.643$, $n_E = 1.623$, $n_O - n_E = 0.020$. Also: $n_O = 1.654$ (for $5H_2O$). Color green. Made by partial dehydration of zeunerite.[74] PD 8.76, 3.71, 3.28; 4–0112*.

$Ba(UO_2)_2(PO_4)_2 \cdot 6H_2O$ **(Uranocircite)** is tetragonal with[75] $a = 6.95$, $c = 8.44$ Å. Crystals like those of autunite. Perfect {001} and distinct {100} cleavages. H. 2. G. 3.53. Uniaxial negative with[67] $n_O = 1.613$, $n_E = 1.604$, $n_O - n_E = 0.009$. Again:[75] $n_O = 1.621$, $n_E = 1.607$, $n_O - n_E = 0.014$ Na. Also may be biaxial negative with small 2V and two sets of lamellar twinning; then $n_X = 1.610 \pm .003$, $n_Y \approx n_Z = 1.623 \pm .003$, $n_Z - n_X = 0.013$. When heated the biaxial sample becomes uniaxial at 100°–150° C. Color canary-yellow with X nearly colorless, Y and Z pale canary-yellow. Made from autunite. PD 3.58, 8.19, 2.08; 8–413.

$Pb(UO_2)_2(PO_4)_2 \cdot 8.4H_2O)$ is tetragonal (or nearly so). Crystals may be eight-sided basal plates. Uniaxial negative with[67] $n_O = 1.625\text{--}1.627$, $n_E = ?$. Also may be biaxial with small 2V. Made from autunite.

$Ca(UO_2)_2(VO_4)_2 \cdot nH_2O$ **(Tyuyamunite)** is orthorhombic with[23] $a = 10.40$, $b = 19.41$, $c = 8.26$ kX. Crystals laths or flakes. Perfect {010} and distinct {001} and {100} cleavages. G. 3.67–4.35, increasing with decreasing water content. $X = b$; $Y = c$.[76] $(-)2V = 48°$ ca., $n_X = 1.75\text{--}1.80$ calc., $n_Y = 1.927\text{--}1.932$, $n_Z = 1.965\text{--}1.968$, $n_Z - n_X = 0.17\text{--}0.21$. On dehydration the refractive indices increase, but the optic angle does not change. Color yellow with X nearly colorless, Y pale canary-yellow, Z canary-yellow. Made by treating $K_2(UO_2)_2(VO_4)_2 \cdot 3H_2O$ with a solution of calcium bicarbonate. PD 10.2, 5.02, 3.20; 6–0017.

$KAl_2(PO_4)_2OH \cdot 4H_2O(?)$ **(Minyulite)** is orthorhombic(?). Crystals acicular. Probably a cleavage parallel to elongation. H. 3.5. G. 2.45. $X = c$. $(+)2V$ large.[77] $n_X = 1.531$, $n_Y = 1.534$, $n_Z = 1.538$, $n_Z - n_X = 0.007$. Colorless to white. PD 5.6, 3.37, 6.8; 2–0143.

[74] Weiss-Frondel: *Am. Min.* XXXVI, p. 249 (1951). Names used here as proposed by Frondel in *Dana's System of Mineralogy*, II, p. 989 (1951).

[75] Baldanza: *Periodico Min. Roma* XXII, p. 249 (1953).

[76] Merwin in Hillebrand: *Am. J. Sci.* CCVIII, p. 208 (1924).

[77] Simpson and LeMesurier: *J. Roy. Soc. West Australia* XIX, p. 13 (1933).

KAl$_2$(PO$_4$)$_2$F·4H$_2$O(?) is orthorhombic.[13] Crystals slender prisms. G. 2.44. X = c. (+)2V near 90°, n_X = 1.528, n_Y = 1.530, n_Z = 1.533, n_Z − n_X = 0.005. Colorless. PD 5.6, 3.37, 6.8; 2–0143.

KAl$_2$(PO$_4$)$_2$OH·2H$_2$O is orthorhombic[13] in slender prisms. G. 2.55. Y parallel with rods. (+)2V = 85°–90°, n_X = 1.536, n_Y = 1.541, n_Z = 1.547, n_Z − n_X = 0.011. Colorless. Another phase is monoclinic (in prisms) with β = 102°–103°. G. 2.55. Y = b; Z ∧ c = 2°–3°. (+)2V = 71°, n_X = 1.562, n_Y = 1.564, n_Z = 1.568, n_Z − n_X = 0.006. Colorless. Made by treating kaolinite with phosphate solution.[78] PD 5.6, 3.37, 6.8; 2–0143.

KFe$_2$(PO$_4$)$_2$OH·2H$_2$O is monoclinic[13] (in prisms) with β = 102°. G. 2.93. X = b; Z ∧ c = 30°. (+)2V = 81°, r > v. n_X = 1.706, n_Y = 1.720, n_Z = 1.741, n_Z − n_X = 0.035. Color yellow. PD 6.79, 5.99, 3.06; 9–446.

NH$_4$Al$_2$(PO$_4$)$_2$OH·2.5H$_2$O is monoclinic (in prisms) with[13] β = 102°. X = b; Z ∧ c = 8°. (+)2V = 60°, n_X = 1.564, n_Y = 1.566, n_Z = 1.572, n_Z − n_X = 0.008. Colorless.

KAl$_2$(PO$_4$)$_2$OH·0.5H$_2$O is monoclinic (in prisms) with[13] clino- and orthodomes. Y = b; Z ∧ c = 34°. (−)2V = 71°, n_X = 1.565, n_Y = 1.571, n_Z = 1.574, n_Z − n_X = 0.009. Colorless.

Pb$_2$UO$_2$(PO$_4$)$_2$·H$_2$O (Parsonsite) is monoclinic.[78a,78b] Crusts of powder and {010} lath-like crystals. β about 81°. H. 2.5–3. G. 5.37. Water content variable. Y = b; Z ∧ c usually 12°–14°, but varies from 2° to 36°. (−)2V = ?, n_X = 1.85, n_Y = ?, n_Z = 1.862, n_Z − n_X = 0.012, but varying much (with H$_2$O content?). Color pale yellow, not pleochroic. PD 4.25, 3.28, 2.13; 8–311.

3. Formula Type A$_m$B$_n$(XO$_4$)$_p$Z·xH$_2$O with (m + n):p = 5:2

Ca(UO$_2$)$_4$(PO$_4$)$_2$(OH)$_4$·2(−7?)H$_2$O(?) (Phosphuranylite) is ortho-rhombic with a = 15.85, b = 17.42, c = 13.76 Å. Crystals {100} plates long ∥ c with good {001} and {010} cleavages. H. about 2. G. about 4.1. X = a; Y = b. (−)2V = small to 51° Na, r > v. n_X = 1.682, n_Y = 1.706, n_Z = 1.708, n_Z − n_X = 0.026. The indices vary notably (with variations in H$_2$O?); for example:[78c] n_X = 1.658, n_Y = 1.699, n_Z = 1.699, n_Z − n_X = 0.041, and again: n_X = 1.695, n_Y = ?, n_Z ≈ 1.77, n_Z − n_X = 0.082. Color yellow with X very pale or colorless, Y yellow, Z golden yellow. Made[79] from solution held at 180° C. or by alteration of autunite. PD 7.91, 3.96, 3.15; 8–289*.

Pb(UO$_2$)$_4$(PO$_4$)$_2$(OH)$_4$·7(−2?)H$_2$O (Renardite) is orthorhombic with

[78] Kittrick and Jackson: *Science* CXX, p. 508 (1954).
[78a] Frondel: *Am. Min.* XXXV, p. 245 (1950).
[78b] Bignand: *Bull. Soc. Fr. Min.* LXXVIII, p. 1 (1955).
[78c] Frondel: *Am. Min.* XXXV, p. 756 (1950).
[79] Bignand, Goni, and Guillemin: *Bull. Soc. Fr. Min.* LXXVII, p. 1299 (1954).

$a = 16.01$, $b = 17.5$, $c = 13.7$ Å. U.C. 6. Crystals are {100} tablets or laths. Good {100} cleavage. G. > 4. X = a; Y = c. $(-)2V = 41°$ calc., r > v. $n_X = 1.715$, $n_Y = 1.736$, $n_Z = 1.739$, all ±0.003, $n_Z - n_X = 0.018$. Color yellow with X and Y yellow, Z colorless. Probably forms a complete series of mix-crystals with[78c] $Ca(UO_2)(PO_4)_2(OH)_4 \cdot 2H_2O$. Made as described by Bignand.[78b] PD 7.97, 3.99, 5.93; 8–328.

G. PHOSPHITES, ETC.

$Na_2HPO_3 \cdot 5H_2O$ is orthorhombic[79a] with $a:b:c = 0.70:1:0.78$. Crystals prismatic. Y = c; Z = a. $(+)2V = 43°16'$ Li, $44°7'$ Na, $44°45'$ Tl. $n_Y = 1.4434$ Na, $n_Z - n_X =$ weak. Colorless.

$NaH_2PO_3 \cdot 2.5H_2O$ is monoclinic[80] with $a:b:c = 1.202:1:0.796$, $\beta = 109°53'$. Crystals basal tablets. M.P. 42° C. Y = b; Z $\wedge$ $c = -54°33'$. $(+)2V = 77°36'$ Li, $77°38'$ Na, $77°40'$ Tl, r < v very weak. $n_X = 1.4193$ Na, $n_Y = 1.4281$ Li, 1.4309 Na, 1.4334 Tl, $n_Z = 1.4493$ Na, $n_Z - n_X = 0.030$ Na. Colorless.

H. METAPHOSPHATES, ETC.

KPO_3 is uniaxial positive.[81] M.P. 813° C. $n_O = 1.465$, $n_E = 1.483$, $n_E - n_O = 0.018$. Colorless.

$Na_3K(PO_3)_4$ is orthorhombic(?). M.P. 552° C. $(-)2V = 40°$. $n_X = 1.493$, $n_Y = 1.500$, $n_Z = 1.514$, $n_Z - n_X = 0.021$. Colorless. PD 2.97, 3.10, 8.9; 8–232.

α-CaP_2O_6 is orthorhombic with micaceous basal cleavage and poor {010} cleavage.[82] X = a; Y = b. $(-?)2V =$ almost 90°. $n_X = 1.587$, $n_Y = 1.591$, $n_Z = 1.595$, $n_Z - n_X = 0.008$. Also reported to be tetragonal[11] and uniaxial negative with $n_O = 1.595$, $n_E = 1.588$, $n_O - n_E = 0.007$.

β-CaP_2O_6 forms euhedral plates, laths, etc., with {010} cleavage and parallel extinction.[82] $(-)2V = 80°$ calc., $n_X = 1.573$, $n_Y = 1.587$, $n_Z = 1.596$, $n_Z - n_X = 0.023$. Colorless. CaP_2O_6 glass has $n = 1.542$.

$NaAsO_3$ is orthorhombic.[26] G. 2.30. $(+)2V = 88°$ calc. $n_X = 1.479$, $n_Y = 1.502$, $n_Z = 1.5265$, $n_Z - n_X = 0.0475$. Colorless.

NH_4PO_3 is monoclinic;[83] crystals platy with G. 2.21. $(+)2V =$ large, $n_X = 1.490$, $n_Y = ?$, $n_Z = 1.505$, $n_Z - n_X = 0.015$. Colorless. Made by reaction of $(NH_4)_2S$ and $Pb(PO_3)_2$ and precipitation with alcohol. Colorless.

[79a] Dufet: *Bull. Soc. Fr. Min.* XIII, p. 199 (1890).
[80] Dufet: *Bull. Soc. Fr. Min.* XII, p. 477 (1889).
[81] Morey: *J. Am. Chem. Soc.* LXXVI, p. 4724 (1954).
[82] Hill, Faust, and Reynolds: *Am. J. Sci.* CCXLII, pp. 457, 542 (1944).
[83] Colony, in Kiehl and Hill: *J. Am. Chem. Soc.* XLIX, p. 123 (1927).

Also described as orthorhombic[84] with $a = 10.40$, $b = 10.8$, $c = 12.75$ Å. U.C. 16. X $= b$. Biaxial negative. Is this another phase?

NaPO₃ has two (or three?) crystal phases.[4] α-NaPO₃ crystallizes just below the melting point (627° C.). It is biaxial with $(-)2V = 80°$, $n_X = 1.474$, $n_Y = 1.478$, $n_Z = 1.480$, $n_Z - n_X = 0.006$. It is also made by dehydrating $NaH_2PO_4 \cdot 2H_2O$; then reported to have[85] $(-)2V = $ large, $n_X = 1.473$, $n_Y = ?$, $n_Z = 1.486$, $n_Z - n_X = 0.013$. β-NaPO₃ is probably orthorhombic;[4] Y $= b$; Z $= a$. $(+)2V = 78°$, $n_X = 1.498$, $n_Y = 1.510$, $n_Z = 1.529$, $n_Z - n_X = 0.031$. Also reported[86] as $n_X = 1.502$, $n_Y = ?$, $n_Z = 1.525$. NaPO₃ glass has[4] $n = 1.4847$. Colorless. PD 2.86, 3.08, 4.98; 2-0776*.

Na₄Ca(PO₃)₆ is biaxial.[87] M.P. 738° C. $(-)2V = 80°$, $n_X = 1.518$, $n_Y = 1.564$, $n_Z = 1.581$, $n_Z - n_X = 0.063$. Colorless.

CaAs₂O₆ is monoclinic[10] (or triclinic?) with $\beta = 70°$. G. 3.195. Extinction at 18° (23°?) to elongation. $n_X = 1.629$, $n_Y = ?$, $n_Z = 1.635$, $n_Z - n_X = 0.006$.

NaPO₃·2H₂O is triclinic with[88] $(001) \wedge (100) = 64°16'$, $(001) \wedge (010) = 82°33'$; $(100) \wedge (010) = 73°28'$. Perfect basal cleavage. $(+)2V = $ large, r > v. Mean refractive index 1.400, $n_Z - n_X = 0.009$. Also reported as biaxial with[89] $(-)2V = 77° \pm 3°$. Another phase (?) is uniaxial negative[4] with $n_O = 1.441$, $n_E = 1.432$, $n_O - n_E = 0.009$.

CaV₂O₆·4H₂O (Rossite) is triclinic with[90] $\alpha = 98°18'$, $\beta = 120°12'$, $\gamma = 89°34'$. Crystals often vertically elongated and flattened on {010}. Good {010} cleavage. H. 2–3. G. 2.45. Y $\wedge b$ about 45°; Z near c. $(-?)2V = $ large with strong dispersion. $n_X = 1.710$, $n_Y = 1.770$, $n_Z = 1.840$, $n_Z - n_X = 0.130$. Color yellow. Made from water solution.

CaV₂O₆·2H₂O (Metarossite) forms flaky masses.[90] $(+)2V = $ large with strong dispersion. $n_X = 1.840$, $n_Y > 1.85$, $n_Z > 1.85$. Yellow to colorless in flakes. Made by partial dehydration of $CaV_2O_6 \cdot 4H_2O$.

I. HYPOPHOSPHATES, ETC.

K₂H₂P₂O₆·3H₂O is orthorhombic[91] with $a:b:c = 0.992:1:0.901$. Crystals vertical columnar with {100}, {010}, {110}, {101}, etc. X $= c$; Y $= a$.

[84] Romers, Ketelaar, and MacGillavry: *Nature* CLXIV, p. 960 (1949).

[85] Colony, in Beans and Kiehl: *J. Am. Chem. Soc.* XLIX, p. 1878 (1927).

[86] Partridge, Hicks and Smith: *J. Am. Chem. Soc.* LXIII, p. 454 (1941).

[87] Morey: *J. Am. Chem. Soc.* LXXIV, p. 5783 (1952).

[88] Kerr in Kiehl and Coats: *J. Am. Chem. Soc.* XLIX, p. 2180 (1927).

[89] Quimby: *Chem. Rev.* XL, p. 141 (1947).

[90] Foshag and Hess: *Proc. U. S. Nat. Mus.* LXXII, Art. 11, pp. 1 and 9 (1927). β from *Dana's System of Mineralogy*, II, p. 1053 (1951).

[91] Dufet: *Bull. Soc. Fr. Min.* XIV, pp. 217 and 219 (1891).

$(-)2V = 62°$, r < v very weak. $n_X = 1.4768$, $n_Y = 1.4843$, $n_Z = 1.4870$ Na, $n_Z - n_X = 0.0102$. Colorless.

$K_2H_2P_2O_6 \cdot 2H_2O$ is monoclinic[91] with $a:b:c = 0.745:1:0.798$, $\beta = 98°29'$. Crystals basal tablets with {110}, {221}, etc. X $\wedge$ c $= -36°30'$; Z $= b$. $(-)2V = 36°9'$ Na, r < v very weak. $n_X = 1.4893$, $n_Y = 1.5314$, $n_Z = 1.5363$ Na, $n_Z - n_X = 0.049$. Colorless.

$Na_2H_2P_2O_6 \cdot 6H_2O$ is monoclinic with[92] $a:b:c = 2.013:1:2.0381$. $\beta = 126°47'$. Crystals basal tablets or short prisms. Perfect {001} and poor {110} cleavages. Twinning on {10$\bar{1}$}. G. 1.85. Y $= b$; Z $\wedge$ c $= +35°17'$ Na. $(+)2V = 55°36'$ Li, $57°20'$ Na, $58°10'$ Tl. $n_X = 1.4822$ Li, 1.4855 Na, 1.4883 Tl, $n_Y = 1.4861$ Li, 1.4897 Na, 1.4927 Tl, $n_Z = 1.5006$ Li, 1.5041 Na, 1.5074 Tl, $n_Z - n_X = 0.0186$ Na. Colorless. Made from water solution.

$Na_3HP_2O_6 \cdot 9H_2O$ is monoclinic with[92] $a:b:c = 1.552:1:1.510$, $\beta = 102°2'$. Crystals basal tablets with {101}, {034}, {110}, etc. Twinning on axis a. G. 1.74. X $\wedge$ c $= -10°$ Li, $-11°$ Na, $-12°$ Tl; Z $= b$. $(-)2V = 82°2'$ Li, $82°0'$ Na, $81°56'$ Tl, r > v very weak. $n_X = 1.4622$ Li, 1.4653 Na, 1.4682 Tl, $n_Y = 1.4705$ Li, 1.4738 Na, 1.4769 Tl, $n_Z = 1.4769$ Li, 1.4804 Na, 1.4836 Tl, $n_Z - n_X = 0.0182$ Na. Colorless.

$Na_4P_2O_7 \cdot 10H_2O(?)$ is monoclinic with[92] $a:b:c = 1.172:1:1.908$, $\beta = 100°16'$. Crystals domatic, terminated by prisms, etc. Lamellar twinning on {001}; {010} and {101} cleavages. G. 1.82. Y $= b$; Z $\wedge$ c $= -39.5°$. $(+)2V = 48°58'$ Li, $48°56'$ Na, $48°43'$ Tl, r > v very weak. $n_X = 1.4777$ Na, $n_Y = 1.4789$ Li, 1.4822 Na, 1.4852 Tl, $n_Z = 1.5036$ Na, $n_Z - n_X = 0.0259$ Na. Colorless. PD 4.38, 6.52, 5.46; 8–240/1.

J. PYROPHOSPHATES, ETC.

$K_4P_2O_7$ melts at 1105° C. It is uniaxial positive[93] with $n_O = 1.495$, $n_E = 1.502$, $n_E - n_O = 0.007$. Colorless.

$K_5P_3O_{10}$ melts incongruently[93] at 642° C. It is uniaxial negative with $n_O = 1.520$, $n_E = 1.516$, $n_O - n_E = 0.004$.

β-$Ca_2P_2O_7$ is tetragonal.[82] Uniaxial positive with $n_O = 1.630$, $n_E = 1.639$, $n_E - n_O = 0.009$. Again:[11] $n_O = 1.624$, $n_E = 1.628$, $n_E - n_O = 0.004$. It inverts at 1270° C. to α-$Ca_2P_2O_7$ which forms equant crystals with two good cleavages and common polysynthetic twinning.[82] M.P. 1358° C. $(-)2V = 50°$, $n_X = 1.584$, $n_Y = 1.599$, $n_Z = 1.605$, $n_Z - n_X = 0.021$. Again:[11] $n_X = 1.585$, $n_Y = 1.60$, $n_Z = 1.605$, $n_Z - n_X = 0.020$. A third phase[82] is known. Colorless. PD 3.00, 3.20, 3.07; 2–0647*.

[92] Dufet: *Bull. Soc. Fr. Min.* X, pp. 102–111 (1887).

[93] Morey: *J. Am. Chem. Soc.* LXXVI, p. 4724 (1954).

CaH$_2$P$_2$O$_7$ is uniaxial negative with[11] $n_O = 1.578$, $n_E = 1.518$, $n_O - n_E = 0.060$. PD 3.35, 3.19, 3.74; 9–354.

Na$_2$H$_2$P$_2$O$_7$ forms fine needles with positive elongation.[4] $n_1 = 1.510$, n_2 ($\parallel$ needles) $= 1.517$.

Pb$_2$As$_2$O$_7$ is orthorhombic with[94] G. 6.85. M.P. 802° C. Biaxial with $n_Y = 2.03$.

Na$_2$H$_2$P$_2$O$_7$·6H$_2$O is monoclinic with $a:b:c = 2.026:1:2.049$. $\beta = 123°19'$. Crystals basal tablets with perfect {001} cleavage. G. 1.86. X $\wedge$ $c = -42.5°$; Z $= b$. $(-)2V = 15°13'$ Li, $31°56'$ Na, $36°10'$ Tl, r < v extreme; $n_X = 1.4573$ Li, 1.4599 Na, 1.4623 Tl, $n_Y = 1.4616$ Li, 1.4645 Na, 1.4672 Tl, $n_Z = 1.4617$ Li, 1.4649 Na, 1.4677 Tl, $n_Z - n_X = 0.005$ Na. Colorless. Made by adding acetic acid to a warm solution of the normal salt.

Na$_4$P$_2$O$_7$·10H$_2$O is monoclinic with $a:b:c = 1.287:1:1.895$, $\beta = 98°16'$. Crystals domatic. G. 1.82. X $= b$; Z nearly exactly normal to {101}. $(+)2V = 60.5°$. $n_X = 1.4470$ Li, 1.4499 Na, 1.4526 Tl, $n_Y = 1.4496$ Li, 1.4525 Na, 1.4551 Tl, $n_Z = 1.4575$ Li, 1.4604 Na, 1.4629 Tl, $n_Z - n_X = 0.0104$ Na. Colorless. Made from water solution. PD 4.38, 6.52, 5.46; 8–240/1.

Na$_4$P$_2$O$_7$ is biaxial with[4] $(+)2V = 40°$. $n_X = 1.475$, $n_Y = 1.477$, $n_Z = 1.496$, $n_Z - n_X = 0.021$. Colorless.

Mg$_2$P$_2$O$_7$ is monoclinic[95] with $a:b:c = 0.795:1:1.088$, $\beta = 104°11'$. Crystals basal tablets with perfect {110} and good {001} cleavages. H. 4. G. 3.06. M.P. 1383° C. X $\wedge$ $c = +15°$ (nearly normal to {001}); Y $= b$. $(+)2V = 20.5°$. $n_X = 1.602$, $n_Y = 1.604$, $n_Z = 1.615$ Na, $n_Z - n_X = 0.013$. Colorless. Made from fusion. PD 3.02, 2.98, 4.14; 8–38.

Mn$_2$P$_2$O$_7$ is monoclinic with[95] $a:b:c = 0.783:1:?$, $\beta = 105°01'$. Crystals prismatic with perfect {110} and poor {001} cleavages. H. 4. G. 3.71. M.P. 1196° C. X $\wedge$ $c = -4°$; Y $= b$. $(+)2V =$ nearly 90°. $n_X = 1.695$, $n_Y = 1.704(?)$, $n_Z = 1.710$ Na, $n_Z - n_X = 0.015$. Color brownish pink with X light pink, Y and Z nearly colorless to very pale yellow (in thick plates). Miscible in all proportions with Mg$_2$P$_2$O$_7$. Made from fusion. PD 3.10, 2.95, 2.60; 3–0555.

Na$_5$P$_3$O$_{10}$ has at least two phases.[4] One phase (α) is biaxial with $(+)2V = 21°$, $n_X = 1.477$, $n_Y = 1.478$, $n_Z = 1.504$, $n_Z - n_X = 0.027$. The other (β-)phase[4] is also biaxial with $(+)2V = 57°$, $n_X = 1.470$, $n_Y = 1.477$, $n_Z = 1.502$, $n_Z - n_X = 0.032$. Colorless. Both made from the melt, the first by very slow cooling, the second by rapid cooling. PD 2.68, 4.55, 2.60; 2–0922*.

Na$_5$P$_3$O$_{10}$·6H$_2$O has two cleavages at right angles. It is biaxial with[4]

[94] *Int. Crit. Tables*, I, 1926.

[95] Andersen: *J. Wash. Acad. Sci.* IV, p. 318 (1914).

$(+)2V = 20°$, $n_X = 1.449$, $n_Y = 1.450$, $n_Z = 1.482$, $n_Z - n_X = 0.033$. Colorless. Made from water solution.

CaP$_4$O$_{11}$ has the optic plane normal to a good cleavage.[82] $(-)2V = 15°$, $n_X = 1.470$, $n_Y = 1.497$, $n_Z = 1.499$, $n_Z - n_X = 0.029$. Colorless.

Ca$_2$P$_6$O$_{17}$ has the optic plane normal to a good cleavage.[82] $(-)2V = 23°$, $n_X = 1.477$, $n_Y = 1.511$, $n_Z = 1.513$, $n_Z - n_X = 0.036$. Colorless.

K. COMPOUND PHOSPHATES, ETC.

Ca$_{10}$(PO$_4$)$_6$O·Ca$_2$SiO$_4$ (Steadite) is hexagonal with fair basal cleavage. Uniaxial negative with[16] mean index 1.65–1.67 and weak birefringence. Color pale buff to brown. Found in some slags.

4(Na$_3$PO$_4$·11H$_2$O)·NaNO$_3$ is uniaxial positive with[38] $n_O = 1.444$, $n_E = 1.450$, $n_E - n_O = 0.006$. Colorless. Made from water solution.

Ca$_3$(PO$_4$)$_2$·2Ca$_2$SiO$_4$ (Nagelschmidtite) is orthorhombic(?). Crystals tabular or granular. G. 3.065. M.P. about 1800°–1900° C. Good basal and fair {110} cleavages.[16] $(+)2V = 0°–20°$. $n_X = 1.642$–1.680, $n_Y = 1.642$–1.675, $n_Z = 1.661$–1.690, $n_Z - n_X = 0.004$–0.010. Colorless. Made[96] by sintering the powdered constituents, or by fusion. PD 2.66, 2.80, 1.94; 5–0646.

Ca$_3$(PO$_4$)$_2$·Ca$_2$SiO$_4$ (Silicocarnotite) is monoclinic[16] and pseudo-hexagonal. M.P. 1700°–1850° C. $(-)2V = $ large; $n_X = 1.632$, $n_Y = 1.636$, $n_Z = 1.640$, $n_Z - n_X = 0.008$. Color blue with X colorless, Y pale blue, Z sky-blue. Found in some slags.

Na$_3$PO$_4$·NaBO$_2$·18H$_2$O is biaxial with[38] $(-)2V = 60°$ calc. $n_X = 1.445$, $n_Y = 1.451$, $n_Z = 1.453$, $n_Z - n_X = 0.008$. PD 2.78, 3.73, 2.86; 2–0841.

Mg$_3$B$_2$(OH)$_6$(PO$_4$)$_2$·6H$_2$O (Lueneburgite) is probably monoclinic. In fibrous masses; also in pseudo-hexagonal tablets. A prismatic cleavage with an angle of about 73°. H. near 2. G. 2.05. Y $= b$(?). $(-)2V = 62°$ calc. $n_X = 1.520$,[24] $n_Y = 1.54$, $n_Z = 1.545$, $n_Z - n_X = 0.025$. Color white or brownish white. Artificial.[97]

[96] Barrett and McCaughey: *Am. Mineralogist* XXVII, p. 680 (1942).

[97] Berdesinski: *Naturwiss.* XXXVIII, p. 476 (1951).

X. Silicates

A. INTRODUCTION

X-ray studies have proved that in silicates each silicon atom is surrounded by four oxygen atoms arranged at the corners of a tetrahedron, as illustrated in Figs. 10-1 and 10-2. In Fig. 10-1 the silicon and oxygen atoms are assumed to be of the same size so as to show their relative positions more plainly. Actually, the oxygen atoms are much larger than the silicon atoms, as shown in Fig. 10-2. If such tetrahedral groups are not

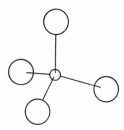

Fig. 10-1. Positions of centers of atoms in SiO_4-tetrahedron.

linked directly by sharing one (or more) oxygen atoms, the formula of the substance will include one or more SiO_4 groups,[1] as in zircon, $ZrSiO_4$ and forsterite, Mg_2SiO_4. No SiO_4 tetrahedron is linked to a neighboring tetrahedron by sharing more than one oxygen atom, but one tetrahedron may be linked thus to one, two, three or four other tetrahedra. If it is linked to only one other, as shown in Figs. 10-3 and 10-4 the formula must contain Si_2O_7 as in $Ca_2MgSi_2O_7$ (åkermanite). If it is linked to two other tetrahedra it may form a trigonal ring, as in $BaTiSi_3O_9$ (benitoite) (Fig.

[1] A few silicates (called "subsilicates") contain one or more oxygen atoms not directly connected with a silicon atom, as in sillimanite, $AlOAlSiO_4$, and kornerupine, $Mg(AlO)_2AlSiO_4$.

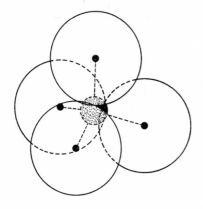

Fig. 10-2. Packing diagram of atoms
in SiO₄-tetrahedron.

10-5), or a tetragonal ring (Fig. 10-6), or a hexagonal ring as in $Be_3Al_2Si_6O_{18}$
(beryl) (Fig. 10-7); finally it may form a continuous chain as in $MgSiO_3$
(enstatite) (Fig. 10-8). In all these examples the formula includes SiO_3 or
a multiple thereof.

If the SiO_4 tetrahedron is linked to three other tetrahedra, it forms a

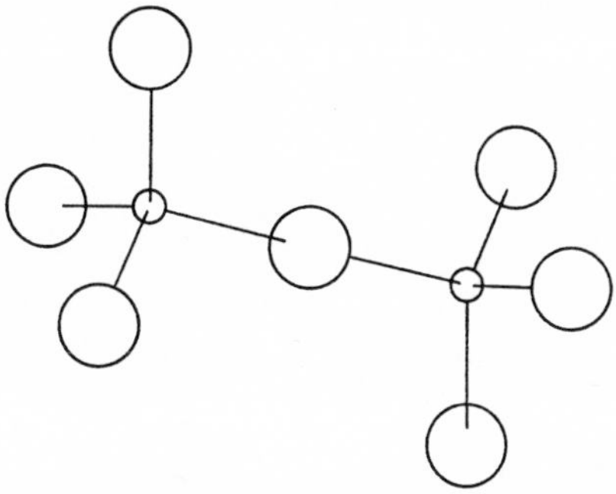

Fig. 10-3a. Positions of centers of atoms in the type of Si_2O_7-group found in $Sc_2Si_2O_7$
(thortveitite).

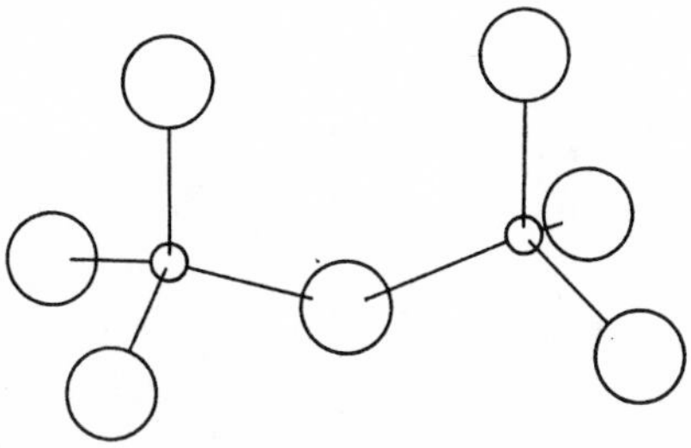

Fig. 10-3b. Positions of centers of atoms in the type of Si_2O_7-group found in
$Ca_2MgSi_2O_7$ (åkermanite).

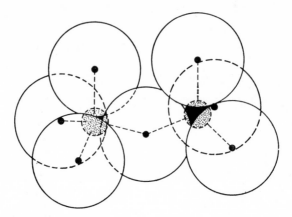

Fig. 10-4. Arrangement of atoms in Si₂O₇-group, åkermanite type.

continuous sheet, as in micas (Fig. 10-9) and the formula includes[2] $(Si,Al)_2O_5$ or a multiple thereof, as in $KAl_2(OH)_2Si_3AlO_{10}$. Finally, if linked to four other tetrahedra, it forms a continuous three-dimensional network, as in sodalite (Fig. 10-9) and the formula must include $(Si,Al)_2O_4$ or some

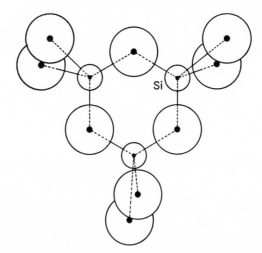

Fig. 10-5. Arrangement of atoms in trigonal Si₃O₉-group found in BaTiSi₃O₉ (benitoite).

multiple thereof. No other cases are known except that not all the tetra-hedra in a single substance are necessarily linked to their neighbors in the

[2] The replacement of some Si atoms by Al will be described later.

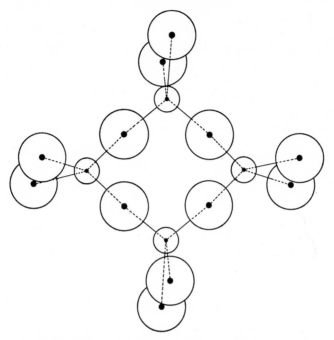

Fig. 10-6. Arrangement of atoms in square Si_4O_{12}-group probably present in $(Fe_{1-x}Mn_x)$—$Ca_2Al_2BO_3OHSi_4O_{12}$ (axinite).

same way (forming "heterosilicates"). On this basis silicates may be classified as follows:[3]

Class	Grouping of SiO_4 tetra-hedra	Links between SiO_4 tet-rahedra	Oxygen atoms for $4(Si + Al)$	Examples	
				Formula	Mineral
1. Nesosilicates	Singles	0	16	Mg_2SiO_4	Forsterite
2. Sorosilicates	Doubles	1	14	$Ca_2MgSi_2O_7$	Åkermanite
3. Cyclosilicates	Rings	2	12	$BaTiSi_3O_9$	Benitoite
4. Inosilicates	Chains	2	12	$MgSiO_3$	Enstatite
5. Phyllosilicates	Sheets	3	10	$Mg_3(OH)_2Si_4O_{10}$	Talc
6. Tectosilicates	Frameworks	4	8	$KSiAlO_4$	Kaliophilite

In the SiO_4 tetrahedra of silicates some of the silicon atoms may be replaced by Al (or by Be or B) atoms. This changes the electric charge of the

---

[3] The names of the classes were given by Strunz (*Mineral. Tabellen*, 1941) and Fleischer (1947 Reprint 117, A.S.T.M.). The prefixes mean: *neso*, island; *soro*, group; *cyclo*, ring; *ino*, thread (or chain); *phyllo*, sheet; *tecto*, framework.

tetrahedra. For example, SiO_2 has zero charge; for convenience it may be written as $Si_{12}O_{24}$; if one quarter of the Si atoms are replaced by Al atoms, then the formula becomes $Si_9Al_3O_{24}$ which is not neutral but has a negative charge of -3; if this is satisfied by K atoms the formula is $K_3Si_9Al_3O_{24}$, or, as usually written, $KAlSi_3O_8$ (orthoclase). If one-third of the Si atoms are replaced by Al atoms the formula becomes $Si_8Al_4O_{24}$ with a charge of -4;

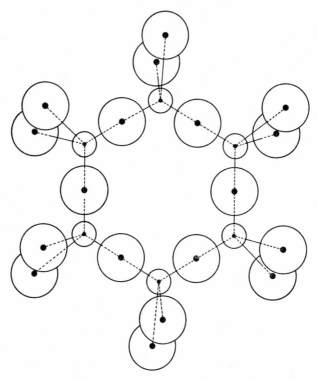

Fig. 10-7. Arrangement of atoms in hexagonal Si_6O_{18}-group found in $Al_2Be_3Si_6O_{18}$ (beryl).

if this is satisfied by K atoms the formula is $K_4Si_8Al_4O_{24}$ or $KAlSi_2O_6$ (leucite). If half the Si atoms are replaced by Al atoms, the formula becomes $Si_6Al_6O_{24}$ with a charge of -6; if this charge is satisfied by Na atoms the formula is $Na_6Si_6Al_6O_{24}$ or $NaAlSiO_4$ (nepheline). Thus the three-dimensional framework may serve as the basis of silicates with the same Si (without Al) to O ratio in their formulas as phyllosilicates or inosilicates or nesosilicates. Al atoms can proxy for Si atoms not only in three-dimensional frameworks but in other silicate structures.

Some silicates have their silicon tetrahedra linked to their neighbors in more than one way. For example, $Ca_{10}(Mg,Fe)_2(OH)_4Al_4Si_9O_{34}$ (vesuvianite) contains single tetrahedra (SiO_4) and also pairs of tetrahedra (Si_2O_7) in different parts of the same structure. To show this the formula may be

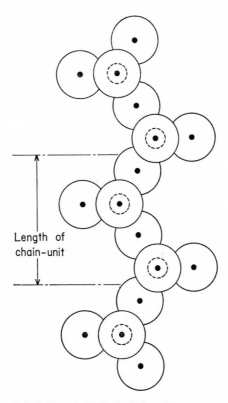

Length of chain-unit

Fig. 10-8. Arrangement of atoms in Si_2O_6-chain found in pyroxenes such as $CaMgSi_2O_6$ (diopside). Two such chains, sharing lateral oxygens, form the Si_4O_{11}-band found in amphiboles such as $Ca_2Mg_5Si_8O_{22}(OH)_2$ (tremolite).

written: $Ca_{10}(Mg,Fe)_2Al_4\begin{Bmatrix}(SiO_4)_5 \\ (Si_2O_7)_2\end{Bmatrix}(OH)_4$. Therefore, it could be included in the nesosilicates or the sorosilicates. Amphibole has half its tetrahedra linked to two others and half to three others; this can be shown in a generalized formula as $R_7\begin{Bmatrix}Si_2O_6 \\ Si_2O_5\end{Bmatrix}(OH)_2$, which becomes $(Mg,Fe)_7Si_4O_{11}(OH)_2$ for anthophyllite. In a few silicates Be, like Al, may replace some Si in the

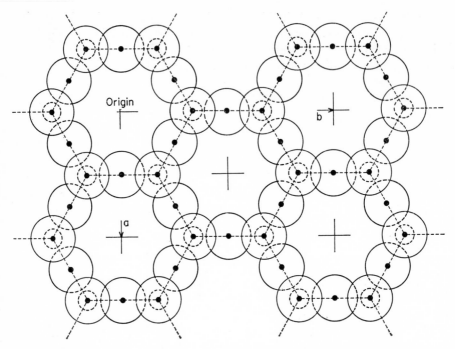

Fig. 10-9. Arrangement of atoms in Si_2O_5-sheet forming the basis of most layer-silicates.

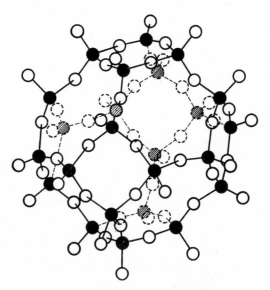

Fig. 10-10. Positions of centers of atoms in a portion of a porous three-dimensional framework with composition $(Si_{1-x}Al_x)O_2$. After Jaeger.

tetrahedrons; accordingly beryl may be considered to have a three-dimensional framework with the formula $Al_2(Si_6Be_3)O_{18}$, although it clearly has hexagonal Si_6O_{18} rings also; it is a cyclosilicate only if the BeO_4 tetrahedra are considered to be unlike the SiO_4 tetrahedra.

Silicates which have their SiO_4 tetrahedra grouped in sheets (and formulas including Si_2O_5 or a multiple) have other elements also in parallel layers. Some compounds containing no silica have structures characterized by similar sheets, as illustrated by brucite and moissanite. The number of such sheets in the unit cell is constant for one type of a compound, but may vary widely in different types of a single compound. For example, SiC (moissanite) has 6, 15, 21, 33, 51, etc., layers in different types.[4] In phyllosilicates, the Si atoms in the SiO_4 tetrahedra may be replaced (in part) by Al atoms. For example, $Al_4(OH)_8Si_4O_{10}$ (kaolinite) has five planes of atoms.

Five planes of atoms in $Al_4(OH)_8Si_4O_{10}$ (Kaolinite).

Plane	Coordination with O + OH ions	Ions	Spacing (Å)
1		O_6	
			0.60
2	Tetrahedral	Si_4	
			1.59
3		$O_4(OH)_2$	
			1.06
4	Octahedral	Al_4	
			1.06
5		$(OH)_6$	
			3.06
1		O_6	

Talc and pyrophyllite each have fourteen planes of atoms per unit cell. The first group of seven planes is chemically exactly repeated in the next seven planes; however, all fourteen planes are required in the unit cell because the second group is displaced horizontally with respect to the first group. The excellent basal cleavage in such compounds is due to the lack of strong bonds between planes 7 and 8 and also between planes 14 and 1; there is consequently wide spacing between these planes.

Similar conditions are found in silicates such as $KAl_2(OH)_2Si_3AlO_{10}$ (potash mica), $KMg_3(OH)_2Si_3AlO_{10}$ (phlogopite mica). $Mg_5Al_2Si_3O_{10}(OH)_8$

[4] Ramsdell: *Am. Min.* XXXII, p. 64 (1947); Wyckoff: *Crystal Structures*, Ch. III, par. C3, New York, 1948–1951.

Fourteen Planes of Atoms.

Plane number	Coordination with O + OH ions.	$Mg_3(OH)_2Si_4O_{10}$ (Talc)	$Al_2(OH)_2Si_4O_{10}$ (Pyrophyllite)
1		O_6	O_6
2	Tetrahedral	Si_4	Si_4
3		$O_4(OH)_2$	$O_4(OH)_2$
4	Octahedral	Mg_6	Al_4
5		$O_4(OH)_2$	$O_4(OH)_2$
6	Tetrahedral	Si_4	Si_4
7		O_6	O_6
8		O_6	O_6
9	Tetrahedral	Si_4	Si_4
10		$O_4(OH)_2$	$O_4(OH)_2$
11	Octahedral	Mg_6	Al_4
12		$O_4(OH)_2$	$O_4(OH)_2$
13	Tetrahedral	Si_4	Si_4
14		O_6	O_6
1		O_6	O_6

(clinochlore—a variety of chlorite), etc. An outline of the arrangement of the silicates appears at the beginning of this chapter.

B. TECTOSILICATES (FRAMEWORKS OF TETRAHEDRA): $A_m(XO_2)_n$

SiO₂ has this type of formula (with $m = 0$) but, although it is often considered to be the foundation of all silicates and has a related structure consisting of SiO_4 tetrahedra, it is described among the oxides.

NaSiAlO₄[1] has four crystal phases.[2] The high temperature or α-phase is isometric of unknown index, presumably about 1.51; it is stable above 1248° C. and inverts at 687° C. on cooling to a metastable triclinic phase (carnegieite) which has complicated lamellar twinning and G. 2.51; M.P. 1526° C. $(-)2V = 12°-15°$, $n_X = 1.509$, $n_Y = 1.514-$, $n_Z = 1.514$, $n_Z - n_X = 0.005$. On further cooling a second inversion may occur at 227° C., marked (on heating) by an abrupt increase in birefringence. The low temperature phase (nepheline) is hexagonal with $a = 9.98$, $c = 8.44$ Å. Crystals basal tablets or short prisms with poor $\{10\bar{1}0\}$ and $\{0001\}$ cleavages. G. 2.619. M.P. 1526° C., after inversion at 1248° C. Gelatinizes with

[1] Whenever Al (or Fe, Be or B or, rarely, Y, V, La, Pr, Nd or Sm) follows Si in the formula it means that that element takes the place of Si in a tetrahedron of the crystal structure. So far as the formula is concerned it therefore counts as Si.

[2] Bowen and Greig: *Am. J. Sci.* CCX, p. 204 (1925).

acids. Uniaxial negative with[2] $n_O = 1.537$, $n_E = 1.533$, $n_O - n_E = 0.004$. Again:[3] $n_O = 1.532$, $n_E = 1.528$, $n_O - n_E = 0.004$. Also:[3a] $n_O = 1.526$, $n_E = 1.522$, $n_O - n_E = 0.004$. Colorless. All these phases easily made from fusion. $NaSiAlO_4$ and $KSiAlO_4$ are miscible in all proportions *at high temperature;* they form discontinuous series at low temperature. $CaAl_2Si_2O_8$ is miscible with $2NaAlSiO_4$ up to about 37 mol. per cent; it has no perceptible effect on n_O, but increases n_E, producing an isotropic condition at 23 per cent $CaAl_2Si_2O_8$. $NaSiAlO_4$ is miscible with $CaAlAlO_4$ up to about 60 per cent of the latter. This produces a marked increase in the refractive indices[4] as shown in Fig. 10-11, n_O increasing less rapidly than n_E, so that

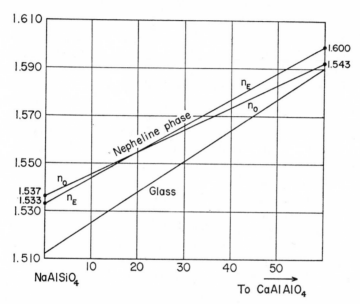

Fig. 10-11. Variations in the properties of the series, $NaAlSiO_4$—$CaAlAlO_4$. After Goldsmith, *Amer. Mineral.* XXXIV, p. 471 (1949).

the crystals are isotropic with 20 per cent of $CaAlAlO_4$ with $n = 1.555$; with 60 per cent of $CaAlAlO_4$ $n_O = 1.593$, $n_E = 1.600$, $n_E - n_O = 0.007$. $HAlSiO_4$ and $SiSiO_4$ are miscible in $NaSiAlO_4$ up to about 25 mol. per cent; they decrease the refringence, birefringence and density only a little. $NaSiAlO_4$ saturated with about 25 per cent Na_2SiO_3 has[5] $n_Z = 1.518$ and inverts at 1163° C. instead of at 1248° C. $NaAlSiO_4$ glass has $n = 1.510$.

[3] Winkler: *Am. Min.* XXXII, p. 131 (1947).
[3a] Saalfeld: *N. Jahrb. Miner. Monatshefte*, 1955, p. 207.
[4] Goldsmith: *Am. Min.* XXXIV, p. 471 (1949).
[5] Tilley: *Tsch. Min. Pet. Mitt.* XLIII, p. 406 (1933).

Pure $NaSiAlO_4$ is rare in nature, but with about 15 to 30 mol. per cent $KSiAlO_4$ (and often some Ca and H) it forms the natural mineral called nepheline; since its composition is variable its properties vary as follows: $n_O = 1.536–1.549$, $n_E = 1.532–1.544$, $n_O - n_E = 0.003–0.005$. PD (at 750° C.) 4.29, 2.61, 1.50; 2–0259.

KSiAlO₄ has three (or four?) crystal phases. At high temperature it intercrystallizes freely with $NaSiAlO_4$—is this the isometric or the triclinic phase of the latter? Another phase, made from fusion of $KAlSiO_4$, $K_3Al_2(SiF_4)_3$ and LiF_2, is orthorhombic[6] with $a = 9.01$, $b = 15.67$, $c = 8.57$ Å. Distinct {001} and poor {100} cleavages. Commonly twinned to pseudo-hexagonal forms. G. 2.60. M.P. 1800° C. X = a; Y = b. $(-)2V = 40°$, $n_X = 1.528$, $n_Y = 1.536$, $n_Z = 1.537$, $n_Z - n_X = 0.009$. Colorless. It inverts at 1540° C. to metastable **kaliophilite** which is hexagonal with $a = 27.0$, $c = 8.51$ Å. Crystals thick prismatic with poor {10$\bar{1}$0} and {0001} cleavages (or parting?). H. 6. G. 2.61. M.P. 1800° C. Gelatinizes with HCl. Uniaxial negative with $n_O = 1.537$, $n_E = 1.533$, $n_O - n_E = 0.004$. Again: $n_O = 1.530$, $n_E = 1.526$, $n_O - n_E = 0.004$. Colorless. Another phase (kalsilite) is also hexagonal, but trapezohedral,[7] with $a = 5.17$, $c = 8.67$ Å. No cleavage seen. G. 2.59. Uniaxial negative with $n_O = 1.542$, $n_E = 1.537$, $n_O - n_E = 0.005$. Again:[8] $n_O = 1.537$, $n_E = 1.530$, $n_O - n_E = 0.007$. Colorless. $KSiAlO_4$ glass has $n = 1.508$. PD 3.10, 2.60, 3.41; 9–471* [which polymorph?].

NaSiBO₄ is isometric.[9] M.P. 760° C. Isotropic with $n = 1.572$. Colorless.

K₂SiAl₂O₆ is isometric.[10] Crystals octahedral. Soluble in HCl. Isotropic with $n = 1.540$. Colorless. Made from fusion.

CsSi₂AlO₆ is isometric[11] with $a = 13.66$. Isotropic with $n = 1.523$. It forms mix-crystals with $NaSi_2AlO_6 \cdot H_2O$.

TlSi₂AlO₆ is isometric[11] and isotropic with $n = 1.637$. PD 3.60, 3.35, 5.54; 6–0212*.

KSi₂AlO₆ (Leucite) is isometric (above about 600° C.) with $a = 13.40$ Å. Crystals trapezohedral {211}. H. 5.5–6. G. 2.47. M.P. 1686° C. Unstable below about 600° C. Isotropic with[12] $n = 1.495$ at 750° C. and about 1.509 at 21° C. The low-temperature β-phase is tetragonal[11] with $a = 12.92$,

---

[6] Kunze: *Heidelb. Beit. Min. Pet.* IV, p. 99 (1954).

[7] Bannister and Hey: *Min. Mag.* XXVI, p. 218 (1942).

[8] Rigby and Richardson: *Min. Mag.* XXVIII, p. 75 (1947).

[9] Morey: *J. Soc. Glass Tech. Sheffield* XXXV, p. 270 (1951).

[10] Bowen: *Am. J. Sci.* CXCIII, p. 115 (1917); Morey and Bowen: *Am. J. Sci.* CCIV, p. 1 (1922).

[11] Barrer *et al.*: *J. Chem. Soc. London*, 1951, p. 1267; *ibid.*, 1952, p. 1561; *ibid.*, 1953, p. 1466, p. 1879, p. 4029, and p. 4035.

[12] Rinne and Kolb: *N. Jahrb. Min.* II, p. 157 (1910).

$c = 13.70$ Å. It is characterized by complex multiple twinning, by means of which crystals retain an external pseudo-isometric form. $n_O = 1.508$, $n_E = 1.509$, $n_E - n_O = 0.001$. Again:[11] $n = 1.512$. Colorless, white or gray. Made from fusion. Also made by dehydrating analcite and replacing its Na with K. Then $n = 1.51$. Inclusions of glass, magnetite, etc., are common, sometimes radially arranged or parallel with leucite crystal faces. PD 5.33, 3.42, 3.24; 6–0124*.

KSi₂FeO₆ (Fe-Leucite) is pseudo-isometric (like leucite). G. 2.59. Mean index[13] is 1.619. Birefringence higher than that of leucite. Another phase (KFeSi₂O₆) is K-acmite. See p. 279.

RbSi₂AlO₆(·H₂O?) has two phases.[11] At high temperature it is tetragonal with $a = 13.64$, $c = 13.33$ Å and $n = 1.521$. At low temperature it is also tetragonal, but with $a = 13.2$, $c = 13.6$ Å. and $n = 1.481$. It forms mix-crystals with KSi₂AlO₆. PD 3.31, 2.87, 3.61; 10–385*.

LiSiAlO₄ is reported to have three hexagonal crystal phases (!) as well as one orthorhombic phase. It dissociates at 1397° C. One phase is hexagonal scalenohedral[14] with $a = 13.54$, $c = 9.01$ Å. H. 6.5.[15] G. 2.64. M.P. 1388° C. Uniaxial positive with $n_O = 1.573$, $n_E = 1.583$, $n_E - n_O = 0.010$. Again:[15] $n_O = 1.572$, $n_E = 1.587$, $n_E - n_O = 0.015$. White to pale gray. Made hydrothermally. Another phase is hexagonal with[15] $a = 5.27$, $c = 11.25$ Å. U.C. 3. G. 2.35. No cleavage. Uniaxial negative with $n_O = 1.524$, $n_E = 1.5195$, $n_O - n_E = 0.0045$. Again:[16] $n_O = 1.527$–1.531, $n_E = 1.521$–1.523, $n_O - n_E = 0.006$–0.008. Made from fusion. The low temperature phase, called **eucryptite,** is hexagonal with distinct basal cleavage. G. 2.67. Uniaxial negative[17] with $n_O = 1.545$, $n_O - n_E = $ weak. Colorless. Another phase is described as orthorhombic with Z parallel[18] with elongation. (+)2V = large, $n_X = 1.575$, $n_Y = 1.578$, $n_Z = 1.586$, $n_Z - n_X = 0.011$. Made from fusion. The glass has $n = 1.530$–1.535; again:[19] G. 2.429 and $n = 1.541$.

RbSiAlO₄ is hexagonal[20] and isomorphous with nepheline. Uniaxial negative with $n_O = 1.530$, $n_E = 1.526$, $n_O - n_E = 0.004$. Colorless. It is reported to be isometric and isotropic with[11] $n = 1.531$. PD 3.18, 2.67, 2.27; 10–13.

[13] Rigby: *Thin Section Mineralogy of Ceramic Materials,* 1948, p. 148, 149.

[14] Mrose: *Bull. Geol. Soc. Am.* LXIII, p. 1283 (1952).

[15] Winkler: *Acta Cryst.* I, p. 27 (1948) and VI, p. 99 (1953).

[16] Hatch: *Am. Min.* XXVIII, p. 471 (1943).

[17] Larsen: *U. S. Geol. Surv. Bull.* 679 (1921).

[18] Barrer and White: *J. Chem. Soc. London,* 1951, p. 1267.

[19] Roy and Osborn: *J. Am. Chem. Soc.* LXXI, p. 2086 (1949).

[20] Trömel: *Ver. K. Wilhelm Inst. Silikatfor.* III, p. 103 (1930); Eitel, Herlinger, and Trömel: *Naturwiss.* XVIII, p. 469 (1930).

NaSiYO₄ is hexagonal with[20] $a = 10.79$, $c = 8.80$ kX. Uniaxial negative with $n_O = 1.832$, $n_E = 1.804$, $n_E - n_O = 0.028$. Colorless.

NaSiLaO₄ is hexagonal with[20] $a = 11.01$, $c = 8.96$ kX. Uniaxial negative with $n_O = 1.867$, $n_E = 1.840$, $n_O - n_E = 0.027$. Colorless.

NaSiPrO₄ is hexagonal[20] and isomorphous with nepheline. Uniaxial negative with $n_O = 1.889$, $n_E = 1.861$, $n_O - n_E = 0.028$. Colorless.

NaSiNdO₄ is hexagonal[20] with $a = 10.89$, $c = 8.85$ kX. Uniaxial negative with $n_O = 1.889$, $n_E = 1.861$, $n_O - n_E = 0.028$. Colorless.

NaSiSmO₄ is hexagonal[20] and isomorphous with nepheline. Uniaxial negative with $n_O = 1.898$, $n_E = 1.867$, $n_O - n_E = 0.031$. Colorless.

KSiLaO₄ is hexagonal[20] with $a = 11.0$, $c = 8.96$ kX. Uniaxial negative with $n_O = 1.867$, $n_E = 1.840$, $n_O - n_E = 0.027$. Colorless.

LiSiLaO₄ is hexagonal[20] and isomorphous with nepheline. Uniaxial negative with $n_O = 1.870$, $n_E = 1.843$, $n_O - n_E = 0.027$.

CsSiAlO₄ is isotropic with[11] $n = 1.574$. PD 3.23, 2.71, 2.00; 10–14.

CaSi₂La₂O₈ is hexagonal with[20] $a = 11.01$, $c = 8.85$ Å. Uniaxial negative with $n_O = 1.880$, $n_E = 1.874$, $n_O - n_E = 0.006$. Colorless.

CaSi₂Nd₂O₈ is hexagonal with[20] $a = 10.89$, $c = 8.85$ Å. Uniaxial negative with $n_O = 1.903$, $n_E = 1.898$, $n_O - n_E = 0.005$. Colorless.

LiSi₄AlO₁₀ (Petalite) is monoclinic domatic with $a = 11.77$, $b = 5.13$, $c = 15.17$ Å. $\beta = 112°44'$. Crystals {001} or {010} tablets or elongated along a. Perfect {001} and good {201} cleavages. H. 6.5. G. 2.42. F. 5 with phosphorescence. Insoluble except in HF. X $\wedge$ a (= {001} cleavage) = 2° to 8° in acute β; Z = b. (+)2V = 83°34', r < v weak (with weak crossed dispersion also). $n_X = 1.504$, $n_Y = 1.510$, $n_Z = 1.516$, $n_Z - n_X = 0.012$. $n_Y(F) - n_Y(C) = 0.007$. Color red, green or white; colorless in thin section. On heating it dissociates at 950° C. or less.[16] The glass has G. 2.29 and $n = 1.495$. PD 3.73, 3.65, 3.50; 9–475*.

FELDSPAR GROUP

The minerals of the feldspar group are tectosilicates of aluminum and potassium, sodium, calcium or barium. The potassium, sodium and calcium types are the most abundant constituents of igneous rocks. They are all monoclinic or triclinic and have perfect basal and good side-pinacoid cleavages. The chief types are:

Monoclinic

KSi₃AlO₈	{Sanidine—high temperature} Orthoclase {Adularia—low temperature}
NaSi₃AlO₈	Barbierite
BaSi₂Al₂O₈	Celsian

Triclinic

KSi₃AlO₈	Microcline

KSi$_3$AlO$_8$ Microcline

NaSi$_3$AlO$_8$ Analbite (hypothetical, but abundant in anorthoclase)

NaSi$_3$AlO$_8$ Albite $\Big\}$ Plagioclase $\Big\{$ high temperature

CaSi$_2$Al$_2$O$_8$ Anorthite   low temperature

The following artificial compounds are considered to be feldspars:

Monoclinic

RbSi$_3$AlO$_8$ intercrystallizes with orthoclase
KSi$_3$FeO$_8$
KSi$_3$GaO$_8$ KGe$_3$AlO$_8$ KGe$_3$GaO$_8$

Triclinic

KSi$_3$FeO$_8$ SrSi$_2$Al$_2$O$_8$
     MnSi$_2$Al$_2$O$_8$
NaSi$_3$GaO$_8$ CaSi$_2$Ga$_2$O$_8$
NaGe$_3$AlO$_8$ CaGe$_2$Al$_2$O$_8$
NaGe$_3$GaO$_8$ CaGe$_2$Ga$_2$O$_8$

High-temperature forms can be distinguished from low-temperature forms only by very careful observation of optical and crystallographic properties. They are distinct because of varying states of disorder in the arrangement of the Al and Si in tetrahedral sites, and in the arrangement of Na, Ca, and K in the non-tetrahedral sites. It is rather probable that the degree of disorder is sensitive not only to variations in temperature but also to variations of pressure, and it is possible that other factors such as the composition, pH, etc., of the medium from which the crystals form, may also affect the degree of order.

KSi$_3$AlO$_8$ has at least three crystal phases; two of them are monoclinic (often collectively called **orthoclase**), namely, high-temperature sanidine and low-temperature adularia. Lowest-temperature form, microcline, is triclinic. **Sanidine** has $a = 8.4$, $b = 12.9$, $c = 7.1$ Å, $\beta = 115°35'$. U.C. 4. Crystals equant, {010} tablets, or elongated along a. Perfect {001} and distinct {010} cleavages. H. 6. G. 2.57. Carlsbad twinning (on {010}) common. In some crystals of sanidine Z is normal to (010); in other crystals it is parallel with (010), the optic angle passing through 0° between these two conditions, and Z and Y interchanging their position. X makes an angle of about 5° to 8° with a (the trace of the basal cleavage in (010)) in the obtuse angle β. The optic plane may be normal to (010) in red light and parallel thereto in blue light. If the optic plane is parallel with (010) the dispersion is inclined (weak) with r > v; if it is normal to (010) the dispersion is horizontal (weak) with r < v. (−)2V very small. $n_X = 1.520–1.523$, $n_Y \approx n_Z = 1.525–1.53$, $n_Z − n_X = 0.005–0.006$. Sanidine often contains some Na; the refringence, birefringence, extinction angle and specific gravity increase gradually with increase in sodium (as shown in Fig. 10-12). Colorless. Made from fusion. PD 3.25, 3.21, 3.75; 10–357*.

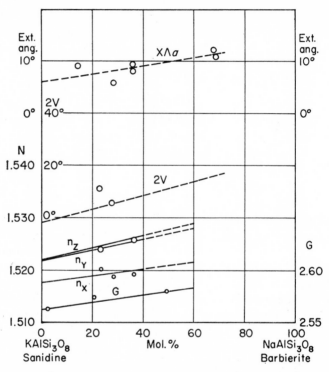

Fig. 10-12. Variations in the properties of the series $KAlSi_3O_8$—$NaAlSi_3O_8$, quenched from high temperature (sanidine—barbierite).

Adularia, the low-temperature phase of orthoclase, is also monoclinic, with $a = 8.45$, $b = 12.9$, $c = 7.15$ Å, $\beta = 116°3'$. Crystals much like those of sanidine. Perfect {001} and distinct {010} cleavages. H. 6. G. 2.57. Carlsbad twinning common (rotation about c, contact plane (010)). X ∧ a (trace of basal cleavage in (010)) is about 5° in obtuse β. (+)2V = 50° to 70° (or even up to 85°), r > v with weak horizontal dispersion. $n_X = 1.519–1.526$, $n_Y = 1.523–1.530$, $n_Z = 1.524–1.533$, $n_Z − n_X = 0.005–0.007$. Adularia, like sanidine, often contains some Na; the refringence, birefringence, extinction angle and specific gravity all increase with increase of Na, as shown in Fig. 10-13. Colorless. **Microcline** can be changed artificially to sanidine.[20a] It is triclinic pinacoidal with $a = 8.44$, $b = 13.00$, $c = 7.21$ Å, $\alpha = 90°7'$, $\beta = 115°50'$, $\gamma = 89°55'$. U.C. 4. Crystals resemble those of orthoclase but usually have two sets of multiple-twinning

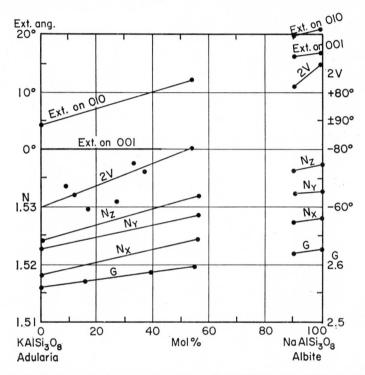

Fig. 10-13. Variations in the properties of the series $KAlSi_3O_8$—$NaAlSi_3O_8$ stabilized at relatively low temperature (adularia—albite).

lamellae nearly at right angles. Perfect {001} and distinct {010} cleavages. H. 6. G. 2.55. Fusion begins at 1170° C. (with formation of leucite) and is complete at 1530° C. X makes an angle of about 5° with the {001} cleavage in (010) and about 15° with the {010} cleavage in (001). Z is nearly normal to {010}. $(-)2V$ = about 83°, r > v with notable horizontal dispersion. $n_X = 1.518$, $n_Y = 1.522$, $n_Z = 1.525$, $n_Z - n_X = 0.007$. Colorless. Made by coating a (010) cleavage piece of low albite with[21] powdered KSi_3AlO_8 and heating at 1060° C. for six hours. PD 3.24, 4.21, 3.83; 10–479.

[20a] Goldsmith and Laves: *Geochim. Cosmochim. Acta* V, p. 1 (1954).

[21] Laves: *J. Geol.* LIX, p. 511 (1951); [*Min. Abst.* XI, p. 470].

RbSi₃AlO₈ is a Rb analogue of potash feldspar,[11] like sanidine. It is biaxial with $n_X = 1.524$, $n_Y = ?$, $n_Z = 1.529$, $n_Z - n_X = 0.005$. It forms a (continuous?) series of mix-crystals with KSi₃AlO₈ in which there is only a small change in indices; for example: crystals with Rb:K = 52:48 have a mean index of 1.524; with Rb:K = 20:80, the mean index is 1.521; and with Rb:K = 0:100, $n_X = 1.517$, $n_Z = 1.523$. Colorless. Formed hydrothermally. PD 3.31, 2.87, 3.61; 10–376.

KSi₃FeO₈ is monoclinic and triclinic[22] corresponding with orthoclase and microcline. The microcline phase shows common twinning on {100}, {001}, or {021}; G. 2.712. Extinction on (010) is at 7°–8° to a; Y = b. $n_X = 1.601$, $n_Y = ?$, $n_Z = 1.609$, $n_Z - n_X = 0.008$. Color yellow. Made by passing SiO₂ and Fe₂O₃ into fused potassium vanadate and cooling slowly. KSi₃FeO₈ glass has $n = 1.586$. PD 3.18, 4.02, 3.80; 9–462(?).

To determine more accurately the role of Al and Si in the crystal structure of feldspars artificial isomorphous compounds have been made in which Al is replaced by Ga and Si by Ge, or both; such compounds have the following properties as compared with feldspar:[23]

	NaSi₃AlO₈	NaSi₃GaO₈	NaGe₃AlO₈	NaGe₃GaO₈
M.P.	1118° C.	1015° C.	1067° C.	952° C.
n (glass)	1.489	1.519	1.592	1.636
n_X	1.525	n_X' 1.552	1.606	1.638
n_Z	1.536	n_Z' 1.558	1.619	1.654

	KSi₃AlO₈	KSi₃GaO₈	KGe₃AlO₈	KGe₃GaO₈
M.P.	1170° C.	1000–1020° C.	1122° C.	ca. 1000° C.
n (glass)	1.488	1.513	1.578	1.617
n_X	1.518	n_X' 1.533	1.590[24]	1.615
n_Z	1.526	n_Z' 1.539	1.595	1.628

	CaSi₂Al₂O₈	CaSi₂Ga₂O₈	CaGe₂Al₂O₈	CaGe₂Ga₂O₈
M.P.	1553° C.	Liq. temp. 1323° C.	Liq. > 1400° C.	Liq. 1321° C.
n (glass)	1.5755	1.633	1.658	1.745
n_X	1.576	n_X' 1.625	1.641	1.705
n_Z	1.588	n_Z' 1.631	1.647	1.711

	Ca₂Si₄Al₃GaO₁₆	CaSi₂AlGaO₈	CaSiGeAl₂O₈
M.P.	ca. 1495° C.	1530° C.	1465° C.
n (glass)	1.591	1.608	1.611
n_X'	1.591	1.604	1.608
n_Z'	1.596	1.611	1.615

[22] Gaubert: *C. R. Cong. Soc. Sav. Sci.*, p. 402 (1925); Faust: *Am. Min.* XXI, p. 735 (1936).

[23] Goldsmith: *J. Geol.* LVIII, p. 518 (1950).

[24] Correction made by J. R. Goldsmith in pers. comm. June 6 and July 6, 1955. He also suggested that the indices of the Ca—Ga and Ca—Ge compounds should show greater birefringence.

$NaSi_3AlO_8$ has three or four crystal phases. One phase is pseudo-monoclinic, but known only with 10–15 per cent KSi_3AlO_8; it is called anorthoclase (or analbite). It has two sets of multiple twinning much like those in microcline, but finer; X' makes an angle of 6° to 12° with a in (010). The optic plane is nearly normal to {010}. $(-)2V = 42°$ to 54°, r > v, $n_X = 1.523$, $n_Y = 1.528$, $n_Z = 1.529$. $n_Z - n_X = 0.006$. Again:[25] $(-)2V = 60°$, $n_X = 1.5198$, $n_Y = 1.5242$, $n_Z = 1.5276$, $n_Z - n_X = 0.0078$. PD 3.21, 3.24, 4.11; 9–478. The triclinic phases of $NaSi_3AlO_8$ are the common ones (high- and low-temperature albite) which intercrystallize freely with $CaSi_2Al_2O_8$. See Fig. 10–14. $NaSi_3AlO_8$, $CaSi_2Al_2O_8$ and KSi_3AlO_8 are the main com-

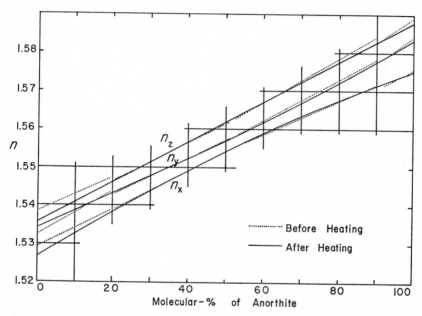

Fig. 10–14a. Variation of refractive indices in plagioclase. The solid lines refer to properties of material heated to equilibrium at temperatures a little below the melting points and then quenched. Data of Smith, *Amer. Mineral.* XLIII, p. 1179 (1958), and of Smith in Hess, *Geol. Soc. Amer., Mem.* LXXX, p. 191 (1960). Modified from Smith's figures.

ponents of the very abundant minerals known as feldspars, and the $NaSi_3AlO_8$—$CaSi_2Al_2O_8$ series is plagioclase. This series was formerly supposed to consist of units of definite composition which were named oligoclase, andesine, labradorite, and bytownite. It is now known to be a contin-

[25] Ho: *Contr. Nat. Res. Inst. Geol. Acad. Sinica, Nanking,* 1933, No. 4, p. 31 [*Min. Abst.* V, p. 439].

uous series[25a] which has been artificially divided so that albite means pure
$NaSi_3AlO_8$ and also the series from 100 to 90 per cent $NaSi_3AlO_8$ with 0 to 10
per cent $CaSi_2O_8$. Oligoclase varies in composition from 90 to 70 per cent
$NaSi_3AlO_8$ + 10–30 per cent $CaSi_2Al_2O_8$ (expressed as $Ab_{90}An_{10}$ to $Ab_{70}An_{30}$).
Andesine varies from $Ab_{70}An_{30}$ to $Ab_{50}An_{50}$, labradorite from $Ab_{50}An_{50}$ to

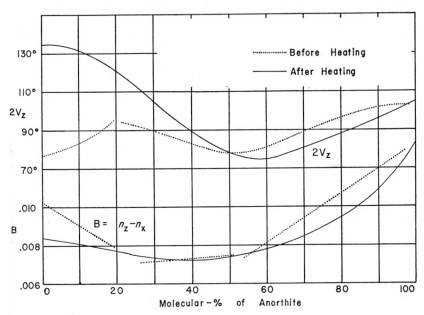

Fig. 10–14b. Variation of birefringence ($n_Z - n_X$) and optic angle ($2V_Z$) in plagioclase.
The solid lines are for material heated to high temperature and quenched; Data of
Smith, *op. cit.* Modified from Smith's figures.

$Ab_{30}An_{70}$, bytownite from $Ab_{30}An_{70}$ to $Ab_{10}An_{90}$ and anorthite from $Ab_{10}An_{90}$
to Ab_0An_{100}.

$Ab_{100}An_0$ to $Ab_{90}An_{10}$ (High-temperature or α-albite) is triclinic with
$a = 8.23$, $b = 13.00$, $c = 7.25$ Å, $\alpha = 94°3'$, $\beta = 116°20'$, $\gamma = 88°9'$.
Crystals varied; often {010} tablets or prismatic. Perfect {001} and good
{010} cleavages. Often twinned in one or more ways. H. 6–6.5. G. 2.61–
2.625. The extinction angle on (010) is 9° to 12°[26] (14°–22°[27]); on (001) it
is 0°–2°[26] (3°–4°[27]), and the maximum extinction angle in the zone normal

[25a] More accurately a multiple series or system, for in addition to the simple variation
of chemical composition, various states of order and disorder are possible in the arrangement of Si and Al in tetrahedral sites, requiring in one case (anorthite) a doubled
c-axis. Temperature of equilibrium or crystallization governs this, and can be estimated
roughly from optical and crystallographic measurements.

[26] Tuttle and Bowen: *J. Geol.* LVIII, p. 572 (1950).

[27] Tröger: *Tabellen Opt. Bestim. gestein. Miner.* 1952, p. 99, 101, etc.

to (010) is $26°–37°$. $(-)2V = 45°–55°$. $n_X = 1.527–1.533$, $n_Y = 1.532–1.539$, $n_Z = 1.534–1.542$. $n_Z - n_X = 0.007–0.009$. Colorless. Made from fusion. PD 3.18, 3.75, 3.21; 10–393*. This phase seems to invert[26] slowly at about 700° C. to low-temperature or **β-albite** whose crystal forms and properties are very nearly the same as those of α-albite except for the optic angle and extinction angles. The extinction angle on (010) is $7°–20°$; on (001) it is $3°$, and the maximum extinction angle[28] in the zone normal to (010) is $12°–20°$. $(+)2V = 75°–83°$. $n_X = 1.528–1.535$, $n_Y = 1.533–1.540$, $n_Z = 1.539–1.545$, $n_Z - n_X = 0.010$. Again:[29] for pure $NaSi_3AlO_8$: $n_X = 1.5274$, $n_Y = 1.5314$, $n_Z = 1.5379$, $n_Z - n_X = 0.0105$. PD 3.20, 3.78, 6.39; 9–466*. Pure **$NaSi_3AlO_8$** glass has G. 2.382 and $n = 1.4964$ Li, 1.4891 Na, 1.4916 Tl.

$Ab_{90}An_{10}$ to **$Ab_{70}An_{30}$** (High-temperature or **α-oligoclase**) is triclinic with $a = 8.16$, $b = 12.90$, $c = 7.13$ Å, $\alpha = 93°4'$, $\beta = 116°22'$, $\gamma = 90°4'$. Crystals varied; often {010} tablets or prismatic. Perfect {010} and good {001} cleavages. H. 6–6.5. G.[28] 2.625–2.645. The extinction angle on (010) is $0°–14°$, on (001) it is $0°–3°$. $(-)2V = 55°–75°$. $n_X = 1.535–1.545$, $n_Y = 1.539–1.549$, $n_Z = 1.542–1.552$, $n_Z - n_X = 0.007$ *ca.* It seems to invert slowly at about 700° C. to low-temperature or **β-oligoclase** which differs from the α-phase chiefly in extinction and optic angles. The β-phase has an extinction angle on (010) of $12°–3°$, on (001) it is $0°–1°$ and the maximum angle in the zone normal to (010) is $0°–12°$. The optic angle, $2V_X$, is $97°–82°$. $n_X = 1.535–1.545$, $n_Y = 1.54–1.549$, $n_Z = 1.545–1.552$, $n_Z - n_X = 0.010–0.007$. Colorless. PD 3.18, 4.03, 3.20; 9–457 (α- or β-?).

$Ab_{70}An_{30}$ to **$Ab_{50}An_{50}$** (High-temperature or **α-andesine**) is triclinic with $a = 8.14$, $b = 12.86$, $c = 7.17$ Å, $\alpha = 93°23'$, $\beta = 116°28'$, $\gamma = 89°59'$. Crystals varied. Perfect {010} and good {001} cleavages. H. 6–6.5. G. 2.645–2.675. The extinction angle on (010) is $0°–17°$, on (001) it is $0°–5°$ and the maximum in the zone normal to (010) is $12°–27°$. $2V_X = 75°–115°$, $n_X = 1.545–1.555$, $n_Y = 1.549–1.558$, $n_Z = 1.552–1.562$, $n_Z - n_X = 0.007$ *ca.* It seems to invert slowly at about 700° C. to low-temperature or **β-andesine** which differs from the α-phase as follows: the extinction angle on (010) is $3°–17°$; on (001) it is $0°–5°$ and the maximum angle in the zone normal to (010) is $20°–32°$. $2V_X = 82°–105°$, $n_X = 1.546–1.556$, $n_Y = 1.550–1.559$, $n_Z = 1.553–1.563$, $n_Z - n_X = 0.007$ *ca.* Colorless. PD 3.21, 3.18, 4.04; 10–359.

$Ab_{50}An_{50}$ to **$Ab_{30}An_{70}$** (**Labradorite**) is triclinic with $a = 8.21$, $b = 12.95$, $c = 14.16$ Å. $\alpha = 93°31'$, $\beta = 116°3'$, $\gamma = 89°59'$. Only one phase is known. Crystals often {010} tablets or varied. Perfect {010} and good

---

[28] Van der Kaaden: *Optical Studies on Natural Plagioclase Feldspars*, Proefschrift, Utrecht, 1951.

[29] *Am. J. Sci.* Bowen Vol. (250A), p. 85 (1952).

{001} cleavages. H. 6–6.5. G. 2.66–2.72. Extinction angle on (010) is 16°–28°; on (001) it is 5°–14°, and the maximum extinction angle in the zone normal to (010) is 29°–40°. $(+)2V = 75°–90°$, r > v. $n_X = 1.555$–1.563, $n_Y = 1.558$–1.567, $n_Z = 1.563$–1.572, $n_Z - n_X = 0.008$–0.009. Colorless. Made from fusion. PD 3.20, 3.18, 4.04; 9–465*.

$Ab_{30}An_{70}$ to **$Ab_{10}An_{90}$** (**Bytownite**) is triclinic with $a:b:c = 0.636:1:0.554$. $\alpha = 93°22'$, $\beta = 116°0'$, $\gamma = 94°4'$. Crystals often {010} tablets. Perfect {010} and good {001} cleavages. H. 6–6.5. G. 2.72–2.74. Extinction angle on (010) is 28°–36°; on (001) it is 14°–30°, and the maximum angle in the zone normal to (010) is 40°–57°. $(-)2V = 77°–90°$, r < v. $n_X = 1.563$–1.572, $n_Y = 1.567$–1.578, $n_Z = 1.572$–1.582, $n_Z - n_X = 0.009$–0.010. Colorless. Made from fusion. PD 3.20, 4.03, 3.75; 9–467.

$Ab_{10}An_{90}$ to **Ab_0An_{100}** (**Anorthite**) is triclinic with $a = 8.21$, $b = 12.95$, $c = 14.16$ Å. $\alpha = 93°13'$, $\beta = 115°56'$, $\gamma = 91°12'$. Crystals varied, often {010} tablets. Perfect {010} and good {001} cleavages. H. 6–6.5. G. 2.74–2.765. Extinction angle on (010) is 37°–40°; on (001) it is 30°–39°. $(-)2V = 77°$. $n_X = 1.572$–1.577, $n_Y = 1.578$–1.584, $n_Z = 1.582$–1.590, $n_Z - n_X = 0.010$–0.013. Colorless. Made from fusion.

$CaSi_2Al_2O_8$ has at least three crystal phases,[30] but two of these are only metastable. One such phase is made by heating $CaSi_2Al_2O_8$ glass to 2000° C. in a graphite crucible in a nitrogen atmosphere, cooling slowly to 1258° C. and allowing to crystallize. It is also made (with H_2O under pressure) at temperatures[31] below 375° C. It is hexagonal with $a = 5.11$, $c = 14.738$ Å. U.C. 1. Crystals basal plates with perfect basal cleavage. H. 5–6. G. 2.74. Uniaxial positive[31] with $n_O = 1.585$, $n_E = 1.590$, $n_E - n_O = 0.005$. Another metastable phase crystallizes at about 950° C.—more easily if some $NaSi_3AlO_8$ is present. It is orthorhombic with $a = 8.224$, $b = 8.606$, $c = 4.836$ Å. U.C. 2. It has poor cleavage parallel with the optic plane; conchoidal fracture. H. 6. G. 2.70. $(-)2V = 39°$, $n_X = 1.553$, $n_Y = 1.580$, $n_Z = 1.584$, $n_Z - n_X = 0.031$. Made by crystallizing the glass. The stable phase **anorthite** is triclinic with $a = 8.21$, $b = 12.95$, $c = 14.16$, $\alpha = 93°13'$, $\beta = 115°56'$, $\gamma = 91°12'$. Crystals often {010} tablets. H. 6. G. 2.765. M.P. 1550° C. Soluble in HCl. Multiple twinning common. The optic plane makes a large angle with (010), the Z axis being at about 43° to (010) and about 50° to (001), while the X axis makes an angle of about 32° with (010) and about 35° with (001). The extinction angle is 35° on (001) and 37° to 38° on (010). Extinction normal to X is at 19.5° to (001) and 32° to (010); extinction normal to Z is at 66° to (001) and 52° to[31] (010). $(-)2V = 77°$. $n_X = 1.5755$, $n_Y = 1.5832$, $n_Z = 1.5885$, $n_Z - n_X = 0.013$. Again: $n_X = 1.5768$, $n_Y = 1.5846$, $n_Z = 1.5903$, $n_Z - n_X = 0.0135$.

[30] Davis and Tuttle: *Am. J. Sci.* Bowen Vol. (250A), p. 107 (1952).
[31] Goldsmith and Ehlers: *J. Geol.* LX, p. 386 (1952).

Colorless. Made from fusion. $CaSi_2Al_2O_8$ glass has G. 2.70 and $n = 1.5719$ Li, 1.5755 Na, 1.5786 Tl. This phase is an end-member of the plagioclase series whose properties are shown in Fig. 10-14. PD 3.21, 3.19, 4.05; 10–379*.

$BaSi_2Al_2O_8$ has three crystal phases.[32] The high-temperature or **α-phase** is hexagonal. Crystals are basal plates with basal cleavage. G. 3.3. M.P. 1715° C. Uniaxial positive with $n_O = ?$, $n_E = 1.5712$. Again:[33] $n = 1.567$, $n_E - n_O = 0.004$. Colorless. It may take in crystal solution up to 30 per cent KSi_3AlO_4; then $n_E = 1.5681$. Found in slags. Colorless. Made by heating celsian at 1500° for four days.[31] Another phase of $BaSi_2Al_2O_8$ (called **paracelsian**) is monoclinic[34] and pseudo-orthorhombic with $a:b:c = 0.947:1:0.895$, $\beta = 90°10'$. Crystals often prismatic and vertically striated. Complex twinning common. Poor prismatic cleavage. G. 3.31–3.32. X nearly normal to (100); Z = b. $(-)2V = 50°-53°$ ca., r < v. $n_X = 1.5634$ Li, 1.5702 Na, 1.5734 Tl, $n_Y = 1.5793$ Li, 1.5824 Na, 1.5867 Tl, $n_Z = 1.5843$ Li, 1.5869 Na, 1.5901 Tl, $n_Z - n_X = 0.0167$ Na. This phase alters easily to celsian. The phase commonly found in nature (called **celsian**) is monoclinic prismatic with $a = 8.63$, $b = 13.10$, $c = 7.29$ Å, $\beta = 115°9'$. Isomorphous with orthoclase. Crystals short prismatic or {010} plates. Perfect {001}, distinct {010} and poor {110} cleavages. Common Carlsbad and other twinning. H. 6. G. 3.8 (−3.57?). M.P. 1640° C. Soluble in HCl. $X \wedge c = +3°$; Y = b; $Z \wedge a$ (the {001} cleavage) $= +28°$. $(+)2V =$ about 80°, $n_X = 1.587$, $n_Y = 1.593$, $n_Z = 1.600$, $n_Z - n_X = 0.013$. With 6 per cent of other isomorphous compounds:[35] $(+)2V = 86°22'$, $n_X = 1.5835$, $n_Y = 1.5886$, $n_Z = 1.5941$, $n_Z - n_X = 0.0106$. A variety[36] with 4 per cent CaO has: Y = b, $Z \wedge a = 29°$, $(-)2V = 76°$, $n_X = 1.572$, $n_Y = 1.5795$ calc., $n_Z = 1.584$, $n_Z - n_X = 0.012$. PD 3.29, 2.97, 3.99; 10–356.

$SrSi_2Al_2O_8$ seems to be isomorphous with $CaSi_2Al_2O_8$ and therefore triclinic. It is fibrous without twinning. G. 3.12. $(-)2V = 70°$, $n_X = 1.574$,[37] $n_Y = 1.582$, $n_Z = 1.586$, $n_Z - n_X = 0.012$. It may take in crystal solution[32] up to 30 per cent KSi_3AlO_8 and then $n_X = 1.567$, $n_Y = ?$, $n_Z = 1.577$, $n_Z - n_X = 0.010$. The extinction angle normal to X is 4° to 8° to the cleavage and elongation direction. This angle does not vary with the potash content. The maximum extinction angle Z' to elongation is 20°. Colorless. PD 3.27, 3.22, 3.43; 10–15.

[32] Dittler and Lasch: *Sitz. Akad. Wiss. Wien* I, 140, p. 633 (1931).
[33] Faber: *Chem. Erde*, X, p. 67 (1936)
[34] Spencer: *Min. Mag.* XXVI, p. 231 (1942); Smith: *Acta Cryst.* VI, p. 613 (1953).
[35] Strandmark: *Geol. För. Förh.* XXV, p. 289 (1903); XXVI, p. 97 (1904); *Zeit. Krist.* XLIII, p. 89 (1907).
[36] Segrist: *Min. Mag.* XXVII, p. 166 (1946).
[37] Eskola: *Am. J. Sci.* CCIV, p. 331 (1922).

MnSi$_2$Al$_2$O$_8$ is probably isomorphous with anorthite and therefore triclinic. It has an extinction angle[38] of 43°. $(-)2V = ?$, $n_X = 1.605$, $n_Y = ?$, $n_Z > 1.626$, $n_Z - n_X > 0.021$. Similar crystals probably with some Ca have $n_X = 1.59$, $n_Z = 1.61$.

ZEOLITES

Zeolites are tectosilicates of aluminum and another base, usually calcium or sodium, containing water that can be largely expelled without destroying the crystal structure. The crystal easily reabsorbs its water, if exposed to water vapor, or it can absorb other materials in place of the water, such as air, ammonia, alcohol, iodine, etc. Moreover, the second base is generally readily exchangeable in a saturated solution of some other base; for example, the calcium in stilbite can be replaced by Na, K, NH$_4$, Ba, Ag or Cu and vice versa. Base-exchange properties make it difficult to establish chemical formulas.

Some zeolites are chemically correctly described as hydrated feldspars but they are not so closely related crystallographically as are the feldspars. The following zeolites will be included here:

NaSi$_2$AlO$_6$·H$_2$O	Analcite	Isometric
Na$_2$CaSi$_{10}$Al$_4$O$_{28}$·20H$_2$O(?)	Faujasite	Isometric
KSiAlO$_4$·nH$_2$O	K-Nepheline	Hexagonal(?)
NaSi$_2$AlO$_6$·3H$_2$O	Gmelinite	Hexagonal
CaSi$_4$Al$_2$O$_{12}$·6H$_2$O(?)	Chabazite	Hexagonal
CaSi$_3$Al$_2$O$_{10}$·5H$_2$O	Levynite	Hexagonal
NaSiAlO$_4$·nH$_2$O		Orthorhombic
LiSiAlO$_4$·2H$_2$O		Orthorhombic
BaSi$_3$Al$_2$O$_{10}$·4H$_2$O	Edingtonite	Orthorhombic
CaSi$_2$Al$_2$O$_8$·4H$_2$O	Gismondite	Orthorhombic
NaCa$_2$Si$_5$Al$_5$O$_{20}$·6H$_2$O	Thomsonite	Orthorhombic
Na$_2$CaSi$_{20}$Al$_4$O$_{48}$·14H$_2$O(?)	Mordenite	Orthorhombic(?)
Na$_2$Si$_3$Al$_2$O$_{10}$·2H$_2$O	Natrolite	Orthorhombic
NaSi$_3$AlO$_8$·H$_2$O		Monoclinic
CaSi$_3$Al$_2$O$_{10}$·3H$_2$O	Scolecite	Monoclinic
Na$_2$Ca$_2$Si$_9$Al$_6$O$_{30}$·8H$_2$O	Mesolite	Monoclinic
CaSi$_4$Al$_2$O$_{12}$·4H$_2$O(?)	Laumontite	Monoclinic
Ca$_4$Si$_8$Al$_8$O$_{32}$·12H$_2$O(?)	Phillipsite	Monoclinic
Ba$_2$Si$_{11}$Al$_4$O$_{30}$·10H$_2$O(?)	Harmotome	Monoclinic
CaSi$_6$Al$_2$O$_{16}$·7H$_2$O(?)	Stilbite	Monoclinic
CaSi$_6$Al$_2$O$_{16}$·5H$_2$O(?)	Heulandite	Monoclinic
CaSi$_5$Al$_2$O$_{14}$·4H$_2$O(?)	Epistilbite	Monoclinic

[38] Snow: *J. Am. Ceram. Soc.* XXVI, p. 11 (1943).

$NaSi_2AlO_6 \cdot H_2O$ (Analcite) is isometric with $a = 13.68$ Å. U.C. 16. Crystals often trapezohedral or more complex. Penetration twinning common. Very poor cubic cleavage. H. 5–5.5. G. 2.22–2.29. F. 2.5 to colorless glass. Gelatinizes with HCl. Isotropic with $n =$ usually 1.486, but variable from 1.472 to 1.489. But large crystals are often very weakly birefringent[39] with complicated twinning and $(-)2V =$ small to large, mean index $n = 1.487$ Na, $n_Z - n_X = 0.001$. Colorless. Made in a steel bomb or even a closed tube. Natural analcite often contains excess SiO_2 and H_2O and Al_2O_3; also minor K_2O, CaO, etc.[40] Its birefringence increases as it loses H_2O when heated;[40] for example, a crystal with $n_Z - n_X = 0.00032$ with total H_2O 8.2 per cent, has $n_Z - n_X = 0.00072$ after losing 3.6 per cent H_2O, $n_Z - n_X = 0.00134$ after losing 6.3 per cent H_2O, and $n_Z - n_X = 0.00212$ after losing 8.0 per cent H_2O. But the birefringence decreases to zero[41] if the mineral is heated to 200°–250° C. in water vapor. PD 3.43, 5.61, 2.93; 7–363/4*. When heated in air until cloudy and then immersed in oil, analcite is triclinic with negative birefringence[42] and so much like the high-temperature form of leucite that it has been called *natronleucite*. The Na of analcite can be replaced more or less by other elements; with[11] K it has $n = 1.490$; with K and loss of water to only 1.51 H_2O[43] it becomes leucite with $n = 1.51$; with NH_4 and the same loss of water it becomes NH_4-leucite with $n = 1.524$; with Ag and no loss of water it has $a = 13.7$ Å and $n = 1.56$; with Rb and loss of water to 1.9 H_2O it has $n = 1.51$; with Tl and loss of water to 0.5 H_2O it has $n = 1.64$.

$Na_2CaSi_{10}Al_4O_{28} \cdot 20H_2O(?)$ (Faujasite) is isometric hexoctahedral[44] with distinct {111} cleavage. H. 5. G. 1.92. F. 3. Decomposed by acid. Isotropic with $n = 1.48$ *ca*. Loss of a little water changes it to uniaxial positive with $n = 1.48$ *ca*. and weak birefringence; the birefringence decreases on heating and at about 150° C. (having lost 12 H_2O) the substance is again isotropic. Further heating changes it to uniaxial negative. Upon cooling in damp air the water is taken up again and the optic changes are reversed. Colorless or white. PD 15.0, 3.75, 5.68; 2–0010. K-faujasite is said to have been made[2] in octahedral crystals but the index ($n = 1.394$) is surprisingly low.

$KSiAlO_4 \cdot nH_2O$ has been called K-nepheline hydrate.[45] It is uniaxial negative with $n_O = 1.5256$, $n_O - n_E =$ very weak. Colorless. Made hydrothermally. PD 2.56, 4.47, 3.32; 2–1019 (?).

[39] Stewart: *Min. Mag.* XXVI, p. 1 (1941).
[40] Friedel: *Bull. Soc. Fr. Min.* XIX, p. 363 (1896).
[41] Klein: *Sitz. Akad. Wiss. Berlin*, 1897, p. 290.
[42] Rinne: *Sitz. Akad. Wiss. Berlin* XLVI, p. 1163 (1890).
[43] Barrer: *J. Chem. Soc. London*, 1950, p. 2342.
[44] Witteborg: *Zeit. Krist.* LXXXIII, p. 374 (1932).
[45] Baur and Becke: *Zeit. anorg. Chem.* LXXII, p. 119 (1911).

$LiSi_4AlO_{10} \cdot 2.5H_2O$ is probably tetragonal,[18] but has no visible birefringence. $n = 1.480$. (Possibly a phyllosilicate.)

$Na_{26}Si_{22}Al_{18}O_{84} \cdot 12H_2O(?)$ is hexagonal[46] with G. 2.36. Uniaxial negative with $n_O = 1.502$, $n_E = 1.495$, $n_O - n_E = 0.007$. Colorless.

$Na_{56}Si_{42}Al_{38}O_{169} \cdot 24H_2O(?)$ is hexagonal.[46] Crystals six-sided basal plates. Mean index $n = 1.498$. Birefringence about 0.022. Closely resembles analcite. Colorless.

$NaSi_2AlO_6 \cdot 3H_2O$ (Gmelinite) varies in composition toward chabazite, CaAl replacing some NaSi; K may be present. Crystals hexagonal or rhombohedral with $c/a = 1.017$ and vertical striations. Distinct rhombohedral cleavage and basal parting. H. 4.5. G. 2.04–2.17. F. 3 with intumescence. Decomposed by HCl. Usually biaxial, retaining external hexagonal forms by twinning on $\{110\}$ and $\{1\bar{1}0\}$ of a monoclinic (or triclinic?) structure, the "rhombohedral" cleavage actually being parallel to (001), (100) and (010). Some crystals strictly uniaxial; others are uniaxial in some parts and biaxial elsewhere. $(\pm)2V = $ small, $n_X = 1.464$–1.479, $n_Y = ?$, $n_Z = 1.465$–1.480, $n_Z - n_X = 0.001$–0.009, usually very weak. Gmelinite from Iceland[47] has $(-)2V = 0°$–$30°$, $n_Z - n_X = 0.002$; dehydrated it has $(+)2V < 10°$, $n_Z - n_X = 0.027$. Saturated with iodine it is pleochroic with a clear brown, c red-brown to opaque. Saturated with bromine it has a nearly colorless, c reddish yellow. Heated with boiling glycerine it becomes pleochroic with a colorless, c red-brown. Gmelinite can have Na replaced by K with loss of 4 per cent H_2O and increase of density from 2.045 to 2.090. The change can be reversed by immersion in NaCl solution. PD 4.10, 12.0, 2.96; 9–419.

$CaSi_4Al_2O_{12} \cdot 6H_2O(?)$ (Chabazite) varies in composition toward gmelinite, NaSi (and KSi) replacing some CaAl. Crystals hexagonal with $a = 13.75$, $c = 14.94$ Å. U.C. 4. Often simple rhombohedrons resembling cubes since the rhombohedral angle is $88°14'$. Distinct rhombohedral cleavage. H. 4–5. G. 2.08–2.16. F. 3 with intumescence. Decomposed by HCl. Crystals often biaxial, the external hexagonal form being retained by twinning of a monoclinic (or triclinic?) structure which has $a:b:c = 0.463:1:0.341$, $\beta = 96°29'$. $(\pm)2V = 0°$–$32°$, $n_X = 1.478$–1.485, $n_Y = ?$, $n_Z = 1.480$–1.490, $n_Z - n_X = 0.002$–0.010, usually very weak. These variations may be due to variations in composition, the Ca-rich samples being positive and the Na-rich negative, but Rinne found[42] that fully hydrated

---

[46] Friedman: *J. Geol.* LIX, p. 19 (1951). As the formulas are doubtful it seems possible that these two are actually $NaSi_2AlO_6 \cdot H_2O$ (analcite) with some intercrystallized $HNaSiAl_2O_6 \cdot H_2O$.

[47] Grandjean: *C. R. Acad. Sci. Paris* CXLIX, p. 866 (1909) and *Bull. Soc. Fr. Min.* XXXIII, p. 5 (1910).

chabazites are positive, slight heating changes them to negative, and further heating changes them back to the positive condition, but with strong birefringence. Made by heating in a closed tube with carbonated water at 200° C. Colorless. PD 2.95, 4.35, 9.5; 10–370. Hydration is easily changed; base exchange also is easily produced; for example, with[11] about a third of the Ca replaced by Li, $n = 1.48$; with 11 per cent of the CaO replaced by Ag_2O, $n = 1.49$. However, Grandjean found[47] that a sample of chabazite with its normal tenor of water had: X = c, $(-)2V = 65°$, mean index $n = 1.49$, $n_Z - n_X = 0.0014$; after driving out the water it had: $(+)2V < 12°$, Z = c, $n_Z - n_X = 0.0089$; when rehydrated the birefringence decreased and the optic sign changed again. Saturated with $(NH_4)_2O$ it was[43] uniaxial positive with a mean $n = 1.487$ and $n_Z - n_X = 0.004$. Saturated with iodine at 300° C. and cooled in a desiccator it was positive and nearly uniaxial with $n_Z - n_X = 0.009\pm$ and X and Y pink, Z yellow. Saturated with calomel at 500° C. and then cooled it had: $(-)2V = 0°$, $n_O - n_E = 0.045$; the calomel shattered the crystals; saturated with Hg at 300° C. and cooled in a desiccator it had $(-)2V = 74°$, $n_Z - n_X = 0.028$ and X very pale yellow, Y dark yellow, Z darker reddish yellow; by addition of water the birefringence decreased and the mineral darkened with X brown, Y dark brown, Z opaque. The mineral took up 35 per cent Hg and then 25 per cent H_2O; upon heating the water went off and then the Hg without destroying the crystal. Saturated with sulfur the mineral was negative with $n_Z - n_X = 0.036$. Chabazite after partial dehydration can take up CS_2 which causes a great increase in birefringence with a change of the interference color from gray to higher order white. After partial dehydration it can take up CO_2, which changes vibration directions and increases the birefringence. Similar results can be obtained with alcohol or chloroform or benzol. The birefringence of chabazite[48] decreases to practically zero when the mineral is saturated with Na, but treatment with $AgNO_3$ or $CuCl_2$ produces almost no change in birefringence. Chabazite has been changed artificially[49] to the pure Na-, K-, Tl-, NH_4-, Cu-, Ag-, Ba-, Ca- or Mg- compounds, but optic data are lacking.

$CaSi_3Al_2O_{10} \cdot 5H_2O$ **(Levynite)** is hexagonal with $c/a = 0.836$. Crystals rhombohedral. H. 4–4.5. G. 2.09–2.16. Easily fusible. Uniaxial negative with $n_O = 1.496$, $n_E = 1.491$, $n_O - n_E = 0.005$. It may be biaxial (2V = 0°–30°, due to strain or inversion?) and then $n_Z - n_X = 0.0075$; dehydrated and then saturated with[49] dry air it has $(+)2E = 85°–120°$, $n_Z - n_X = 0.0075$ and n_Y much less than before; saturated with Hg it is biaxial negative with $n_Z - n_X = 0.030$ and a dark red-brown to opaque, c yellow.

[48] Zoch: Chem. Erde, I, p. 219 (1915).
[49] Rinne: N. Jahrb. Min. II, 1897, p. 28; Fortsch. Min. III, p. 178 (1913).

2NaSiAlO$_4$·H$_2$O is orthorhombic with[50] (−)2V = large, n_X = 1.503, n_Y = 1.506, n_Z = 1.508, $n_Z − n_X$ = 0.005. Colorless. PD 3.40, 4.39, 2.95; 10–460.

4NaSiAlO$_4$·H$_2$O is orthorhombic with[50] (−)2V = moderate, n_X = 1.534, n_Y = 1.546, n_Z = 1.548, $n_Z − n_X$ = 0.014. Colorless. PD 2.95, 4.07, 4.67; 10–459.

LiSiAlO$_4$·2H$_2$O(?) is orthorhombic(?). Crystals[50] like rods with Z parallel with elongation. Biaxial. n_X = 1.525, n_Z = 1.535, $n_Z − n_X$ = 0.010. Colorless. PD 6.42, 4.29, 3.15; 5–0181. The Li can be replaced by other elements as follows:

> 33.8% of Li replaced by Na, mean index n = 1.54
> 12.9% of Li replaced by Ca, mean index n = 1.56
> 88.1% of Li replaced by Ag, mean index n = 1.66
> 28.1% of Li replaced by K, mean index n = 1.54
> 85.6% of Li replaced by Ba, mean index n = 1.55
> 79% of Li replaced by Tl, mean index n = 1.70
> ?% of Li replaced by Rb, mean index n = 1.55
> 11.1% of Li replaced by NH$_4$, mean index n = 1.54

BaSi$_3$Al$_2$O$_{10}$·4H$_2$O (Edingtonite) is orthorhombic with a = 9.56, b = 9.68, c = 6.53 Å. U.C. 2. Crystals pseudo-tetragonal with perfect {110} cleavage. H. 4. G. 2.7–2.78. F. 5. Gelatinizes with acid. X = c, Y = b.[51] (−)2V = 53°52′, n_X = 1.541, n_Y = 1.553, n_Z = 1.557, $n_Z − n_X$ = 0.016. With about 6 per cent CaO: (−)2E = 10°–15°, n_X = 1.542, $n_Y ≈ n_Z$ = 1.550, $n_Z − n_X$ = 0.008. Edingtonite may have 8.79 per cent Na$_2$O introduced by base exchange and then Z = c, $n_X′$ = 1.518, $n_Z′$ = 1.525; or with 15.35 per cent K$_2$O introduced it has: X = c, $n_X′$ = 1.547, $n_Z′$ = 1.555; or with 35.66 per cent Ag$_2$O introduced it has n_Y = 1.645, $n_Z − n_X$ = very weak; or with 44.13 per cent Tl$_2$O introduced it has Z = c, n_Y = 1.710, $n_Z − n_X$ = very weak. Colorless.

CaSi$_2$Al$_2$O$_8$·4H$_2$O (Gismondite) is orthorhombic with a = 13.68, b = 14.28, c = 10.60 Å. Usually contains some KSi (or NaSi) replacing CaAl. Crystals often pyramidal. Distinct {101} cleavage. H. 4.5. G. 2.27. F. 3 with intumescence. Gelatinizes with HCl. Basal sections often show four segments with extinction inclined at 5° (monoclinic?). X = b; Z nearly normal to {100}. (−)2V = 82°–86°, n_X = 1.5308, n_Y = 1.5402, n_Z = 1.5484, $n_Z − n_X$ = 0.0176. Again:[52] n_X = 1.538, n_Y = 1.543, n_Z = 1.548, $n_Z − n_X$ = 0.010. Upon heating gismondite becomes optically orthorhom-

---

[50] Barrer and White: *J. Chem. Soc. London*, 1952, p. 1561. *Pers. comm.* Aug. 9, 1955.
[51] Hey: *Min. Mag.* XXIII, p. 483 (1934).
[52] Dunham: *Am. Min.* XVIII, p. 369 (1933).

bic with $(-)2V$ = small. X = c, $n_Z - n_X$ = weak. PD 7.30, 3.24, 2.73; 2–0096. After dehydration[47] crystals will take up Hg causing little change in optic properties, but if then exposed to moisture the Hg changes its condition, the mineral darkens so that one direction is gray, yellow or colorless and the other direction is bluish black like ink, or purple.

$NaCa_2Si_5Al_5O_{20} \cdot 6H_2O$ (**Thomsonite**) is orthorhombic hemimorphic (m2m)[53] with a = 13.07, b = 13.07, c = 13.23 Å. U.C. 4. The b-axis shows pyroelectricity. NaSi may be replaced by CaAl (or the reverse) so that the Na:Ca ratio varies from about 1:1 to about 1:3. There may be also a little replacement of Ca by Na_2 (secondary?). Crystals prismatic to fibrous, vertically striated; also {010} plates. Perfect {010} and poor {100} cleavages. H. 5–5.5. G. 2.25–2.40. F. 2 with intumescence. Gelatinizes with HCl. Y = c; Z = b. $(+)2V$ = 47°–75°, r > v distinct. n_X = 1.511–1.530, n_Y = 1.513–1.532, n_Z = 1.518–1.545, $n_Z - n_X$ = 0.006–0.020; F − C for n_Y = 0.0074. See Fig. 10-15. PD 2.86, 2.95, 2.68; 9–490. Removing $4H_2O$ lowers

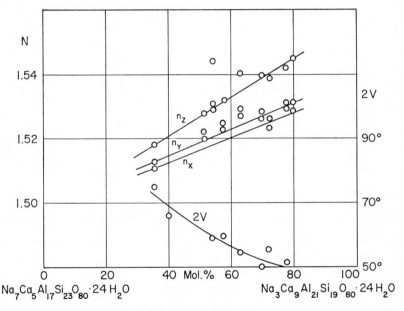

Fig. 10-15. Variations in optical properties of the thomsonite series. Data from Hey, *Mineral. Mag.* XXIII, p. 51 (1932).

the refringence about 0.025. See Fig. 10-16. Heated until cloudy and then immersed in oil the birefringence[50] is reduced. The sodium in thomsonite may be replaced artificially to some extent by K,[53] NH_4, Ag or Tl. Introduc-

[53] Hey: *Min. Mag.* XXIII, p. 51 (1932).

tion of 3.25 per cent K_2O causes practically no change in optic properties, but increases the specific gravity from 2.373 to 2.381. Introduction of 10.37 per cent Ag_2O gives G. 2.52, and raises the indices from $n_X = 1.529$, $n_Y = 1.531$, $n_Z = 1.542$, $n_Z - n_X = 0.013$ to $n_X = 1.582$, $n_Y = 1.588$,

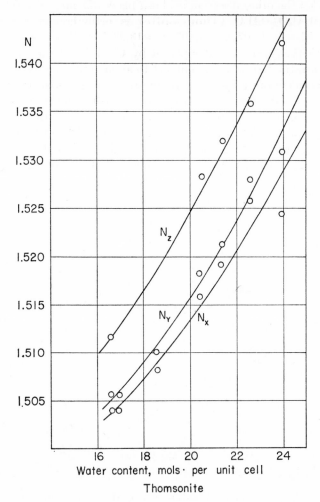

Fig. 10-16. Variations in optical properties of the thomsonite series. Data from Hey, *Mineral. Mag.* XXIII, p. 51 (1932).

$n_Z = 1.600$, $n_Z - n_X = 0.018$. Similarly, the introduction of 11.74 per cent Tl_2O gives G. 2.595, $n_X = 1.568$, $n_Y = 1.574$, $n_Z = 1.585$, $n_Z - n_X = 0.017$. Heated until cloudy and then immersed in oil thomsonite is still orthorhombic usually with unchanged optic orientation and decreased birefringence, but much heating may cause the optic plane to become normal to (001). Colorless.

$Na_2CaSi_{20}Al_4O_{48} \cdot 14H_2O(?)$ **(Mordenite)** is orthorhombic(?) with $a = 18.25$, $b = 20.35$, $c = 7.50$ Å. U.C. 2. The ratio of Ca to Na (and K) varies notably; the tenor of H_2O and of SiO_2 is also variable. Crystals prismatic, vertically striated. Perfect {100} and good {010} cleavages. H. 5. G. 2.1. F. 3–4 to clear glass. Insoluble in HCl. Optically seems to be monoclinic since $X \wedge c = 4°$, but X-rays indicate orthorhombic symmetry. $Z = b$. 2V large,[54] seeming to vary through 90°. $n_X = 1.471$–1.478, $n_Y = 1.477$ ca., $n_Z = 1.473$–1.482, $n_Z - n_X = 0.002$–0.005. Again:[55] mean index $n = 1.467$. Colorless, yellowish or pinkish. PD 3.48, 3.22, 9.10, 6–0239/40.

$Na_2Si_3Al_2O_{10} \cdot 2H_2O$ **(Natrolite)** is orthorhombic with $a = 18.3$, $b = 18.6$, $c = 6.57$ Å. U.C. 8. Crystals prismatic, vertically striated, pseudotetragonal, acicular to fibrous along c. Perfect {110} cleavage and {010} parting. H. 5–5.5. G. 2.25. F. 2. Gelatinizes with HCl. $Y = b$; $Z = c$. Negative relief distinct. $(+)2V = 60°$–63°, r < v weak. $n_X = 1.473$–1.480, $n_Y = 1.476$–1.482, $n_Z = 1.485$–1.493, $n_Z - n_X = 0.011$–0.013. Colorless. PD 2.86, 5.90, 4.38; 3–0705. Natrolite heated until cloudy and then immersed in oil becomes monoclinic,[42] {001} becoming {010} and the former prism faces becoming {101} and {$\bar{1}$01}; optical properties not much changed but $X \wedge c = 7°$ and $Z = b$. It reverts easily to its former condition on cooling in moist air. Natrolite made by base exchange from scolecite,[56] but still containing 5.38 CaO, has Z parallel with elongation and a mean index, $n = 1.484$ with $n_Z - n_X = 0.01$. When a sample of natrolite having $n_X = 1.479$, $n_Y = 1.482$, $n_Z = 1.491$, $n_Z - n_X = 0.012$ has 6.38 per cent of K_2O introduced artificially[57] (base exchange) it has $n_X = 1.478$, $n_Y = 1.481$, $n_Z = 1.488$, $n_Z - n_X = 0.010$; when it has 19.40 K_2O introduced it has G. 2.365, $n_X = 1.480$, $n_Y = 1.483$, $n_Z = 1.490$, $n_Z - n_X = 0.010$. PD 7.0, 2.96, 3.09; 3–0062. With 6.55 Li_2O introduced it has G. 2.135, $n_X = 1.489$, $n_Y = 1.492$, $n_Z = 1.501$, $n_Z - n_X = 0.012$; when it has 14.39 $(NH_4)_2O$ introduced it has G. 2.073, $(n_X + n_Y) \div 2 = 1.507$, $n_Z = 1.515$; when it has 41.23 Ag_2O introduced it has G. 3.09, $X = c$, $n_X = 1.577$, $(n_Y + n_Z) \div 2 = 1.585$; when it has 52.23 Tl_2O introduced it has G. 3.92, $(n_X + n_Y) \div 2 = 1.620$, $n_Z = 1.629$. PD 3.01, 4.90, 4.43; 2–0636. K, Li and Ag natrolite have been made also from mesolite.

$NaSi_3AlO_8 \cdot H_2O(?)$ is monoclinic with[50] $a = 8.10$, $b = 6.10$, $c = 4.88$ Å, $\beta = 105°20'$. Crystals six-sided tablets. Perfect basal cleavage. $(+)2V = ?$,

[54] Shannon: *U. S. Nat. Mus. Bull.* 131, p. 346 (1926); Koch: *Am. Min.* II, p. 243 (1917).

[55] Barrer and White: *J. Chem. Soc. London*, 1952, p. 1561.

[56] Hey: *Min. Mag.* XXIV, p. 227 (1936).

[57] Hey: *Min. Mag.* XXIII, p. 243 (1932).

mean $n = 1.49$, $n_Z - n_X$ = weak. X-ray pattern not like that of ussingite.

$CaSi_3Al_2O_{10} \cdot 3H_2O$ **(Scolecite)** is monoclinic with $a = 18.48$, $b = 18.95$, $c = 6.54$ Å. $\beta = 90°42'$. U.C. 8. Crystals slender prismatic, vertically striated, often in fibrous masses. Good {110} cleavage. H. 5. G. 2.3. F. 2, curling into wormlike forms (whence the name). Gelatinizes with HCl. $X \wedge c = 15°-18°$ in obtuse β; $Z = b$. $(-)2V = 36°$ *ca.*, r < v distinct. $n_X = 1.5122$, $n_Y = 1.5187$, $n_Z = 1.5194$, $n_Z - n_X = 0.0083$. Colorless. Made by heating constituents in a closed tube at 150° C. Scolecite inverts at about 200° to 250° C. with a loss of one third of its water to a phase called metascolecite[58] which has X normal to (010) (= (100) of scolecite) and $Y \wedge c = 18°$, $(-)2V = 65°$, r < v, mean index $n = 1.523$, $n_Z - n_X =$ very weak. But this phase may take on as much water[56] as scolecite and then $Y \wedge c = 18°$, the mean index $n = 1.505$, $n_Z - n_X = 0.01$ *ca.* Scolecite loses all the rest of its water between 335° and 345° C. irreversibly; it then has $Z \wedge c = 85°-88°$, $(-)2V = 65°$, r < v, $n_Y = 1.541$ and very weak birefringence. The crystal structure breaks down at about 550° C. When Ag replaces Ca (at least to some extent) $X \wedge$ elongation = 1°-5°; mean index $n = 1.525-1.54$, $n_Z - n_X = 0.01$. When Tl replaces Ca the extinction on the cleavage is 12° with negative elongation and a mean index $n = 1.53$.

$Na_2Ca_2Si_9Al_6O_{30} \cdot 8H_2O$ **(Mesolite)** is monoclinic with $a = 56.7$, $b = 6.54$, $c = 18.44$ Å, $\beta = 90°0' \pm 20'$. U.C. 8. Crystals often fibers along b. Perfect {301} and {$\bar{3}01$} cleavages. H. 5. G. 2.27. F. easy, to vermicular forms. Gelatinizes with HCl. $X \wedge c = 8°$, $Y = b$ (= elongation). $(+)2V$ = about 85° at 15° C., with r < v strong, but the optic angle increases rapidly on heating, becoming 90° at 20° C. and negative above 20°; then measured about X it decreases rapidly becoming 0° at 59° C.; above 59° C. the optic plane is nearly parallel with 001. PD 2.85, 3.19, 6.61; 3–0711. Mesolite loses half its water (reversibly) at about 250° C.; and the remainder (irreversibly) at about 350° C.: it is then called metamesolite and has its optic plane parallel with the elongation, while a negative acute bisectrix is nearly normal to one of the cleavages; the crystal structure breaks down at about 670° C. At ordinary temperature $n_X = 1.5048$, $n_Y = 1.5050$, $n_Z = 1.5053$, $n_Z - n_X = 0.0005$ (Görgey).[59] Again:[60] $n_X = 1.5073$, $n_Y = 1.5074$, $n_Z = 1.5075$, $n_Z - n_X = 0.0002$ Na. Mesolite when treated with[60] K-solution changes to K-natrolite with positive elongation and $n_Y = 1.483$; when treated with $LiNO_3$ solution it becomes Li-natrolite with positive elongation, $n_Y = 1.491$ and $n_Z - n_X = 0.013$; when treated with $AgNO_3$ solution it becomes Ag-natrolite with negative elongation,

---

[58] Cavinato: *Mem. Accad. Lincei Roma*, II, p. 320 (1927); *Min. Abst.* IV, p. 320 (1930).
[59] Görgey: *Tsch. Min. Pet. Mitt.* XXVIII, p. 77 (1909).
[60] Hey: *Min. Mag.* XXIII, p. 421 (1933).

$n_Y = 1.552$, and $n_Z - n_X = 0.002$. But it is also possible to produce base exchange[60] in mesolite without causing a change to natrolite; thus by replacing one third of the Ca with Na the crystal has G. 2.22 (?), positive elongation, $n_Y = 1.499$ and $n_Z - n_X = 0.004$. By introducing 6.37 per cent $(NH_4)_2O$ the crystal has G. 2.144, positive elongation, $n_Y = 1.511$, $n_Z - n_X$ = weak. By introducing 20.86 per cent Ag_2O the crystal has G. 2.63−, negative elongation, $n_Y = 1.542$ and $n_Z - n_X = 0.004$. By introducing 42.75 per cent Tl_2O the crystal has G. 2.35±, positive elongation, $n_Y = 1.588$ and $n_Z - n_X$ = very weak.

$CaSi_4Al_2O_{12} \cdot 4H_2O(?)$ **(Laumontite)** is monoclinic with $a = 14.90$, $b = 13.12$, $c = 7.55$ Å, $\beta = 111°30'$. U.C. 12. NaSi (and KSi) can replace CaAl to a limited extent. Apparently Ca may also be replaced in part by Na_2 (or K_2). Crystals prismatic resembling pyroxene. Twinning on {100}. Perfect {010} and {110} cleavages. H. 3–4. G. 2.23–2.41. F. 2.5 with swelling. Gelatinizes with HCl. $Y = b$; $Z \wedge c = 8°–11°$ in acute β. $(-)2V = 33°–47°$, r < v distinct, and[61] weak inclined dispersion. $n_X = 1.509–1.514$, $n_Y = 1.518–1.522$, $n_Z = 1.521–1.525$, $n_Z - n_X = 0.010–0.012$. Colorless (or tinted by ferric iron). Laumontite may easily lose about one eighth of its water, often then falling to a powder; it has been called then **leonhardite** (or caporcianite) and has $a = 14.75$, $b = 11.10$, $c = 7.55$ Å, $\beta = 112°$. $Y = b$; $Z \wedge c = 8°–35°$; $(-)2V = 26°44'$, r < v; $n_X = 1.502–1.507$, $n_Y = 1.512–1.516$, $n_Z = 1.514–1.518$, $n_Z - n_X = 0.011–0.012$. The reverse change is also easily accomplished.

$Ca_4Si_8Al_8O_{32} \cdot 12H_2O(?)$ **(Phillipsite)** is monoclinic prismatic with $a = 10.00$, $b = 14.25$, $c = 8.62$ Å. $\beta = 125°40'$. U.C. 1. It commonly contains KSi (and NaSi) replacing some CaAl; Ba may also be present. Crystals often penetration twins resembling orthorhombic or tetragonal forms, long parallel c. Distinct {001} and {010} cleavages. H. 4–4.5. G. 2.2. F. 3 to white enamel. Gelatinizes with HCl. $X = b$; $Z \wedge c = 11°–30°$ in acute β. $(+)2V = 60°$ to $80°$ (or more?), r < v weak. Indices vary; apparently the most siliceous crystals have the lowest indices with n = about 1.48 and $Z \wedge c$ about 10° while the least siliceous samples have n about 1.51 and $Z \wedge c$ about 30°. A sample from Honolulu has $n_X = 1.493$, $n_Y = 1.497$, $n_Z = 1.500$, $n_Z - n_X = 0.007$. PD 7.64, 6.91, 3.18; 2–0084. A crystal[62] with 5.5 CaO, 5.7 Na_2O and 5.5 K_2O may be changed by immersion in 2.5 per cent KCl for 24 hours at 180° C. to contain 5.7 Na_2O and 12.3 K_2O; this causes no noticeable change in birefringence or extinction angle but lowers the indices about 0.003. Another sample[42] heated until cloudy and then immersed in oil has its extinction angle ($Z \wedge c$) reduced from 19° to 9°; in moist air the change is not reversed; on further heating the birefringence

[61] Coombs: *Am. Min.* XXXVII, p. 812 (1952).
[62] Koenigsberger and Müller: *N. Jahrb. Min. Bl. Bd.* XLIV, p. 402 (1921).

decreases distinctly, X and Z change places, the extinction angle $(X \wedge c)$ rises to 17° in acute angle β, the optic sign becomes negative and the optic angle changes to almost zero.

$Ba_2Si_{11}Al_4O_{38} \cdot 10H_2O(?)$ **(Harmotome)** is monoclinic prismatic with[63] $a = 9.80$, $b = 14.10$, $c = 8.66$ Å, $\beta = 124°50'$. U.C. 1. It may contain some K, Na, Ca. Crystals like those of phillipsite, elongated along c. Distinct {010} and poor {001} cleavages. H. 4.5. G. 2.44–2.50. F. 3 to white glass. Decomposed by HCl. $X \wedge c = 58°$ in obtuse β; $Z = b$. $(+)2V = 79°$, $n_X = 1.503$, $n_Y = 1.505$, $n_Z = 1.508$, $n_Z - n_X = 0.005$. Colorless. PD 8.24, 7.17, 6.26; 9–480. On heating the extinction angle increases (to 82° at 130° C.). The optic angle decreases on heating,[42] becoming 32° at 730° C. (Heat due to grinding in making a thin section may reduce 2V to 32°.) Further heating to 400° C. and then cooling in a desiccator changes the optic angle to $(-)2V = 50°$ ca., the optic plane to (010), the birefringence to 0.026, and lowers the refringence; upon rehydration the changes are (about) reversed. If saturated with mercury vapor and then cooled the mineral can scarcely be distinguished from the dehydrated condition, but if exposed to moisture the mercury changes its state, the mineral darkens and becomes pleochroic with a and c blue-black or purple and b clear gray, yellow or colorless. Harmotome heated until cloudy and then immersed in oil[32] has its optic plane changed in position, so that $X \wedge a = 23°$ ca. and also has its birefringence much increased; in this condition it is said to be triclinic.

$CaSi_6Al_2O_{16} \cdot 7H_2O(?)$ **(Stilbite)** is monoclinic prismatic with $a = 13.60$, $b = 18.13$, $c = 11.29$ Å, $\beta = 129°10'$. U.C. 4. Usually contains some NaSi in place of CaAl (and Na_2 in place of Ca?). Crystals twinned as crosses on {100} to pseudorhombic forms. Perfect {010} and poor {100} cleavages. H. 3.5–4. G. 2.09–2.20. F. 3 with exfoliation to white enamel. Decomposed by HCl. $X \wedge c = 5°$ (3°–12°) in acute β; $Y = b$. $(-)2V = 30°-50°$, $n_X = 1.484-1.492$, $n_Y = 1.493-1.498$, $n_Z = 1.495-1.501$, $n_Z - n_X = 0.009-0.011$. Colorless. PD 4.08, 9.1, 4.68; 10–433. Heated until cloudy and then immersed in oil it becomes orthorhombic with {100} as the optic plane[64] and $Z = c$, but this is accomplished only after a long series of changes, as follows: normal stilbite has $X \wedge c = -5°$, and $(-)2V = 30°$ ca. After heating to 125° C. it has about $5H_2O$, and the extinction angle and optic angle are both about 0°; by further loss of water on heating, $X \wedge c$ gradually increases to about $+5°$ and the optic angle gradually opens in a plane

[63] Meier: *Am. Min.* XXIV, p. 540 (1939); Sekanina and Wyart: *Bull. Soc. Fr. Min.* LX, p. 139 (1937).

[64] Orientation of Tschermak (*Sitz. Akad. Wiss. Wien*, CXXVI, p. 600, 1917) in which (100) = Dana's (001), (010) = Dana's (010), (101) = Dana's (100), (001) = Dana's (Ī01), etc.

normal to $\{010\}$, passes 90° with change of sign and becomes 0° about Z ($= b$) with X $= c$ at about 150° C. with about $4H_2O$. By further loss of water on heating, Y (formerly X) gradually moves from c to Y $\wedge$ $c = 3°–7°$, the optic angle opens about Z ($= b$) in a plane normal to $\{010\}$, passes 90° with a second change of sign and becomes 0° about X ($= a$) at about 185° C. with about $3H_2O$. By further heating, Z (formerly Y) moves toward c until Z $\wedge$ $c = 0°$, the optic angle opens about X (which is in the obtuse angle β at 83°–87° with c) in (010), passes 90° with a third change of sign and becomes 0° about Z ($= c$). This is the fourth uniaxial condition; it occurs at about 250° C. with about $2H_2O$. The mineral is now orthorhombic. With further heating the birefringence gradually decreases; with about $1H_2O$ at about 350° C. the mineral is still orthorhombic; with further heating it becomes microscopically isotropic. All these changes can be produced by dehydration in H_2SO_4 without heating. After complete dehydration the process is not reversible. Stilbite can be changed artificially[48] by base exchange into pure Ca-, Na-, K-, NH_4-, Ba-, Ag-, or Cu-stilbite. Optic data on these are lacking, but after immersion in KCl solution for 24 hours at 180° C. (probably leading to K-stilbite) it has:[62] X $\wedge$ $c = 6°$, $n_X = 1.478$, $n_Y = 1.481$, $n_Z = 1.483$, $n_Z - n_X = 0.005$. NH_4-stilbite is nearly isotropic with an extinction angle near zero. Ag-stilbite has weakened birefringence. Na-stilbite has birefringence about the same as Ca-stilbite. Cu-stilbite is bluish green.

$CaSi_6Al_2O_{16}\cdot5H_2O(?)$ **(Heulandite)** is monoclinic prismatic with $a = 7.45$, $b = 17.80$, $c = 15.85$ Å, $\beta = 91°26'$; U.C. 4. Usually contains some NaSi replacing CaAl (and also Na_2 replacing Ca secondary?); also may contain some Sr. Crystals $\{010\}$ tablets or equant. Perfect $\{010\}$ cleavage. H. 3.5–4. G. 2.2. F. 2, after swelling to vermicular forms. X $\wedge$ $c = 68°–82°$ (also reported as 35° $ca.$;[65] also X $\wedge$ a is reported[66] as variable from $+89°$ through 0° to $-86°$ in different sectors and in different crystals); Z $= b$. $(+)2V = 32°$ $ca.$, r > v, with distinct crossed dispersion. $n_X = 1.496$–1.498, $n_Y = 1.497$–1.499, $n_Z = 1.501$–1.505, $n_Z - n_X = 0.005$–0.007, $n_Z - n_X = 0.005$.[67] When rich in silica ($SiO_2 = 61.83$): n_X and $n_Y = 1.487$–1.488, $n_Z = 1.488$–1.489, $n_Z - n_X = 0.001$. Colorless. Made by heating the constituents at 170° C. in carbonated water[68] in a closed tube. Digestion in a KCl solution for a week produces K-heulandite (Ca replaced by K); in the same way NH_4-, Na-heulandite, etc., can be produced—but optic data are lacking. Heating a sample from Iceland reduced the optic angle to 0° at 80° C. with about $5H_2O$; then X and Y change places and the optic angle

[65] Shannon: *Bull. U. S. Nat. Mus.* 131, p. 346 (1926).
[66] Resegotti: *Atti R. Acc. Sci. Torino* LXIV, p. 105 (1929) [*Min. Abst.* V, p. 83].
[67] Parsons: *Univ. Toronto Stud., Geol. Ser.* XIV, p. 52 (1922).
[68] Doelter: *N. Jahrb. Min.* I, p. 128 (1890).

increases from 0° to 90° and then (with change of sign) decreases again to 0° at about 180° C.; meanwhile the extinction angle decreases to 0° at about 150° C. with about $4H_2O$ and the mineral is orthorhombic; then Y and Z change places and the optic angle increases to pass through 90° once more and become uniaxial positive at about 280° C. with about $2H_2O$. With further heating the optic plane changes position again. Above 350° C. a second orthorhombic form exists with weaker birefringence. Studying another sample from Iceland Slawson[69] concluded that the mineral is always biaxial but seems to be uniaxial in some cases because the optic plane rotates through the position of the black cross. The relations between temperature, optic angle and rotation of the optic plane from the position at ordinary temperature are about as follows, as derived from Slawson's curves:

Temp. C.	2E	Rotation
25°	74°38'	0°
100°	80°	10°
150°	66°	13°
200°	34°	45°
250°	61°	96°
300°	120°	114°

Gaubert found that the optic properties are influenced by three different factors,[70] namely, "optic anomalies" (probably due to variations in composition), temperature, and tenor of water. Change in temperature from 0° to 109° without change in tenor of water causes a rotation of the optic plane with increase in the optic angle. Loss of water without change of temperature causes a decrease of the optic angle, the mineral becoming uniaxial with a loss of 1.8 per cent H_2O ($= \frac{1}{2}H_2O$ in the formula); with a loss of 2.2 per cent H_2O the optic angle is about 20° in a plane normal to the original condition; with a loss of 3 per cent H_2O the optic angle is very large in a new plane. Heulandite at 230° C. has indices as follows: $n_X = 1.4651$, $n_Y = 1.4733$, $n_Z = 1.4747$, $n_Z - n_X = 0.0096$. At $-79°$ C. the optic angle is nearly 0° and the optic plane is nearly parallel with 001. Heulandite heated in boiling glycerine and then plunged into methylene iodide has:[71] G. 2.19, $(+)2V = 45°56'$, $n_X = 1.5004$, $n_Y = 1.5015$, $n_Z = 1.5078$, $n_Z - n_X = 0.0074$. Heated in the same way and plunged into acetylene tetrabromide it has G. 2.16, $n_X = 1.4994$, $n_Y = 1.5009$, $n_Z = 1.5071$, $n_Z - n_X = 0.0077$, $\therefore$ $(-)2V = 52°$, calc.

[69] Slawson: Am. Min. X, p. 305 (1925).

[70] Gaubert: C. R. Acad. Sci. Paris CLXXXVII, p. 1057 (1928); ibid., CXC, p. 802 (1930); Wyart: ibid., CXCI, p. 1343 (1930); also Bull. Soc. Fr. Min. LII, p. 162 (1929).

[71] Gaubert: Bull. Soc. Fr. Min. XXX, p. 104 (1907).

CaSi$_5$Al$_2$O$_{14}$·4H$_2$O(?) **(Epistilbite)** is monoclinic with $a:b:c =$ 0.4194:1:0.2881, $\beta = 90°40'$. Usually contains some NaSi replacing CaAl; it is closely related to heulandite but not the same. Crystals prismatic with common twinning. Perfect {010} cleavage. H. 4. G. 2.25. F. 5 with intumescence. Decomposed by HCl. $Y = b$; $Z \wedge c = 10°$ in acute β. $(+)2V = 44°$, $r < v$ marked. $n_X{}^{52} = 1.505$, $n_Y = 1.515$, $n_Z = 1.519$, $n_Z -$ $n_X = 0.014$. Colorless. When heated until cloudy and then immersed in oil,[42] it becomes orthorhombic with $X = b$ and $Y = a$; in an intermediate condition it must be uniaxial. Upon reabsorption of water it reverts to its original condition.

Al(OH)$_2$SiAlO$_4$ is only a sample of the possible ratios of Al$_2$O$_3$·SiO$_2$ and H$_2$O in alumina-silica hydrogels. Such gels are apparently amorphous[71a] and isotropic. After ignition $n = 1.48$ to 1.68 increasing with increase in alumina; thus, if Al$_2$O$_3$:SiO$_2$ = 0:1, $n = 1.48$–1.485; if the ratio is 1:6.5, $n = 1.48$–1.49; if it is 1:4.3, $n = 1.495$–1.505; if 1:2.8, $n = 1.520$–1.535; if 1:1.9, $n = 1.535$–1.545; if 1:0.9, $n = 1.58$–1.595; if 1:0, $n = 1.68$. The determination of the refractive index of the colloidal constituent of clay might be used to determine whether the alumina is present as a hydrate or as a silicate.

Sodalite Group

The sodalite group includes four minerals which are tectosilicates of aluminum and sodium with some NaCl, NaOH, NaS$_2$, Na$_2$SO$_4$ or CaSO$_4$. They are isometric with rather complicated formulas as follows:

6NaSiAlO$_4$·2NaCl	or Na$_4$ClSi$_3$Al$_3$O$_{12}$	Sodalite
6NaSiAlO$_4$·2NaOH	or Na$_4$(OH)Si$_3$Al$_3$O$_{12}$	OH-Sodalite
6NaSiAlO$_4$·2NaS$_2$	or Na$_4$S$_2$Si$_3$Al$_3$O$_{12}$	Lazurite
6NaSiAlO$_4$·2CaSO$_4$	or Na$_3$CaSO$_4$Si$_3$Al$_3$O$_{12}$	Hauynite
6NaSiAlO$_4$·Na$_2$SO$_4$	or Na$_8$SO$_4$Si$_6$Al$_6$O$_{24}$	Noselite

Na$_4$ClSi$_3$Al$_3$O$_{12}$ (Sodalite) is isometric with $a = 8.87$ Å. U.C. 2. Crystals dodecahedral; often granular. Poor {110} cleavage. H. 5.5–6. G. 2.35. F. 3.5–4.0 to colorless glass. Gelatinizes even in acetic acid. Isotropic with $n = 1.483$ (to 1.488). A Bolivian sample[72] had $n = 1.4806$ Li, 1.4837 Na, 1.4868 Tl. Rarely birefringent about inclusions. Colorless, gray, yellow, blue, greenish, pale red. In thin flakes colorless, yellow, blue or pink. Some samples are pink when freshly broken, fading quickly on exposure to light. Some sodalite fluoresces in ultraviolet light. Made[73] by heating

[71a] Šplíchal: *Min. Abst.* I, p. 288 (1922).

[72] Brendler: *Am. Min.* XIX, p. 28 (1934.)

[73] Friedel and Friedel: *Bull. Soc. Fr. Min.* XIII, p. 129 (1890). See also Medved: *J. Chem. Phys.* XXI, p. 1309 (1953).

muscovite with soda and NaCl to 500° C. PD 3.63, 2.08, 6.3; 3–0338.

$Na_4OHSi_3Al_3O_{12}$ **(OH-Sodalite)** is isometric with $a = 8.77-8.90$ Å. Isotropic with $n = 1.495$.

$Na_4SSi_3Al_3O_{12}$ **(Lazurite)** is isometric with $a = 9.11$ Å. U.C. 2. Often in dodecahedrons or cubes. The tenor of S is variable. Ca may also be present. The Na can be replaced by[74] K, NH_4, Rb, Cs, Ag, Mg, Ca, Sr, Ba, Zn, methyl, ethyl or butyl, but optic data are lacking. Poor {110} cleavage. H. 5–5.5. G. 2.38–2.45. Isotropic with $n = 1.500$. Color rich Berlin blue or azure blue or greenish blue or violet blue. The richly colored varieties are highly prized. Made abundantly for use in "ultramarine" paint.

$Na_3CaSO_4Si_3Al_3O_{12}$ **(Hauynite)** is isometric with $a = 9.10$. U.C. 6. Crystals often twinned; also dodecahedral, etc. Rather distinct {110} cleavage. H. 5.5–6. G. 2.4–2.5. Isotropic with $n = 1.4961$. Color blue, green, red, yellow. Made by heating muscovite with soda and $CaSO_4$ to 500° C. PD 3.72, 2.63, 6.45; 2–0331.

$Na_8SO_4Si_6Al_6O_{24}$ **(Noselite or Nosean)** is isometric with $a = 9.05$ Å. Crystals often dodecahedral; often granular. H. 5.5. G. 2.3–2.4. Gelatinizes easily with acids. Isotropic with $n = 1.486-1.494$; rarely birefringent (due to strain?). Colorless, white, gray, blue, brown, red or black from inclusions or alteration products. PD 3.69, 2.61, 2.13; 2–0339.

$Na_8(WO_4)Si_6Al_6O_{24}$ **(WO₄-Nosean)** is isometric[74a] with $a = 9.16$ kX. Crystals cubo-octahedral. Isotropic with $n = 1.490$. Colorless. Made by crystallization between 800° and 1000° C.

SCAPOLITE GROUP

The scapolite group includes a main series of tectosilicates of aluminum and sodium or calcium with NaCl or $CaCO_3$ but NaCl may be replaced at least in part by NaF, KCl, (KOH?), $NaHCO_3$ or $NaHSO_4$ while $CaCO_3$ may be replaced in part by $CaSO_4$, $MgCO_3$, $CaCl_2$ or perhaps CaF_2. The chief compounds are:

$3NaSi_3AlO_8 \cdot NaCl$ or $Na_4ClSi_9Al_3O_{24}$ Marialite
$3CaSi_2Al_2O_8 \cdot CaCO_3$ or $Ca_4CO_3Si_6Al_6O_{24}$ Meionite

Scapolite is sometimes called wernerite and the marialite-meionite series is divided as follows:

Marialite	$Ma_{100}Me_0$	to	$Ma_{80}Me_{20}$	$c/a = 0.446$
Dipyre	$Ma_{80}Me_{20}$	to	$Ma_{50}Me_{50}$	$c/a = 0.444$
Mizzonite	$Ma_{50}Me_{50}$	to	$Ma_{20}Me_{80}$	$c/a = 0.442$
Meionite	$Ma_{20}Me_{80}$	to	Ma_0Me_{100}	$c/a = 0.439$

[74] Jaeger and van Melle: *Proc. K. Ak. Wet. Amsterdam* XXX, p. 249, 479, 885 (1927); *ibid.* XXXII, p. 156, 167 (1929).

[74a] Saalfeld: *N. Jahrb. Miner. Monatshefte*, p. 207 (1955).

$Na_4ClSi_9Al_3O_{24}$ (with 0–20% $Ca_4CO_3Si_6Al_6O_{24}$) **(Marialite)** is tetragonal dipyramidal with c/a = 0.446. NaCl may be replaced at least in part by NaF, KCl, (KOH?), $NaHCO_3$ or $NaHSO_4$. Crystals long prismatic, vertically striated. Distinct {100} and poor {110} cleavages. H. 5.5–6. G. 2.58–2.60. Uniaxial negative (as found in nature—but the pure compound may be positive—see Fig. 10-17), with n_O = 1.532–1.545, n_E = 1.534–1.538,

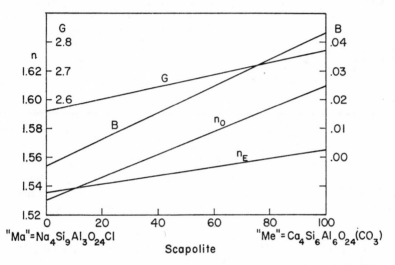

Fig. 10-17. Properties of the scapolite series $Na_4Al_3Si_9O_{24}Cl$—$Ca_4Al_6Si_6O_{24}CO_3$.

$n_O - n_E$ = −0.002–0.007. Colorless. Refringence, birefringence and specific gravity all increase in scapolite with increase of Ca. PD 3.44, 3.03, 3.78; 2–0412.

80–50% $NaClSi_9Al_3O_{24}$ + 20–50% $Ca_4CO_3Si_6Al_6O_{24}$ (the portion of the scapolite or wernerite series called dipyre) is tetragonal dipyramidal with c/a = 0.444. Variations in composition noted above. Crystals prismatic with distinct {100} and poor {110} cleavages. H. 5.5–6. G. 2.6–2.67. Uniaxial negative with n_O = 1.545–1.57, n_E = 1.538–1.55, $n_O - n_E$ = 0.007–0.02. Colorless.

50–20% $Na_4Si_9Al_3O_{24}$ + 50–80% $Ca_4CO_3Si_6Al_6O_{24}$ (the portion of the scapolite or wernerite series known as **mizzonite**) is tetragonal dipyramidal with c/a = 0.442. Variation in composition as noted above. Crystals prismatic with distinct {100} and poor {110} cleavages. H. 5.5–6. G. 2.67–2.73. Uniaxial negative with n_O = 1.57–1.59, n_E = 1.55–1.56, $n_O - n_E$ = 0.02–0.03. Colorless.

$Ca_4CO_3Al_6Si_6O_{24}$ (with 0–20% $Na_4ClSi_9Al_3O_{24}$) **(Meionite)** is tetragonal dipyramidal with c/a = 0.4393. $CaCO_3$ may be replaced in part by $CaSO_4$,

$MgCO_3$, $CaCl_2$ or CaF_2. Crystals long prismatic, vertically striated. Distinct {100} and poor {110} cleavages. H. 5.5–6. G. 2.70–2.75. M.P. 1100°–1200° C. Decomposed by HCl. Uniaxial negative with n_O = 1.590–1.600, n_E = 1.560–1.563, $n_O - n_E$ = 0.030–0.037. Colorless. Made by crystallizing a glass[75] of the given composition in a steel bomb with a 10 per cent NaCl solution. PD 3.47, 3.08, 2.07; 2–0405.

$Na_3CaCO_3(OH)_2Si_3Al_3O_{12}$ **(Cancrinite)** is hexagonal pyramidal with a = 12.75, c = 5.18 Å. U.C. 2. CO_3 may be replaced by SO_4 or Cl; Ca by NaH, KH, etc. Crystals prismatic with perfect {10$\bar{1}$0} cleavage. H. 5–6. G. 2.42–2.5. F. 2 with intumescence. Effervesces and gelatinizes with acids. Uniaxial negative with[76] n_O = 1.550, n_E = 1.519, $n_O - n_E$ = 0.031. With $CaCO_3$ replaced in part by Na_2CO_3 (or $NaHCl_3$?) and Ca:Na = 1:1, n_O = 1.525, n_E = 1.505, $n_O - n_E$ = 0.020. With NaOH, but no $CaCO_3$ n_O = 1.500, n_E = 1.497, $n_O - n_E$ = 0.003. With AgOH in place of NaOH, n_O = 1.647, n_E nearly equals n_O. But with AgOH, n_O may also = 1.670, n_E = 1.649, and $n_O - n_E$ = 0.021. With increasing Na and SO_4 the refringence, birefringence and specific gravity all decrease. Colorless. PD 3.19, 4.61, 3.61; 3–0503. Made by heating under pressure a mixture of sodium silicate, alumina and sodium carbonate; also by treating nephelite and labradorite with sodium carbonate at high temperatures.

C. PHYLLOSILICATES (SHEETS OF TETRAHEDRA): $A_m(X_2O_5)_nZ_q$

$K_2MgSi_5O_{12}(?)$ has two phases.[1] The α-phase is isometric with a = 13.39 Å. M.P. 1089° C. Crystals octahedrons, cubes, etc. Isotropic with n = 1.501. The β-phase forms fibers with G. 2.395 and very weak birefringence (about 0.001 or 0.002) and n = 1.505 Na. PD 3.25, 3.38, 5.34; 10–21. The glass has G. 2.38 and n = 1.498. Colorless. Made from fusion.

$CaCuSi_4O_{10}$ is tetragonal with G. 3.04,[2] 2.95.[3] Uniaxial negative with n_O = 1.6354, n_E = 1.6053, $n_O - n_E$ = 0.0301. Color azure blue with O deep blue, E pale rose. Made from fusion and called Vestorian blue; supposed to be the equivalent of an artificial blue pigment used by the early Egyptians.

$FeBaSi_4O_{10}$ **(Gillespite)** is ditetragonal dipyramidal[4] with a = 7.495, c = 16.05 Å. U.C. 4. Perfect {001} and poor {100} cleavages. H. 3. G. 3.4.

[75] Shepherd, Rankin and Wright: Am. J. Sci. CLXXVIII, p. 305 (1909).

[76] Eitel: N. Jahrb. Min. II, 1922, p. 45; also Die Feldspathvertreter, 1925, p. 232.

[1] Roedder: Am. J. Sci. CCXLIX, p. 81 and 224 (1951).

[2] Fouqué: C. R. Acad. Sci. Paris, CVIII, p. 325 (1889).

[3] Laurie: Proc. Roy. Soc. London, LXXXIX, A, p. 418 (1914).

[4] Pabst: Am. Min. XXVIII, p. 372 (1943).

F. easy. Uniaxial negative with $n_O = 1.621$, $n_E = 1.619$, $n_O - n_E = 0.002$. Color rose-red with O pale pink, E deep rose-red. Leached by HCl all the Fe and Ba are removed leaving hydrous silica ($8SiO_2 \cdot 5H_2O$) in glistening scales resembling those produced from biotite by treatment with H_2SO_4. They have G. 1.8–2.0 and are uniaxial negative[5] (or slightly biaxial) with variable indices (due to variable tenor of H_2O?) such as $n_O = 1.465$, $n_E = 1.455$, $n_O - n_E = 0.010$ and $n_O = 1.449$, $n_E = 1.441$, $n_O - n_E = 0.008$. Colorless. PD 3.39, 4.41, 3.22; 3–0402.

$K_8CaSi_{10}O_{25}$ is hexagonal;[6] plates have parallel extinction. Uniaxial negative with $n_O = 1.548$, $n_E = 1.537$, $n_O - n_E = 0.011$. Colorless.

$K_2Mg_5Si_{12}O_{30}$ is hexagonal.[1] Crystal six-sided tablets often with second order pyramids. No cleavage. G. 2.58. M.P. 1174° C. Uniaxial positive with $n_O = 1.543$, $n_E = 1.550 \pm 0.002$, $n_E - n_O = 0.008$ Na. Nearly the same indices as those of quartz. Colorless. Made from fusion.

$K_2MgSi_3O_8(?)$ is hexagonal.[1] M.P. 1134° C. Uniaxial negative with $n_O = 1.530$, $n_E = 1.524$, $n_O - n_E = 0.006$. It inverts to a second phase (on cooling) which has G. 2.56 and a "gross index" of 1.527. Colorless. Made from fusion. PD 3.10, 3.21, 2.67; 10–30 (β-phase); 3.12, 3.99, 2.61; 10–20 (α-phase).

$K_8CaSi_{10}O_{25}$ is hexagonal.[7] Crystals platy. M.P. 946° C. Uniaxial negative with $n_O = 1.551$, $n_E = 1.539$, $n_O - n_E = 0.012$. Colorless. Made from fusion.

$K_2Pb_4Si_8O_{21}(?)$ forms fibers or laths with parallel extinction.[8] Indices $n_X = 1.69 \pm 0.01$, $n_Z = 1.79 \pm 0.01$. ". . . extinction is parallel and the optic axis is parallel with the longitudinal axis [of the fibers]."[9]

$Na_2Si_2O_5$ has at least two crystal phases. The high temperature α-phase is orthorhombic[10] with $a = 15.45$, $b = 4.909$, $c = 6.43$ Å. U.C. 4. Crystals {100} plates with perfect {100} and distinct {010} cleavages. G. 2.48, M.P. 874° C. Inverts reversibly at 678° C. X = a; Y = b. (−)2V = 50°–55°. $n_X = 1.497$, $n_Y = 1.505$, $n_Z = 1.508$, $n_Z - n_X = 0.011$. Again:[11] $n_X = 1.504$, $n_Y = 1.514$, $n_Z = 1.518$, $n_Z - n_X = 0.014$. The glass has $n = 1.504$. Colorless. Made from fusion. The low temperature phase is monoclinic[10] with $a = 12.31$, $b = 4.849$, $c = 8.124$ Å, $\beta = 104°7'$. Crystals thin

[5] Schaller: *Am. Min.* XIV, p. 319 (1929).

[6] H. E. Merwin: *pers. comm.* April 2, 1931; Morey, Kracek and Bowen: *J. Soc. Glass Tech.* XIV, p. 149 (1930).

[7] G. R. Rigby: *Thin Section Mineralogy of Ceramic Materials*, 1948.

[8] Geller and Bunting: *J. Res. Bur. Stand.* XVII, p. 277 (1936).

[9] Geller and Bunting[8] do not state the optic sign. The fibrous habit suggests that it is probably positive.

[10] Donnay and Donnay: *Am. Min.* XXXVIII, p. 163 (1953).

[11] Morey and Bowen: *J. Phys. Chem.* XXVIII, p. 1167 (1924); *Trans. Soc. Glass Tech.* IX, p. 226 (1925).

{100} pseudo-hexagonal plates. Perfect {100} and distinct {010} cleavages. Very commonly twinned on {100}, G. 2.6. $(-)2V = 48°$ calc.[10] $n_X = 1.500$, $n_Y = 1.510$, $n_Z = 1.515$, $n_Z - n_X = 0.015$. $Z = b$; X nearly normal to {100}, $Y \approx c$. Colorless.

$K_2Si_2O_5$ is orthorhombic.[12,13] Crystals six-sided plates with angles of about 40° and 80°; if these plates are basal, the cleavages are: {001} perfect, {010} distinct, {100} imperfect. Lamellar twinning nearly parallel with elongation b. Crystals from fusion are elongated parallel with Z; from solution parallel with Y. Crystals hygroscopic. G. 2.538. M.P. 1036° C. $X = c$; $Y = b$. $(-)2V =$ rather large. $n_X = 1.503$, $n_Y = 1.509$ $ca.$, $n_Z = 1.513$, $n_Z - n_X = 0.010$. The glass has G. 2.474. Colorless. Made from fusion and from solution.

$Li_2Si_2O_5$ is orthorhombic with[10] $a = 5.80$, $b = 14.66$, $c = 4.81$. U.C. 4. Crystals rectangular tablets with three rectangular cleavages, one being perfect, the others nearly perfect. G. 2.454. M.P. 1032° C. (incongruently). Y normal to the best cleavage; Z parallel to the two best cleavages.[14] $(+)2V = 50°$–$60°$, $n_X = 1.547$, $n_Y = 1.550$, $n_Z = 1.558$, $n_Z - n_X = 0.011$. Again:[15] $n_X = 1.525$, $n_Y = ?$, $n_Z = 1.545$, $n_Z - n_X = 0.020$. Colorless. Made from fusion. PD 3.67, 3.75, 1.98; 4–0436.

$LiKSi_2O_5$ is orthorhombic(?). M.P. 870° C.[16] $2V = 53°$, $n_X = 1.536$, $n_Y = ?$, $n_Z = 1.540$, $n_Z - n_X = 0.004$. Colorless.

$Li_2K_4Si_6O_{15}$ is orthorhombic(?). M.P. 815° C. (two or three inversions[16]). $(-?)2V = 85°$–$90°$. $n_X = 1.510$, $n_Y = 1.5125$ $ca.$ $n_Z = 1.515$, $n_Z - n_X = 0.005$. Colorless.

$Ba_2Si_3O_8(?)$ is orthorhombic[17] and granular with three pinacoids; cleavages,[18] one (assumed to be {001}) perfect, the others poor. Lamellar twinning on a prism face inclined 30° to a. G. 3.93. M.P. 1450° C. $X = c$; $Y = a$. $(+)2V = 54°$. $n_X = 1.617$ C, 1.620 D, 1.627 F, $n_Y = 1.622$ C, 1.625 D, 1.632 F, $n_Z = 1.641$ C, 1.645 D, 1.652 F, $n_Z - n_X = 0.025$ D. Colorless. Made from fusion. PD 3.79, 3.33, 3.28; 6–0206. It forms a complete series of mix-crystals with $BaSi_2O_5$ whose properties vary continuously as shown in Fig. 10–18.

$Na_2Ca_3Si_6O_{16}(?)$ (Devitrite) is orthorhombic;[19] crystals often prismatic.

[12] Morey and Fenner: *J. Am. Chem. Soc.* XXXVI, p. 215 (1914).

[13] Kracek, Bowen and Morey: *J. Phys. Chem.* XXXIII, p. 1857 (1929); also Goranson and Kracek, *ibid.*; XXXVI, p. 913 (1932).

[14] Merwin: *J. Phys. Chem.* XXXIV, p. 2647 (1930).

[15] Jaeger and van Klooster: *Proc. K. Akad. Wet. Amsterdam* XVI, p. 857 (1914).

[16] Vail: *Am. Chem. Soc. Monog.* 116, I (1952).

[17] $Ba_2Si_3O_8$ is included here because it is completely miscible with $BaSi_2O_5$. See also p. 268.

[18] Eskola: *Am. J. Sci.* CCIV, p. 331 (1922).

[19] Morey and Bowen: *J. Soc. Glass Tech.* IX, p. 226 (1925); Wyckoff and Morey: *Am. J. Sci.* CCXII, p. 419 (1926).

It dissociates to $CaSiO_3$ and liquid at 1045° C. Z parallel with elongation. $(+)2V = 75°$. $n_X = 1.564$, $n_Y = 1.570$, $n_Z = 1.579$, $n_Z - n_X = 0.015$. Colorless. Made from fusion. Similar acicular devitrification products of glass have been described under the name **rivaite** by Zambonini[20] and

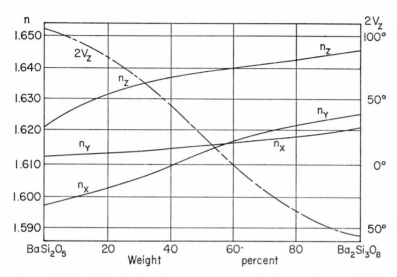

Fig. 10-18. Variations in properties of the series $BaSi_2O_5$—$Ba_2Si_3O_8$. Modified from data of Eskola, *Am. Jour. Sci.* IV, p. 331 (1922).

under the name réaumurite by Lacroix.[21] **Rivaite** is reported to have the optic plane normal to the elongation and Z normal to the laths with $(-)2V =$ small; $n_Y = 1.56$, $n_Z - n_X =$ weak. This is probably wollastonite according to Bowen.[22] **Réaumurite** has Z parallel with the elongation according to Gaubert[23] with biaxial character and $n_X = 1.540$, $n_Z = 1.545–1.55$, $n_Z - n_X$ weak.

$K_2Ca_3Si_6O_{16}$ forms orthorhombic[24] needles and long prisms and plates. Z = elongation, $(-)2V = ?$. $n_X = 1.56$, $n_Z = 1.57$, $n_Z - n_X = 0.01$. Decomposes above 960° C to $K_2Ca_2Si_6O_{15}$ and glass. Made from fusion.

$K_2Ca_2Si_6O_{15}$ forms stout prisms[24] with highly inclined extinction. $(+)2V$ = large, $n_X = 1.575$, $n_Y = ?$, $n_Z = 1.59$. Decomposes above 1115° C. to wollastonite + $CaSiO_3$ + glass. Made from fusion.

$K_2PbSi_4O_{10}$ forms rectangular plates with parallel extinction. M.P. 757°

[20] Zambonini: *Rend. Acc. Napoli*, XVIII, p. 223 (1912).
[21] Lacroix: *Bull. Soc. Fr. Min.* XXXVIII, p. 16 (1915).
[22] Bowen: *Am. Min.* VII, p. 64, (1922).
[23] Gaubert: *C. R. Acad. Sci. Paris*, 1925, p. 1853.
[24] Morey, Kracek and Bowen: *J. Soc. Glass Tech.* XIV, p. 149 (1930).

C. $(+)2V = 75°$ *ca.* $n_X = 1.590$, $n_Y = 1.612$, $n_Z = 1.650$, all ± 0.005, $n_Z - n_X = 0.06$. The glass has $n = 1.606$; it softens at 463° C. PD 3.70, 3.22, 3.08; 3–0317.

$Na_6Be_6Si_{14}O_{37}(?)$ is orthorhombic[25] with G. 2.55. $n_X = 1.532$, $n_Y = ?$, $n_Z = 1.545$, $n_Z - n_X = 0.013$ and $(+)2E = 60°$; therefore $(+)2V = 38°$ and $n_Y = 1.533$.

$KHSi_2O_5$ is orthorhombic[26] in pseudo-hexagonal prismatic to tabular crystals. G. 2.417. M.P. 515° C. Good {100} and {010} cleavages. X = b, Y = c, Z = a. $(+)2V = 40°$ *ca.* $n_X = 1.495$, $n_Y = 1.501$ calc. $n_Z = 1.535$, $n_Z - n_X = 0.040$. Hardly soluble in water even at 100° C. Alters with reduction of index to 1.480. Loses weight (H_2O) when heated in air at 420° C. Colorless. Made hydrothermally.

$K_4CaSi_6O_{15}$ is monoclinic or triclinic;[7] crystals prisms or plates with slightly inclined extinction. M.P. 959° C. $(-)2V = 60° \pm 5°$. $n_X = 1.535$, $n_Y = 1.541$, $n_Z = 1.543$, $n_Z - n_X = 0.008$. Colorless. Made from fusion.

$Na_2Mg_2Si_6O_{15}$ is monoclinic.[7] Z $\wedge$ $c = 24°$. $(+)2V = $ large. $n_X = 1.540$, $n_Y = 1.5425$ calc., $n_Z = 1.546$, $n_Z - n_X = 0.006$. Colorless. Made from fusion.

$K_2Ca_2Si_9O_{21}(?)$ is monoclinic[24] or triclinic. Crystals prismatic with slightly inclined extinction. $(-)2V = $ large. $n_X = 1.515$, $n_Y = 1.526$ est., $n_Z = 1.535$, $n_Z - n_X = 0.020$. Colorless. Made from fusion.

$K_4CaSi_6O_{15}$ is monoclinic[24] or triclinic; crystals are plates with inclined extinction. $(-)2V = 60° \pm 5°$. $n_X = 1.535$, $n_Y = 1.541$, $n_Z = 1.543$, $n_Z - n_X = 0.008$. Colorless. Made from fusion.

$BaSi_2O_5$ **(Sanbornite)** is triclinic[27] with angles α, β and γ not far from 90°. It has perfect {001} and poor {010} and {100} cleavages; polysynthetic twinning on {010}. H. 5. G. 4.19. The optic plane is nearly normal to {010}; Z is nearly normal to {001}. Extinction angle on (001) is 3.5° and on (010) it is 5.5°. $(-)2V = 66°$ *ca.* $n_X = 1.597$, $n_Y = 1.616$, $n_Z = 1.624$, $n_Z - n_X = 0.027$. Colorless. $BaSi_2O_5$ is also orthorhombic[28] with three pinacoidal cleavages. M.P. 1420° C. G.[18] 3.73 and X = b; Y = a (nearly the same as sanbornite). $(-)2V = 75°$ *ca.*, $n_X = 1.595$ C, 1.597 D, 1.602 F, $n_Y = 1.610$ C, 1.612 D, 1.617 F, $n_Z = 1.618$ C, 1.621 D, 1.632 F, $n_Z - n_X = 0.024$ D. PD 4.05, 2.22, 3.17; 10–45 (α-, or high-temp. form): 3.09, 4.0, 3.32; 10–46 (β-form). The glass has $n = 1.6085$. $BaSi_2O_5$ forms a continuous series of mix-crystals with $BaSi_3O_8$ in which the optic properties vary continuously as shown in Fig. 10–18.

[25] Gaubert: *Bull. Soc. Fr. Min.* L, p. 504 (1927).

[26] Morey and Fenner: *J. Am. Chem. Soc.* XXXIX, p. 1173 (1917); Morey: *J. Am. Chem. Soc.* XXXVI, p. 215 (1914).

[27] Rogers: *Am. Min.* XVII, p. 161 (1932).

[28] Bowen: *J. Wash. Acad. Sci.* VIII, p. 265 (1918).

$K_2Si_2O_5 \cdot H_2O$ is granular.[26] It dissociates at 405° C., altered by H_2O below 280° C. Soluble in water. $(+)2V$ = very small. Mean index, n, estimated at 1.50, $n_Z - n_X$ = strong. Colorless.

$CaSi_2O_5 \cdot 2H_2O$ **(Okenite)** is triclinic in minute blade-shaped crystals; often fibrous. Perfect {010} cleavage. Twinning on {010}. H. 5. G. 2.28–2.33. F. 2.5. Gelatinizes with HCl. Extinction parallel with c in {010}, but it may reach 34° in the vertical zone. Positive elongation. Optically negative(?). Indices vary notably (due to variable tenor of H_2O?), n_Z from 1.536[29] to 1.553.[30] Color white or pale. Made by recrystallization in[31] carbonated water in a sealed tube. PD 21., 8.8, 3.56; 9–469*.

$Na_2Al_2Si_2O_8 \cdot H_2O(?)$ **(Lembergite)** is orthorhombic[32] with a prism angle of 112°; it seems to be closely related to kaolinite and chemically it is called nepheline hydrate.[33] $(+)2V = 66°45'$, r < v. $n_X = 1.569$, $n_Y = 1.570$, $n_Z = 1.573$, $n_Z - n_X = 0.004$. The optic sign changes to negative on heating to 115° (dehydrated). Produced artificially and said to occur in nature. PD 3.40, 4.39, 2.95; 10–460* (identity?).

$Mg_3(OH)_2Si_4O_{10}$ **(Talc)** is monoclinic with $a = 5.27$, $b = 9.13$, $c = 18.88$ Å, $\beta = 100°15'$. U.C. 4. It often contains a little FeO, Al_2O_3 and extra H_2O. Crystals rare; usually in compact masses. Perfect {001} cleavage. H. 1. G. 2.82. F. 6, after exfoliation. X nearly normal to {001}; Z = b. $(-)2V = 0°–30°$, r > v. $n_X = 1.540$, n_Y nearly = $n_Z = 1.575$, $n_Z - n_X = 0.035$. Indices vary (due to Fe or H_2O?); for example:[34] $n_X = 1.538–1.545$, $n_Z = 1.575–1.590$, $n_Z - n_X = 0.030–0.050$. After losing half its water below red heat the optic properties are nearly the same; the rest of the water is lost between 875° and 960° C. Color pale green or colorless. Made under pressure at moderate temperatures. PD 2.49, 4.58, 1.53; 3–0881.

$Fe_3(OH)_2Si_4O_{10}$ **(Minnesotaite)** is the iron analogue of talc.[35] It is monoclinic with $a = 5.4$, $b = 2.4$, $c \sin \beta = 19.1$ Å. Forms colorless needles with positive elongation, or plates showing nearly centered acute bisectrix interference figures with $(-)2V < 5°$. $n_X = 1.586$ (earlier reported 1.580), $n_Y = n_Z = 1.618$ (earlier, 1.615), $n_Z - n_X = 0.032$. Natural material usually contains Fe''', Mg, and excess of H_2O. H. 2.5. G. 3–3.1. Greenalite decomposes to minnesotaite + fayalite at 470° C., minnesotaite decom-

[29] Hey: *Min. Mag.* XXIII, p. 81 (1932).

[30] Tilley and Alderman: *Min. Mag.* XXIII, p. 513 (1934).

[31] Doelter: *N. Jahrb. Min.* I, p. 123 (1890).

[32] Lagorio: *Trav. Soc. Nat. Varsovie* VI, Livr. XI, p. 7 (1895).

[33] Dominikiewicz: *Min. Abst.* V, p. 255 (1933).

[34] Doelter and Dittler: *Ber. Akad. Wiss. Wien,* CXXI (1), p. 897 (1912).

[35] Flaschen and Osborn: *Am. Min.* XXXIX, p. 328 (1954); also *Econ. Geol.* LII, p. 923, 1957.

poses to fayalite and quartz at slightly higher temperatures. PD 9.53, 2.52, 4.77; 6–0025.

$Mg_6(OH)_8Si_4O_{10}$ (**Chrysotile**) is monoclinic prismatic with $a = 14.66$, $b = 9.24$, $c = 5.33$, $\beta = 93°16'$. U.C. 1. Crystals fibrous and flexible in the variety called asbestos. Poor {110} cleavages at 130°. H. 2–2.5. G. 2.36–2.50. F. 6. Y = b; Z $\wedge$ c (elongation) = nearly 0°. (+)2V = 30–35° (but may seem smaller due to superposition of lamellae). $n_X = 1.542$, $n_Y = 1.543$ calc., $n_Z = 1.555$, $n_Z - n_X = 0.013$. Again:[36] $n_X = 1.53–1.54$, $n_Z = 1.54–1.55$. With some Ni or Fe indices may be up to .02 higher. Color green, yellow, gray. Made by hydrothermal methods[36a] under pressure at temperatures below 500° C.

$(Ni,Mg)_6(OH)_6Si_4O_{11} \cdot H_2O$ (**Garnierite**) is monoclinic like chrysotile. With 47 per cent NiO it has (+)2V = 0°–10°. $n_X = 1.622$, $n_Y \approx n_Z = 1.630$, $n_Z - n_X = 0.008–0.010$. Color dark green with X < Z. PD 9.8, 1.52, 2.65; 2–0060.

$Fe''_9Fe'''_2(OH)_{16}Si_8O_{20}(?)$ (**Greenalite**) is monoclinic,[37] resembling chrysolite with $a = 14.5$, $b = 18.6$, $c = ?$ Crystallization mostly submicroscopic but distinct to X-rays. Granular. G. 3$\pm$. Isotropic, or nearly so, with $n = 1.660$ C, 1.674 D, 1.686 F. Hawley[37a] found n as low as = 1.650 (on submicroscopic material containing some opal?). PD 2.57, 7.12, 3.56; 2–1012. Color green to yellow or brown.

$Mg_3Si_4O_{11} \cdot nH_2O$ (**Sepiolite**) is monoclinic with $a = 23.2$, $b = 15.7$, $c = 5.32$ Å, $\beta = 90°–93°$. Always finely fibrous often with amorphous and other material, the mixture being called meerschaum, with mean index of about 1.54. H. 2–2.5. G. 2. Z very near c. (−)2V = very near 0°. $n_X = 1.515–1.520$, $n_Y \approx n_Z = 1.525–1.529$, $n_Z - n_X = 0.009\pm$. Heated above 100° C. n_Z becomes 1.535 ca. Color white or pale. Made under pressure;[37b] also found in boiler deposits.[37c]

$Mg_5Al(OH)_8Si_3AlO_{10}$ (**Clinochlore**) is monoclinic with $a = 5.2–5.3$, $b = 9.2–9.3$, $c = 28.3–28.6$ Å. $\beta = 96°50'$ ca. Often contains a little Fe (for Mg). It is a variety of chlorite. Crystals lamellar with perfect basal cleavage. H. 2–2.5. G. 2.7. Y = b; X nearly normal to {010}. (+)2V = 0°–40°. $n_Y = 1.57–1.58$, $n_Z - n_X = 0.004–0.010$ ca. Nearly always green (but it can be gray, olive, pink or white) with X and Y pale green, Z pale yellow-green to colorless. Made by hydrothermal methods[36a] under pressure at 520°–680° C.

[36] Noll: *Zeit. anorg. Chem.* CCLXI, p. 1 (1950).

[36a] Yoder: *Am. Jour. Sci. Bowen* Vol. (CCL-A), p. 560 (1952).

[37] Gruner: *Am. Min.* XXI, p. 449 (1936).

[37a] Hawley in Winchell: *Optical Mineralogy* Part II, p. 380 (1951).

[37b] Bowen and Tuttle: *Geol. Soc. Am. Bull.* LX, p. 439 (1949).

[37c] Clark: *Min. Mag.* XXVIII, p. 359 (1948).

$Mg_3(OH)_4Si_2O_5$ **(Antigorite)** is monoclinic prismatic with $a = 5.3$, $b = 9.25$, $c = 13.52$ Å, $\beta = 91°4'$. U.C. 2. It is a chief component of the chlorite group, and may contain a little Fe and Al. Usually lamellar with perfect {001} cleavage. H. 2–2.5. G. 2.62. Y $= b$; X nearly normal to {001}. $(-)2V =$ moderate. $n_Y = 1.55$–1.58, $n_Z - n_X = 0.004$–0.010. Color greenish, brownish or yellowish. Made artificially.[38] PD 7.30, 3.63, 2.52; 7–417*.

$AlOHSi_2O_5$ **(Pyrophyllite)** is monoclinic prismatic with $a = 5.15$, $b = 8.88$, $c = 18.60$ Å, $\beta = 99°55'$. U.C. 8. Lamellar masses with perfect {001} cleavage. H. 1–1.5. G. 2.84. F. 6 after enlarging. X normal to cleavage; Z parallel to elongation of blades. $(-)2V = 53$–$60°$, r $>$ v weak. $n_X = 1.552$, $n_Y = 1.588$, $n_Z = 1.600$, $n_Z - n_X = 0.048$. Colorless or stained. Made by hydrothermal methods under pressure. PD 3.07, 4.43, 2.42; 3–0574.

MICA GROUP

The mica group consists of phyllosilicates of aluminum and potassium (rarely sodium), usually with magnesium, iron or lithium. All micas also contain some OH or F or both. Micas are normally monoclinic, but may be hexagonal or triclinic. They have very perfect basal cleavage giving thin elastic laminae. The chief components are:

$K_2Mg_6(OH)_4Si_6Al_2O_{20}$	Phlogopite
$K_2Mg_5Al(OH)_4Si_5Al_3O_{20}$	Eastonite
$NaAl_2(OH)_2Si_3AlO_{10}$	Paragonite
$KAl_2(OH)_2Si_3AlO_{10}$	Muscovite

The following micas have been made containing fluorine in place of hydroxyl:

$NH_4Mg_3F_2Si_3AlO_{10}$	NH_4O_{10}F-Phlogopite
$K(Fe,Mg)_3F_2Si_3AlO_{10}$	F-Biotite
$KLiFeAl(F,OH)_2Si_3AlO_{10}$	F-Zinnwaldite

Several of the micas have been observed with two or more distinct crystal structures, differing in the pattern or sequence in which successive layers fit over one another. Such stacking-polymorphs would differ very little in their respective lattice energies; with few exceptions (as when the stacking sequence produces rhombohedral or hexagonal symmetry), they cannot be distinguished optically.

$KMg_3(OH)_2Si_3AlO_{10}$ **(Phlogopite)** has three (or more) phases, two

---

[38] van Niewenburg and Blumendal: *Rec. Trav. Chim. Pays Bas* L, p. 129 and 789 (1931); *N. Jahrb. Min.* I, p. 82 (1933).

being monoclinic (one layer or two layers) and one, three-layer trigonal, The one-layer monoclinic phase has[39] $a = 5.31$, $b = 9.20$, $c = 10.31$ Å. $\beta = 99°54'$. Perfect $\{001\}$ cleavage with $\{010\}$ and $\{111\}$ parting. H. 2.5–3. G. 2.79. X nearly $\perp$ $\{001\}$. Y = b. $(-)2V = 0°–10°$ $ca.$ $n_X = 1.548$, $n_Y \approx n_Z = 1.588$, $n_Z - n_X = 0.040$. Colorless—but in nature it often contains some Fe (replacing Mg) and then is yellowish brown or greenish and pleochroic with X colorless, Y and Z reddish brown. Made from components under considerable pressure. PD 9.94, 3.35, 2.61; 10–495* (1M-type).

$K_2Mg_5Al(OH)_4Si_5Al_3O_{20}$ (Eastonite) forms a complete series with $K_2Mg_6(OH)_4Si_6AlO_{20}$ and in both the Mg can be replaced in whole or in any amount by Fe; these four are the end-members of the biotite system of micas. Crystals have three (or more) phases, but are usually monoclinic and almost hexagonal. Perfect basal cleavage; also $\{010\}$ and $\{011\}$ parting. H. 2.5–3. G. 2.86. F. 5. X very nearly normal to $\{001\}$ (cleavage). Y = b. $(-)2V =$ small, r < v weak. $n_X = 1.542$, $n_Y = 1.577$ $ca.$ $n_Z = 1.578$, $n_Z - n_X = 0.036$. Color pale, but usually with enough iron to be yellow or brown. Made under high pressure at rather high temperature.[39] PD 10.1, 3.37, 2.66; 2–0045 ("biotite").

$KMg_3F_2Si_3AlO_{10}$ (F-Phlogopite) is monoclinic domatic with $a = 5.299$, $b = 9.188$, $c = 10.135$ Å, $\beta = 99°55'$. U.C. 4. This is phlogopite mica with OH replaced by F. With Mg replaced by Fe it is F-biotite. Crystals six-sided prisms; often lamellar. Perfect $\{001\}$ cleavage, with $\{010\}$ and $\{111\}$ parting. H. 2.5–3. G. 2.85. X nearly normal to $\{001\}$; Y = b. $(-)2V = 9°–14°$, r < v weak. $n_X{}^{40} = 1.519$, $n_Y = 1.545$, $n_Z = 1.547$, $n_Z - n_X = 0.028$. Again:[41] $n_X = 1.522$, $n_Y = 1.5485$, $n_Z = 1.549$, $n_Z - n_X = 0.027$. Also:[42] $n_X = 1.544$, $n_Y = 1.546$, $n_Z = 1.566$, $n_Z - n_X = 0.029$. Also[43] (with 6.43 CaO): $n_X = 1.520$, $n_Y \approx n_Z = 1.558$, $n_Z - n_X = 0.038$. Colorless. Made[40,41] by heating the components in a sealed container. PD 9.96, 3.33, 1.99; 10–494.

$NH_4Mg_3F_2Si_3AlO_4$ (NH$_4$-Phlogopite) has been made from vermiculite.[44] It has: $n_X = 1.54\pm$, 1.55, 1.56, $n_Y \approx n_Z = 1.57+$, 1.58, 1.59, $n_Z - n_X = 0.03$.

$K(Fe,Mg)_3F_2Si_3AlO_{10}$ (F-Biotite) with Fe:Mg = 2:1 is monoclinic like phlogopite; it is a F-biotite and has:[43] $(-)2V = 0°$, $n_X = 1.551$, $n_Y =$

[39] Yoder and Eugster: *Am. Min.* XXXIX, p. 326 (1954) and *Geochim. Cosmochim. Acta* VI, p. 157 (1954).

[40] Van Valkenburg and Pike: *J. Res. Nat. Bur. Stand.* XLVIII, p. 360 (1952).

[41] Kohn and Hatch: *Am. Min.* XL, p. 10 (1955).

[42] Noda: *Bull. Chem. Soc. Japan*, XXIII, p. 40 (1950).

[43] Grigoriev: *Cent. Min.* A, 1934, p. 219.

[44] Gruner: *Am. Min.* XXIV, p. 428 (1939).

$n_Z = 1.596$, $n_Z - n_X = 0.045$. Color brown. Made from components[43] with CaF_2 at high temperature (1200° C.).

$NaAl_2(OH)_2Si_3AlO_{10}$ (**Paragonite**) is monoclinic with $a = 5.12$, $b = 8.87$, $c = 19.33$ Å, β not far from 90°. Often contains some K in place of Na. H. 2. G. 2.85. F. 6. Insoluble. X nearly normal to {001};[45] $Z = b$. $(-)2V = 40°$ ca. $n_X = 1.564$–1.577, $n_Y = 1.599$–1.605, $n_Z = 1.600$–1.609, $n_Z - n_X = 0.028$–0.038. Colorless. PD 1.48, 2.51, 3.18; 10–420*.

$KAl_2(F,OH)_2Si_3AlO_{10}$ (**Muscovite**) is monoclinic prismatic with $a = 5.18$, $b = 9.02$, $c = 20.04$ Å, $\beta = 95°30'$. U.C. 4. The natural mineral usually contains OH with little or no F; the F-bearing type is easier to make. Crystals usually tabular with six sides; often lamellar massive. Perfect {001} cleavage; also {110} and {010} parting. H. 2.5–3. G. 2.76–3.0. F. 5.7 to gray or yellow glass. Insoluble. X makes an angle of 0°–2° with a normal to {001}; $Z = b$. $(-)2V = 45°$ ca., r > v distinct. $n_X = 1.552$, $n_Y = 1.582$, $n_Z = 1.588$, $n_Z - n_X = 0.036$. Colorless (or, with some Fe''', brown). Made[46] by heating in a sealed container. PD 10.1, 3.36, 4.49; 7–25*.

$KLiFeAl(F,OH)_2Si_3AlO_{10}$ (**Zinnwaldite**) is monoclinic prismatic with $a = 5.26$, $b = 9.07$, $c = 20.10$ Å, $\beta = 100°$. U.C. 4. Crystals usually short prisms or lamellar. Perfect {001} cleavage. H. 2.5–4. G. 3.0 ca. F. 1.5–2.5. X $\wedge$ $c = 0°$–4°; Y $= b$. $(-)2V = 30°$ ca. $n_X = 1.55$ ca., $n_Y = 1.58$ ca., $n_Z = 1.58$ ca., $n_Z - n_X = 0.03$ ca. Color violet, yellow, gray, brown and pleochroic with X yellowish or reddish, Y and Z brownish gray or brown. Made[47] by fusion of $KAlSiO_4$ with potassium fluosilicate. PD 10.0, 2.62, 3.34; 10–435*.

$Al_4(OH)_8Si_4O_{10}$ has three phases.[47a] The low temperature γ-phase (**kaolinite**) is triclinic pinacoidal with $a = 5.14$, $b = 8.93$, $c = 7.37$ Å, $\alpha = 91°48'$, $\beta = 104°30'$, $\gamma = 90°$. U.C. 2. Crystals pseudo-hexagonal flakes often curved in vermicular groups with twinning as in mica. Perfect {001} cleavage. H. 2.–2.5. G. 2.61. F. 7. Insoluble in acids. Loses water at about 450° C. X makes an angle of 3° with a normal to {001}; $Z = b$. $(-)2V = 20°$–55°, r > v weak. $n_X = 1.561$, $n_Y = 1.565$, $n_Z = 1.566$, $n_Z - n_X = 0.006$. With more H_2O (18.7%) $n_X = 1.526$, $n_Y = ?$, $n_Z = 1.543$, $n_Z - n_X = 0.017$. Colorless or rarely tinted buff. PD 7.15, 3.57, 2.33; 5–0143/4*. Made by heating the constituents[48] in an autoclave at

[45] Barrer and White: *J. Chem. Soc. London*, 1952, p. 1561.
[46] Baur and Becke: *Zeit. anorg. Chem.* LXXII, p. 119 (1911).
[47] Doelter: *Tsch. Min. Pet. Mitt.* X, p. 67 (1888); *N. Jahrb. Min.* II, p. 178 (1888).
[47a] Ross and Kerr: *Am. Min.* XV, p. 34 and 144 (1930).
[48] Van Nieuwenburg and Pieters: *Rec. Trav. Chim. Pays-Bas* XLVIII, p. 27 (1929).

200–260 atmospheres for 288 hours. It has also been made at ordinary temperature while dickite (the β-phase) has been made at 350° and nacrite (the α-phase) is probably stable at still higher temperatures. **Dickite** is monoclinic domatic with $a = 5.15$, $b = 8.95$, $c = 28.68$ Å., $\beta = 96°49'$. U.C. 4. Crystals basal scales with perfect $\{001\}$ cleavage. H. 2.5–3. G. 2.62. F. 7. Loses water at about 550° C. X $\wedge$ $\perp \{001\}$ $= +15°$ to 20° (3° greater for red than for blue); $Z = b$. $(+)2V = 68°–80°$, r < v. $n_X = 1.560$, $n_Y = 1.562$, $n_Z = 1.566$, $n_Z - n_X = 0.006$. Extinction angle in (010) (Y $\wedge$ a = trace of cleavage) distinctly greater in red than in violet light. Colorless. PD 7.15, 3.58, 2.33; 10–446*. Made at 350° C. **Nacrite** is also monoclinic domatic with $a = 5.15$, $b = 8.95$, $c = 28.70$ Å, $\beta = 91°43'$. U.C. 4. Pseudohexagonal by twinning. Perfect $\{001\}$ and good $\{010\}$ and $\{110\}$ cleavages. H. 2.5–3. G. 2.5 ca. F. 7, but exfoliates. Retains part of its water to 600° C. or more. Y $\wedge$ a = 10°–12°; Z = b. $(-)2V = 40°$, r > v. Also $(+)2V = 90°$ ca. r < v. $n_X = 1.557$, $n_Y = 1.562$, $n_Z = 1.563$, $n_Z - n_X = 0.006$. With 0.34 Fe_2O_3: $(-)2V = 80°$, $n_X = 1.560$, $n_Y = 1.563$, $n_Z = 1.566$, $n_Z - n_X = 0.006$. On dehydration n_X is still 1.561 at 350° C., 1.540 at 400° C., 1.509 at 500° C., then suddenly increases to 1.528 at 800° C. PD 7.23, 3.59, 1.49; 7–320*.

$KCa_4FSi_8O_{20} \cdot 8H_2O$ **(Apophyllite)** is ditetragonal dipyramidal with $a = 9.00$, $c = 15.8$ Å. U.C. 2. Na may replace some K and OH some F. Crystals prismatic with perfect $\{001\}$ and poor $\{110\}$ cleavages. H. 4.5–5. G. 2.3–2.4. F. 1.5 with exfoliation. Decomposed to silica by HCl. Uniaxial and positive or, less commonly, negative; sometimes basal sections are divided into sectors some of which are biaxial with axial planes crossed for red and blue light as in brookite; the biaxial condition may be produced by lateral pressure or change of temperature. Strikingly abnormal interference colors and interference figures are due to marked dispersion of the birefringence, which may be zero in any part of the spectrum, the corresponding color then being absent in the interference tints. The abnormal colors may disappear at about 275° C. (due to inversion?). Wenzel[49] found:

	Positive			Isotropic (Na)			Negative		
	n_O	n_E	$n_Z - n_O$	n_O	n_E	$n_E - n_O$	n_O	n_E	$n_O - n_E$
Li	1.532	1.534	0.002	1.5381	1.5384	0.003	1.5415	1.5415	0.0000
Na	1.535	1.537	0.002	1.5418	1.5418	0.0000	1.5433	1.5429	0.0004
Tl	1.538	1.540	0.002	1.5438	1.5438	0.0000	1.5448	1.5439	0.0009

Colorless or stained by impurities. Made by heating the powdered mineral to about 160° C. under pressure[50] in water with CO_2. Biaxial types[51] with

[49] Wenzel: *N. Jahrb. Min. Bl. Bd.* XL, p. 565 (1917).
[50] Doelter: *N. Jahrb. Min. Bl. Bd.* XLI, p. 565 (1917).
[51] Cornu: *Cent. Min.* 1906, p. 79.

OH (in place of F) are positive with $r < v$ and have higher indices than those which have $r > v$. PD 3.94, 2.98, 1.58; 7–170.

$Ca_4(OH)_2Si_6O_{15} \cdot 3H_2O$ **(Gyrolite)** is hexagonal with[52] $a = 9.72$, $c = 132.8$ Å. Crystals lamellar with perfect basal cleavage. H. 3–4. G. 2.34–2.45. F. difficult, with swelling. Soluble in acid. Uniaxial negative with[53] $n_O = 1.545$, $n_E = 1.535$, $n_O - n_E = 0.010$. Again:[54] $n_O = 1.548$, $n_E = 1.536$, $n_O - n_E = 0.012$. Colorless or white. Made by hydrothermal methods. PD 22., 3.12, 11.0; 9–449.

$(Mg,Fe)_3(OH)_2Si_3AlO_{10} \cdot 4H_2O(?)$ **(Vermiculite)** is monclinic with $a = 5.33$, $b = 9.18$, $c = 28.85$ Å, $\beta = 93°15'$. Composition uncertain and variable. Crystals lamellar with much swelling when heated. X is normal to $\{001\}$. $(-)2V = 0°–8°$.[55] $r < v$ weak. $n_X = 1.525$, $n_Y \approx n_Z = 1.545$, $n_Z - n_X = 0.020$ with 4.24 Fe_2O_3 and 0.68 FeO. And with 6.35 Fe_2O_3 and 8.61 FeO (also 1.74 TiO_2) $n_Y > 1.586$. Color brown or green with X colorless, Y and Z pale brown. Mg can be replaced by Ni artificially.[56] With 11.25 NiO a sample had:[57] $(-)2V = 0°–8°$, $r > v$ weak, $n_X = 1.542$, $n_Y \approx n_Z = 1.573$, $n_Z - n_X = 0.031$. Pleochroic with X pale green, Y and Z pale yellowish to brownish green. PD 14.2, 3.52, 1.53; 10–418*.

$KFe_2(Fe,Mg,Al)_5Si_8O_{20} \cdot 4H_2O(?)$ **(Stilpnomelane)** varies notably in composition and the formula is quite uncertain. The Fe may be nearly all ferrous or ferric. It is monoclinic with $a = 5.39$, $b = 9.40$, $c \sin \beta = 12.12$ Å, $\beta = 97°$ ca. U.C. 1. Perfect $\{001\}$ cleavage. H. 1.5. G. 2.6–2.83. X nearly normal to $\{001\}$. $(-)2V$ very small, $n_X = 1.546$, $n_Y \approx n_Z = 1.576$, $n_Z - n_X = 0.030$ and G. 2.59 for a ferrous iron sample and $n_X = 1.625$, $n_Y \approx n_Z = 1.735$, $n_Z - n_X = 0.110$ and G. 2.83 for a ferric iron sample. A sample from Lahn with G. 2.823, $n_X = 1.565$, $n_Y \approx n_Z = 1.623$ and $n_Z - n_X = 0.058$, after oxidizing before the blowpipe had $n = 1.77$ and after base exchange[58] of Tl for K (in Clerici solution) had G. 3.066, $n_X = 1.574$, $n_Y \approx n_Z = 1.651$, $n_Z - n_X = 0.077$; and after this had been heated in the oxidizing flame it had $n = 1.80$. PD 11.9, 4.04, 3.03; 2–0036.

$Al(OH)Si_2O_5 \cdot 2H_2O(?)$ **(Leverrierite)** is one of the formulas in the montmorillonite system; it is monoclinic (or orthorhombic?) with[59] $a = 5.15$, $b = 8.95$, $c = 15$–15.5 Å. It varies much in composition. Crystals thin lamellar or vermicular with perfect basal cleavage. H. 1.5. G. 2.5–2.6. X is

[52] Mackay and Taylor: *Min. Mag.* XXX, p. 80 (1953).

[53] Flint, McMurdie and Wells: *J. Res. Nat. Bur. Stand.* XXI, p. 617 (1938) and XXVI, p. 13 (1941).

[54] Bogue: *Chemistry of Portland Cement*, 1947, p. 396.

[55] Shannon: *Am. J. Sci.* CCXV, p. 20 (1928).

[56] Ross, Shannon and Gonyer: *Econ. Geol.* XXIII, p. 528 (1928).

[57] Ross and Shannon: *Am. Min.* XI, p. 90 (1926).

[58] Holzner: *N. Jahrb. Min. Bl. Bd.* LXVI, A, p. 213 (1933).

[59] Nagelschmidt: *Min. Mag.* XXV, p. 140 (1938).

(nearly) normal to $\{001\}$; $Y = b$. $(-)2V = 0°$–$33°$ (rarely large). Optic properties vary with tenor of MgO and H_2O but much more with tenor of Fe_2O_3. Data follow:[60]

$\dfrac{100Fe'''}{Fe''' + Al} = 1.4$	9.3	42.9	81.9	87.4
$(-)2V$ =	12°–25°	30°		26°
n_X = 1.488	1.543	1.559	1.589	1.585
n_Y =	1.565 –	1.588 –	1.600	1.593
n_Z = 1.513	1.565	1.588	1.610	1.608
$n_Z - n_X$ = 0.025	0.022	0.029	0.021	0.023

Without Fe montmorillonite is colorless, but it is often colored dark olive green to yellow, orange or brown by iron; then pleochroic with X colorless, yellow-green or yellow-brown, Y brown, green or yellow, Z brown, green or yellow. PD 14., 4.41, 2.51; 3–0016*.

$Fe(OH)Si_2O_5 \cdot 2H_2O$ (Nontronite) is monoclinic(?) with $a = 5.23$, $b = 9.11$, $c = 15$–15.5 Å. In nature it often contains some Na and Al. Crystals thin lamellar with perfect basal cleavage. H. 1.5. G. 2.6. X nearly normal to $\{001\}$; $Y = b$. $(-)2V = 40°$ $ca.$[61] $n_X = 1.617$, $n_Y = 1.637$ calc., $n_Z = 1.640$, $n_Z - n_X = 0.023$. Color green, yellow or brown and pleochroic. It forms a complete series with $Al(OH)Si_2O_5 \cdot 2H_2O$ (Leverrierite). With increasing Al the indices and optic angle decrease and for $Al(OH)Si_2O_5 \cdot 2H_2O$ $(-)2V = 10°$ $ca.$ $n_X = 1.485$, $n_Y = 1.509$ calc., $n_Z = 1.510$, $n_Z - n_X = 0.025$. The properties also vary with varying tenor of H_2O; for example, for a sample with about 60 per cent of Fe replaced by Al, n_Y at 15° = 1.585, at 75° = 1.615, at 160° = 1.655, and at 290° = 1.69. Nontronite decomposes at 350° C. The nontronite-leverrierite series is part of the montmorillonite system. PD 15.6, 4.55, 1.82; 2–0004*.

$K_2Ca_3Si_6O_{16}$ has[61a] two phases. The high temperature α-phase is orthorhombic.[10] Crystals prismatic with parallel extinction. Decomposes at 1115° C. $(+)2V$ = large. $n_X = 1.575$, $n_Y = 1.582$ est., $n_Z = 1.590$, $n_Z - n_X = 0.015$. Colorless. The low temperature β-phase is also orthorhombic. Crystals acicular with parallel extinction. Inverts at 960° C. $(-)2V = ?$. $n_X = 1.56$, $n_Y = ?$, $n_Z = 1.57$, $n_Z - n_X = 0.01$. Colorless.

$NaBe(OH)Si_3O_7$ is dimorphous.[61b] One phase **(epididymite)** is orthorhombic with $a = 12.63$, $b = 7.32$, $c = 13.58$ Å. Crystals basal plates. Twinning on $\{001\}$. Perfect $\{001\}$ and $\{100\}$ cleavages. H. 6. G. 2.548.

---

[60] Winchell: *Am. Min.* XXX, p. 510 (1945).
[61] Hamilton and Furtwängler: *Tsch. Min. Pet. Mitt.* II, p. 397 (1951).
[61a] Classification doubtful.
[61b] Ito: *Am. Min.* XXXII, p. 442 (1947).

F. 3. $Y = c$; $Z = a$. $(+)2V = 31°$, r > v. $n_X = 1.5440$, $n_Y = 1.5441$, $n_Z = 1.5464$, $n_Z - n_X = 0.0024$. Colorless. The other phase **(eudidymite)** is monoclinic prismatic with $a = 12.62$, $b = 7.37$, $c = 13.99$ Å, $\beta = 103°43'$. Crystals basal plates with lamellar twinning on {001}. Perfect {001} and poor {110} cleavages. H. 6. G. 2.553. $Y = b$; $Z \wedge c = -58.5°$. $(+)2V = 30°$, r > v distinct. $n_X = 1.545$, $n_Y = 1.546$, $n_Z = 1.551$, $n_Z - n_X = 0.006$. Colorless.

$K_2Ca_2(Si_3O_7)_3$ is monoclinic or triclinic.[61a] Crystals prisms or plates with a small extinction angle. $(-)2V = $ large. $n_X = 1.515$, $n_Y = 1.53$ (est.), $n_Z = 1.535$, $n_Z - n_X = 0.020$. Colorless.

D. INOSILICATES (CHAINS OF TETRAHEDRA):
$A_m(XO_3)_n$ OR $A_m(X_4O_{11})_nZ_q$

$Na_4CaSi_3O_9$ is isometric,[1] Crystals octahedral, etc. Decomposes at 1141° C. Isotropic with $n = 1.571$. Colorless. PD 2.68, 1.89, 1.54; 1–1064.

$K_4CaSi_3O_9$ is isometric(?). Crystals octahedral.[2] Decomposes at 1005° C. Isotropic with $n = 1.572$. Colorless.

$K_4Be_3Si_4O_{12}$ is isometric with[3] G. 2.53 and $n = 1.523$; also weakly birefringent like leucite.

$Li_4K_{10}Si_7O_{21}$ is isometric.[4] M.P. 900° C. Isotropic with[5] $n = 1.540$. Colorless.

Li_2SiO_3 has at least two crystal phases; one is tetragonal[6] with $a = 9.39$, $c = 5.92$ Å. Crystals acicular. Uniaxial positive with $n_O = 1.587$, $n_E = 1.599$, $n_E - n_O = 0.012$. Again:[7] $n_O = 1.591$, $n_E = 1.611$, $n_E - n_O = 0.020$. Colorless. Another phase is pseudo-hexagonal and orthorhombic with[8] $a = 5.43$, $b = 9.41$, $c = 4.66$ Å. Crystals prismatic with poor cleavage parallel with elongation. G. 2.48. M.P. 1202° C. $Y = b$; $Z = c$. $(+)2V = $ small. $n_X \approx n_Y = 1.65$, $n_Z = 1.67$ ca., $n_Z - n_X = 0.02$ ca. Colorless. Made from fusion with LiCl. The glass has G. 2.35 and $n = 1.548$. PD 4.70, 2.72, 1.57; 4–0273.

$Na_{10}Fe_2Si_8O_{24}$ is hexagonal.[9] Crystals are prismatic. M.P. 838° C. Uni-

[1] Wyckoff and Morey: *Am. J. Sci.* CCXII, p. 419 (1926).

[2] Morey, Kracek and Bowen: *J. Soc. Glass Tech.* XIV, p. 149 (1930). Also H. E. Merwin: *pers. comm.* Apr. 2, 1931.

[3] Gaubert: *Bull. Soc. Fr. Min.* L, p. 504 (1927).

[4] Kracek: *J. Am. Chem. Soc.* LXI, p. 2863 (1939).

[5] Vail: *Am. Chem. Soc. Monog.* 116, I (1952).

[6] Barrer and White: *J. Chem. Soc. London*, 1951, p. 1267.

[7] Kracek: *J. Phys. Chem.* XXXIV, p. 2641 (1930). But described as having negative elongation.

[8] Donnay and Donnay: *Am. Min.* XXXVIII, p. 163 (1953).

[9] Bowen and Schairer: *Am. J. Sci.* XVIII, p. 365 (1929).

axial positive with $n_O = 1.609$, $n_E = 1.625$, $n_E - n_O = 0.016$. Colorless. The glass has $n = 1.583$.

ZnSiO₃ is hexagonal or orthorhombic.[10] It forms masses of needles somewhat like mullite. M.P. 1429° C. G. 3.52. $n_X = 1.616$, $n_Z = 1.623$, $n_Z - n_X = 0.007$. Found in some fireclay zinc retorts.[10]

BaSiO₃ is orthorhombic[11] in needles or grains. G. 4.4. M.P. 1604° C. Cleavage normal to Z. $(+)2V = 29°$, $r > v$ strong. $n_X = 1.669$ C, 1.673 D, 1.682 F, $n_Y = 1.670$ C, 1.674 D, 1.684 F, $n_Z = 1.673$ C, 1.678 D, 1.688 F, $n_Z - n_X = 0.005$ D. Colorless. Made from fusion. PD 3.43, 3.36, 3.73; 6–0247.

Ba₂Si₃O₈(?) is orthorhombic and isomorphous with BaSiO₃. It has three pinacoidal cleavages,[11] the best being normal to Z. G. 3.93. $(+)2V = 58°$, $n_X = 1.620$, $n_Y = 1.625$, $n_Z = 1.645$, $n_Z - n_X = 0.025$. Colorless. Made from fusion. PD 3.79, 3.33, 3.28; 6–0206. It forms a series of mix-crystals with BaSiO₃. (See also p. 256.)

Na₂SiO₃ is orthorhombic[12] in needles with prismatic cleavage. M.P. 1086° C. G. 2.61. Z parallel with prisms. $(-)2V = 80°$, $n_X = 1.513$, $n_Y = 1.520$, $n_Z = 1.528$, $n_Z - n_X = 0.015$. Again:[13] $n_X = 1.49$, $n_Y = 1.50$, $n_Z = 1.51$, $n_Z - n_X = 0.02$. Colorless. PD 3.04, 2.40, 2.57; 1–0836.

LiNaSiO₃ is orthorhombic[11] in prisms with prismatic cleavage and positive elongation. M.P. 847° C. $(+)2V = $ large, $n_X = 1.552$, $n_Y = 1.557$, $n_Z = 1.571$, $n_Z - n_X = 0.019$. It forms a complete series of mix-crystals with Na₂SiO₃ whose optic properties are shown in Fig. 10–19.

Na₂Ti₂Si₂O₉ (Lorenzenite) is orthorhombic[15] with $a = 8.66$, $b = 14.42$, $c = 5.18$ Å. Crystals acicular with distinct {010} cleavage. H. 6. G. 3.43. F. easy. $X = b$; $Y = a$. $(-)2V = 38°–40°$, $r > v$ distinct. $n_X = 1.91$, $n_Y = 2.01$, $n_Z = 2.02$, $n_Z - n_X = 0.12$. Brown to black with X and Y pale reddish yellow, Z pale yellow. Synthesized.[15]

K₂SiO₃ is orthorhombic(?). M.P. 960° C. Z parallel cleavage. $(+)2V = 35°$, $r < v$ strong. $n_X = 1.520$, $n_Y = 1.521$, $n_Z = 1.528$, $n_Z - n_X = 0.008$. Colorless. Made from fusion.

Al₄OSi₂Al₂O₁₂ (Mullite) is orthorhombic with[16] $a = 7.49$, $b = 7.63$, $c = 2.87$ Å. It often contains more Al; Fe‴ and Ti may be present; also F and OH. Crystals prismatic with distinct {010} cleavage. G. 3.0. M.P. 1810° C.

---

[10] Rigby: *Thin Section Mineralogy of Ceramic Materials*, 1948, p. 150–151.

[11] Eskola: *Am. J. Sci.* CCIV, p. 331 (1922).

[12] Morey and Bowen: *J. Phys. Chem.* XXVIII, p. 1167 (1924).

[13] Wills: *Encycl. Chem. Tech.* XII, p. 304 (1954).

[14] Kracek (and Merwin): *J. Am. Chem. Soc.* LXI, p. 2157 (1939).

[15] Schurtz: *Am. Min.* XL, p. 335 (1955). Schurtz' *a b c* changed to *a c b* to make $b > a > c$. Ramsayite is probably the same.

[16] Taylor: *Zeit. Krist.* LXVIII, p. 503 (1928).

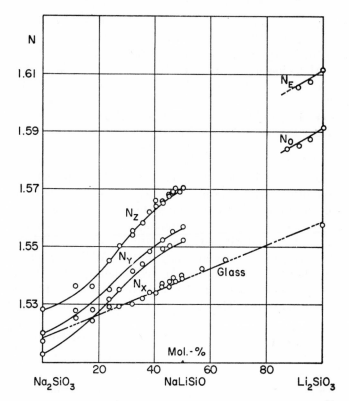

Fig. 10-19. Variations in properties of the series Na_2SiO_3—$NaLaSiO_3$—Li_2SiO_3. Modified after Kracek.[14]

$Y = b$; $Z = c$. Optic properties vary notably with varying tenor of Fe_2O_3 and TiO_2. Data follow:

Fe_2O_3	TiO_2	(+)2V	n_X	n_Y	n_Z	$n_Z - n_X$	Authority
0.0 (art.)	0.0	45°−50°	1.642	1.644	1.654	0.012	Bowen[17]
0.50	0.79	?	1.651	?	1.668	0.017	Bowen[18]
0.86	1.12	?	1.653	?	1.672	0.019	Bowen[18]
?	1.86	?	1.648	?	1.679	0.031	Sawatari[19]

Colorless to pink or red with X and Y colorless, Z rose-pink. A second phase[20] has $X = c$, $n_X = 1.600$, $n_Z = 1.610$. Rare in nature, but very com-

[17] Bowen and Grieg: *J. Am. Ceram. Soc.* VII, p. 238 (1924).
[18] Bowen, Grieg and Zies: *J. Wash. Acad. Sci.* XIV, p. 183 (1924).
[19] Sawatari: *Min. Abst.* VI, p. 70 (1935).
[20] Hugill: *Trans. Brit. Ceram. Soc.* XXXIX, p. 121 (1940) [*Min. Abst.* VIII, p. 95].

mon in porcelain, etc., being the only compound of Al_2O_3 and SiO_2 stable at high temperature. PD 3.38, 2.20, 3.41; 6–0258/9*.

$Na_3Ca_3Si_5O_{17}$ is orthorhombic(?) in rectangular crystals with pinacoids and prisms. Melts incongruently at 1125° C. $(+)2V = $ large.[21] Mean index $n = 1.620$, $n_Z - n_X = 0.002$. Colorless. Made from fusion. PD 3.98, 2.88, 2.73; 10–53.

$Li_2K_{10}Si_7O_{20}$ is orthorhombic(?) M.P. 880° C. $2V = 13°$. $n_X = 1.550$, $n_Y = ?$, $n_Z = 1.555$, $n_Z - n_X = 0.005$. Colorless.

PYROXENE GROUP

The pyroxene group includes compounds very closely related in crystallographic and other physical properties as well as in chemical composition although they crystallize in two crystal systems (orthorhombic and monoclinic). In all of them the common crystal form is the unit prism with angles of about 87° and 93° and with good prismatic cleavage parallel with these faces. Chemically the pyroxenes are metasilicates, ABX_2O_6, where A = Ca, Na, Mn, Mg, Fe; B = Mg, Fe, Mn, Al, and minor amounts of Ti, Cr, V, etc.; X = Si, Al, and probably Ti, Fe''', V. All of these except V are common in natural pyroxenes. The chief pyroxene components are as follows:

Orthorhombic

$MgSiO_3$	⎰Protoenstatite ⎱Enstatite
$(Mg,Fe)SiO_3$	Hypersthene
$(Fe,Mg)SiO_3$	Ferrosilite
$m(Ca,Mg,Fe)_2Si_2O_6 + n(Al,Fe)_4O_6$	Mellonite—Artificial only

Monoclinic

$MgSiO_3$	Clinoenstatite
$(Mg,Fe)SiO_3$	Clinohypersthene
$(Fe,Mg)SiO_3$	Clinoferrosilite
$(Mg,Fe)SiO_3 + nCaSiO_3$	Pigeonite
$CaMgSi_2O_6$	Diopside
$CaFeSi_2O_6$	Hedenbergite
$CaMnSi_2O_6$	Johannsenite
$mCa(Mg,Fe)Si_2O_6 + n(Mg,Fe)_2Si_2O_6$ and pAl_2O_3	Augite
$NaFeSi_2O_6$	Acmite
$NaAlSi_2O_6$	Jadeite
$LiAlSi_2O_6$	Spodumene

[21] Segnit: *Am. J. Sci.* CCLI, p. 586 (1953).
[22] Morey and Bowen: *Trans. Soc. Glass Tech.* IX, p. 226 (1925). (See p. 288.)

MgSiO$_3$ has three crystal phases. One, called protoenstatite, is stable[23] above 990° C.; another, known as enstatite, is stable below 990° C.; a third, called clinoenstatite, is metastable below 985° C. and stable above 1160° C. **Protoenstatite** is orthorhombic with $a = 9.25$, $b = 8.92$, $c = 5.25$ Å. It was made by heating MgSiO$_3$ with LiF at 1100° C. for a week. Crystals are laths with Z parallel to elongation (c). $(+)2V = 70°$ ca. The refractive indices have not been measured but are said to be about the same as those of enstatite. PD 3.16, 1.96, 1.49; 3–0523. **Enstatite** is also orthorhombic with[24] $a = 18.20$, $b = 8.89$, $c = 5.20$ Å. Crystals short prismatic or {100} or {010} tablets. Distinct {110} cleavages at about 88°; {010} or rare {100} parting. H. 5.5. G. 3.1–3.3. Y $= b$; Z $= c$. $(+)2V = 55°$ ca., r $<$ v weak. $n_X = 1.650$, $n_Y = 1.653$, $n_Z = 1.658$, $n_Z - n_X = 0.008$. Colorless. Made from fusion at temperatures below 990° C. PD 3.17, 2.87, 2.49; 7–216. **Clinoenstatite** is monoclinic with $a = 9.12$, $b = 8.86$, $c = 5.24$ Å, $\beta = 92°45'$. Crystals short prismatic or {100} tablets. Good {110} cleavages at about 88°. Common twinning on {100}. Begins to dissociate at 1557° and melts at 1577°. H. 6. G. 3.2. X $= b$; Z $\wedge$ $c = 22°$. $(+)2V = 53°$. $n_X = 1.651$, $n_Y = 1.654$, $n_Z = 1.660$, $n_Z - n_X = 0.009$. Colorless. Made from MgSiO$_3$ with Ca- or Mg-vanadate. PD 2.87, 2.97, 1.60; 3–0696.

MgSiO$_3$ forms a continuous series of mix-crystals (solid solutions) in both its orthorhombic (enstatite) and its monoclinic phase with FeSiO$_3$, to at least 85 per cent of the latter. Orthorhombic MgSiO$_3$ with not over 13% (by some writers the limit is set at 20%) to 50%, hypersthene; with 50% to 87% (or 80%) ferrohypersthene, and with more FeSiO$_3$, ferrosilite or orthoferrosilite. The whole series has been named enstenite.[25] Ferrohypersthene is pale to olive green, or brown. Hypersthene is green to brown, and pleochroic with X brownish red, Y reddish yellow, and Z green or blue. Optic data[26] follow:

---

[23] Atlas: *J. Geol.* LX, p. 125 (1952); also *pers. comm.* June 10th 1955.

[24] a b c with $a > b$ to show the relation between orthorhombic and monoclinic pyroxenes.

[25] Winchell: *Am. J. Sci.* VI, p. 504 (1923.)

[26] Hess: *Am. J. Sci.*, Bowen Vol. (250A), p. 173 (1952), gives equations and/or charts showing values for a, b, c, $n_Z - n_X$, and 2V. Hess's data for 2V fit remarkably well the hyperbola equation, $\sin^2 V_X = 0.158[1 - (x - 0.5)^2/.062]$, from which the values of 2V in the table were calculated. Values of n_X were obtained by difference from Hess's values of n_Z and $n_Z - n_X$, shown in his Fig. 2. Variations of lattice constants and refractive indices are linear within the accuracy of the data according to Hess.

Boundary limits	Enstatite	Hyper-sthene		Ferrohy-persthene	Ferrosilite
	$x = 0.87$		$x = 0.50$	$x = 0.13$	
$x = Mg/(Mg + Fe'' + Fe''')$	1.00	0.75	0.50	0.25	0.00
a	18.228	18.279	18.330	18.382	18.433
b	8.805	8.869	8.932	9.001	9.065
c	5.185	5.203	5.222	5.240	5.258
n_X	1.6569	1.6843	1.7117	1.7390	1.7664
n_Y (calc.)	1.658_5	1.692_0	1.724_5	1.752_4	1.770_6
n_Z	1.6650	1.6959	1.7268	1.7576	1.7885
$n_Z - n_X$	0.0081	0.0116	0.0151	0.0186	0.0221
$2V_Z$	53°	111°	133°	111°	53°
$2V_X$	127°	69°	47°	69°	127°
G	3.215	3.352	3.588	3.775	3.962

Data in the above table are for "Bushveld type"[:6] specimens having an average of about 2.75% (wt.) of $(Fe''',Al)_2O_3$. The optic sign is $(-)$ in the middle three-fourths of the series, but $(+)$ for the last 0.13 at each end. Exsolution lamellae containing clinopyroxene that holds most of the Ca that was probably in solid solution in the enstenite when it formed at high temperature, are fairly common in orthopyroxenes of the Bushveld type, which cooled slowly after crystallizing. The lamellae commonly cause a characteristic bronze-like luster. Materials containing less of the sesquioxide components have lower refractive indices, smaller c, and larger a and b. Many natural specimens have significantly higher tenor of sesquioxides (Al,Fe''') substituting for Mg, and Al for Si (or perhaps OH for O) to maintain valency balance. $2V_X$ seems to be a few degrees larger in specimens from volcanic lavas that presumably cooled quickly, but the cause of this difference has not been determined. PD 3.20, 2.89, 1.49; 2–0520 ("hypersthene").

(Ca,Mg,Fe'', Fe''', Al)$_2$(Si,Al)$_2$O$_6$ (Mellorite) is formed in ceramic materials. It is orthorhombic with perfect prismatic cleavages at 88°. It is probably a pyroxene. $(+)2V = 75°$ ca. (calc.). $n_X = 1.92$, $n_Y = 1.95$ ca., $n_Z = 2.00$, $n_Z - n_X = 0.08$. Strongly pleochroic with sage green to deep reddish brown in longitudinal sections, and pale yellow-brown to deep reddish brown in cross sections.

(Mg$_{1-x}$Fe$_x$)$_2$Si$_2$O$_6$ (Clinoenstenite) is monclinic. It rarely forms macroscopic crystals. Colorless to yellow, brown, green, or black, with increasing Fe. Pleochroism faint to strong, X yellowish green, Y brownish pink, Z greenish; again, X and Y smoky brown, Z pale yellow; again, X pink or flesh colored, Y pale yellowish green, Z pale green. Made from fusion.

Properties of intermediate members of the series may be obtained by linear interpolation between either end and the middle of the series, whose constants were obtained by algebraic extrapolation using many clinopyroxenes as basis, and least squares procedures to obtain the several regression coefficients, and assuming an ordered distribution of Fe and Mg in the lattice.

Lattice Constants—See Fig. 10–20

	Clino-enstatite, x = 0			Clino-hypersthene, x = 0.5			Clino-ferrosilite, x = 1		
Reference	27	27a	27b	27	27a	27b	27	27a	27b
a	9.618		9.618	9.717		9.69	9.84		9.7
$a \sin \beta$		9.03			9.18			9.33	
b	8.826	8.84	8.828	8.994	8.97	8.95	9.118	9.10	9.1
c	5.187		5.186	5.244		5.25	5.257		?
β	108°25′		108°22′	109°03′		>108°33′	107°25′		109° ±

Optical Properties—See Fig. 10–21a, 10–21b

Reference	27c	27		28	27		28	27	
n_X	1.651	1.6484 ± .0031		1.710	1.7079 ± .0043		1.763	1.7677 ± .0045	
n_Y	1.654	1.6503	.0030	1.715	1.7089	.0041	1.763+	1.7691	.0042
n_Z	1.660	1.6605	.0033	1.735	1.7370	.0045	1.794	1.7976	.0046
$n_Z - n_X$	0.009	0.0121	.0045	0.025	0.0291	.0059	0.031	0.0299	.0061
$Z < c$	22	22.4	1.9	40	41.4	1.9	34.5	44.1	2.7
G	3.19	3.209	.044		3.519	.046		3.797	.069

Clinoenstenite containing small amounts of Ca and Al is very common in nature in the minerals known as **pigeonite** (with Mg > Fe) and **ferropigeonite** (with Mg < Fe). Replacement of Mg by Ca in position A of the generalized formula ABC_2O_6 increases the indices, birefringence, extinction angle, and specific gravity and decreases the optic angle 2V. Replacement of Fe by Ca in position A decreases these constants, except that the extinction angle is virtually unaffected. Ca almost certainly cannot fit into position B in pigeonite. Pigeonite, like clinoenstenite, has X = b, as long as the already small optic angle 2V is not reduced to (and beyond)

[27] Winchell: *Am. J. Sci.* CCLVIII, p. 529 (1960); CCLIX, p. 295 (1961).
[27a] Brown: *Am. Min.* XLIV, p. 15 (1960).
[27b] Kuno and Hess: *Am. J. Sci.* CCLI, p. 741 (1953).
[27c] Hess: *Am. Min.* XXXIV, p. 621 (1949).
[28] Bowen: *Am. J. Sci.* (5), XXX, p. 481 (1935).

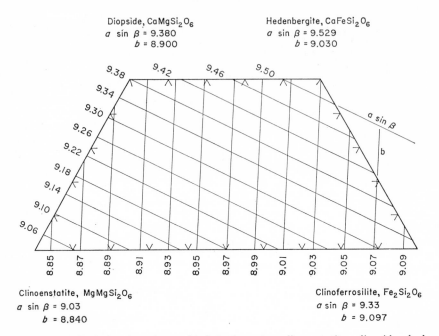

Diopside, CaMgSi$_2$O$_6$
a sin β = 9.380
b = 8.900

Hedenbergite, CaFeSi$_2$O$_6$
a sin β = 9.529
b = 9.030

Clinoenstatite, MgMgSi$_2$O$_6$
a sin β = 9.03
b = 8.840

Clinoferrosilite, Fe$_2$Si$_2$O$_6$
a sin β = 9.33
b = 9.097

Fig. 10-20. Variations in a sin β and in b, in the system clinoenstatite—diopside—hedenbergite—clinoferrosilite, (Ca,Fe,Mg)(Mg,Fe)Si$_2$O$_6$. After Brown, *Am. Mineral.* XLV, p. 15 (1960).

zero by increasing substitution of Ca. Pigeonite with more Ca has Y = b. Z $\wedge$ c = *ca.* 40°, (+)2V = 0 to 30°, $n_X \approx n_Y$ = 1.69–1.71, n_Z = 1.70–1.75. See Figs. 10–21a, 10–21b. Pigeonite has been found in slags.[29]

CaMgSi$_2$O$_6$ (Diopside) is monoclinic[30] with[27] a = 9.750, b = 8.926, c = 5.252 Å., β = 105°55′. U.C. 4. See Fig. 10–20. Crystals short prismatic. Often twinned on {100}. Distinct {110} cleavages; often {100} parting. H. 5–6. G. 3.275. M.P. 1391° C. Y = b; Z $\wedge$ c = 38.5°, greater for red than for blue. (+)2V = 58°, r > v weak. n_X[27] = 1.6658, n_Y = 1.6720, n_Z = 1.6946, $n_Z - n_X$ = 0.0288; colorless. Made from fusion. PD 2.98, 3.23, 2.94; 9–460*. Glass of the same composition has n = 1.6071 D.

CaFeSi$_2$O$_6$ (Hedenbergite) forms a continuous solid solution series with diopside. The properties of the series, as derived from regression studies of many natural specimens, are shown in Fig. 10–21, in which pure hedenbergite is shown with the following properties: n_X = 1.7260 ± .0025, n_Y = 1.7318 ± .0026, n_Z = 1.7551 ± .0027, $n_Z - n_X$ = 0.0291, Z $\wedge$ c = 42.5° ± 1.7°, G = 3.538 ± .041, and a = 9.873, b = 9.049, c = 5.264, β = 104°14′.

[29] Bowen: *J. Wash. Acad. Sci.* XXIII, p. 83 (1933).
[30] Warren and Biscoe: *Zeit. Krist.* LXXX, p. 391 (1931).

Some observed values for $Ca(Mg,Fe)Si_2O_6$ are:

MgO	FeO	(+)2V	n_X	n_Y	n_Z	$n_Z - n_X$	$Z \wedge c$	G.
18.5	0	58°	1.664	1.6715	1.694	0.030	38.5°	3.275
9.61	10.6[31]	59°	1.692	1.699	1.721	0.029	43°18′	3.42
5.70	18.57[32]	60°	1.708	1.714	1.736	0.028	43°	3.41
6.6	18.1[33]	Lge.	1.704	1.714	1.735	0.031		
1.06	22.94[34]	62.5°	1.7225	1.730	1.7505	0.028	47.5°	3.535
	22.9[35]		1.726	1.735	1.752	0.026	48°	

For $(Ca,Fe)FeSi_2O_6$ some observed values are:[36]

CaSiO₃%		FeSiO₃%		n_X	n_Y	n_Z	$n_Z - n_X$
Wt.	Mol.	Wt.	Mol.				
47	50	53	50	1.732	1.740	1.757	0.025
40	43	60	57	1.737	1.745	1.763	0.026
30	33	70	67	1.744	1.753	1.772	0.028
20	22.5	80	77.5	1.751	1.761	1.781	0.030

This series ranges in color from white (pure diopside) through yellow, green and brown to black. Rarely blue. If colored it may be pleochroic with X pale green, Y yellowish green or brown, Z green. Made from fusion. It is stable[36] below 965° C.

For $(Ca,Mg)MgSi_2O_6$ some observed values are:[37]

CaMg	Mg₂	n_X	n_Z	2V	$Z \wedge c$	Y
100	0 Wt.%	1.664	1.694	59° ± 3°	38.5°	∥b
74.5	25.5	1.660	1.684	56° ± 3°	36°	∥b
56	44	1.655	1.675	47° ± 6°	34°	∥b
37	63	1.653	1.671	tiny	30°	∥b
19	81	1.651	1.665	20° ± 6°	26°	⊥b
0	100	1.651	1.660	53° ± 3°	22°	⊥b

For $(Ca,Fe,Mg)(Mg,Fe,Al)(Si,Al)_2O_6$ (augite), with small amounts of Al, optical properties can be estimated from Fig. 10–21 by making corrections for the Al, considered as replacing Mg in the B position and Si in the C position of the general formula ABC_2O_6, as follows:[27] If x_1 atoms of

[31] Eckermann: *Geol. För. Förh. Stockholm* XLIV, p. 203 (1922).

[32] Hess: *Am. Min.* XXXIV, p. 621 (1949).

[33] Schaller: *Am. Min.* XIV, p. 319 (1929).

[34] Wyckoff, Merwin, and Washington: *Am. J. Sci.* X, p. 389 (1925).

[35] Bowen *et al.*: *Am. J. Sci.*, CCXXVI, p. 260 (1933); indices n_X and n_Z in *pers. comm.* Oct. 23, 1934.

[36] Bowen *et. al.*: *Am. J. Sci.* XXVI, p. 193 (1933).

[37] Bowen: *Am. J. Sci.* (4) XXXVIII, p. 207 (1914).

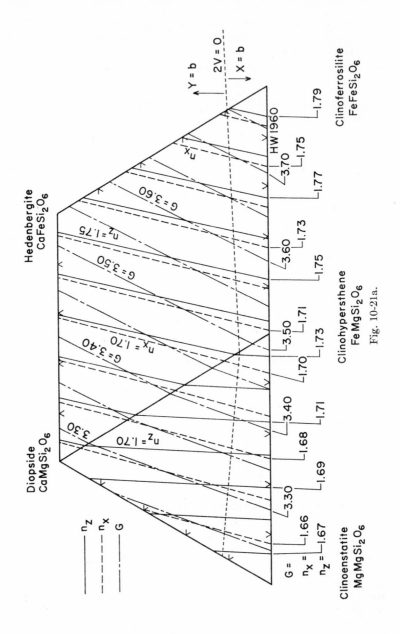

Fig. 10-21a.

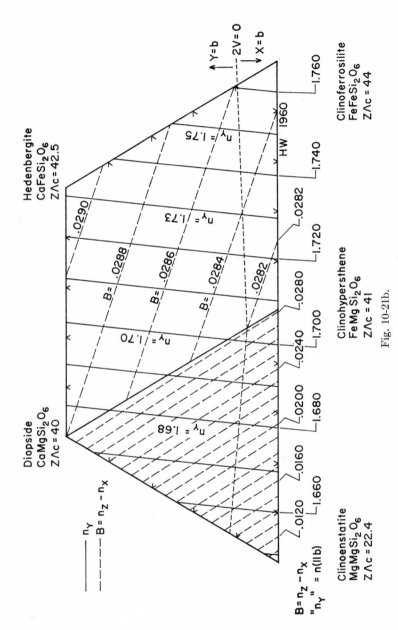

Fig. 10-21a, 10-21b. Variations in optical properties in the system clinoenstatite—diopside—hedenbergite—clinoferro-silite, $(Ca,Fe,Mg)(Mg,Fe)Si_2O_6$.

Fig. 10-21b.

Al (per six oxygens) replace Si, and x_3 atoms of Al replace Mg in position B, x_4 atoms of Fe''' replace Mg in B, and x_5 atoms of Ti replace Mg in B, then we can write,

$$n_X = n'_X + 0.0460x_1 - 0.0341x_3 + 0.0810x_4 + 0.1186x_5$$
$$n_Y = n'_Y + 0.0469x_1 - 0.0567x_3 + 0.0889x_4 + 0.1198x_5$$
$$n_Z = n'_Z + 0.0387x_1 - 0.0714x_3 + 0.0815x_4 + 0.1251x_5$$

where the primed n's are values obtained from Fig. 10–21, assuming that all Al not replacing Si, and all Fe''' and Ti are counted as Mg in reading the chart. With Fe and Ti, the color tends to be darker than without them. For example, X greenish yellow, Y brownish red or violet, Z greenish yellow, reddish, or violet.

Some observed values for analyzed specimens of natural augite are:

FeO	(+)2V	n_X	n_Y	n_Z	$n_Z - n_X$	$Z \wedge c$	G
0.8[38]	59°	1.678	1.685	1.703	0.025	40°	3.18
4.6[39]	59°	1.687	1.694	1.713	0.026	41°	
24.6[40]	49°	1.726	1.732	1.753	0.027	44°	3.48

Artificial $CaMgSi_2O_6$ (Diopside) may take Al_2O_3 or Fe_2O_3 or TiO_2 in crystal solution with results as follows:[41]

$CaMgSi_2O_6$	Al_2O_3	n_X	n_Z	$n_Z - n_X$
100	0	1.664	1.694	0.030
95	5	1.667	1.690	0.023
90	10	1.668	1.693	0.025
$CaMgSi_2O_6$	Fe_2O_3			
98	2	1.670	1.702	0.032
96	4	1.677	1.705	0.028
94	6	1.684	1.710	0.027
92	8	1.691	1.716	0.025
$CaMgSi_2O_6$	TiO_2			
98	2	1.667	1.695	0.028
96	4	1.677	1.704	0.027

Expressed in another way, Al_2O_3, etc., probably enters diopside in the

[38] Ries: *Ann. N. Y. Acad. Sci.* IX, p. 164 (1896).
[39] Wolff: *Bull. Geol. Soc. Am.* XLIX, p. 1619 (1938).
[40] Wager and Deer: *Med. Gronl.* CV, no. 4 (1930).
[41] Segnit: *Min. Mag.* XXX, p. 218 (1953).

form of coupled substitution of Al for Mg and Al for Si, respectively, in octahedral and tetrahedral coordination. With 40 molecular percent[42] of $CaAlSiAlO_6$, $Z \wedge c = 35°$, $(+)2V = 62°$, $n_X = 1.684$, and $n_Z = 1.714$.

CaMnSi₂O₆ (Johannsenite) is monoclinic[43] and isostructural with diopside. Crystals prismatic to fibrous. Good prismatic cleavage. G. 3.6 calc., 3.2–3.5 measured. $Y = b$; $Z \wedge c = 48°$. $(+)2V = 70°$ ca. $n_X = 1.710$, $n_Y = 1.719$, $n_Z = 1.738$, $n_Z - n_X = 0.028$. Color brownish or grayish. Made by inversion of bustamite at about 830° C.

NaFeSi₂O₆ (Acmite or Aegirine) is monoclinic with $a:b:c = 1.099:1:0.601$, $\beta = 106°49'$. Crystals long prismatic, often vertically striated. Distinct prismatic cleavages at 87°. H. 6–6.5. G.[27] 3.584. M.P. 990° C. $Z \wedge c^{27} = 104°$, being 2° less in red than in blue. (The natural mineral, being partly $CaMgSi_2O_6$, etc., has $X \wedge c = $ about 5°–2°.) $Y = b$. $(-)2V = 60°$ calc., r > v. By regressions,[27] $n_X = 1.7710$, $n_Y = 1.8103$, $n_Z = 1.8271$, $n_Z - n_X = 0.0561$. Color brown or green and pleochroic with absorption $X > Y > Z$. PD 2.99, 2.54, 6.5; 3–0621. Made from fusion[9] with NaCl. $NaFeSi_2O_6$ forms a continuous solid solution series with $CaMgSi_2O_6$ whose properties are as follows:

Fe_2O_3	$2V_Z$	n_X	n_Y	n_Z	$n_Z - n_X$	$Z \wedge c$	G.
0[44]	58°	1.664	1.6715	1.694	0.030	38.5°	3.275
?[45]	70°	1.683		1.714	0.031	44°	
?[45]	95°	1.726	1.748calc.	1.766	0.040	71°	
21.73[46]	99°	1.742	1.768	1.787	0.045		3.52
32.0[47]	114°	1.762	1.799	1.814	0.052		
34.6[48]	120°	1.776	1.816	1.836	0.060	$\begin{cases} 98° \text{ (red)} \\ 100° \text{ (blue)} \end{cases}$	3.55

KFeSi₂O₆ (K-Acmite) is monoclinic. Crystals prismatic. $X \wedge c = 0°–2°$; $Y = b$. $(-)2V = ?$, mean index[49] $n > 1.80$, $n_Z - n_X = 0.03$ est. Color yellow-green; pleochroic. Made in a steel bomb. Another phase (KSi_2FeO_6) is Fe-leucite—see p. 227.

NaAlSi₂O₆ (Jadeite) is monoclinic and isostructural with diopside, with which it forms solid solutions. The cell[49a] has $a = 9.45$, $b = 8.57$, $c = 5.25$,

---

[42] Zvetkov: *Mem. Soc. Russe Min.* LXXIV, p. 215 (1945); *Min. Abst.* XI, p. 92 (1950).

[43] Schaller: *Am. Min.* XXIII, p. 575 (1938).

[44] Morey: *Encycl. Chem. Tech.* XII, p. 268–303 (1954).

[45] Ostrovsky: *Bolyankin Jubilee Vol. Acad. Sci. U.S.S.R.* p. 505 (1946). *Min. Abst.* X, p. 464 (1949).

[46] Goranson: *Am. Min.* XII, p. 37 (1927).

[47] Villiers: *Min. Abst.* X, p. 125 (1947).

[48] Washington and Merwin: *Am. Min.* XII, p. 233 (1927).

[49] Rigby: *Thin Section Mineralogy of Ceramic Materials* (1948), p. 148.

[49a] Yoder: *Am. J. Sci.* CCXLVIII, p. 225 (1950).

$\beta = 107°15\frac{1}{2}'$. It also forms solid solutions with acmite, $NaFeSi_2O_6$. Natural jadeite is found only in deep-seated rocks. The thermodynamic calculations[49b] indicate that it can form only under conditions of moderately low temperature and very high pressure. Distinct cleavages at 87°. H. 6–7. G. 3.3–3.5 (by regression[27] 3.27 ± .05). Y = b, Z $\wedge$ c = 98° in red light, 100° in blue (by regression 104° ± 2°). A specimen from Tibet[49c] gave Z $\wedge$ c = 34.5°, (+)2V = 70°. n_X = 1.655 (1.6560 ± .0051 by regression), n_Y = 1.659 (1.6647), n_Z = 1.667 (1.6743 ± .0057), $n_Z - n_X$ = 0.012 (0.0183 ± .0076). PD 2.83, 2.42, 2.92; 9–463*.

μ-$(Ca_{1-x}Sr_x)SiO_3$[49d] is apparently uniaxial positive with n_O = 1.623 ± .002, n_E = 1.630 ± .002 for x = 0.19, and n_O = 1.639, n_E = 1.650 for n = 0.41 (originally given as for crystallization from glasses having 25% and 50% by weight, respectively, of $SrSiO_3$). Formed from glasses at 350° C. to 855° C., under pressures of water vapor from zero to 20,000 pounds per square inch. The phase has also been found in devitrified glasses for which the content (by weight) of $SrSiO_3$ is as low as 2.5%.

$LiAlSi_2O_6$ (Spodumene) is another clinopyroxene, with a = 9.50, b = 8.30, c = 5.24 kX, β = 110°28'. U.C. 4. The glass has n = 1.518 and G. 2.37. Crystals prismatic, often flattened on {100} and vertically striated. Distinct {110} cleavage at 87°. H. 6–7. G. 3.0–3.2. M.P. 1380° C., after inversion at 720° C. Y = b; Z $\wedge$ c = 23°–26°. (+)2V = 58°–66° ca, r < v, with horizontal dispersion. Like other pyroxenes spodumene seems to take Al_2O_3 (and Fe_2O_3) in crystal solution perhaps as $HAlSi_2O_6$ (up to about 20 per cent!).

$LiAlSi_2O_6$%	87.3[50]	81.3[51]	79.1[52]	75.9[52]
n_X	1.661	1.653	1.656	1.648
n_Y	1.666	1.659	1.660	1.655
n_Z	1.676	1.677	1.672	1.662
$n_Z - n_X$	0.015	0.024	0.016	0.014
Z $\wedge$ c	?	25°	23°	24°
G	3.13	3.14	3.097	3.023

Color white, yellowish, greenish, emerald green or lilac; deeply colored varieties are pleochroic with X > Y > Z. The low temperature phase[6] has been made at about 400° C. and the high temperature phase is easily

[49b] Adams: *Am. J. Sci.* CCLI, p. 299 (1953).
[49c] Washington: *Proc. U. S. Nat. Mus.* LX, pt. 14, p. 1 (1922).
[49d] Buckner, Roy, and Roy: *Am. J. Sci.*, CCLVIII, p. 132 (1960).
[50] Quensel: *Geol. För. Förh. Stockholm*, LX, p. 201 (1938).
[51] Grip: *Geol. För. Förh. Stockholm*, LXII, p. 380 (1940).
[52] Schwartz and Leonard: *Am. J. Sci.* CCXI, p. 257 (1926).

made from fusion[53] and also by heating the natural mineral above 720° C. The inversion is not reversible; it is accompanied by a notable increase in volume of about 30 per cent, the density decreasing from about 3.2 to 2.41. M.P. 1423° C. After inversion $LiAlSi_2O_6$ is tetragonal, uniaxial positive with $n_O = 1.519$, $n_E = 1.524$, $n_E - n_O = 0.005$. Again:[54] $n_O = 1.516$, $n_E = 1.522$, $n_E - n_O = 0.006$. With some excess SiO_2: $n_O = 1.516$, $n_E = 1.517$, $n_E - n_O = 0.001$. PD 2.96, 2.83, 2.48; 9–29 (which phase?).

$BaSiO_3 \cdot 6H_2O$ is orthorhombic dipyramidal[55] with $a:b:c = 0.8555:1:0.563$. Crystals prismatic and varied. G. 2.59–2.60. $X = a$;[56] $Y = b$. $(-)2V = 39°40'$, r > v strong. $n_X = 1.542$, $n_Y = $ about 1.548, $n_Z = $ about 1.549, $n_Z - n_X = 0.007$ Na. Colorless. Made from solution.

$CaSiO_3 \cdot 0.5H_2O$ (Riversideite) is[57] orthorhombic(?). Crystals acicular. $(+)2V = $ moderate. $n_X = 1.600$, $n_Y = 1.601$, $n_Z = 1.605$, $n_Z - n_X = 0.005$. Colorless. PD*. (Many "calcium metasilicate hydrates" are listed.)

$CaSiO_3 \cdot H_2O$ (Tobermorite) is orthorhombic[57] with[58] $a = 11.3$, $b = 22.6$, $c = 7.33$ Å. G. 2.44. H. 2.5. Perfect {010} and good {100} cleavages. $X = b$; $Y = c$ (elongation). $(+)2V = $ small, $n_X = 1.570$, $n_Y = 1.571$, $n_Z = 1.575$, $n_Z - n_X = 0.005$. Colorless. PD 10.0, 3.05, 2.93; 6–0020*.

$CaSiO_3 \cdot 2H_2O$ (Plombierite) is orthorhombic[57](?) but usually mainly an uncrystallized gel. Mean refractive index, $n_Y = 1.550$. PD 3.09, 2.81, 1.83; 10–416.

$6CaO \cdot 3SiO_2 \cdot H_2O$ forms platy or prismatic crystals with negative elongation and extinction angle 15°. $(-)2V < 30°$. $n_X = 1.650$, $n_Y = 1.661$, $n_Z = 1.664$. Formed, and stable, at temperatures up to 800° C., and moderate pressures of water vapor. X-ray powder data include lines at d = 2.290, 3.435, 3.067, 2.986, 2.823.[58a]

$9CaO \cdot 6SiO_2 \cdot H_2O$ is difficult to distinguish from rankinite. $n_X = 1.649$, $n_Z = 1.654$. Stable at temperatures up to 800° C., under moderate water vapor pressures. X-ray powder data include stronger lines at d = 2.883, 3.057, 2.673, 2.424, 1.964, 1.833.[58a]

$8CaO \cdot 3SiO_2 \cdot 3H_2O$(?) forms poorly developed crystals with inclined extinction of about 18° and negative elongation. $(+?)2V = $ very small. $n_X = 1.630$, $n_Z = 1.636$. X-ray powder data include stronger lines at d = 1.690, 5.435, 3.043, 4.220, 2.920, 2.716.[58a] It appears to be a calcium analogue of chondrodite.

$K_2SiO_3 \cdot 0.5H_2O$ is orthorhombic(?). M.P. > 660° C. Easily soluble in

[53] Hatch: *Am. Min.* XXVIII, p. 471 (1943).
[54] Roy and Osborn: *J. Am. Chem. Soc.* LXXI, p. 2086 (1949).
[55] a b c changed to b c a to make b > a > c.
[56] Wahl: *Zeit. Krist.* XXXVI, p. 156 (1902).
[57] McConnell: *Min. Mag.* XXX, p. 293 (1954).
[58] a b c changed to a c b to make b > a > c.
[58a] Roy: *Am. Min.,* XLIII, p. 1009 (1958).

water. Z parallel cleavage and elongation. $(+?)2V = $ near $90°$. Mean index[59] $n = 1.50$ (est.), $n_Z - n_X = $ strong. Colorless. Made in a steel bomb.

$K_2SiO_3 \cdot H_2O$ is orthorhombic(?). Crystals equant. Decomposes at $370°$ C. to form $K_2SiO_3 \cdot 0.5H_2O$. $(+)2V = $ small. Mean index $n = 1.50$ est., $n_Z - n_X = $ strong. Colorless. Made in a steel bomb.

$Na_2SiO_3 \cdot 9H_2O$ is orthorhombic with[60] $a:b:c = 0.692:1:0.342$. Crystals equant or $\{100\}$ tablets. No good cleavage. G. 1.646. M.P. $48°$ C. $X = c$; $Y = b$. $(+?)2V = $ near $90°$. $n_X = 1.451$, $n_Y = 1.455+$, $n_Z = 1.460$, $n_Z - n_X = 0.009$. Colorless. Made from solution. PD 2.79, 3.83, 2.92; 1–1007.

$Na_2SiO_3 \cdot 8H_2O$ is monoclinic prismatic[60] with $a:b:c = 0.664:1:0.715$, $\beta = 114°37'$. Crystals prismatic or $\{\bar{1}01\}$ plates. G. 1.67. M.P. $48°$ C. $X \wedge c = 12°$; $Y = b$. $(-)2V = 63°$, $n_X = 1.457+$, $n_Y = 1.463$, $n_Z = 1.465+$, $n_Z - n_X = 0.008\pm$. Dispersion (F − C) for $n_Y = 0.0090+$. Colorless. Made from solution in water.

$Na_2SiO_3 \cdot 6H_2O$ has two phases; crystals grown at room temperature are monoclinic sphenoidal. Crystals triangular $\{100\}$ plates with $\{\bar{1}\bar{1}1\}$, $\{2\bar{1}\bar{1}\}$, etc. They invert at $63°$ and melt at $70°$ C. $X \wedge c = 22°$; $Z = b$. $(+)2V = $ large. $n_X = 1.465$, $n_Y = 1.473$, $n_Z = 1.485$, $n_Z - n_X = 0.020$. Crystals grown at $50°$ C. are monoclinic prismatic with $a:b:c = 1.921:1:1.073$, $\beta = 102°9'$. Crystals short prismatic[5] or tabular. G. 1.807. $Y \wedge c = 20°$; $Z = b$. $n_X = 1.488$, $n_Y = ?$, $n_Z = 1.495$, $n_Z - n_X = 0.007$. Colorless. Made from solution.

$CaSiO_3 \cdot 1.5H_2O$ **(Crestmoreite)** is monoclinic with $\{100\}$(?) cleavage.[61] H. 3. G. 2.6. F. easy. Decomposed by HCl. Z $\wedge$ elongation $= 12°$. $(-)2V = $ large,[62] r $>$ v. $n_X = 1.593$, $n_Y = 1.603$, $n_Z = 1.607$, $n_Z - n_X = 0.014$. Color snow white. Found in boiler deposits. This is said to be an intimate intergrowth of tobermorite and wilkeite.[57]

$Na_2SiO_3 \cdot 5H_2O$ is triclinic pinacoidal with $a:b:c = 0.736:1:0.901$, $\alpha = 128°8'$, $\beta = 98°13'$, $\gamma = 109°50'$. Crystals $\{100\}$ plates with $\{010\}$, $\{001\}$, etc. G. 1.75. M.P. $72°$ C. $(+)2V = 70°$, r $>$ v weak.[57] $n_X = 1.447$, $n_Y = 1.454$, $n_Z = 1.467$, $n_Z - n_X = 0.020$. Colorless. Made from solution. PD 3.33, 3.19, 6.40; 3–0432.

AMPHIBOLE GROUP

The minerals of the amphibole group are orthorhombic or monoclinic inosilicates of magnesium, iron and calcium often with sodium, aluminum

---

[59] Morey: *Am. Chem. Soc. J.* XXXV, p. 215 (1914); XXXIX, p. 1173 (1917).

[60] Baker, Woodward and Pabst: *Am. Min.* XVIII, p. 206 (1933).

[61] E. E. Fairbanks: *pers. comm.* April 20, 1926.

[62] Larsen: *U. S. Geol. Surv. Bull.* 679 (1921) and 848 (1934).

and ferric iron (containing also OH, F or extra O). They usually show vertical elongation and also have good prismatic cleavage at an angle of about 124°. The chief compounds are:

Orthorhombic

$(Mg,Fe)_7(OH)_2Si_8O_{22}$ Anthophyllite

Monoclinic

$(Fe,Mg)_7Si_8O_{22}(OH)_2$	Cummingtonite
$Ca_2(Mg,Fe)_5Si_8O_{22}(OH)_2$	Tremolite ⎤
$Ca_2(Mg,Fe)_3Al_2Si_6Al_2O_{22}(OH)_2$	Tschermakite ⎥
$NaCa_2(Mg,Fe)_5Si_7AlO_{22}(OH)_2$	Edenite ⎬ Hornblende
$NaCa_2(Mg,Fe)_4AlSi_6Al_2O_{22}(OH)_2$	Hastingsite ⎥
$Na_2Mg_3Al_2Si_8O_{22}(OH)_2$	Glaucophane ⎦

Other amphiboles are found in nature, such as $Na_2Fe''_2Fe'''_2(OH)_2Si_8O_{22}$, called riebeckite; these can probably be made artificially.

$Mg_7Si_8O_{22}(OH,F)_2$ has two crystal phases, one being orthorhombic and the other monoclinic. In nature such crystals usually contain little or no fluorine, but artificial products contain little or no hydroxyl, though otherwise they are the same in composition and very similar in properties. The orthorhombic phase, called **anthophyllite**, has $a = 18.52$, $b = 18.04$, $c = 5.27$ Å. Crystals prismatic with $\{110\}$ cleavage at 125°37'. G. 2.9–3.2. H. 5.5–6. F. 4–6. $Y = b$; $Z = c$. $(+)2V =$ large. $n_X = 1.584$, $n_Y = 1.590$, $n_Z = 1.597$, $n_Z - n_X = 0.013$. PD 3.05, 3.24, 8.26; 9–455. With fluorine in place of hydroxyl the indices are about 0.02 less. Orthorhombic $Mg_7Si_8O_{22}(OH)_2$ forms a continuous solid solution series with $Fe_7Si_8O_{22}(OH)_2$ to at least 50 per cent of the latter; with about 20 mol. per cent of the Fe component $n_X = 1.618$, $n_Y = 1.628$, $n_Z = 1.638$, $n_Z - n_X = 0.020$; with about 40 mol. per cent of Fe, $n_X = 1.641$, $n_Y = 1.650$, $n_Z = 1.660$, $n_Z - n_X = 0.019$. Orthorhombic $Mg_7Si_8O_{22}(OH)_2$ also intercrystallizes with $Mg_5Al_2Si_6Al_2O_{22}(OH)_2$ which raises the indices and changes the optic sign to negative.

$(Mg_{1-x}Fe_x)_7Si_8O_{22}(OH,F)_2$ **(kupfferite** for $x < .2$, **cummingtonite** for $.2 < x < .8$, **grunerite** for $x > .8$) is monoclinic with $a = 19.4$–18.8, $b = 17.8$–17.9, $c = 5.25$–5.27, $\beta = 106°$. The naturally occurring hydroxyl series is unknown with $x < .25$. With $x = .40$,[63] $(+)2V = 65°$, $n_X = 1.640$,

---

[63] Bowen and Schairer: *Am. Min.* XX, p. 543 (1935).

$n_Y = 1.647$, $n_Z = 1.665$, $n_Z - n_X = 0.025$, and $Z \wedge c = 20°$. With 77.5 mol. per cent Fe,[63] $2V = 90°$ ca, $n_X = 1.666$, $n_Y = 1.684$, $n_Z = 1.704$, $n_Z - n_X = 0.038$ and $Z \wedge c = 14°$. With 100 mol. per cent Fe,[63] $(-)2V = 86°$, $n_X = 1.686$, $n_Y = 1.709$, $n_Z = 1.729$, $n_Z - n_X = 0.043$ and $Z \wedge c = 10°$. This is called **grunerite**. The Mg component is called **kupfferite**. Color pale to dark brown (darker with increasing Fe) with X colorless or pale yellow, Y pale yellow to brownish, Z brownish yellow to (greenish) brown. The artificial F-cummingtonite series is complete. Its properties may be summarized as follows:

Mol. % Mg	Mol. % Fe	n_X	n_Y	n_Z	$n_Z - n_X$	$Z \wedge c$
100	0	1.583	1.590	1.598	0.015	8°
73	27	1.604	1.613	1.623	0.019	20°
48	52	1.625	1.634	1.645	0.020	23°
25	75	1.647	1.657	1.671	0.024	16°
0	100	1.665	1.676	1.690	0.025	12°

Cummingtonite, like anthophyllite, may contain some Al_2O_3 [as $(Mg,Fe)_5Al_2Si_6Al_2(OH,F)_2$]. It may also contain MnO at least to 14 per cent and ZnO at least to 10 per cent. Colorless (with no Fe), grading to dark brown (with no Mg); pleochroic about the same as the hydroxyl series. Made by fusion with some NaF added as a catalyst. PD 2.75, 3.07, 8.38; 7–382.

A general formula for the hornblende system is $A_{0-1}B_2C_5D_8O_{22}E_2$, where A is Na (or K in part); B is usually Ca or Na, also Mn, and perhaps K; C is Mg, Fe″, Mn, Fe‴, Al, or Ti; D is Si with up to about 25% Al, perhaps also Fe‴, or Ti^{iv}; and E is OH, F, Cl, O or perhaps H_2O. Other elements are commonly present in traces in natural specimens. Many different compositions containing F in position E are easily made; it is also possible to oxidize some of the iron in position C with concomitant change of OH to O by removal of H, and *vice versa*. Numerous special endmembers have received names, of which the most important follow ("chlor-," "fluor-," or "oxy-" prefixed to a name refers to position E):

$Ca_2Mg_5Si_8O_{22}(OH)_2$ = tremolite
$Ca_2Fe_5Si_8O_{22}(OH)_2$ = ferrotremolite
$Ca_2Mg_3Al_2Si_6Al_2O_{22}(OH)_2$ = tschermakite
$Ca_2Fe_3Al_2Si_6Al_2O_{22}(OH)_2$ = ferrotschermakite
$Na_2Mg_3Al_2Si_8O_{22}(OH)_2$ = glaucophane
$Na_2Fe_3Fe_2Si_8O_{22}(OH)_2$ = riebeckite
$NaCa_2Mg_5Si_7AlO_{22}(OH)_2$ = edenite
$NaCa_2Fe_5Si_7AlO_{22}(OH)_2$ = ferroedenite
$NaCa_2Mg_4AlSi_6Al_2O_{22}(OH)_2$ = pargasite
$NaCa_2Fe_4AlSi_6Al_2O_{22}(OH)_2$ = hastingsite

$$NaNa_2Mg_4AlSi_8O_{22}(OH)_2 = \text{Mg-arfvedsonite}$$
$$NaNa_2Fe_4AlSi_8O_{22}(OH)_2 = \text{arfvedsonite}$$
$$\text{etc.}$$

Tremolite is monoclinic with $a = 9.8$, $b = 17.9$, $c = 5.28$, $\beta = 105°12'$. Crystals long prismatic to acicular or fibrous. Perfect {110} cleavage at 124°. Also {010} and {100} or {001} parting. H. 5–6. G. 2.98. Y = b; Z $\wedge$ $c = 18°$ $ca.$ $(-)2V = 88°$, $n_X = 1.599$, $n_Y = 1.613$, $n_Z = 1.625$, $n_Z - n_X = 0.026$. Colorless. Artificial fluor-tremolite[64] has Y = b; Z $\wedge$ $c = 21°$. $(-)2V = 86°30'$. $n_X = 1.581$. $n_Y = 1.593$, $n_Z = 1.602$, $n_Z - n_X = 0.021$. With 9.1 Al_2O_3 Z $\wedge$ $c = 20.5°$, $n_X = 1.573$, $n_Y = ?$, $n_Z = 1.594$, $n_Z - n_X = 0.021$. PD 2.69, 3.10, 8.4; 9–437*. With more than one tenth of the magnesium replaced by iron the mineral is called **actinolite** and has G. 3.0–3.18. $(-)2V = 80°$ $ca.$ Z $\wedge$ $c = 17°–15°$. $n_X = 1.615–1.655$, $n_Y = 1.625–1.665$, $n_Z = 1.64–1.68$, $n_Z - n_X = 0.025$ $ca.$ PD 2.71, 3.11, 8.42; 7–366. Tremolite with no iron is colorless, but it grades into actinolite which is green with X pale yellow, Y yellow-green, Z emerald-green.

Tremolite may also have half its Ca replaced by Na_2; it is then called soda-tremolite or **richterite**. PD 8.55, 2.71, 3.38; 10–456*. Fluor-richterite[64a] made from fusion has $a = 9.823$, $b = 17.957$, $c = 5.268$ Å, $\beta = 104°20'$. PD 3.13, 8.42, 2.80; 10–428*. Crystals acicular with prismatic cleavage. G. 3.035. Y = b; Z $\wedge$ $c = 22°$. $(-)2V = 72°$. $n_X = 1.603$, $n_Y = 1.614$, $n_Z = 1.622$, $n_Z - n_X = 0.019$. Colorless.

Common hornblende varies remarkably in composition including (as endmembers) not only tremolite, tschermakite and hastingsite, but also edenite ($NaCa_2Mg_5Si_7AlO_{22}(OH)_2$) and corresponding ferrous and ferric iron formulas. Heating ferrous hornblende to about 850° C. expels H from OH and oxidizes the iron, changing the properties substantially. This heating also changes the color from green to dark brown.

Since **hornblende** is so variable in composition its properties also vary, but all varieties are monoclinic prismatic with $a:b:c$ about $= 0.55:1:0.29$, $\beta = 106°$. Crystals usually long prismatic to acicular. Perfect {110} cleavage at 124°. Also pinacoidal parting. H. 5–6. G. 3.0–3.5 increasing with iron content. Y = b; Z $\wedge$ $c = 10°–30°$ (unless it is oxidized), being smallest in ferrotremolite and largest in hastingsite. $2V_X$ is about 40° in ferroedenite and hastingsite and about 130° in edenite. The refringence (n_Z) ranges from about 1.63 in tremolite and edenite to about 1.75 in ferrotschermakite. The birefringence varies from about 0.02 to about 0.03. Endmembers have approximately the following properties:[65]

---

[64] Comeforo and Kohn: *Am. Min.* XXXIX, p. 537 (1954).

[64a] Kohn and Comeforo: *Am. Min.* XL, p. 410 (1955).

[65] Winchell: *Am. Min.* XXX, p. 27 (1945).

Endmember	Name	Sign, 2V	n_Z	$n_Z - n_X$	$Z \wedge c$	G
$Ca_2Mg_5Si_8O_{22}(OH)_2$	Tremolite	$-88°$	1.628	0.03	18°	2.98
$NaCa_2Mg_5Si_7AlO_{22}(OH)_2$	Edenite	$+50°$	1.63	0.02	25°	3.06
$NaCa_2Mg_4AlSi_6Al_2O_{22}(OH)_2$	Hastingsite	$+85°$	1.64	0.02	28°	3.15
$Ca_2Mg_3Al_2Si_6Al_2O_{22}(OH)_2$	Tschermakite	$-80°$	1.657	0.02	20°	3.13
$Ca_2Fe_5Si_8O_{22}(OH)_2$	Ferrotremolite	$-75°$	1.735	0.025	12°	3.40
$NaCa_2Fe_5Si_7AlO_{22}(OH)_2$	Ferroedenite	$-20°$	1.73	0.02	15°	3.42
$NaCa_2Fe''_4Fe'''Si_6Al_2O_{22}(OH)_2$	Ferrohastingsite	$-35°$	1.74	0.02	18°	3.45
$Ca_2Fe'''_3Fe'''_2Si_6Al_2O_{22}(OH)_2$	Ferrotschermakite	$-70°$	1.75	0.03	18°	3.42

When any kind of hornblende is heated to about 800° C. the hydrogen may be driven off; this has important effects upon varieties with significant amounts of iron. Barnes[66] has shown that the change is accompanied by oxidation of the iron. After heating a sample of actinolite with about 20 per cent of the iron molecule the extinction angle had changed from 15° to 10°, the optic angle from 73° to 56° and the indices from $n_X = 1.6133$, $n_Y = 1.6313$, $n_Z = 1.6413$, $n_Z - n_X = 0.028$ to $n_X = 1.6301$, $n_Y = 1.6634$, $n_Z = 1.6728$, $n_Z - n_X = 0.0427$; also the color changed from green to brown with X greenish brown, Y deep brown, Z dark brown. Except for the color change these modifications in the Mg_5 to Mg_4Fe series are summarized in relation to composition in Fig. 10–22.

$NaCa_2Mg_5Si_7AlO_{22}F_2$ **(Fluor-edenite)** is monoclinic with[67] $a = 9.85$, $b = 18.00$. $c = 5.28$ Å, $\beta = 104°50'$. Crystals acicular with prismatic cleavage. G. 3.077. $Y = b$; $Z \wedge c = 18°$. $(-)2V = 69°$. $n_X = 1.605$, $n_Y = 1.617$, $n_Z = 1.624$, $n_Z - n_X = 0.019$. Colorless. Made from fusion. PD 3.13, 8.41, 3.27; 10–431.

$NaCa_2Mg_5Si_7Bo_{22}F_2$ **(Fluor-boron-edenite)** is monoclinic with[67] $a = 9.81$, $b = 17.96$, $c = 5.27$ Å, $\beta = 104°27'$. Crystals acicular with prismatic cleavage. G. 3.042. $Y = b$; $Z \wedge c = 12°$. $(-)2V = 75°$. $n_X = 1.588$, $n_Y = 1.598$, $n_Z = 1.605$, $n_Z - n_X = 0.017$. Colorless. Made from fusion. PD 3.12, 8.39, 3.26; 10–427.

$K_2Si_4O_9$ is monoclinic(?). Crystals platy.[68] Twinning common. G. 2.335. M.P. 765° C. after inversion at 592° C. Extinction inclined. $(+)2V =$ rather large. $n_X = 1.477$, $n_Y = 1.479$ (est. from sign and n_X, n_Z), $n_Z = 1.482$, $n_Z - n_X = 0.005$. Colorless. Made from fusion. The glass has G. 2.38 and $n_X = 1.495$.

[66] Barnes: *Am. Min.* XV, p. 393 (1930).
[67] Kohn and Comeforo: *Am. Min.* XL, p. 410 (1955).
[68] Goranson and Kracek: *J. Phys. Chem.* XXXVI, p. 913 (1932).

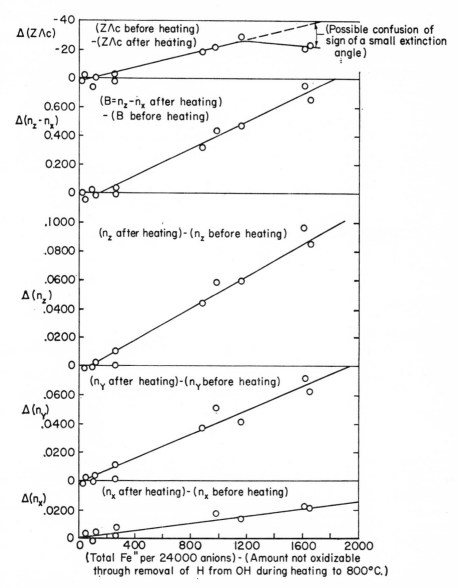

Fig. 10-22. Changes in optical properties associated with oxidation of ferrous to ferric iron by heating amphiboles in air. Data of Barnes (*Amer. Mineral.* XV, p. 393, 1930) on analyzed clinoamphiboles as summarized by Winchell (*Amer. Mineral.* XVI, p. 250, 1931; *ibid.*, XXV, p. 27, 1945).

E. CYCLOSILICATES (RINGS OF TETRAHEDRA):

$$A_m(XO_3)_n, \ A_m(Si_3O_9)_n, \ A_m(Si_4O_{12})_n, \quad \text{OR} \quad A_m(Si_6O_{18})_n$$

BaTiSi$_3$O$_9$ (Benitoite) is hexagonal[1] with a = 6.60, c = 9.71 Å. Crystals pyramidal or tabular with poor $\{10\bar{1}1\}$ cleavage. H. 6–6.5. G. 3.65. F. 3, to transparent glass. Soluble in HF. Uniaxial positive with n_O = 1.757, n_E = 1.804, $n_E - n_O$ = 0.047. Color blue, purple, colorless, varying even in a single crystal. Colored parts are pleochroic with O colorless, E purple, indigo, or greenish blue. Made hydrothermally.[2]

Ca$_2$BaSi$_3$O$_9$ is hexagonal(?) with good prismatic cleavage.[3] Uniaxial negative with n_O = 1.677 C, 1.681 D, 1.685 Tl, 1.690 F, n_E = 1.664 C, 1.668 D, 1.672 Tl, 1.678 F, $n_O - n_E$ = 0.013. Colorless. Made from fusion.

Sr$_3$Si$_3$O$_9$ is hexagonal.[3] Crystals basal plates with fair basal cleavage. M.P. 1580° C. G. 3.65. Uniaxial positive with n_O = 1.596 C, 1.599 D, 1.602 Tl, 1.606 F, n_E = 1.634 C, 1.637 D, 1.641 Tl, 1.646 F, $n_E - n_O$ = 0.038 D. Colorless. Made from fusion. PD 2.92, 2.07 3.57; 6–0415. The glass has G. 3.54 and n = 1.632. Only one crystal phase known, though it forms a series with monoclinic Ca$_3$Si$_3$O$_9$ in which the twinning of the latter is indistinct in mix-crystals containing 37.5, 56.25 and 62.5 Sr$_3$Si$_3$O$_9$ and absent in crystals with more Sr. Data on mix-crystals follow:

Wt. % CaSiO$_3$	100	75	50	25	0
Wt. % SrSiO$_3$	0	25	50	75	100
n_X	1.610 D	1.608	1.606	1.602	1.599
n_Z	1.654 D	1.651	1.646	1.642	1.637
$n_Z - n_X$	0.044	0.043	0.040	0.040	0.038

Na$_2$Ca$_2$Si$_3$O$_9$ forms rectangular crystals[4] with lamellar twinning. M.P. 1284° C. n_X = 1.596, n_Y = ?, n_Z = 1.599, $n_Z - n_X$ = 0.003. Colorless. PD 2.63, 1.86, 3.37; 1–1078. (See also p. 270, footnote 22.)

Be$_3$Al$_2$(Si$_6$O$_{18}$) (Beryl) is hexagonal with a = 9.21, c = 9.17 Å. The formula of beryl is simplified; other elements often present in small amounts include Na, K, Li, Cs, H. Crystals prismatic with poor basal cleavage. H. 7.5–8. G. 2.66–2.85. M.P. about 1420° C. Uniaxial negative, but some crystals have a very small optic angle (2E up to 10°); in such cases the hexagonal form is due to twinning of three or six orthorhombic units as in aragonite. In cross sections the center of such twins may be uniaxial.

---

[1] Payne: *Min. Abst.* VII, p. 518 (1940).
[2] Rase and Roy: *Am. Min.* XL, p. 542 (1955).
[3] Eskola: *Am. J. Sci.* IV, p. 331 (1922).
[4] Rigby: *Thin Section Mineralogy of Ceramic Materials*, 1949, p. 150.

PD 2.87 3.25, 7.98; 9–430. Refringence, birefringence and density vary considerably with the tenor of alkalies which may reach 7 per cent.

Alkalies	Minimum	Maximum
n_O	1.568	1.602
n_E	1.564	1.594
$n_O - n_E$	0.004	0.008
G	2.66	2.85

Artificial beryl glass has $n = 1.526$ and G. 2.385. With 2 per cent[5] of Cr_2O_3 synthetic emerald has $n_O = 1.578$, $n_E = 1.573$ Na. Color green, blue, yellow, white and pink. Green beryl is the gem called emerald. Colorless in thin section; more or less pleochroic in thin section with O < E, or, rarely, O > E.

$NaMg_3Al_6(OH)_4(BO_3)_3Si_6O_{18}$ **(Tourmaline)** is hexagonal (ditrigonal pyramidal) with $a = 15.8$–16.0, $c = 7.1$–7.2. Tourmaline varies greatly in composition and the formula is still uncertain. It is approximately as given above for **dravite**, $NaFe_3Al_6(OH)_4(BO_3)_3Si_6O_{18}$ for **schorlite**, $Na_2Li_3Al_5(OH)_4(BO_3)_3Si_6O_{18}$ for **elbaite**, $NaMn_3Al_6(OH)_4(BO_3)_3Si_6O_{18}$ for **tsilaisite**, and $CaMg_4Al_5(OH)_4(BO_3)_3Si_6O_{18}$ for **uvite**). There is a continuous series from dravite to schorlite (and to uvite) and also from schorlite to elbaite, but none is known from dravite to elbaite. As in other silicates Al_2 may proxy for MgSi to a limited extent. Tourmaline may contain some Cr, Fe''', K, F. Tourmaline crystals are usually prismatic, vertically elongated and striated; some crystals show distinct hemimorphism. Difficult $\{11\bar{2}0\}$ and $\{10\bar{1}1\}$ cleavages. H. 7–7.5. G. 2.9–3.2. Dravite has a fusibility of about 4, and schorlite of about 5.5, but elbaite is infusible. Insoluble even in HF. Uniaxial negative, but (under strain?) may be slightly biaxial, 2E up to 10°. Data follow:

	Dravite		Schorlite		Elbaite		With $Cr_2O_3 =$ 10.86
	Average	Range	Average	Range	Average	Range	
n_O	1.650	1.63 –1.655	1.668	1.64 –1.69	1.646	1.635–1.65	1.687
n_E	1.628	1.61 –1.63	1.639	1.62 –1.66	1.625	1.615–1.63	1.641
$n_O - n_E$	0.022	0.022–0.025	0.029	0.025–0.034	0.021	0.015–0.023	0.046
G		3.03 –3.10		3.12 –3.22		3.01 –3.13	3.12

Color black, brown, less commonly blue, green, red, colorless. A single crystal may vary in color—in zones or at opposite ends of the vertical axis. Pleochroism variable, but the absorption is always O > E. PD 2.58, 4.00,

---

[5] Rogers and Sperisen: *Am. Min.* XXVII, p. 762 (1942).

4.26; 3–0842*. Made by a hydrothermal method[6] with fused tourmaline and solutions of magnesium and alkali borates in a steel bomb at temperatures of 400° to 500° C. The glass of iron tourmaline has G. 2.67 and n = 1.582.

$Mg_2Al_3Si_5AlO_{18}$ **(Cordierite)** has two or more crystal phases. The high temperature α-phase[7] (made by devitrifying glass at about 1200° C.) is isostructural with beryl and has a = 9.782, c = 9.365 Å. Uniaxial negative with n_O = 1.528, n_E = 1.524, $n_O - n_E$ = 0.004. Also anomalously biaxial. It has been named **"α-indialite"** because found in India (near a burning coal seam). The low temperature β-phase is also (probably) hexagonal with a = 9.792, c = 9.349 Å. Uniaxial negative with n_O = 1.541, n_E = 1.537, $n_O - n_E$ = 0.004. This is named **β-indialite.** Both phases of "indialite" may invert to (pseudo-hexagonal) orthorhombic cordierite by slight deformation, and low temperature β-cordierite inverts to α-cordierite at about 800° C. **α-Cordierite** has[8] a = 9.7, b = 17.1, c = 9.3 Å. Crystals prismatic. X = c; Y = a. Optic angle varies through 90° so the sign can be plus or minus. $2V_X$ = 70°–100°, (r < v weak when $2V_X$ < 90°). n_X = 1.53–1.54, n_Y = 1.545 ca. n_Z = 1.54–1.55, $n_Z - n_X$ = 0.01 ca. **β-Cordierite** is also orthorhombic with similar axial lengths. Distinct {010} and poor {100} and {001} cleavages. Twinning in three or six parts is common. H. 7–7.5. G. 2.57–2.66. X = c; Y = a. $2V_X$ = 40°–105°. n_X = 1.52–1.55. n_Y = 1.525–1.526 ca., n_Z = 1.53–1.57, $n_Z - n_X$ = 0.01 ca. These variations in refringence are due chiefly to the fact that Fe may replace Mg in any amount, but this does not explain the variations in optic angle. (With no Fe: n_X = 1.537, n_Z = 1.541, $n_Z - n_X$ = 0.004.) Cordierite is usually light to dark blue but may be greenish, yellow or brown. Color usually absent in thin section, but in thick plates:

X clear yellow, green, brown or reddish
Y dark violet, dark blue, green, dark brown
Z clear blue of various shades, yellow, brown.

When rich in iron: X colorless, Y and Z violet even in thin section. Made hydrothermally. PD 8.58, 3.38, 3.04; 9–472*.

$Fe_2Al_3Si_5AlO_{18}$ **(Fe-Cordierite)** is orthorhombic[9]—see above. Also (−)2V = large. n_X = 1.551, n_Y = 1.564, n_Z = 1.574, $n_Z - n_X$ = 0.023. PD 8.54, 4.06, 3.43; 9–473.

[6] Frondel, Hurlbut and Collette: *Am. Min.* XXXII, p. 680 (1947).

[7] Miyashiro, Iiyama, Yamasaki and Miyashiro: *Am. J. Sci.* CCLIII, p. 185 (1955). This description of the crystallization products of $(Mg, Fe)_2Al_3Si_3AlO_{18}$ (given briefly above) is interesting but needs further study. See also Karkhanavala and Hummel: *J. Am. Ceram. Soc.* XXXVI, p. 389 (1953).

[8] $a\ b\ c$ changed to $b\ a\ c$ to make $b > a > c$.

[9] Schairer and Yagi: *Am. J. Sci.* Bowen Vol. p. 471 (1952).

$Mn_2Al_3Si_5AlO_{18}$ (**Mn-Cordierite**). X parallel length of needles. M.P. 1200° C. $(-)2V =$ small. $n_X = 1.537, n_Y \approx n_Z = 1.558, n_Z - n_X = 0.021$.

$Ca_5Mg_2Si_6O_{19}(?)$ is orthorhombic[10](?) in elongated grains. It dissociates at about 1365° C. It may form mix-crystals with $CaSiO_3$, etc. Elongation parallel to Y. $(+)2V = 80°\pm, n_X = 1.621, n_Y = 1.627, n_Z = 1.635, n_Z - n_X = 0.014$. Colorless. Made from fusion.

$Pb_3Si_3O_9$ (**Alamosite**) is monoclinic[11] with $a:b:c = 1.375:1:0.924, \beta = 95°50'$. Crystals fibrous parallel with b with {010} cleavage. H. 4.5. G. 6.49. M.P. 764° C. Soluble in HNO_3 leaving silica jelly. $Y = b. (-)2V = 65°$, r < v strong with weak inclined dispersion. $n_X = 1.947, n_Y = 1.961, n_Z = 1.968, n_Z - n_X = 0.023$ (meas.). Colorless or white with adamantine luster. PD 3.58, 3.36, 5.82; 3–0344.

$Ca_3Si_3O_9 \cdot H_2O$ (**Xonotlite**) is monoclinic[12] with $a = 8.55, b = 7.34, c = 7.03$ kX, β near 90°. U.C. 2. Crystals long parallel with b, with cleavage, probably {001}. H. 6.5. G. 2.71. F. 2.5. Soluble in HCl. Y (nearly) = $a; Z = b. (+)2V =$ very small. $n_X \approx n_Y = 1.583, n_Z = 1.593, n_Z - n_X = 0.010$. Colorless to pink; color may fade on exposure to light. Found in boiler deposits. PD 3.09, 1.96, 2.83; 3–0568.

$Ca_3Si_3O_9$ has three phases. The high temperature α-phase (called **pseudowollastonite**) is pseudo-orthorhombic and triclinic with $a = 6.90, b = 11.58, c = 19.65$ Å, $\alpha \approx 90°, \beta = 90°48', \gamma \approx 90°$. U.C. 8. Stable between 1200° C. and 1540° C. which is M.P. Crystals are pseudo-hexagonal plates or laths with negative elongation and Z normal to plates. H. 5. G. 2.905. $(+)2V =$ very small,[13] $n_X = 1.610, n_Y = 1.611, n_Z = 1.654, n_Z - n_X = 0.044$. It may show lamellar twinning on {001} with X $\wedge$ $a = 2°$. Colorless. PD 3.20, 2.79, 1.96; 10–486. Found in slags and made from fusion. It inverts at 1125° C. to the β-phase (called **parawollastonite**) which is monoclinic with $a = 15.33, b = 7.28, c = 7.07$ Å, $\beta = 95°25'$. Crystals often {100} or {001} tablets with perfect {100} and good {001} and {$\bar{1}$02} cleavages; also poor {$\bar{1}$01} and {101} cleavage or parting. Twinning on {100}. H. 4.5–5. G. 2.915. PD 2.97, 3.83, 3.52; 10–489. Inverts to the α-phase at 1200° C and melts at 1540° C. Decomposed by HCl. X $\wedge$ $c = 34°$; Y = $b. (-)2V = 35°–40°$, r > v weak with distinct inclined dispersion. $n_X = 1.614, n_Y = 1.629, n_Z = 1.631, n_Z - n_X = 0.017$. Colorless or nearly so. Easily made from the α-phase. The γ- (or β'-) phase[14] (the mineral **wollastonite**) is triclinic with $a = 7.88, b = 7.27, c = 7.03$ Å, α about 90°, $\beta = 95°16', \gamma = 103°22'$. Crystals often {100}

[10] Ferguson and Merwin: *Am. J. Sci.* CXCVIII, p. 81 (1919).

[11] Palache and Merwin: *Zeit. Krist.* XLVI, p. 513 (1909).

[12] Berman: *Am. Min.* XXII, p. 391 (1937). Clark: *Min. Mag.* XXVIII, p. 359 (1948).

[13] Rankin and Wright: *Am. J. Sci.* XXXIX, p. 1 (1915).

[14] Peacock: *Am. J. Sci.* XXX, p. 495 (1935).

or {001} tablets with perfect {100} and good {001} and {$\bar{1}$02} cleavages. H. 4.5–5. G. 2.915. M.P. 1540° C. $X' \wedge c = 31°$. The optic plane makes an angle of 4° with b, the axis of the cleavage zone. $(-)2V = 39°$, r > v. $n_X = 1.620$, $n_Y = 1.632$, $n_Z = 1.634$, $n_Z - n_X = 0.014$. Colorless or nearly so. PD 2.97, 3.83, 3.52; 10–487. The glass has $n = 1.628$ D. Wollastonite can have Fe (and Mn) replacing some Ca. With 8.3 FeO and 1.2 MnO, G. 3.1 and $X' \wedge c = 44°$ in a section normal to the cleavage zone; also $(-)2V = 60°$; $n_X = 1.640$, $n_Y = 1.650$ calc., $n_Z = 1.653$, $n_Z - n_X = 0.013$. With[15] 67 mol. per cent $Fe_3Si_3O_9$: $(-)2V = 85°$; $n_X = 1.716$, $n_Y = 1.725$ ca., $n_Z = 1.734$, $n_Z - n_X = 0.018$. With about 64 per cent:[16] $(-)2V = 72.5°$; $n_X = 1.705$, $n_Y = 1.718$, $n_Z = 1.725$, $n_Z - n_X = 0.020$. Wollastonite is found in slags and made from fusion.

Ca(Fe,Mn,Mg)$_2$Si$_3$O$_9$ **(Vogtite)** is triclinic[17] with $a:b:c = 1.093:1:0.729$, $\alpha = 99°37'$, $\beta = 99°21'$, $\gamma = 83°53'$. Crystals {110} plates with perfect {110} and {1$\bar{1}$0} cleavages. G. 3.39. The optic axes are nearly normal to the cleavages; extinction normal to X is at 5° and normal to Z is at nearly 0°. $(-)2V = 65°30'$. $n_Y = 1.701$, $n_Z - n_X = 0.018$ ($\therefore$ $n_X = 1.685$, $n_Z = 1.703$, calc.—A.N.W.). Color pale yellow, not pleochroic. Forms in acid steel-furnace slags.

CaMn$_4$Si$_5$O$_{15}$ (Rhodonite) is triclinic pinacoidal[18] with $a = 7.77$, $b = 12.45$, $c = 6.74$ kX, $\alpha = 85°10'$, $\beta = 94°4'$, $\gamma = 111°29'$. Crystals often {001} tablets with perfect {100} and {010} and good {001} cleavages. H. 5.5–6. G. 3.75. M.P. about 1200° C. Properties of the pure compound have not been measured but are approximately as follows: $(+)2V = 60°$, r < v weak; $n_X = 1.729$, $n_Y = 1.731$, $n_Z = 1.739$, $n_Z - n_X = 0.010$. PD 2.94, 2.97, 2.76; 5–0614. The glass has $n = 1.700$ and G. 3.48. Natural rhodonite usually contains 4–40 mol. per cent of $(Ca,Fe,Zn,Mg)_3Si_3O_9$. With 17 per cent $Ca_3Si_3O_9$ and 6 per cent $Fe_3Si_3O_9$ X is normal to a plane making angles of 51°40' with {001} and 51°47' with {010}; Z is normal to a plane making angles of 80°55' with {001} and 50°7' with {010}; the extinction on {110} is at 32°26' to {100} and 44°16' to {001}; the extinction on {1$\bar{1}$0} is at 10°48' to {110} and 97°56' to {001}; the extinction on {001} is at 54°27' to {100} and 39°37' to {010}. With 25 per cent $Ca_3Si_3O_9$: $(+)2V = 63°$; $n_Y = 1.708$, $n_Z - n_X = 0.0103$. With 50 per cent $Ca_3Si_3O_9$. $(+)2V = 43°$; $n_Y = 1.678$, $n_Z - n_X = 0.0106$. With about 50 per cent $(Fe,Zn)_3Si_3O_9$: $(+)2V = 45°$; $n_X = 1.742$, $n_Y = 1.745$, $n_Z = 1.759$, $n_Z - n_X = 0.017$. With 50 per cent $Mg_3Si_3O_9$: $(+)2V = 43°$; $n_Y = 1.678$,

[15] Bowen, Schairer and Posnjak: *Am. J. Sci.* XXVI, p. 193 (1933).

[16] Koppen: *Neues Jb. Min. Geol., Mh.*, A, 1948, p. 136 [*Min. Abst.* XI, p. 93].

[17] Hallimond: *Min. Mag.* XVIII, p. 368 (1919).

[18] Perutz: *Min. Mag.* XXIV, p. 573 (1937). (100), (010) and (001) = ($\bar{1}$$\bar{1}$0), (1$\bar{1}$0) and (001) of the old orientation.

$n_Z - n_X = 0.010$ $ca.$ Color pink, red, yellow, gray; alters easily and then brown to black. Colorless in thin section, but in thick plates X clear reddish yellow, Y pinkish red, Z pale reddish yellow.

$Ca_2PbSi_3O_9$ is biaxial with[19] G. 3.99 and $n_X = 1.795$.

$Ca_3Mn_3(Si_3O_9)_2$ **(Bustamite)** is triclinic[19a] with $a = 7.64$, $b = 7.16$, $c = 6.87$ kX, $\alpha = 92°8'$, $\beta = 94°54'$, $\gamma = 101°35'$. Closely related to low temperature $Ca_3Si_3O_9$ but apparently not forming an isomorphous series with it. Perfect {100}, good {110} and {1$\bar{1}$0} and poor {010} cleavages. X nearly normal to {100} in which $Z' \wedge c = 36°$. $(-)2V = 44°$, r < v weak with strong crossed dispersion.[20] $n_X = 1.662$, $n_Y = 1.674$, $n_Z = 1.676$, $n_Z - n_X = 0.014$. PD 2.89, 1.78, 1.67; 3–0693. It may contain Fe and Mg. With[21] Ca:Fe+Mg:Mn = 34:18:48, G. 3.43. $(-)2V = 35°$. $n_X = 1.692$, $n_Y = 1.705$, $n_Z = 1.707$, $n_Z - n_X = 0.015$. Color pink, fading in light. It inverts below 830° C. to $CaMnSi_2O_6$ (johannsenite) which is a pyroxene.

$HNaCa_2Si_3O_9$ **(Pectolite)** is triclinic[22] with $a = 7.91$, $b = 7.08$, $c = 7.05$ Å, $\alpha = 90°24'$, $\beta = 95°14'$, $\gamma = 102°42'$. Crystals long parallel a. Perfect {010} and {001} cleavages. H. 4.5–5. G. 2.74–2.88. F. 2. $X' \wedge c = 10°$ (19°—Palache[23]) nearly in the plane of β. Z nearly normal to {010} and $Z' \wedge b = 13°$. Elongation positive. $(+)2V = 60°$ $ca.$ $n_X = 1.595$,[24] $n_Y = 1.604$, $n_Z = 1.632$, $n_Z - n_X = 0.037$. PD 2.89, 3.08, 1.71; 2–0759. In nature it may contain some Fe, Mg, Mn replacing Ca. For example with[25] 1.50 per cent (Fe,Mn)O it has: $(+)2V = 53°34'$; $n_X = 1.610$, $n_Y = 1.614$, $n_Z = 1.642$, $n_Z - n_X = 0.032$. Colorless or white. Found in boiler deposits.

$HNa(Ca,Mn)_2Si_3O_9$ **(Schizolite)** is triclinic with[26] $a = 8.09$, $b = 7.24$, $c = 7.05$ kX, $\alpha = 90°(11?')$, $\beta = 95°22'$, $\gamma = 101°56'$. Mn may exceed Ca; Fe, Ce, K may be present in the natural mineral. Schizolite is probably a manganoan pectolite, but a series is not yet known. Crystals like those of pectolite. Perfect {100} and {001} cleavages. H. 5–5.5. G. 2.97–3.13. $Y \wedge a = 9°$; Z near b. Elongation ±. $(+)2E = 82°40'$, r < v distinct. $n_X = 1.631$, $n_Y = 1.636$, $n_Z = 1.660$, $n_Z - n_X = 0.029$. Again:[27] $(+)2V =$

[19] *Int. Crit. Tables* I, p. 144 (1926).

[19a] Berman and Gonyer: *Am. Min.* XXII, p. 215 (1937).

[20] Larsen and Shannon: *Am. Min.* VII, p. 95 (1922).

[21] Tilley: *Min. Mag.* XXVII, p. 236 (1946).

[22] Bowen: *J. Wash. Acad. Sci.* XXIII, p. 87 (1933).

[23] Palache: *U. S. Geol. Surv. Prof. Pap.* 180, p. 65 (1935).

[24] Harada: *J. Fac. Sci. Hokkaido Univ. Sapporo,* Ser. 4, II, p. 354 (1934) [*Min. Abst.* VI, p. 92].

[25] Kostyleva: *Min. Abst.* III, p. 111 (1926).

[26] Ito: *Zeit. Krist.* C, p. 437 (1939).

[27] Gerasimovsky: *Trans. Lomonossov Inst. Geochem. Cryst. Min., Acad. Sci. U.S.S.R.,* 1936, No. 7. [*Min. Abst.* VII, p. 209].

$51°$, $n_X = 1.633$ calc., $n_Y = 1.641$, $n_Z = 1.677$, $n_Z - n_X = 0.044$. Color light red, altering to brown.

HCa₂Fe″Fe‴Si₅O₁₅ (Babingtonite) is triclinic[28] with $a = 7.36$, $b = 11.52$, $c = 6.58$ kX, $\alpha = 91°31'$, $\beta = 93°51'$, $\gamma = 104°4'$. Structurally related to rhodonite. Crystals short prisms with perfect $\{001\}$ and poor $\{1\bar{1}0\}$ cleavages. H. 5.5–6. G. 3.36. F. 3 to black magnetic glass. Insoluble in acids. The optic plane is nearly parallel with $\{1\bar{1}0\}$ and nearly normal to $\{001\}$; extinction is at $44°$ on $\{\bar{1}11\}$, at $31°$ on $\{1\bar{1}1\}$ and at about $40°$ on $\{1\bar{1}0\}$. $(+)2V = 76°$, r > v strong. $n_X = 1.720$, $n_Y = 1.731$, $n_Z = 1.753$, $n_Z - n_X = 0.033$ Na. Again: $(+)2V = 60°–65°$, $n_X = 1.713$, $n_Y = 1.726$, $n_Z = 1.746$, $n_Z - n_X = 0.033$. Color greenish or brownish in mass; in thin sections X dark emerald to bluish green, Y pale violet-brown or lilac, Z dark to pale brown or grass green. Formed in Bessemer slags; also a laboratory product.[29]

F. SOROSILICATES (GROUPS OF TETRAHEDRA): $A_m(X_2O_7)_n$

Ca₂MgSi₂O₇ (Åkermanite) is tetragonal scalenohedral with $a = 7.840$, $c = 5.015$ Å. Crystals short prismatic with poor $\{001\}$ cleavage. H. 5–6. G. 2.95. M.P. 1458° C. Uniaxial positive with[1] $n_O = 1.632$, $n_E = 1.639$, $n_E - n_O = 0.007$. Colorless. Made from fusion. PD 2.87, 1.76, 3.09; 4–0681. Ca₂MgSi₂O₇ forms a continuous series of mix-crystals (called **melilite**) with **Ca₂AlSiAlO₇ (gehlenite)**. Data follow:

Wt. per cent					
Ca₂MgSi₂O₇	Ca₂AlSiAlO₇	n_O	n_E	Sign	n of glass
100	0	1.632	1.639	+	1.641
90	10	1.637	1.643	+	
75	25	1.643	1.647	+	
60	40	1.648	1.649	+	
50	50	1.653	1.652	−	1.638
40	60	1.657	1.654	−	
20	80	1.664	1.657	−	
0	100	1.669	1.658	−	1.638

Ca₂MgSi₂O₇ also forms mix-crystals with **Ca₂ZnSi₂O₇ (hardystonite)** and at least a partial series with Ca₂MnSi₂O₇, Ca₂Fe″Si₂O₇ and Ca₂Fe‴SiAlO₇. With 1.70 NiO and 0.21 CoO, uniaxial negative[2] with $n_O = 1.656$, $n_E = 1.652$, $n_O - n_E = 0.004$.

---

[28] Richmond: *Am. Min.* XXII, p. 630 (1937).
[29] Buchrucker: *Zeit. Krist.* XVIII, p. 624 (1891).
[1] Ferguson, Buddington and Merwin: *Am. J. Sci.* CC, p. 131 (1920).
[2] Lapin: *Min. Abst.* X, p. 463 (1949).

$Ca_2FeSi_2O_7$ **(Ferroåkermanite)** is tetragonal. G. 3.23. Poor {001} cleavage. Uniaxial negative with[3] $n_O = 1.690$, $n_E = 1.673$, $n_O - n_E = 0.017$. Stable only below 775° C. 80 per cent $Ca_2FeSi_2O_7$ with 20 per cent $Ca_2MgSi_2O_7$ has $n_O = 1.670$, $n_E = 1.658$, $n_O - n_E = 0.012$. **Justite** is found in slags; it is about 50 per cent $Ca_2FeSi_2O_7$ with about 35 per cent $Ca_2(Zn,Mn)Si_2O_7$; it has $n_O = 1.670$, $n_E = 1.657$, $n_O - n_E = 0.013$.

$Ca_2AlSiAlO_7$ **(Gehlenite)** is tetragonal with $a = 7.69$, $c = 5.10$ Å. Crystals short prismatic with good {001} cleavage. H. 5–6. G. 3.04. M.P. 1590° C. Uniaxial negative with $n_O = 1.669$, $n_E = 1.658$, $n_O - n_E = 0.011$. Colorless. Made from fusion. PD 2.85, 1.75, 3.07; 9–216*. The glass has G. 2.884 and $n = 1.638$. Forms mix-crystals with $Ca_2MgSi_2O_7$ (åkermanite) whose properties are given above. Also with $Ca_2ZnSi_2O_7$ (hardystonite) and $Ca_2FeSi_2O_7$; also a partial series with $NaCaAlSi_2O_7$, $Ca_2MnSi_2O_7$. $Ca_2AlSiAlO_7$ with 30 mol. per cent of $NaCaAlSi_2O_7$ is uniaxial negative with $n_O = 1.644$, $n_E = 1.628$, $n_O - n_E = 0.016$. $Ca_2AlSiAlO_7$ can take up to 15 per cent $Na_2Si_3O_7$ in solid solution and then[4] it is uniaxial negative with $n_O = 1.644$, $n_E = 1.628$, $n_O - n_E = 0.016$. But $Na_2Si_3O_7$ does not intercrystallize with $Ca_2MgSi_2O_7$.

$Ca_2Fe'''SiAlO_7$ **(Ferrigehlenite)** is tetragonal with $a = 7.54$, $c = 4.855$ Å. M.P. 1285° C. Uniaxial negative[5] with $n_O = 1.666$, $n_E = 1.661$, $n_O - n_E = 0.005$.

$Ca_2ZnSi_2O_7$ **(Hardystonite)** is tetragonal scalenohedral with $a = 7.83$, $c = 4.99$ Å. H. 3–4. G. 3.40. Basal cleavage and {100} and {001} parting. Uniaxial negative with[6] $n_O = 1.6718$, $n_E = 1.6624$, $n_O - n_E = 0.0094$. Color white.

$NaCaAlSi_2O_7$ is tetragonal with[7] $a = 8.511$, $c = 4.807$ Å. It decomposes at 1080° C. Uniaxial negative with $n_O = 1.580$, $n_E = 1.575$, $n_O - n_E = 0.005$. Colorless.

$K_2Pb_2Si_2O_7$ forms hexagonal[8] plates with basal cleavage. M.P. 918° C. Uniaxial negative with $n_O = 1.93$, $n_E = 1.72$, $n_O - n_E = 0.21$. PD 2.98, 7.5, 4.08; 3–0625. The glass has $n = 1.775$. It softens at 395° C. Made from fusion.

$NaCaBeSi_2O_6F$ **(Leucophanite)** is orthorhombic[9] and pseudo-tetragonal with $a = 7.38$, $b = 7.38$, $c = 9.96$ kX. Crystals basal tablets with perfect {001} and {010} cleavages. Common twinning on {110} or {001}. H. 4.

[3] Schairer: *Am. Min.* XXIX, p. 90 (1944).

[4] Goldsmith: *J. Geol.* LVI, p. 437 (1948).

[5] Buddington: *Am. J. Sci.* CCIII, p. 35 (1922).

[6] R. B. McCormick: Unpubl. thesis, Univ. Wis. 1936.

[7] Nurse and Midgley: *J. Iron Steel Inst. London*, CLXXIV, p. 121 (1953). [*Min. Abst.* XII, p. 197 (1953)].

[8] Geller and Bunting: *J. Res. Bur. Stand.* XVII, p. 277 (1936).

[9] Zachariasen: *Norsk Geol. Tidsk.* XII, p. 577 (1931).

G. 2.96. X = c; Y = a. $(-)2V = 39°$, r > v. $n_X = 1.571$, $n_Y = 1.595$, $n_Z = 1.598$, $n_Z - n_X = 0.027$. Color white, green or yellow. Colorless in section. Made from fusion of $BeCO_3$, $CaCO_3$, SiO_2 and NaF.

$Na_6Si_2O_7 \cdot 11H_2O$ is orthorhombic with $a:b:c = 0.884:1:1.10$. Crystals prismatic or varied. M.P. 88°. X = a; Y = b. $(+)2V = 65°$. $n_X = 1.504$, $n_Y = 1.510$, $n_Z = 1.524$, $n_Z - n_X = 0.020$. Colorless.

$Na_6Si_2O_7$ is orthorhombic(?).[10] G. 2.96. M.P. 1122° C. $(+)2V = ?$, $n_X = 1.524$, $n_Y = ?$, $n_Z = 1.529$, $n_Z - n_X = 0.005$. Colorless. Made from fusion. The glass has G. 2.6.

$LiK_5Si_2O_7$ is orthorhombic(?). M.P. 830° C. $n_X = 1.515$. $n_Y = ?$, $n_Z = 1.520$, $n_Z - n_X = 0.005$.

$Na_2ZrSi_2O_7$ forms long needles, perhaps monoclinic,[11] with a very small extinction angle. $n_X = 1.688$, $n_Y = ?$, $n_Z = 1.710$, $n_Z - n_X = 0.022$. Colorless.

$Zn_4(OH)_2Si_2O_7 \cdot H_2O$ **(Hemimorphite)** is orthorhombic with[12] $a = 8.38$, $b = 10.70$, $c = 5.11$ kX. Crystals often in sheaflike aggregates. Perfect {110} and poor {101} cleavages. H. 5. G. 3.45. F. 6, glows brightly. Gelatinizes with HCl. Y = a; Z = c. $(+)2V = 46°$, r > v strong. $n_X = 1.614$, $n_Y = 1.617$, $n_Z = 1.636$, $n_Z - n_X = 0.022$. Colorless, white, pale blue or green, gray, brown. PD 3.10, 6.60, 3.29; 5–0555.

$Na_2Ca_2Si_2O_7$ is probably monoclinic.[13] Crystals laths often twinned with inclined extinction. $2V$ = large; all indices near 1.665, $n_Z - n_X = 0.003$. Colorless. PD 2.76, 2.71, 2.61; 10–16.

$Na_2Mg_2Si_2O_7$ is monoclinic[14] with Z $\wedge$ $c = 38°$. $(+)2V$ = large; $n_X = 1.641$, $n_Y = 1.646$ (est.), $n_Z = 1.654$, $n_Z - n_X = 0.013$. Colorless.

$Ca_3Si_2O_7$ **(Rankinite)** is monoclinic.[15] Dissociates to Ca_2SiO_4 at about 1475° C. X $\wedge$ $a = 15°$; Y = b. $(+)2V = 64°$ $ca.$ $n_X = 1.641$, $n_Y = 1.645\pm$, $n_Z = 1.650$, $n_Z - n_X = 0.009$ Na. Colorless. PD 3.14, 2.69, 3.77; 9–327. Made from fusion at about 1450° C.

$Cu_4Si_2O_7F_2$ **(Cuspidine)** is monoclinic[16] with $a:b:c = 0.724:1:1.934$, $\beta = 90°38'$. Crystals small pseudo-rhombic with good {001} cleavage. Lamellar twinning. H. 5–6. G. 2.95 $ca.$ Soluble in HNO_3. Y = b; Z $\wedge$ $c = 6°$. $(+)2V = 63°$, r > v. $n_X = 1.592$, $n_Y = 1.595$, $n_Z = 1.606$, $n_Z - n_X = 0.014$. Colorless or pink. Made from fusion. It forms a complete series with custerite.

[10] Vail: *Am. Chem. Soc. Monog.*, 116 (1952).
[11] D'Ans and Löffer: *Zeit. anorg. Chem.* CXCI, p. 1 (1930).
[12] Ito and West: *Zeit. Krist.* LXXXIII, p. 1 (1932).
[13] Segnit: *Am. J. Sci.* CCLI, p. 586 (1953).
[14] Manuilova: *Trans. Conf. Exp. Min. Petrog. Acad. Sci. U.S.S.R.*, p. 96 (1937). [*Min. Abst.* VII, p. 287 (1939)].
[15] Agrell: *J. Iron Steel Inst. London*, CLII, p. 19P (1945).
[16] Lapin: *C. R. Acad. Sci. U.S.S.R.* XXXI, p. 694 (1941) [*Min. Abst.* IX, p. 11].

$Cu_4(OH)_2Si_2O_7$ **(Custerite)** is monoclinic[17] with $a:b:c = 0.724:1:1.934$, $\beta = 90°38'$. Three directions of cleavage on {001} and {110} make a pseudo-cubic form. Lamellar twinning. H. 5–6. G. 2.95 ca. $X = b$; $Z \wedge c = 6.5°$. $(+)2V = 60°$, r > v; $n_X = 1.586$, $n_Y = 1.589$, $n_Z = 1.598$, $n_Z - n_X = 0.012$. Colorless or greenish gray. It forms a series with cuspidine.

$Ca_3Si_2O_7 \cdot 3H_2O$ **(Afwillite)** is monoclinic sphenoidal with[18] $a = 11.39$, $b = 5.47$, $c = 13.09$ Å, $\beta = 98°26'$. Crystals elongated along b with perfect {001} and poor {100} cleavages. H. 4. G. 2.63. Soluble in HCl. $X \wedge c = -31.2°$ red, $-30°$Na, -29.9 blue; $Y = b$. $(+)2V = 54°40'$, r < v. $n_X = 1.6169$, $n_Y = 1.6204$, $n_Z = 1.6336$, $n_Z - n_X = 0.0167$. Again:[19] $n_X = 1.614$, $n_Y = 1.617$, $n_Z = 1.630$, $n_Z - n_X = 0.016$. Colorless. PD 3.19, 2.84, 2.74; 9–454. Forms at low temperature (up to 160° C.).

G. NESOSILICATES (ISOLATED TETRAHEDRA):
$$A_m(XO_4)_n Z_q$$

Nesosilicates have SiO_4 (or a multiple) in their formulas because the SiO_4 tetrahedra have no oxygen atoms in common.

GARNET GROUP

The garnet group consists of silicates whose formulas may be summarized as $A_3B_2(SiO_4)_3$ in which A may be Ca, Mg, Fe″ or Mn″ and B may be Al, Fe‴, or Cr. Ti may be present in limited amounts and also Mn‴. Finally SiO_4 may be replaced by PO_4 to about 4 per cent P_2O_5 or by $2H_2O$ as in hibschite and artificial $3CaO \cdot Al_2O_3 \cdot 6H_2O$. There are six chief types of garnet of which at least four have been produced artificially; the six are:

Species	Subspecies	Composition	a (Å)
	Pyrope	$Mg_3Al_2(SiO_4)_3$	11.44
Pyralspite	Almandite	$Fe_3Al_2(SiO_4)_3$	11.53
	Spessartite	$Mn_3Al_2(SiO_4)_3$	11.59
	Uvarovite	$Ca_3Cr_2(SiO_4)_3$	12.05
Ugrandite	Grossularite	$Ca_3Al_2(SiO_4)_3$	11.84
	Andradite	$Ca_3Fe_2(SiO_4)_3$	12.04

Garnet crystals found in nature very rarely approach any single formula but are crystal solutions of two or more end-members, but pyralspite intercrystallizes to only a limited extent with ugrandite.

$Mg_3Al_2Si_3O_{12}$ **(Pyrope)** is isometric hexoctahedral with $a = 11.44$ Å. Crystals rare. No cleavage. H. 7–7.5. G. 3.51. F. 4. Isotropic with $n =$

[17] Tilley: *Min. Mag.* XXVIII, p. 90 (1947).
[18] Gottfried: *Zeit. Krist.* LXXXIV, p. 172 (1933).
[19] Heller and Taylor: *J. Chem. Soc. London* 1952, p. 1018 and 2535.

1.705. Color brown, red or black (some Fe is nearly always present). PD 2.58, 1.54, 1.07; 2–1008.

$Fe_3Al_2Si_3O_{12}$ (**Almandite**) is isometric with $a = 11.53$ Å. Crystals often dodecahedral with striated faces. No cleavage. H. 7–7.5. G. 4.32. F. 3. Isotropic with $n = 1.830$. Color brown, red black. Made under water vapor pressure.[1] PD 2.57, 1.54, 2.87; 9–427.

$Mn_3Al_2Si_3O_{12}$ (**Spessartite**) is isometric with $a = 11.59$ Å. Crystals usually dodecahedral. No cleavage. H. 7–7.5. G. 4.18. M.P. 1200° C. Isotropic with $n = 1.80$. Color red. PD 2.60, 1.56, 1.61; 10–354*. Spessartite forms a complete solid solution series with **yttrogarnet,** $Y_3Al_2Al_3O_{12}$ ($3Y_2O_3 \cdot 5Al_2O_3$) which is isometric ($a = 12.01$ Å), in dodecahedral isotropic crystals with $n = 1.823$. PD 2.69, 1.67, 4.89; 8–178. $Y_3Al_2Al_3O_{12}$ inverts at about 1970° C. to a tetragonal (?) phase called **yttroalumite** which melts at about 2110° C. $(-)2V = 0°$, $n_O = 1.942$, $n_E = 1.927$, $n_O - n_E = 0.015$. Yttroalumite also may be biaxial (due to strain?). PD 2.62, 3.70, 1.50; 9–310. $Mn_3Al_2Si_3O_{12}$ glass has $n = 1.655$. $Y_3Al_2Al_3O_{12}$ has G. 3.92 and $n = 1.719$ (by extrapolation). Made at high temperature under high pressure.[2]

$Ca_3Cr_2Si_3O_{12}$ (**Uvarovite**) is isometric with $a = 12.05$ Å. Crystals dodecahedral or varied. No cleavage. H. 7.5. G. 3.78. F. 7. Isotropic with $n = 1.86$. Color green. Made from fusion.[3] PD 2.65, 1.59, 2.97; 7–70.

$Ca_3Al_2Si_3O_{12}$ (**Grossularite**) is isometric with $a = 11.84$ Å. Crystals usually dodecahedral; also trapezohedral. No cleavage. H. 6.5–7. G. 3.53. F. 3. Isotropic with $n = 1.735$. But the isometric condition is stable above about 800° C. and only metastable[4] at lower temperatures so that, while tiny crystals are usually isotropic, larger crystals are often anisotropic retaining their external isometric faces by means of complex twinning. For example a dodecahedral crystal may contain twelve rhombic pyramids in which each has the optic plane parallel with the long diagonal of the rhombic face and the obtuse bisectrix normal to that face, the optic angle being about 50°–90° with r > v, and $n_Z - n_X$ about 0.003. Colorless, yellow, brown, red. PD 2.65, 1.58, 2.96; 3–0826. Made under pressure at high temperature. $Ca_3Al_2Si_3O_{12}$ forms a continuous series of mix-crystals with $Ca_3Fe_2Si_3O_{12}$ and probably also with $Ca_3Cr_2Si_3O_{12}$, the densities and refractive indices varying continuously as follows:

	$Ca_3Fe_2Si_3O_{12}$		$Ca_3Al_2Si_3O_{12}$		$Ca_3Cr_2Si_3O_{12}$
G.	3.83	↔	3.53	↔	3.78
n	1.895	↔	1.735	↔	1.86

[1] Yoder: *Am. Min.* XL, p. 342 (1955).

[2] Yoder and Keith: *Am. Min.* XXXVI, p. 519 (1951).

[3] Hummel: *Am. Min.* XXXV, p. 324 (1950).

[4] Merwin in Wright: *U. S. Geol. Surv. Prof. Pap.* 87, p. 108 (1915).

$Ca_3Al_2Si_3O_{12}$ also forms mix-crystals in all proportions with $Ca_3Al_2O_6 \cdot 6H_2O$[5] ($Ca_3Al_2(H_4O_4)_3$ or $Ca_3Al_2(H_2)_3O_6(OH)_6$). This compound is isometric and isotropic[6] with G. 2.52 and $n = 1.605$. $Ca_3Al_2Si_3O_{12}$ with $Ca_3Al_2O_6 \cdot 6H_2O$ in the ratio about 2:1 has H. 6.5, G. 3.13 and $n = 1.67$–1.68; also may be weakly birefringent; it has been named **hibschite**.

$Ca_3Fe_2Si_3O_{12}$ (Andradite) is isometric with $a = 12.04$ Å. Crystals usually dodecahedral. No cleavage. H. 6.5–7. G. 3.83. Isotropic with $n = 1.895$. But, like $Ca_3Al_2Si_3O_{12}$, the isometric condition is stable above about 800° C. and only metastable at lower temperatures.[4] So twinning is common with weak birefringence and a large optic angle. See $Ca_3Al_2Si_3O_{12}$. Color brown to red or even black. PD 2.70, 3.02, 1.61; 10–288. Made under pressure at high temperature. Forms a continuous series of mix-crystals with $Ca_3Al_2Si_3O_{12}$—see the latter. Also forms similar series with $Ca_3Fe_2O_6 \cdot 6H_2O$[5] ($Ca_3Fe_2(H_4O_4)_3$ or $Ca_3Fe_2(H_2)_3O_6(OH)_6$). This compound is isometric and isotropic[6] with $n = 1.710$.

Na_2CaSiO_4 is isometric[7] with $a = 7.493$ kX. G. 2.79. F. high. Isotropic with $n \approx 1.60$. Colorless. PD 2.66, 1.53, 1.87; 2–0951. Made from fusion.
Na_2MgSiO_4 is isometric[8] and isotropic with $n = 1.523$.
K_2ZnSiO_4 is isometric[9] and isotropic with $n = 1.622$.
$ZrSiO_4$ (Zircon) is tetragonal with[10] $a = 6.60$, $c = 5.88$ kX. Crystals often prismatic with pyramids. Poor {110} cleavage. G. 4.66–4.7. H. 7.5. F. 7. It may contain some Fe_2O_3, ThO_2, Y_2O_3, HfO_2, U_2O_3, H_2O, etc., which cause variations in refractive indices. PD 3.30, 4.43, 2.52; 6–0266. Also crystals gradually alter to an amorphous state (called *metamict*) apparently due to the effects of radioactivity of U and Th in them. As this alteration progresses the properties change as follows:

	Normal Zircon	Partly altered Zircon (Hyacinth)	Much altered Zircon (Malacon)
n_O	1.92–1.96	1.90–1.92	1.76–1.90
n_E	1.96–2.02	1.92–1.96	1.76–1.92
$n_E - n_O$	0.04–0.06	0.02–0.04	0.00–0.02
G.	4.6–4.71	4.2–4.6	3.9–4.2
H.	7.5	7 *ca.*	6–7

[5] Included here, although hydrous, because of its close relation to garnet.
[6] Flint, McMurdie and Wells: *J. Res. Nat. Bur. Stand.* XXVI, p. 13 (1941).
[7] Wyckoff and Morey: *Am. J. Sci.* XII, p. 419 (1926).
[8] Manuilova: *Trans. 2nd Conf. Exp. Min. Acad. Sci. U.S.S.R.*, 1937, p. 87. [*Min. Abst.* VII, p. 287 (1939)].
[9] Ingerson, Morey and Tuttle: *Am. J. Sci.* CCXLVI, p. 31 (1948).
[10] Wyckoff and Hendricks: *Zeit. Krist.* LXVI, p. 73 (1927).

Color yellow, brown, gray, rarely green or colorless. In thin section colorless to pale brown or gray. Made by heating[11] $SiO_2 + ZrO_2$ to about 2600°–2800° C.

$Na_4Zr_2(SiO_4)_3$ is hexagonal[12] with rhombohedral habit. G. 2.88. M.P. 1540° C. Uniaxial negative with $n_O = 1.715$ D, $n_E = 1.692$, $n_O - n_E = 0.023$. Colorless. Made from fusion.

Be_2SiO_4 **(Phenacite)** is hexagonal[13] with $a = 12.40$, $c = 8.24$ Å. Crystals rhombohedral or prismatic; twinning common on $\{10\bar{1}0\}$. Distinct $\{11\bar{2}0\}$ cleavage. H. 7.5. G. 2.98. M.P. 1560° C. Uniaxial positive with $n_O = 1.654$, $n_E = 1.670$, $n_E - n_O = 0.016$. Colorless, yellow, rose or brown; colorless in thin section. PD 3.12, 3.66, 2.52; 9–431.

Zn_2SiO_4 **(Willemite)** is hexagonal with $a = 12.49$, $c = 8.26$ Å. Space group $R\bar{3}$. Crystals hexagonal prisms with $\{0001\}$ and $\{11\bar{2}0\}$ cleavages. H. 5.5. G. 3.9–4.2. M.P. 1510° C. Uniaxial positive with[14] $n_O = 1.695$ $n_E = 1.715$, $n_E - n_O = 0.020$ Na. With some TiO_2: $n_O = 1.701$, $n_E = 1.724$, $n_E - n_O = 0.023$. In lead slags crystals may contain up to 36 per cent Fe_2SiO_4; with also[15] 7 per cent Mg_2SiO_4: $n_O = 1.701$, $n_E = 1.726$, $n_E - n_O = 0.025$ Na; this variety is pleochroic with O reddish violet, E bluish violet. Green fluorescence is common. PD 2.63, 2.83, 3.49; 8–492. Another phase[16] (β-Zn_2SiO_4) has $(-)2V = 49°$, mean index $n = 1.700$, $n_Z - n_X = 0.009$. Yellow fluorescence. A third phase (γ-Zn_2SiO_4) has $(-)2V = 40°$, $n_X = 1.685$, $n_Y = 1.700$, $n_Z = 1.703$, $n_Z - n_X = 0.018$. Red fluorescence.

Zn_2GeO_4 is hexagonal[16] (forming a complete series ot mix-crystals with Zn_2SiO_4). It melts at 1490° C. and has G. 4.82. It is uniaxial positive with $n_O = 1.769$, $n_E = 1.802$, $n_E - n_O = 0.033$. PD 2.90, 2.70, 1.87; 3–0689.

K_2CaSiO_4 is hexagonal.[17] M.P. 1630° C. Crystals hexagonal bipyramids. Uniaxial positive with $n_O = 1.600$, $n_E = 1.605$, $n_E - n_O = 0.005$. Colorless.

$K_2Ca_{23}Si_{12}O_{48}$ is probably hexagonal. Complex twinning common. Uniaxial positive with[18] $n_O = 1.695$, $n_E = 1.703$, $n_E - n_O = 0.008$. Colorless. With some iron in solid solution: $n_O = 1.713$, $n_E = 1.722$, $n_E - n_O = 0.009$. This may be α-Ca_2SiO_4 with some K_4SiO_4 in crystal solution.

Ca_2SiO_4 has four crystal phases.[19] The high temperature α-phase is stable below (and near) the melting point (2130° C.). On cooling it inverts to

[11] Curtis and Sowman: *J. Am. Ceram. Soc.* XXXVI, p. 190 (1953).
[12] D'Ans and Löffler: *Zeit. anorg. Chem.* CXCI, p. 1 (1930).
[13] Morgan and Hummel: *J. Am. Ceram. Soc.* XXXII, p. 250 (1949).
[14] Klein and Brown: *Trans. Am. Ceram. Soc.* XVII, p. 745 (1915).
[15] Faber: *Chem. Erde* X, p. 67 (1935).
[16] Ingerson, Morey and Tuttle: *Am. J. Sci.* CCXLVI, p. 31 (1948).
[17] Rigby: *Thin Section Mineralogy of Ceramic Materials*, 1948, p. 145, 150.
[18] Taylor: *J. Res. Nat. Bur. Stand.* XXVII, p. 311 (1941).
[19] Bredig: *Am. Min.* XXVIII, p. 594 (1943).

α'-Ca_2SiO_4 (bredigite) and that inverts to β-Ca_2SiO_4 (larnite) at 1420° C. which inverts to γ-Ca_2SiO_4 (shannonite) at 675° C.

α-Ca_2SiO_4 is hexagonal with[20] $a = 5.44$ and $c = 7.02\ kX$. The pure compound inverts at high temperature to α'-Ca_2SiO_4, but with other compounds in solid solution it is metastable; for example, with 13.58 Mg_2SiO_4 and 5.62 Fe_2SiO_4 it is uniaxial positive with $n_O = 1.724$, $n_E = 1.738$, $n_E - n_O = 0.014$. The pure compound has a mean index, n, below 1.707 and weak birefringence. Colorless. Made from fusion, but inverts if pure.

α'-Ca_2SiO_4 (Bredigite) is orthorhombic[21] with $a = 11.08$, $b = 18.55$, $c = 6.76\ kX$. Common pseudo-hexagonal twinning. Distinct $\{110\}$ cleavage. The pure compound melts at 2130° C.; on cooling it promptly inverts to larnite at 1420° C. and then to shannonite at 675° C., but with some Mg, Ba, Mn, Na or K (one or more) in crystal solution it is metastable and with 6.8 MgO, 6.9 BaO and 3.4 MnO it has X = b, Y = a, $(+)2V = 30° \pm 10°$, $n_X = 1.712$, $n_Y = 1.716$, $n_Z = 1.725$, $n_Z - n_X = 0.013$. PD 2.75, 1.96, 2.19; 7–348*. A colored variety has X violet, Y and Z colorless to pale green and $(+)2V = 33°$, $n_X = 1.725$, $n_Y = 1.728$, $n_Z = 1.740$, $n_Z - n_X = 0.015$. Indices vary with variations in composition at least as much as $n_X = 1.712$–1.725, $n_Y = 1.716$–1.728, $n_Z = 1.725$–1.740. The mineral, bredigite, is not found as pure Ca_2SiO_4, but always contains other elements. Found in slags.

β-Ca_2SiO_4 (Larnite) is monoclinic[20] with $a = 5.48$, $b = 6.76$, $c = 9.28\ kX$, $\beta = 94°50'$. Stable between 1420° and 675° C.; metastable below 675° C. Crystals have distinct $\{100\}$ cleavage and common lamellar twinning on $\{100\}$. X $\wedge$ $c = 13°$–14°; Z = b. $(+)2V$ = moderate, $n_X = 1.707$, $n_Y = 1.715$, $n_Z = 1.730$, $n_Z - n_X = 0.023$. Colorless. Made from fusion. PD 2.80, 2.74, 2.78; 9–351*.

γ-Ca_2SiO_4 (Shannonite[22]) is orthorhombic[20] with $a = 6.78$, $b = 5.06$, $c = 11.28\ kX$. Crystals have prismatic cleavage. G. 2.97. Y parallel prisms. $(+)2V = 52°$, $n_X = 1.642 \pm 0.002$, $n_Y = 1.645 \pm 0.002$, $n_Z = 1.654 \pm 0.002$, $n_Z - n_X = 0.015$. Colorless. PD 2.73, 1.91, 3.01; 9–369*. Also described[23] as probably monoclinic with a small extinction angle on fine twinning and $(-)2E = 52°$. It can take about 10 per cent of Fe_2SiO_4 into solid solution and then[24] $n_X = 1.653$, $n_Z = 1.677$, $n_Z - n_X = 0.024$. With

[20] Saalfeld: *Fort. Min.* XXXII, p. 35 (1954).

[21] Tilley and Vincent: *Min. Mag.* XXVIII, p. 255 (1948).

[22] The name "shannonite" from a locality in Tasmania where it apparently does not exist, is nevertheless convenient; Tilley, *Geol. Mag.* LXIV, p. 143 (1928) and LXV, p. 129 (1929). Paul, *Tsch. Min. Pet. Mitt.* originally described γ-Ca_2SiO_4, but rather inaccurately.

[23] Rankin and Wright: *Am. J. Sci.* XXXIX, p. 1 (1915).

[24] Mason: *J. Iron Steel Inst. London* CL, p. 69P (1944). [*Min. Abst.* X, p. 265 (1945)].

some Fe_2SiO_4, Mn_2SiO_4 and Mg_2SiO_4 in solid solution the indices may reach[25] $n_X = 1.66$, $n_Y = 1.68$, $n_Z = 1.69$.

Ca_2SiO_4 forms a complete solid solution series[26] with Ba_2SiO_4, the properties increasing regularly from G. 3.28, $n_X = 1.717$, $n_Z = 1.735$ for Ca_2SiO_4 to G. 5.2, $n_X = 1.810$, $n_Z = 1.830$ for Ba_2SiO_4. It forms a similar series with[27] Sr_2SiO_4. The data for Sr_2SiO_4 are: G. 3.84, $n_X = 1.727$, $n_Z = 1.756$. Ca_2SiO_4 can take some Na_4SiO_4 in solid solution. With[28] 2.7 Na_2O, $n_X = 1.698$, $n_Z = 1.713$.

Ba_2SiO_4 is orthorhombic(?); granular without cleavage or twinning;[29] melting point about that of Pt. $n_X = 1.810$, $n_Z = 1.830$, $n_Z - n_X = 0.02$. Colorless. Made from fusion. PD 3.03, 2.95, 2.91; 6–0366.

OLIVINE GROUP

The compounds of the olivine group are orthosilicates of divalent bases crystallizing in the orthorhombic system. There is a continuous series from Mg_2SiO_4 to Fe_2SiO_4 and from Fe_2SiO_4 to Mn_2SiO_4 and perhaps from Mg_2SiO_4 to Mn_2SiO_4. As in the carbonates there is a double salt between each of these three and Ca_2SiO_4 and no series to that compound. The chief types are the following:

Species	Subspecies	Formula
Olivine	Forsterite	Mg_2SiO_4
	Chrysolite, etc.	$(Mg,Fe)_2SiO_4$
	Fayalite	Fe_2SiO_4
	Knebelite	$(Fe,Mn)_2SiO_4$
	Tephroite	Mn_2SiO_4
	Picrotephroite	$(Mn,Mg)_2SiO_4$
?	Artificial	$CaFeSiO_4$
	Monticellite	$CaMgSiO_4$
	Glaucochroite	$CaMnSiO_4$

It is probable that $CaFeSiO_4$, $CaMgSiO_4$ and $CaMnSiO_4$ are miscible in crystals in all proportions, like the three types of dolomite.

Mg_2SiO_4 (Forsterite) is orthorhombic with $a = 4.77$, $b = 10.26$, $c = 5.99$ Å. Crystals usually somewhat elongated parallel to c; rarely parallel to a; commonly with good development of $\{110\}$, $\{010\}$, $\{021\}$, etc. Twin-

[25] Bowen, Schairer, and Posnjak: *Am. J. Sci.* XXV, p. 273 (1933).

[26] Toropov and Konovalov: *C. R. Acad. Sci. U.S.S.R.* XX, p. 663 (1938) [*Min. Abst.* X, p. 265].

[27] Toropov and Konovalov: *C. R. Acad. Sci. U.S.S.R.* XL, p. 155 (1943) [*Min. Abst.* IX, p. 134].

[28] Segnit: *Am. J. Sci.* CCLI, p. 586 (1953).

[29] Eskola: *Am. J. Sci.* CCIV, p. 331 (1922).

ning rare. Distinct {010} and poor {100} cleavages. H. 6.5–7. G. 3.2. M.P. 1890° C. $X = b$; $Y = c$. $(+)2V = 81°$, $n_X = 1.635$, $n_Y = 1.651$, $n_Z = 1.670$, $n_Z - n_X = 0.035$. Colorless. Made from fusion. With 20 mol. per cent[30] Fe_2SiO_4: $(-)2V = 87°$, $n_X = 1.674$, $n_Y = 1.692$, $n_Z = 1.712$, $n_Z - n_X = 0.038$. With 40 per cent Fe_2SiO_4: $(-)2V = 78°$, $n_X = 1.712$, $n_Y = 1.735$, $n_Z = 1.753$, $n_Z - n_X = 0.041$. Mg_2SiO_4 and $LiAlSiO_4$ are miscible[30a] in limited amounts, Mg_2SiO_4 experimentally to about 25 per cent in $LiAlSiO_4$ and $LiAlSiO_4$ to about 40 per cent in Mg_2SiO_4. The refractive indices in the series $(Mg_{1-x}Fe_x)_2 SiO_4$ are accurately predictable by linear interpolation between the end-members.

Fe_2SiO_4 (Fayalite) is orthorhombic with $a = 4.80$, $b = 10.59$, $c = 6.16$ Å. Crystals like those of Mg_2SiO_4. Distinct {010} and poor {100} cleavages. G. 4.4. M.P. 1205° C. $X = b$; $Y = c$. $(-)2V = 47°$, $n_X = 1.824$, $n_Y = 1.864$, $n_Z = 1.875$, $n_Z - n_X = 0.051$. Color olive green; easily alters to reddish brown or black. PD 2.49, 2.82, 3.54; 9–307*. Made from fusion. With 20 mol. per cent[30] Mg_2SiO_4: $(-)2V = 58°$, $n_X = 1.786$, $n_Y = 1.822$, $n_Z = 1.833$, $n_Z - n_X = 0.047$. With 40 per cent Mg_2SiO_4: $(-)2V = 69°$, $n_X = 1.748$, $n_Y = 1.778$, $n_Z = 1.792$, $n_Z - n_X = 0.044$. With 22 per cent Ca_2SiO_4: $n_X = 1.772$, $n_Z = 1.823$. An impure sample from slag has $(-)2V = 53°$, $n_X = 1.817$, $n_Y = 1.84$, $n_Z = 1.863$, $n_Z - n_X = 0.046$.

Mn_2SiO_4 (Tephroite) is orthorhombic with $a = 4.86$, $b = 10.62$, $c = 6.22$ Å. Crystals like those of Mg_2SiO_4. Distinct {010} and poor {100} cleavages. G. 4.2. M.P. near 1300° C. $X = b$; $Y = c$. $(-)2V = 50°$ $ca.$, $n_X = 1.78$, $n_Y = 1.805$, $n_Z = 1.82$, $n_Z - n_X = 0.04$ $ca.$ Color ash-gray, reddish brown or red. PD 2.56, 3.61, 2.86; 9–485. In thick sections X brownish red, Y reddish, Z greenish blue with $X < Z < Y$. Made from fusion. With some[30] Fe_2SiO_4: $(-)2V = 50°$ $ca.$, $n_X = 1.80$ $ca.$, $n_Y = 1.84$ $ca.$, $n_Z = 1.85$ $ca.$, $n_Z - n_X = 0.05$ $ca.$ With some Mg_2SiO_4: $(-)2V = 85°$, $n_X = 1.71$, $n_Y = 1.727$, $n_Z = 1.74$, $n_Z - n_X = 0.03$. With some Ca_2SiO_4: $(-)2V = 62.5°$, $n_X = 1.723$, $n_Y = 1.752$ calc., $n_Z = 1.759$, $n_Z - n_X = 0.026$. With 17 per cent MnO, 10 per cent ZnO and some FeO: $(-)2V = 77°$, $n_X = 1.758$, $n_Y = 1.786$, $n_Z = 1.804$, $n_Z - n_X = 0.046$.

$CaFeSiO_4$ is orthorhombic[31] with $a:b:c = 0.437:1:0.577$. G. 3.33. Gelatinizes with HCl. M.P. 1208° C. $X = b$; $Y = c$. $(-)2V = 49°$, $r > v$ moderate. $n_X = 1.696$, $n_Y = 1.734$, $n_Z = 1.743$, $n_Z - n_X = 0.047$. Also reported with $n_X > 1.74$. Color pale yellow. Made in a steel bomb. A related type with 35.11 per cent CaO, 18.97 FeO and 11.21 MnO has: G. 3.34, $n_X = 1.6749$, $n_Y = 1.7004$ (636), 1.7054 (578), 1.7133 (513), 1.7162 (470), $n_Z = 1.7105$, $n_Z - n_X = 0.0356$.

---

[30] Winchell: *Optical Mineralogy*, Part 2, p. 499 (1951).
[30a] Dittler and Hofmann: *Chem. Erde* XI, 1937, p. 256.
[31] Bowen, Schairer and Posnjak: *Am. J. Sci.* XXVI, p. 193 (1933).

CaMgSiO₄ (Monticellite) is orthorhombic with $a = 4.815$, $b = 11.08$, $c = 6.37$ Å. Crystals prismatic; also granular. Poor {010} cleavage. G. 3.2. Gelatinizes with HCl. Decomposes at 1300° C. $X = b$;[32] $Y = c$. $(+)2V = 85°$, $n_X = 1.639$, $n_Y = 1.646$, $n_Z = 1.653$, $n_Z - n_X = 0.014$. PD 1.81, 1.59, 2.66; 3–1107/8*. Colorless. Made from fusion at about 1490° C. With 10 per cent[33] Mg₂SiO₄: $(+)2V = 85°$–90°, $n_X = 1.638$–1.640, $n_Y = 1.646$, $n_Z = 1.651$–1.655, $n_Z - n_X = 0.015$. With 16 per cent MgFeSiO₄: $(-)2V = 74.5°$, $n_X = 1.663$, $n_Y = 1.674$, $n_Z = 1.680$, $n_Z - n_X = 0.018$.

CaMnSiO₄ (Glaucochroite) is orthorhombic[34] with $a = 4.91$, $b = 11.12$, $c = 6.49$ Å. Crystals prismatic with poor {001} cleavage. H. 6. G. 3.48. M.P. 1355° C. Gelatinizes with HCl. $X = b$; $Y = c$, $(-)2V = 61°$, r > v. $n_X = 1.685$, $n_Y = 1.723$, $n_Z = 1.736$, $n_Z - n_X = 0.051$. Color bluish green; colorless in thin section. Again:[35] $(-)2V = 68°$, $n_X = 1.699$, $n_Y = 1.724$ calc., $n_Z = 1.734$, $n_Z - n_X = 0.035$.

Ni₂SiO₄ is orthorhombic[36] with $(+)2V = 60°$ calc., $n_X = 1.976$, $n_Y = 1.987$, $n_Z = 2.019$, $n_Z - n_X = 0.043$. PD 2.75, 1.73, 1.48; 3–0780.

Cd₂SiO₄ forms irregular crystals with[37] $n > 1.74$ and moderate birefringence. Colorless.

Pb₂SiO₄ is orthorhombic(?). Crystals prismatic with good basal cleavage normal to the prism faces. M.P. 743° C. Parallel extinction. $(-)2V = 80°$ ca., $n_X = 2.13$, $n_Y = 2.15$, $n_Z = 2.18$, $n_Z - n_X = 0.05$. PD 3.21, 3.11, 2.98; 3–0494. [Indices and optic sign inconsistent. A.N.W.]

Li₄SiO₄ is pseudo-hexagonal and probably orthorhombic. Crystals granular. Lamellar twinning common, rarely in two sets. G. 2.39. M.P. 1255° C. with decomposition. Large extinction angle on twinning. $(+)2V = $ small.[38] $n_X = 1.594$, $n_Y = 1.60$ ca. $n_Z = 1.614$, $n_Z - n_X = 0.020$. Again:[39] $n_X = 1.602 \pm 0.002$, $n_Y = ?$, $n_Z = 1.610 \pm 0.002$. PD 2.66, 3.97, 2.59; 4–0727. Colorless, but may be colored pink by Li₂O or deep lilac by Ni if made in a nickel crucible; then pleochroic. Made from fusion.

Na₄SiO₄ has two phases. The high temperature α-phase[40] is monoclinic(?). It decomposes at 1089° C.; on cooling it inverts at 960° C. Crystals have lamellar twinning; Z is nearly normal to the twinning lines and extinction

[32] Agrell: *J. Iron Steel Inst. London* CLII, p. 19P (1945).

[33] Ferguson and Merwin: *Am. J. Sci.* CXCVIII, p. 81 (1919).

[34] Schaller: *Am. Min.* XX, p. 815 (1935).

[35] Moskwin: *Trav. Inst. Petrog. Acad. Sci. U.S.S.R.*, 1933, No. 4, p. 45 [*Min. Abst.* VII, p. 142].

[36] Grigoriev: *Min. Abst.* VII, p. 142 (1938).

[37] Niewenburg and Blumendal: *Rec. Trav. Chim. Pays-Bas* L, p. 989 (1931).

[38] Jaeger and Klooster: *Proc. K. Akad. Wet. Amsterdam* XVI, p. 857 (1914).

[39] Merwin: *J. Phys. Chem.* XXXIV, p. 2647 (1930).

[40] Kracek: *J. Phys. Chem.* XXXIV, p. 1583 (1930).

varies up to 8° with the twinning planes. Biaxial(?) with $n_X = 1.524$, $n_Y = ?$, $n_Z = 1.537$, $n_Z - n_X = 0.013$. The low temperature β-phase[41] forms acute-angled plates {010?} with extinction at about 15° to the short edge. G. 2.58. $(-)2V = ?$, mean index, $n = 1.536\pm$, $n_Z - n_X =$ rather weak. Colorless. Made from fusion.

$Ca_3AlSiAlO_8$ is orthorhombic(?).[23] Crystallizes as fibers and grains. Z parallel with fibers. $(+)2V =$ rather large, $n_X = 1.675$, $n_Y = 1.679$ $ca.$ $n_Z = 1.685$, $n_Z - n_X = 0.010$. Colorless. Made from glass at about 1300° C.; it dissociates at 1335° C. to Ca_2SiO_4 and $CaAl_2O_4$.

Sr_2SiO_4 is probably monoclinic,[29] commonly twinned on {100}. G. 3.84. F. 7. X $\wedge$ c = 17°; Z = b. $(+)2V = 32°30'$. $n_X = 1.722$ C, 1.7275 D, 1.740 F, $n_Y = 1.727$ C, 1.732 D, 1.744 F, $n_Z = 1.752$ C, 1.756 D, 1.766 F, $n_Z - n_X = 0.0285$ D. No inversion found. Colorless. PD 2.87, 2.83, 2.29; 10–34. Made from fusion. It forms a continuous series with Ca_2SiO_4 (probably the β-phase).

$Ca_3Mg(SiO_4)_2$ (Merwinite) is monoclinic with[42] $a = 5.20$, $b = 9.20$, $c = 6.78$ Å. Multiple lamellar twinning common in two sets intersecting at 43°. Perfect {010} cleavage. H. 6. G. 3.15. M.P. 1598° C. Gelatinizes with HCl. X $\wedge$ c = 36°; Z = b. $(+)2V = 66°$ $ca.$[43] $n_X = 1.706$, $n_Y = 1.712$, $n_Z = 1.724$, $n_Z - n_X = 0.018$. Again:[32] $(+)2V = 69°$, $n_X = 1.708$, $n_Y = 1.714$, $n_Z = 1.725$, $n_Z - n_X = 0.017$. Colorless. PD 2.66, 1.90, 1.53; 4–0728. Found in slags. Perhaps only a solid solution[42] of Mg_2SiO_4 in β-Ca_2SiO_4.

$Ca_2SiO_4 \cdot H_2O$ (Hillebrandite) is orthorhombic[44] with $a = 9.22$, $b = 9.34$, $c = 10.61$ Å. Crystals fibrous with prismatic cleavage. H. 5.5. G. 2.69. Soluble in HCl. Y = a; Z = c. $(-)2V = 42°$ calc., r < v strong. $n_X = 1.605$, $n_Y = 1.61$ $ca.$, $n_Z = 1.612$, $n_Z - n_X = 0.007$. Color porcelain white or greenish. PD 2.92, 4.76, 3.33; 9–51*. In Portland cement. After heating to 500° C. it loses water and becomes γ-Ca_2SiO_4.

$Ca_2SiO_4 \cdot H_2O$ has another orthorhombic phase[45] which forms {100} laths with prismatic cleavage. H. 5. G. 2.8. Cruciform twins not rare. Y = a; Z = c. $(+)2V = 68°$ calc. $n_X = 1.614$, $n_Y = 1.620$, $n_Z = 1.633$, $n_Z - n_X = 0.019$ Na. Colorless. Forms on quartz in lime water at 170° C. PD 3.04, 2.70, 1.90; 3–0594*.

$Ca_2SiO_4 \cdot nH_2O$ is orthorhombic(?). Crystals are fine needles[46] with Z

---

[41] Morey and Fenner: *J. Am. Chem. Soc.* XXXVI, p. 215 (1914).

[42] Bredig: *J. Phys. Chem.* XLIX, p. 537 (1945).

[43] Larsen and Foshag: *Am. Min.* VI, p. 143 (1921).

[44] Heller: *Acta Cryst.* V, p. 724 (1952). *a b c* changed to *b a c*.

[45] Thorvaldson and Shelton: *Can. J. Res.* I, p. 148 (1929).

[46] Vigfusson, Bates and Thorvaldson: *Can. J. Res.* XI, p. 520 (1934).

parallel with elongation. Mean refractive index $1.597 \pm .003$ and weak birefringence. Colorless. PD 3.01, 1.91, 1.89; 9–329*. Probably with less water it forms grains with refractive index $n = 1.62$ to 1.64. After dehydration mean index $n = 1.692$–1.693.

$Ca_{10}Si_5O_{20} \cdot 6H_2O(?)$ forms orthorhombic laths with perfect cleavage normal to elongation.[47] $(+)2V =$ medium, $n_X = 1.614$, $n_Y = 1.620$, $n_Z = 1.623$, $n_Z - n_X = 0.019$ Na. PD 4.19, 3.28, 2.42; 3–0247*. Heated at 450° C. under pressure the crystals were unchanged but the composition became $Ca_6Si_3O_{12} \cdot 2H_2O$ and $n_X = 1.642$, $n_Y = ?$, $n_Z = 1.672$, $n_Z - n_X = 0.030$. PD 2.81, 3.06, 2.85; 3–0735.

$Ca_3(OH)_2SiO_4 \cdot H_2O(?)$ is orthorhombic(?) in tiny needles with Z parallel with elongation. $n_X{}^{47} = 1.589$, $n_Y = ?$, $n_Z = 1.597$, $n_Z - n_X = 0.008$. Colorless.

$Al_2(F,OH)_2SiO_4$ (Topaz) is orthorhombic with $a = 4.61$, $b = 8.78$, $c = 8.38$ Å. Crystals usually prismatic, often vertically striated, with perfect {001} cleavage. H. 8. G. 3.5–3.57, increasing with tenor of F. $X = a$; $Z = c$. Data follow:

$\dfrac{100 \ (OH)}{OH + F}$	1.9	17.3	29.8
$(+)2V$	67°18′	64°38′	48° ca.
n_X	1.6072	1.6123	1.629
n_Y	1.6104	1.6155	1.631
n_Z	1.6176	1.6229	1.638
$n_Z - n_X$	0.0104	0.0106	0.009
G	3.565	3.537	3.509

Colorless, yellow, gray, greenish, reddish or bluish. PD 2.96, 1.40, 1.38; 2–0704/5. The fluorine compound has been made[48] by heating a mixture of Na_2SiF_6, Al_2O_3 and H_2O to 500° C.

HUMITE FAMILY

The four minerals of the humite family are nesosilicates of magnesium with some $Mg(F,OH)_2$. They are related in crystal structure but not isomorphous. They are also related to olivine. The a and b axes are nearly constant throughout the group, but the vertical axis, c, is related to the number of Mg atoms in the formula as follows[48a]:

[47] Bogue: *Chemistry of Portland Cement*, 1947, p. 394–398.

[48] Michel-Lévy and Wyart: *Bull. Soc. Franc. Min.* LXIX, p. 156 (1946).

[48a] a and b axes are interchanged for olivine, norbergite and humite. c' is equal to c for orthorhombic minerals and equal to $c \sin \beta$ in monoclinic minerals.

	a or b	b or a	c	c'	β
Olivine	10.21	4.755	5.98	$c' = 2 \times 2.990$	90°
Norbergite	10.22	4.70	8.72	$c' = 3 \times 2.906$	90°
Chondrodite	10.27	4.733	7.87	$2c' = 5 \times 2.976$	109°2'
Humite	10.23	4.738	20.86	$c' = 7 \times 2.980$	90°
Clinohumite	10.27	4.745	13.68	$2c' = 9 \times 2.984$	100°50'

$Mg(F,OH)_2 \cdot Mg_2SiO_4$ **(Norbergite)** is orthorhombic with $a = 10.22$, $b = 4.70$, $c = 8.72$ Å. H. 6.5. G. 3.14. Gelatinizes with HCl. $X = a$; $Z = b$. $(+)2V = 45°-50°$,[49] $n_X = 1.561-1.563$, $n_Y = 1.566-1.570$, $n_Z = 1.587-1.590$, $n_Z - n_X = 0.027$. Again[50] (with no Fe or OH): $(+)2V = 33°$, $n_X = 1.548$, $n_Y = 1.552$, $n_Z = 1.570$, $n_Z - n_X = 0.022$. Color yellowish brown with $X > Y > Z$, Z being colorless. PD 1.74, 3.08, 2.26; 2–1345. Made from fusion.[50]

$Mg(F,OH)_2 \cdot 2Mg_2SiO_4$ **(Chondrodite)** is monoclinic with $a = 10.27$, $b = 4.70$, $c = 8.72$ Å. $\beta = 109°2'$. Crystals often {010} tablets with poor {001} cleavage. H. 6–6.5. G. 3.1–3.2. F. 7. $X \wedge a = -22°$ to $-30°$; $Z = b$. $(+)2V = 50°$, $r > v$ weak, $n_X{}^{50} = 1.582$, $n_Y = 1.594$, $n_Z = 1.612$, $n_Z - n_X = 0.030$ (measured on the pure artificial F compound; in nature the mineral often contains Fe'' and a little Ti, Al, Fe''' and Mn which raise the indices and optic angle notably, for example: $(+)2V^{51} = 71°$, $n_X = 1.613$, $n_Y = 1.623$, $n_Z = 1.643$ and $(+)2V^{49} =$ large, $n_X = 1.635$, $n_Y = 1.645$, $n_Z = 1.663$). Color yellow, brown or red. Made from fusion.

$Mg(F,OH)_2 \cdot 3Mg_2SiO_4$ **(Humite)** is orthorhombic with $a = 10.23$, $b = 4.738$, $c = 20.86$ Å. Crystals small complex {100} or {001} tablets with poor {001} cleavage. H. 6. G. 3.2–3.3. F. 7. $X = a$; $Z = b$. $(+)2V = 59°$, $n_X = 1.598$, $n_Y = 1.606$, $n_Z = 1.630$, $n_Z - n_X = 0.032$ (measured[50] on the pure artificial F compound). Data on the natural mineral follow:

FeO + MnO	$(+)2V$	n_X	n_Y	n_Z	$n_Z - n_X$	Authority
2.35	?	1.621	1.627	1.649	0.028	Larsen[49]
5.37	69°	1.623	1.634	1.655	0.032	Rankama[52]
12.43	67°54'	?	1.643	?	?	Lacroix
8.43(+2.66 Fe_2O_3)	68°	1.643	1.653	1.675	0.032	Rankama[52]

Color white, yellow, brown; in thin section colorless or pleochroic with X pale to dark golden yellow, Y pale yellow, Z golden yellow and $X > Z > Y$. Made from fusion. PD 1.74, 2.45, 1.48; 7–167/8.

[49] Larsen: *Am. Min.* XIII, p. 354 (1928). The higher indices may be due to some Fe replacing Mg.

[50] Van Valkenburg: *Am. Min.* XL, p. 339 (1955).

[51] Thiele: *Chem. Erde* XIII, p. 64 (1940).

[52] Rankama: *Bull. Com. Géol. Finlande* No. 123, p. 81 (1938).

Mg(F,OH)$_2$·4Mg$_2$SiO$_4$ (Clinohumite) is monoclinic with $a = 10.27$, $b = 4.745$, $c = 13.68$, $\beta = 100°50'$. Crystals complex and varied with poor {001} cleavage. Lamellar twinning on {001} common. H. 6. G. 3.2. F. 7. X $\wedge$ $a = 7°$–$20°$; Z $= b$. (+)2V $= 76°$, r $>$ v weak. $n_X = 1.608$, $n_Y = 1.618$, $n_Z = 1.636$, $n_Z - n_X = 0.028$ (measured[50] on the pure artificial F compound). Data on the natural mineral follow:

FeO + MnO	TiO$_2$	(+)2V	n_X	n_Y	n_Z	$n_Z - n_X$	X $\wedge$ a	Authority
4.83	?	near 90°	1.625	1.638	1.653	0.028	?	Larsen[49]
15.44	0.06	76°	1.652	1.633	?	?	12°–15°	Larsen[49]
5.18	1.92	62°	1.664	1.673	1.698	0.034	7.5°	Larsen[49]
6.50	5.20	58°	1.691	1.700	1.724	0.033	?	Quervain[53]

Color brown, yellow, white. Color in thin section like humite. But with Ti the color becomes brownish red with X deep reddish yellow to blood red, Y and Z orange yellow and X $>$ Y $>$ Z. Made from fusion.

Ca$_3$OSiO$_4$ is hexagonal(?) with poor basal cleavage. Uniaxial negative[54] with $n_O = 1.722$, $n_E = 1.716$, $n_O - n_E = 0.006$. Also reported to have $(-)2V = 0°$ or very small with[32] $n_O = 1.724$, $n_E = 1.719$, $n_O - n_E = 0.005$. Colorless. Found in Portland cement. PD 2.78, 2.60, 2.19; 9–352.

Na$_2$ZrOSiO$_4$ is orthorhombic[12] often in pseudo-hexagonal twins of prismatic form with positive elongation. G. 3.605. M.P. (incongruently) 1477° C. $(-)2V = $ small. $n_X = 1.741$, $n_Y = $ slightly less than 1.790, $n_Z = 1.790$, $n_Z - n_X = 0.049$. Colorless.

Na$_{12}$Fe$_3$O$_8$Si$_5$O$_{20}$ forms rounded grains[55] with M.P. 1091° C. They show intricate polysynthetic twinning. $n_Y = 1.96$, $n_Z - n_X = 0.01\pm$.

Na$_6$OSiO$_4$ is orthorhombic[17](?). Crystals have acute angles and distinct cleavage. M.P. 1122° C. (+?)2V $= ?$, $n_X = 1.524$, $n_Y = ?$, $n_Z = 1.529$, $n_Z - n_X = 0.005$. Colorless. Made from fusion.

(UO$_2$)$_2$SiO$_4$·2H$_2$O(?) (Soddyite) is orthorhombic with $a:b:c = 0.796:1:0.669$. Crystals prismatic. H. 3–4. G. 4.63. $(-)2V = ?$, $n_X = 1.645$, $n_Y = 1.662$, $n_Z = ?$ Again: $n_X = 1.65$, $n_Y = 1.68$, $n_Z = 1.71$, $n_Z - n_X = 0.06$. Color yellow; rarely pleochroic. Made from solution[55a] at 180° C. and higher.

Pb$_4$O$_2$SiO$_4$ has three crystal phases.[56] The high temperature α-phase is stable above 720° C. It forms irregular plates. M.P. 725° C. (+)2V $= 40°$ ca., $n_X = 2.31$, $n_Y = 2.34$, $n_Z = 2.38$, $n_Z - n_X = 0.07$. PD 3.10, 3.03,

---

[53] Quervain: *Schw. Min. Pet. Mitt.* XVIII, p. 591 (1938). Contains 4.69 per cent Fe$_2$O$_3$.

[54] Shepherd and Rankin: *Ind. Eng. Chem.* III, p. 211 (1911); Rankin and Wright: *Am. J. Sci.* XXXIX, p. 1 (1915).

[55] Bowen, Schairer and Willems: *Am. J. Sci.* XX, p. 405 (1930).

[55a] Gruner: *Am. Min.* XXXVIII, p. 342 (1953).

[56] Geller, Creamer and Bunting: *J. Res. Bur. Stand.* XIII, p. 237 (1934).

1.68; 3–0554. The β-phase is stable between 720° C. and 155° C. It forms minute, probably prismatic grains having an average refractive index of about 2.34 and medium birefringence. The γ–phase is stable below 155° C. It is very much like the β-phase but has weaker birefringence. PD 3.02, 3.13, 1.82; 3–0602.

Al_2OSiO_4 has three crystal phases, all three being metastable at ordinary temperature. The α-phase is sillimanite which dissociates to mullite and liquid at about 1545° C. and then to corundum and liquid at about 1810° C. The β-phase is andalusite which changes to mullite and glass at about 1300° C. The γ-phase is kyanite which changes to mullite and glass at about 1300° C. more easily than andalusite.

α-Al_2OSiO_4 (Sillimanite) is orthorhombic with $a = 7.43$, $b = 7.58$, $c = 5.74$ Å. Crystals nearly square prisms often vertically striated, with perfect {010} cleavage. H. 7.5. G. 3.25. M.P. 1816° C. Y = b; Z = c. $(+)2V = 25°-30°$, r > v strong. $n_X = 1.655–1.661$, $n_Y = 1.658–1.670$, $n_Z = 1.677–1.684$, $n_Z - n_X = 0.020–0.023$. F−C for $n_Y = 0.0107$. The index of refraction is lower in dark colored crystals. For example, in a pale brown crystal $n_X = 1.6612$ and $n_Z = 1.6837$, and in a dark brown crystal $n_X = 1.6549$ and $n_Z = 1.6773$. Colorless, yellowish, greenish, brown, blue. Colorless in thin section; in thick sections:

X	Pale brownish	Brownish yellow	Very pale yellow
Y	Brown	Grayish green	Colorless or greenish
Z	Dark brown	Violet blue	Sapphire blue

Made hydrothermally under pressure;[57] also made from kyanite and andalusite.[58] PD 3.36, 2.20, 3.41; 10–369*.

β-Al_2OSiO_4 (Andalusite) is orthorhombic with $a = 7.76$, $b = 7.90$, $c = 5.56$ Å. Crystals nearly square prisms with good {110} cleavage at 90°48′. H. 7. $ca.$ G. 3.1–3.2. Changes to mullite and glass at about 1300° C. X = c; Y = b. Andalusite may have up to one tenth of its normal Al replaced by Mn, Fe, Ti and this modifies the properties as follows:

$\dfrac{100\,(Mn + Fe + Ti)}{Al + Mn + Fe + Ti}$	$(-)2V$	n_X	n_Y	n_Z	$n_Z - n_X$	G	Authority
1.1	86°	1.634	1.639	1.645	0.011	3.13	Macdonald[59]
2.8	75°	1.637	1.641	1.646	0.009	3.16	Macdonald[59]
10.3	71°	1.662	1.671	1.691	0.029	3.22	Wülfing[60]

[57] Michel-Lévy: *C. R. Acad. Sci. Paris* CCXXX, p. 2213 (1950).
[58] Beekman: *Ves. Nat. Kon. Akad. Wet. Amsterdam* XI, 1, p. 295 (1902).
[59] Macdonald and Merriam: *Am. Min.* XXIII, p. 588 (1938).
[60] Wülfing: *Sitz. Akad. Wiss. Heidel.* 1917 A, Abt. 12. Indices require $(+)2V$.

Color red, violet, gray, yellow, green; when altered may be brown, gray, black. Pleochroism variable even in one crystal. Colorless in thin section; in a thick section it may be:

X	Rose red	Blood red	Yellow
Y	Colorless or yellow	Oil green	Green
Z	Colorless or yellow	Olive green	Greenish yellow

Made between 450° and 650° C. under water pressure[61] of 10,000 to 30,000 psi. PD 4.61, 1.49, 5.71; 3–0165*.

γ-Al_2OSiO_4 **(Kyanite)** is triclinic with $a = 7.09$, $b = 7.72$, $c = 5.56\,kX$, $\alpha = 89°58.5'$, $\beta = 101°8'$, $\gamma = 105°57'$. Crystals {100} tablets elongated along c. Perfect {100} and good {010} cleavages; {001} parting. Multiple twinning common. Hardness varies: on {100} it is 4–5 parallel to c and 6–7 parallel to b; on {010} it is 6 parallel to c and 7 normal to c; on {001} it is 5.5 parallel to b and 6.5 parallel to a; on {1$\bar{1}$0} it is 7.5. G. 3.6 ca. Changes to mullite and glass at about 1300° C., more easily than andalusite. X nearly normal to {100}; extinction on (100), $Z' \wedge c = 27°$–$32°$; on (010), $Z' \wedge c = 5°$–$8°$; on (001), $X' \wedge a = 0°$–$2.5°$. It may contain a little Fe_2O_3, Na_2O, K_2O, H_2O which modify the properties as follows:

Fe_2O_3	$(Na,K)_2O$	H_2O	$(-)2V$	n_X	n_Y	n_Z	G	Authority
0.30	?	0.03	82°15′	1.7131	1.7219	1.7285	3.65	Barić[62]
0.33	1.10	0.83	?	1.7171	1.722	1.7290	3.53	Gübelin[63]
0.34	?	?	82°	1.718		1.734	?	Ozerov[64]

Color blue (whence the name), white, rarely gray, green or black. Colorless in thin section. In thick sections it may be pleochroic with X colorless, Y violet blue, Z dark cobalt blue. The color may disappear on heating. PD 1.38, 3.20, 1.93; 3–1164*.

$CaTiOSiO_4$ **(Titanite or Sphene)** is monoclinic with $a = 6.55$, $b = 8.70$, $c = 7.43$ Å, $\beta = 119°43'$. Crystals often wedge-shaped (whence the name sphene) with large {001} and {111} faces; varied. Distinct {110} cleavage. H. 5–5.5. G. 3.4–3.6. Y = b; $Z \wedge c = 47°$–$52°$ and nearly normal to {102}. $(+)2V = 23°$–$35°$, r > v extreme. Titanite may contain 1 to 20 per cent R_2O_3 perhaps as R_2SiO_5; R may be Fe‴, Al, Y,

[61] Roy: *Am. Min.* XXXIX, p. 140 (1954).
[62] Barić: *Zeit. Krist.* XCIII, p. 57 (1936) [*Min. Abst.* VI, p. 529].
[63] Gübelin: *Schw. Min. Pet. Mitt.* XIX, p. 325 (1939).
[64] Ozerov and Bykhover: *Min. Abst.* VII, p. 49 (1938). With 1.80 TiO_2 and 1.81 Cr_2O_3.

Ce, Cb. One O atom may be replaced in part by OH and F. In general refractive indices decrease and the optic angle increases with decrease of Ti. Data follow:

TiO_2	Fe_2O_3	Al_2O_3	$(Ce,Y)_2O_3$	$(+)2V$	n_X	n_Y	n_Z	$Z \wedge c$	Authority
40.89	0.00	0.00	Trace	$23°ca.$	1.901	?	2.093	51°	Sahama[65]
40.10	0.40	0.27	?	$20°ca.$	1.950	1.970	2.092		Bohnstedt[66]
35.26	1.34	1.02	4.51	$33°calc.$	1.90		2.04	36°	Morgante[67]
30.65	6.17	7.32	3.58	$35°-40°$	1.843	1.870	1.943		Young[68]

Color brown, gray, yellow, green, rose-red, black, often varying in a single crystal. Pleochroism often weak or absent in thin section; in thick sections:

X Greenish yellow	Pale brownish yellow	Nearly colorless
Y Greenish pink	Pale brownish yellow	Greenish yellow
Z Salmon pink	Pale yellow	Orange to brownish red

PD 3.20, 2.59, 2.98; 2–0521. Made by fusing a mixture of SiO_2, TiO_2 and $CaCl_2$.[69]

$Pb_2UO_2SiO_4 \cdot H_2O$ (Kasolite) is monoclinic with $a = 13.28$, $b = 7.01$, $c = 6.71$, $\beta = 103°42'$. Crystals minute prisms (along b) with perfect {001} and poor {100} and {010} cleavages. H. 4–5. G. 6.46. $X = b$; $Z \wedge c = 1°$ $ca.$ $(+)2V = 42°58'$ Li, $43°18'$ Na. $n_X = 1.80$ calc., $n_Y = 1.90$, $n_Z = 1.967$ calc., $n_Z - n_X = 0.077$ calc. Color yellow to brown. Made from solution[55a] at 180° C. and higher. PD 3.26, 2.93, 4.18; 8–297.

$Ca_5CO_3(SiO_4)_2$ has two crystal phases. The high temperature α-phase is stable above 1200° C. under a pressure of 90 atmospheres. It is orthorhombic with good {001} and {010} cleavages. $Y = a$. $2V =$ large. $n_X = 1.665$, $n_Y = ?$, $n_Z = 1.680$, $n_Z - n_X = 0.015$. Colorless. The β-phase **(spurrite)** is monoclinic(?) with[70] distinct {001} and poor {100} cleavages at 79°. Multiple twinning. H. 5. G. 3. F. 7. $X = b$; $Z \wedge a =$ nearly 0°, distinct crossed dispersion. $(-)2V = 39.5°$, $r > v$ weak. $n_X = 1.640$, $n_Y = 1.674$, $n_Z = 1.679$, $n_Z - n_X = 0.039$. According to Tilley[71] the dis-

[65] Sahama: *Bull. Com. Géol. Finlande* CXXXVIII, p. 88, 1946.
[66] Bohnstedt: *Tr. Lomonosov Inst.* VII, p. 49 (1936); [*Min. Abst.* VII, p. 210].
[67] Morgante: *Min. Abst.* IX, p. 216 (1946).
[68] Young: *Am. Min.* XXIII, p. 149 (1938).
[69] *Dana's System of Mineralogy*, 1892, p. 716.
[70] Wright: *Am. J. Sci.* CLXXVI, p. 547 (1908).
[71] Tilley: *Min. Mag.* XXII, p. 77 (1929).

tinct cleavage is {100}, $X = b$ and $Y \wedge c = -33°$. Colorless or tinted in mass. PD 3.03, 2.70, 1.97; 4–0640.

XI. Siliceous Glasses

The index of refraction of many glasses produced by chilling substances of definite composition from the liquid state has been given in preceding pages in connection with the description of the crystal phases. However, no kind of commercial glass corresponds with any of these substances of definite composition: such glass varies widely in composition. The refractive index and dispersion of glass are very important in connection with its use for optical purposes; they are definitely related to the composition of the glass, and these relationships are of special interest in the microscopic examination of glass.

Silica (SiO_2) seems to be the characteristic, if not the essential, constituent of all commercial glasses, although in certain rare types it may be replaced partly or wholly by B_2O_3 or P_2O_5. The other constituents vary both in kind and in tenor in the various types of glass. For example, in ordinary "crown" glass (ordinary window glass—type 1), the other constituents are chiefly Na_2O, CaO, and K_2O in variable proportions, in flint glass (also called strass—type 2) the other constituents are chiefly PbO, Na_2O, and K_2O in variable proportions. Glasses of these two types have been known for many years; several other types of glass have come into use, including especially: type 3, opal glass, containing the constituents of type 1 with also CaF_2, SnO_2 or P_2O_5; type 4, borosilicate crown glass containing the constituents of type 1 with also B_2O_3; type 5, barium glasses containing the constituents of either type 1 or type 2 with also BaO; type 6 (not in common use) thallium flint glass containing chiefly SiO_2, PbO and Tl_2O with or without K_2O. Many other types are known, including borate glasses, phosphate glasses, etc., but the types listed are the most important at present.

While glass may be made with nearly any composition, commercial (and many optical) glasses are generally far more restricted. Empirical results[1] show that the most convenient range of physical properties such as stability, workability, reasonable hardness, non-devitrification during cooling, insolubility, and even non-hygroscopicity, are maintained in glasses that consist mainly of $Na_2O \cdot 4SiO_2$ and $K_2O \cdot 6SiO_2$, with other components added in such a way as to maintain the SiO_2 approximately at constant weight (80%) in the whole glass (as by adding $PbO \cdot 14SiO_2$, etc.). Therefore the compositions of most kinds of commercial glass can be expressed approximately in a ternary diagram as shown in Fig. 11–1.

[1] Wright: Optical Glass: U. S. Ord. Dept., Doc. 2037 (1921).

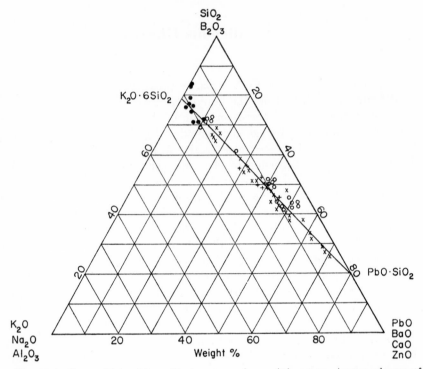

Fig. 11-1. Composition of borosilicate crown glasses (●), crown (crown glasses of this type have less than 20 percent BaO.), and barium crown glasses (O), flint glasses (×), and barium flint glasses (+). Modified, after F. E. Wright: *J. Amer. Ceramic Soc.* III, p. 785 (1920).

The diagram (Fig. 11-1) gives a summary of the composition of commercial glasses, but does not express all the facts. If the percentage of silica exceeds 75 per cent, the melt is too viscous to be satisfactory in the furnace; if the alkalies exceed 20 per cent, the glass produced is soft, hygroscopic and chemically unstable, being more or less soluble in water. Accordingly, a minimum of about 5 per cent of lime (or RO) is needed to give a satisfactory melt and durable glass; other things being equal glass with both alkalies is more durable than glass with either alkali alone; if the lime exceeds 13 per cent the mixture fuses with difficulty and the resultant glass crystallizes very easily; lead oxide may be used up to 80 per cent, but as the percentage of lead oxide increases, so also does the danger of crystallization on cooling, the danger of attack on the melting pot, the softness of the resultant glass, and the depth of its (yellow) color. In some types of glass barium oxide may be used up to about 50 per cent, but with important percentages of BaO it is desirable to use increasing amounts of B_2O_3 and Al_2O_3; mixtures high in BaO attack the crucible seriously, especially if any free silica is present in the clay. Boron oxide may be used up to about 20 per cent, but it is not desirable in lead glasses. Zinc oxide in excess of about 12 per cent is apt to induce crystallization, though small amounts may aid in preventing crystallization. More than 5 per cent of alumina tends[1] to make most glass melts exceedingly viscous, but alumina decreases the danger of crystallization and renders the glass tough and resistant; in dense barium glasses alumina even up to 10 per cent aids in preventing crystallization of barium disilicate and improves the working qualities of the melt and the glass.

Various types of manufactured glass are, in general, so complicated in composition that it is very difficult to draw accurate conclusions regarding the relations between composition and physical properties from analyses of such types accompanied by measures of physical data. Peddle[2] adopted a different method of determining these relationships. He made many kinds of glass of varying, but simple, composition; in any one series the composition was varied as to only one component: by measuring the indices of refraction and densities of the glasses thus made, he was able to reach important conclusions. He began with the simplest case: glasses of the composition $100SiO_2 \cdot xNa_2O$, x varying from 20 to 100 molecules. He tested next the corresponding case: $100SiO_2 \cdot xK_2O$, x again varying from 20 to 100 molecules; in this case no large pieces of glass could be obtained and all the glasses were highly soluble in water—physical data could not be measured on them, but were obtained in two cases by extrapolation from other series. The next test was on a series: $100SiO_2 \cdot \frac{1}{2}xNa_2O$. $\frac{1}{2}xK_2O$, x varying as before; these glasses were intermediate in character between those of the Na_2O and the K_2O series, but not suitable for measurements of physical data. Peddle next considered glasses having only two silica-alkali ratios, $100SiO_2 +$ either 40 or 20 K_2O or Na_2O, and studied alkali-calcium series obtained by adding various amounts of CaO to each of these. He studied also similar series of alkali-lead, and of alkali-barium glasses.

Some of his results may be tabulated as follows:[3]

SODIUM GLASSES—$100SiO_2 \cdot xNa_2O$

	Weight percentage						
x	SiO_2	Na_2O	$Al_2O_3 + Fe_2O_3$	$n(D)$	$n(F) - n(C)$	$\dfrac{n(D) - 1}{n(F) - n(C)}$	G
20	83.00	16.58	0.42	1.4851	0.00790	61.4	2.353
30	76.64	22.98	0.38	1.4952	0.00835	59.3	2.413
40	71.20	28.44	0.36	1.5015	0.00875	57.3	2.457
70	58.68	41.03	0.29	1.5118	0.00962	53.2	2.535
100	49.91	49.84	0.25	1.5168	0.01017	50.8	2.560

[2] Peddle: *J. Soc. Glass Tech.* IV, p. 3–107, 225–251, 299–366 (1920).

[3] Peddle's analyses are all of the "batch" composition; the composition of the resultant glass is slightly different on account of volatilization and pot attack; more accurate data are very scanty.

POTASSIUM GLASSES (by extrapolation)—100SiO₂·xK₂O

x	Weight percentage			n(D)	n(F) − n(C)	$\frac{n(D) - 1}{n(F) - n(C)}$	G
	SiO₂	K₂O	Al₂O₃ + Fe₂O₃				
20	76.00	23.60	0.40	1.4937	.00809	61.2	2.388
40	61.27	38.44	0.29	1.5073	.00888	57.1	2.465

SODIUM POTASSIUM GLASSES (by extrapolation)—200SiO₂·xNa₂O·xK₂O

x	n(D)	n(F) − n(C)	$\frac{n(D) - 1}{n(F) - n(C)}$	G
20......	1.4892	.00803	60.9	2.377
40......	1.5044	.00882	57.15	2.472

SODIUM CALCIUM GLASSES—100SiO₂·20Na₂O·xCaO

x	Weight percentage				n(C)	n(D)	n(F)	n(F) − n(C)	$\frac{n(D) - 1}{n(F) - n(C)}$	G
	SiO₂	Na₂O	CaO	Al₂O₃ + Fe₂O₃						
5	79.90	15.97	3.73	0.40	1.49455	1.4970	1.50270	.00815	61.98	2.412
10	77.03	15.39	7.19	0.39	1.50628	1.5088	1.51469	.00841	60.50	2.458
15	74.37	14.85	10.41	0.37	1.51662	1.5192	1.52527	.00865	60.03	2.499
20	71.86	14.36	13.42	0.36	1.52526	1.5279	1.53414	.00888	59.44	2.537
30	67.36	13.44	18.86	0.34	1.54074	1.5435	1.55008	.00934	58.20	2.603
40	63.37	12.67	23.65	0.31	1.54443	1.5573	1.56423	.00980	56.87	2.659

POTASSIUM CALCIUM GLASSES—100SiO₂·20K₂O·xCaO

x	Weight percentage				n(C)	n(D)	n(F)	n(F) − n(C)	$\frac{n(D) - 1}{n(F) - n(C)}$	G
	SiO₂	K₂O	CaO	Al₂O₃ + Fe₂O₃						
5	73.21	23.01	3.42	0.36	1.49862	1.5011	1.50690	.00828	60.5	2.420
10	70.79	22.75	6.61	0.35	1.50557	1.5081	1.51403	.00846	60.1	2.450
20	66.40	20.87	12.40	0.33	1.51968	1.5223	1.52851	.00883	59.2	2.505
30	62.53	19.65	17.51	0.31	1.53278	1.5355	1.54200	.00922	57.3	2.601
40	59.08	18.57	22.06	0.29	1.54629	1.5491	1.55587	.00958	57.3	2.601

SODIUM POTASSIUM CALCIUM GLASSES—SiO₂·10Na₂O·10K₂O·xCaO

x	Weight percentage					n(C)	n(D)	n(F)	n(F) − n(C)	$\frac{n(D) - 1}{n(F) - n(C)}$	G
	SiO₂	Na₂O	K₂O	CaO	Al₂O₃ + Fe₂O₃						
5	76.21	7.87	11.98	3.56	0.38	1.49673	1.4992	1.50496	.00823	60.65	2.415
10	73.59	7.60	11.56	6.88	0.37	1.50608	1.5086	1.51451	.00843	60.33	2.450
15	71.15	7.35	11.18	9.96	0.36	1.51512	1.5177	1.52377	.00865	59.83	2.485
20	64.88	7.12	10.81	12.85	0.34	1.52267	1.5253	1.53151	.00884	59.42	2.523
30	64.71	6.69	10.17	18.11	0.32	1.53736	1.5401	1.54664	.00928	58.20	2.585
40	61.02	6.31	9.59	22.78	0.30	1.54997	1.5528	1.55963	.00966	57.22	2.626

SODIUM LEAD GLASSES—100SiO₂·20Na₂O·xPbO

x	Weight percentage				n(C)	n(D)	n(F)	n(F) − n(C)	$\frac{n(D) - 1}{n(F) - n(C)}$	G
	SiO₂	Na₂O	PbO	Al₂O₃ + Fe₂O₃						
5	71.91	14.38	13.35	0.36	1.51571	1.5186	1.52561	.00990	52.38	2.628
10	63.44	12.69	23.55	0.32	1.54135	1.5448	1.55326	.01191	45.74	2.911
15	56.76	11.35	31.61	0.28	1.56520	1.5691	1.57871	.01351	42.12	3.152
20	51.34	10.27	38.14	0.25	1.58869	1.5930	1.60365	.01496	39.64	3.368
30	43.12	8.62	48.04	0.22	1.62215	1.6272	1.63982	.01767	35.50	3.390
40	37.17	7.43	55.21	0.19	1.65147	1.6571	1.67131	.01984	33.12	3.940

POTASSIUM LEAD GLASSES—100SiO₂·20K₂O·xPbO

x	Weight percentage				$n(C)$	$n(D)$	$n(F)$	$n(F) - n(C)$	$\dfrac{n(D)-1}{n(F)-n(C)}$	G
	SiO₂	K₂O	PbO	Al₂O₃ + Fe₂O₃						
5	66.55	20.81	12.31	0.33	1.51710	1.5201	1.52739	.01029	50.53	2.616
10	59.25	18.52	21.94	0.29	1.54452	1.5480	1.55652	.01200	45.67	2.849
15	53.40	16.69	29.65	0.26	1.56674	1.5707	1.58046	.01372	41.59	3.089
20	48.60	15.20	35.97	0.23	1.58974	1.5941	1.60488	.01514	39.24	3.290
30	41.18	12.88	45.74	0.20	1.62339	1.6284	1.64123	.01794	35.03	3.640
40	35.74	11.18	52.91	0.17	1.65375	1.6596	1.6397	.02022	32.62	3.942

SODIUM BARIUM GLASSES[4]—100SiO₂·20Na₂O·xBaO

x	Weight percentage				$n(C)$	$n(D)$	$n(F)$	$n(F) - n(C)$	$\dfrac{n(D)-1}{n(F)-n(C)}$	G
	SiO₂	Na₂O	BaO	Al₂O₃ + Fe₂O₃						
5	74.7	15.4	9.5	0.4	(1.50119)	(1.5037)	(1.50961)	(.00842)	(59.8)	(2.557)
10	68.2	14.1	17.4	0.3	1.51757	1.5202	1.52642	.00895	58.8	2.708
15	62.7	13.0	24.0	0.3	1.53297	1.5357	1.54218	.00921	58.2	2.853
20	58.1	12.0	29.7	0.2	1.54546	1.5483	1.55503	.00957	57.3	2.987
30	50.6	10.4	48.8	0.2	1.56680	1.5698	1.57695	.01015	56.1	3.203
40	44.8	9.2	45.8	0.2	1.58635	1.5895	1.59602	.01067	55.3	3.407

POTASSIUM BARIUM GLASSES—100SiO₂·20K₂O·xBaO

x	Weight percentage				$n(C)$	$n(D)$	$n(F)$	$n(F) - n(C)$	$\dfrac{n(D)-1}{n(F)-n(C)}$	G
	SiO₂	K₂O	BaO	Al₂O₃ + Fe₂O₃						
5	69.1	21.7	8.8	0.4	1.50549	1.5080	1.51673	.00844	60.2	2.565
10	63.5	20.0	16.2	0.3	1.51768	1.5203	1.52622	.00884	58.8	2.681
15	58.8	18.4	22.5	0.3	1.52897	1.5317	1.53819	.00922	57.7	2.798
20	54.6	17.2	27.9	0.3	1.54085	1.5437	1.55047	.00962	56.5	2.922
30	47.9	15.1	36.8	0.2	1.56219	1.5652	1.57239	.01020	55.4	3.143
40	42.7	13.4	43.7	0.2	1.58064	1.5938	1.59135	.01071	54.5	3.308

SODIUM POTASSIUM BARIUM GLASSES—100SiO₂·10Na₂O·10K₂O·xBaO

x	Weight percentage					$n(C)$	$n(D)$	$n(F)$	$n(F) - n(C)$	$\dfrac{n(D)-1}{n(F)-n(C)}$	G
	SiO₂	Na₂O	K₂O	BaO	Al₂O₃ + Fe₂O₃						
5	71.8	7.4	11.3	9.2	0.3	1.50333	1.5058	1.51165	.00832	60.8	2.562
10	65.8	6.8	10.3	16.8	0.3	1.51729	1.5199	1.52609	.00880	59.1	2.695
15	60.6	6.3	9.5	23.3	0.3	1.53146	1.5342	1.54067	.00921	58.0	2.821
20	56.2	5.8	8.9	28.8	0.3	1.54476	1.5476	1.55437	.00961	57.0	2.951
30	49.2	5.1	7.7	37.7	0.3	1.56640	1.5694	1.57657	.01017	56.0	3.175
40	43.7	4.5	6.9	44.7	0.2	1.58494	1.5881	1.59567	.01073	54.8	3.349

Some compositions[4a] in the system Ca₂Al₂SiO₇—CaAl₂Si₂O₈—MgAl₂O₄ may be represented by using x for weight per cent. of the first component, and y for the weight per cent. of the last; the second (CaAl₂Si₂O₈) then equals 100 − x − y, and a knowledge of x and y can be used to predict with a fair degree of accuracy the refractive index of the corresponding

---

[4] The results on the glass in this series with 5BaO were obtained by extrapolation.

[4a] DeVries and Osborn, *J. Amer. Ceram. Soc.* XL, p. 6 (1957), give data for 42 compositions in the ranges of x and y stated.

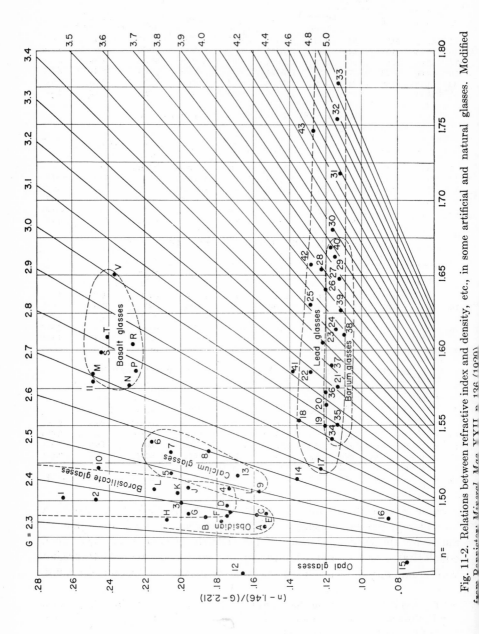

Fig. 11-2. Relations between refractive index and density, etc., in some artificial and natural glasses. Modified from Perrister, *Mineral Mag.* XXII, p. 136 (1929).

glass, provided that $0 < x < 75\%$, and $0 < y < 20\%$, by the following regression equation:[4b]

$$n \text{ (glass)} = 1.5766 + 0.00057x + 0.00066y \pm .0010$$

where the last term (.0010) is the standard error of the regression.

As silica seems to be the characteristic constituent of nearly all glasses Bannister[5] devised a method of distinguishing between the various kinds of glass which is based on the way in which they differ from silica in their physical characters. The index of refraction of SiO_2 glass is taken as 1.46 and its density as 2.21. The chief types of commercial glasses may be identified by their position on a diagram which has the index of refraction as one coordinate and the ratio $(n\text{-}1.46)/(G\text{-}2.21)$ as the other coordinate. A modification of Bannister's diagram is shown in Fig. 11–2. The separation of lead and calcium glasses is very distinct, but calcium glasses grade into borosilicate glasses and barium glasses overlap lead glasses considerably. These conditions are natural since there are so many variables in glass. Opal glasses are quite distinct. Natural glasses composing obsidians and basalt glasses are also shown. The data include several glasses used as imitation gem stones.

Data for Figs. 11–2 and 11–3

Borosolicate Glasses:

1. Imitation gem stone, Bannister's No. 14 in Min. Mag., XXII, p. 136 (1929). No analysis. $n(D) = 1.500$, G. 2.36.

2. Borosilicate crown glass, Wright's No. 12 in J. Am. Ceram. Soc., III, p. 783 (1920). $SiO_2 = 72.0, B_2O_3 = 12.0, Na_2O = 11.0, Al_2O_3 = 5.0.$ $n(D) = 1.4997;$ $\dfrac{n(D) - 1}{n(F) - n(C)} = 64.7$; G. 2.37.

3. Borosilicate crown glass, Morey's No. 5 in Intern. Crit. Tables, II, p. 87 (1927). $SiO_2 = 59.5,$ $B_2O_3 = 21.5,$ $K_2O = 14.4,$ $CaO = 0.3,$ $Al_2O_3 = 1.9,$ $ZnO = 2.3,$ $As_2O_5 = 0.1.$ $n(C) = 1.49573,$ $n(D) = 1.4980,$ $n(F) = 1.50336,$ $\dfrac{n(D) - 1}{n(F) - n(C)} = 65.3$, G. 2.40.

4. Borosilicate crown glass, Wright's No. 15, op. cit. $SiO_2 = 70.6,$ $B_2O_3 = 6.0,$ $Al_2O_3 = 1.0,$ $As_2O_3 = 0.3,$ $Mn_2O_3 = 0.1,$ $K_2O = 10.5,$ $Na_2O = 11.5.$ $n(C) = 1.50446,$ $n(D) = 1.5069,$ $n(F) = 1.51259,$ $\dfrac{n(D) - 1}{n(F) - n(C)} = 62.3$, G. 2.48.

Calcium Glasses:

5. Hard crown glass, Morey's No. 27, op. cit. $SiO_2 = 69.6,$ $CaO = 11.5,$ $K_2O = 18.4,$ $Al_2O_3 = 0.3,$ $As_2O_3 = 0.2.$ $n(C) = 1.51496,$ $n(D) = 1.5175,$ $n(F) = 1.52352,$ $\dfrac{n(D) - 1}{n(F) - n(C)} = 60.5$, G. 2.49.

[4b] Regression formula based on the data of DeVries and Osborn (ref. 4a), calc. by HW.
[5] *Min. Mag.* XXII, p. 136 (1929).

6. Imitation gem stone, Bannister's No. 10, *op. cit.* No analysis. $n(D) = 1.538$. G. 2.57.

7. Imitation gem stone, Bannister's No. 8, *op. cit.* No analysis. $n(D) = 1.532$, G. 2.56.

8. Imitation gem stone, Bannister's No. 12, *op. cit.* No analysis. $n(D) = 1.532$. G. 2.60.

9. Ordinary crown glass, Wright's No. 1, *op. cit.* $SiO_2 = 74.6$, $As_2O_3 = 0.3$, $Mn_2O_3 = 0.1$, $CaO = 5.0$, $K_2O = 11.0$, $Na_2O = 9.0$. $n(D) = 1.5055$, $\dfrac{n(D) - 1}{n(F) - n(C)} = 60.2$, G.2.5.

Intermediate and Special Types:

10. Beryllium glass, Lai and Silverman's No. B_3, in J. Am. Ceram. Soc., XI, p. 535 (1928): $SiO_2 = 73.39$, $BeO = 7.64$, $Na_2O = 18.96$. $(Na_2O \cdot BeO \cdot 4SiO_2)$. $n(D) = 1.5193$, G. 2.45.

11. Imitation gemstone, Bannister's No. 18, *op. cit.* No analysis, but considered to be an iron calcium glass. $n(D) = 1.577$. G. 2.68.

12. Imitation gem stone, opal white, Bannister's No. 24, *op. cit.* No analysis. $n(D) = 1.450$. G. 2.15.

13. Barium borosilicate crown glass, Morey's No. 18, *op. cit.* $SiO_2 = 67.1$, $B_2O_3 = 7.2$, $Al_2O_3 = 0.3$, $As_2O_5 = 0.1$, $CaO = 2.0$, $BaO = 7.2$, $K_2O = 16.2$. $n(C) = 1.51358$, $n(D) = 1.5160$, $n(F) = 1.52167$, $\dfrac{n(D) - 1}{n(F) - n(C)} = 63.8$, G. $= 2.54$.

14. Zinc crown glass, Morey's No. 16, *op. cit.* $SiO_2 = 69.7$, $Al_2O_3 = 0.3$, $As_2O_5 = 0.4$, $CaO = 0.4$, $ZnO = 16.5$, $K_2O = 1.7$, $Na_2O = 11.0$. $n(C) = 1.51225$, $n(D) = 1.5149$, $n(F) = 1.52115$, $\dfrac{n(D) - 1}{n(F) - n(C)} = 57.9$, G. 2.62.

15. Imitation gem stone, opal white, Bannister's No. 26, *op. cit.* No analysis. $n(D) = 1.457$, G. 2.17.

16. Imitation gem stone, dark, brown, Bannister's No. 22, *op. cit.* No analysis, but considered to be colored by iron and titanium. $n(D) = 1.488$, G. 2.52.

Lead Glasses:

17. Flint glass, Wright's No. 47, *op. cit.* $SiO_2 = 68.7$, $Mn_2O_3 = 0.1$, $As_2O_3 = 0.2$, $PbO = 13.3$, $ZnO = 2.0$, $Na_2O = 15.7$. $n(C) = 1.51721$, $n(D) = 1.5202$, $n(F) = 1.52747$, $\dfrac{n(D) - 1}{n(F) - n(C)} = 50.7$, G. 2.7.

18. Flint glass, Wright's No. 53, *op. cit.* $SiO_2 = 59.3$, $As_2O_3 = 0.2$, $PbO = 27.5$, $K_2O = 8.0$, $Na_2O = 5.0$. $n(C) = 1.55024$, $n(D) = 1.5537$, $n(F) = 1.56217$, $\dfrac{n(D) - 1}{n(F) - n(C)} = 46.4$, G. 2.9.

19. Flint glass, Morey's No. 48, *op. cit.* $SiO_2 = 60.6$, $Al_2O_3 = 0.3$. $As_2O_5 = 0.1$, $CaO = 0.3$, $BaO = 2.5$, $PbO = 22.5$, $K_2O = 13.9$. $n(C) = 1.54562$, $n(D) = 1.5491$, $n(F) = 1.55768$, $\dfrac{n(D) - 1}{n(F) - n(C)} = 45.5$, G. 2.95.

20. Flint glass, Morey's No. 55, *op. cit.* $SiO_2 = 55.9$, $Al_2O_3 = 0.2$, $As_2O_5 = 0.1$, $CaO = 0.3$, $PbO = 32.9$, $K_2O = 11.1$. $n(C) = 1.55945$, $n(D) = 1.5632$, $n(F) = 1.57257$, $\dfrac{n(D) - 1}{n(F) - n(C)} = 42.9$, G. 3.07.

21. Flint glass, Wright's No. 56, *op. cit.* $SiO_2 = 53.7$, $Mn_2O_3 = 0.1$, $As_2O_3 = 0.3$

$PbO = 36.6$, $Na_2O = 1.0$, $K_2O = 8.3$. $n(C) = 1.57122$, $n(D) = 1.5752$, $n(F) = 1.58507$, $\dfrac{n(D) - 1}{n(F) - n(C)} = 41.0$, G. 3.22.

22. Imitation gem stone, red. Bannister's No. 7, *op. cit.* No analysis. $n(D) = 1.585$, G. 3.18.

23. Imitation gem stone, green. Bannister's No. 6, *op. cit.* $n(D) = 1.606$, G. 3.42.

24. Flint glass, Morey's No. 92, *op. cit.* $SiO_2 = 48.0$, $Al_2O_3 = 0.2$, $As_2O_5 = 0.1$, $PbO = 45.1$, $CaO = 0.3$, $Na_2O = 5.2$, $K_2O = 1.2$. $n(C) = 1.60867$, $n(D) = 1.6134$, $n(F) = 1.62529$, $\dfrac{n(D) - 1}{n(F) - n(C)} = 36.9$, G. 3.55.

25. Imitation gem stone, yellow, Bannister's No. 5, *op. cit.* No analysis. $n(D) = 1.630$, G. 3.53.

26. Imitation gem stone, yellow, Bannister's No. 4, *op. cit.* No analysis. $n(D) = 1.640$, G. 3.70.

27. Flint glass, Morey's No. 101, *op. cit.* $SiO_2 = 40.6$, $Al_2O_3 = 0.2$, $As_2O_5 = 0.1$, $CaO = 0.2$, $PbO = 51.5$, $K_2O = 7.5$. $n(C) = 1.64149$, $n(D) = 1.6469$, $n(F) = 1.66066$, $\dfrac{n(D) - 1}{n(F) - n(C)} = 33.7$, G. 3.87.

28. Imitation gem stone, purple. Bannister's No. 3. *op. cit.* No analysis. $n(D) = 1.654$, G. 3.79.

29. Imitation gem stone, yellow, Bannister's No. 2, *op. cit.* No analysis. $n(D) = 1.662$, G. 3.97.

30. Flint glass, Wright's No. 78, *op. cit.* $SiO_2 = 38.0$. $As_2O_3 = 0.2$, $PbO = 56.8$. $K_2O = 5.0$. $n(C) = 1.67413$, $n(D) = 1.6801$, $n(F) = 1.69517$, $\dfrac{n(D) - 1}{n(F) - n(C)} = 32.3$, G. 4.1.

31. Flint glass, Wright's No. 80, *op. cit.* $SiO_2 = 33.7$, $As_2O_3 = 0.3$, $PbO = 62.0$, $K_2O = 4.0$, $n(C) = 1.71055$, $n(D) = 1.7174$, $n(F) = 1.73489$, $\dfrac{n(D) - 1}{n(F) - n(C)} = 29.5$, G. 4.49.

32. Flint glass, Wright's No. 82, *op. cit.* $SiO_2 = 28.4$, $As_2O_3 = 0.1$, $PbO = 69.0$ $K_2O = 2.5$. $n(C) = 1.74641$, $n(D) = 1.7541$, $n(F) = 1.77384$, $\dfrac{n(D) - 1}{n(F) - n(C)} = 27.5$, G. 4.78.

33. Flint glass, Wright's No. 83, *op. cit.* $SiO_2 = 27.3$, $As_2O_3 = 0.1$, $PbO = 71.0$, $K_2O = 1.5$. $n(C) = 1.76999$, $n(D) = 1.7782$, $n(F) = 1.79940$, $\dfrac{n(D) - 1}{n(F) - n(C)} = 26.5$, G. 4.99.

33a. Flint glass, Wright's No. 84, *op. cit.* $SiO_2 = 22.0$, $PbO = 78.0$. $n(C) = 1.87938$, $n(D) = 1.8904$, $n(F) = 1.91935$, $\dfrac{n(D) - 1}{n(F) - n(C)} = 22.3$, G. 5.83.

33b. Flint glass, Wright's No. 87, *op. cit.* $SiO_2 = 18.0$, $As_2O_3 = 0.1$, $PbO = 82.0$. $n(C) = 1.94925$, $n(D) = 1.9626$, $n(F) = 1.99807$, $\dfrac{n(D) - 1}{n(F) - n(C)} = 19.7$, G. 6.33.

Barium Glasses:

34. Barium crown glass, Morey's No. 43, *op. cit.* $SiO_2 = 57.1$, $B_2O_3 = 1.8$, $Al_2O_3 = 0.2$, $As_2O_5 = 0.1$, $CaO = 0.3$, $BaO = 26.9$, $K_2O = 13.7$. $n(C) = 1.53802$, $n(D) = 1.5407$, $n(F) = 1.54712$, $\dfrac{n(D) - 1}{n(F) - n(C)} = 59.4$, G. 2.90.

35. Barium flint glass, Wright's No. 89, *op. cit.* $SiO_2 = 56.2$, $As_2O_3 = 0.3$, $PbO = 7.0$, $ZnO = 9.0$, $BaO = 15.0$, $K_2O = 11.0$, $Na_2O = 1.5$. $n(C) = 1.54694$, $n(D) = 1.5500$, $n(F) = 1.55736$, $\dfrac{n(D) - 1}{n(F) - n(C)} = 52.8$, G. 3.0.

36. Barium flint glass, Wright's No. 95, *op. cit.* $SiO_2 = 51.2$, $As_2O_3 = 0.3$, $PbO = 4.0$, $ZnO = 14.0$, $BaO = 20.0$, $K_2O = 5.0$, $Na_2O = 5.5$, $n(C) = 1.56607$, $n(D) = 1.5692$, $n(F) = 1.57679$, $\dfrac{n(D) - 1}{n(F) - n(C)} = 53.1$, G. 3.12.

37. Barium crown glass, Wright's No. 40, *op. cit.* $SiO_2 = 37.5$, $B_2O_3 = 15.0$, $Al_2O_3 = 5.0$, $As_2O_3 = 1.5$, $BaO = 41.0$. $n(C) = 1.58703$, $n(D) = 1.5899$, $n(F) = 1.59673$, $\dfrac{n(D) - 1}{n(F) - n(C)} = 60.8$, G. 3.32.

38. Barium crown glass, Wright's No. 45, *op. cit.* $SiO_2 = 31.0$, $B_2O_3 = 12.0$, $Al_2O_3 = 8.0$, $As_2O_3 = 1.0$, $BaO = 48.0$. $n(C) = 1.60673$, $n(D) = 1.6098$, $n(F) = 1.61710$, $\dfrac{n(D) - 1}{n(F) - n(C)} = 58.8$, G. 3.54.

39. Barium flint glass, Wright's No. 102, *op. cit.* $SiO_2 = 42.8$, $As_2O_3 = 0.5$, $PbO = 32.6$, $ZnO = 5.1$, $BaO = 10.8$, $K_2O = 7.5$, $Na_2O = 0.7$. $n(C) = 1.62233$, $n(D) = 1.6269$, $n(F) = 1.63832$, $\dfrac{n(D) - 1}{n(F) - n(C)} = 34.8$, G. 3.70.

40. Barium flint glass, Morey's No. 104, *op. cit.* $SiO_2 = 36.6$, $Al_2O_3 = 0.2$, $Sb_2O_3 = 0.6$, $As_2O_5 = 0.2$, $K_2O = 4.9$, $CaO = 0.2$, $BaO = 13.6$, $ZnO = 4.7$, $PbO = 39.2$. $n(C) = 1.66297$, $n(D) = 1.6683$, $n(F) = 1.68173$, $\dfrac{n(D) - 1}{n(F) - n(C)} = 35.6$, G. 3.98.

Thallium Glasses:

41. Thallium glass, Bannister's No. 3, *op. cit.* p. 152. $SiO_2 = 36.99$, $PbO = 18.06$, $K_2O = 37.49$, $Tl_2O = 7.46$. $n(C) = 1.581$, $n(D) = 1.586$, $n(F) = 1.599$, $\dfrac{n(D) - 1}{n(F) - n(C)} = 32.5$, G. 3.12.

42. Thallium glass, Bannister's No. 2, *op. cit.* p. 152. $SiO_2 = 38.45$, $PbO = 18.81$, $K_2O = 12.63$, $Tl_2O = 29.38$. $n(C) = 1.650$, $n(D) = 1.657$, $n(F) = 1.673$, $\dfrac{n(D) - 1}{n(F) - n(C)} = 28.6$, G. 3.75.

43. Thallium glass, Bannister's No. 1. *op. cit.* p. 152. $SiO_2 = 27.17$, $PbO = 23.98$, $K_2O = 12.07$, $Tl_2O = 36.36$. $n(C) = 1.736$, $n(D) = 1.744$, $n(F) = 1.766$, $\dfrac{n(D) - 1}{n(F) - n(C)} = 24.8$, G. 4.42.

44. Thallium glass, Bannister's No. 4, *op. cit.* p. 152. $SiO_2 = 20.83$, $PbO = 24.82$, $K_2O = 0.00$, $Tl_2O = 55.01$. $n(C) = 1.9276$, $n(D) = 1.9431$, $n(F) = 1.9808$, $\dfrac{n(D) - 1}{n(F) - n(C)} = 17.7$, G. 6.03.

Natural Rock Glasses:

A. Rhyolite obsidian, Yellowstone Park, C. E. Tilley: Min. Mag. XIX, p. 275 (1922). $n(D) = 1.482$, G. 2.353.

B. Rhyolite obsidian, Clifton, Ariz., B. Ježek and Woldřich: Zeit. Krist. LIII, p. 82 (1913). $n(C) = 1.4850$, $n(D) = 1.4871$, $n(F) = 1.4956$, $\dfrac{n(D) - 1}{n(F) - n(C)} = 46.0$, G. 2.355. $n(C)$ and $n(F)$ by graphic solution from n for Li, Na and Tl.

C. Rhyolite obsidian, Easter Island, Pacific, C. E. Tilley, *op. cit.* n(D) = 1.490, G. 2.400.

D. Rhyolite obsidian, Greenland, B. Ježek, *op. cit.* n(C) = 1.4939, n(D) = 1.4956, n(F) = 1.5002, $\dfrac{n(D) - 1}{n(F) - n(C)}$ = 78.7, G. 2.413.

E. Rhyolite obsidian, Real del Monte, Mexico, B. Ježek. *op. cit.* n(C) = 1.4889, n(D) = 1.4912, n(F) = 1.4970, $\dfrac{n(D) - 1}{n(F) - n(C)}$ = 60.6, G. 2.394.

F. Rhyolite obsidian, Papayan, Colombia, B. Ježek, *op. cit.* n(C) = 1.4830, n(D) = 1.4852, n(F) = 1.4925, $\dfrac{n(D) - 1}{n(F) - n(C)}$ = 51.1, G. 2.352.

G. Rhyolite obsidian, Lipari Island, C. E. Tilley, *op. cit.* n(D) = 1.490, G. 2.363.

H. Rhyolite obsidian, Guamani, Ecuador, B. Ježek, *op. cit.* n(C) = 1.4840, n(D) = 1.4863, n(F) = 1.4941, $\dfrac{n(D) - 1}{n(F) - n(C)}$ = 48.1, G. 2.336.

J. Trachyte obsidian, Pantelleria, C. E. Tilley, *op. cit.* n(D) = 1.508, G. 2.454.

K. Trachyte obsidian, Ascension, C. E. Tilley, *op. cit.* n(D) = 1.506, G. 2.435.

L. Trachyte obsidian, Teneriffe, C. E. Tilley, *op. cit.* n(D) = 1.512, G. 2.467.

M. Basalt glass, Gallanach, Island of Muck, C. E. Tilley, *op. cit.* n(D) = 1.583, G. 2.704.

N. Basalt glass, Portree, Skye, C. E. Tilley, *op. cit.* n(D) = 1.576, G. 2.716.

P. Basalt glass, Vesuvius (1805), C. E. Tilley, *op. cit.* n(D) = 1.586, G. 2.769.

R. Basalt glass, Kau desert, Kilauea, C. E. Tilley, *op. cit.* n(D) = 1.603, G. 2.841.

S. Basalt glass, Caisteal, Island of Muck, C. E. Tilley, *op. cit.* n(D) = 1.598, G. 2.773.

T. Basalt glass, Reunion Isl., C. E. Tilley, *op. cit.* n(D) = 1.608, G. 2.825.

V. Basalt glass, Kildonan, Island of Eigg, C. E. Tilley, *op. cit.* n(D) = 1.649, G. 3.003.

Wright[6] has shown that glasses are well characterized by their refractive index and dispersion. They are equally well characterized by the refractive index and the reciprocal of the dispersion, which is called ν and equals $\dfrac{n(D) - 1}{n(F) - n(C)}$. These values are the coordinates used in Fig. 11-3, which shows that the lead glasses fall along a remarkably smooth curve, the calcium glasses fall close together and the borosilicate glasses form another small group, while the barium glasses scatter over a large area; the thallium glasses of Bannister[5] fall along a curve nearly parallel with that of the lead glasses. Natural acid volcanic glasses or obsidians vary in dispersion much more than in refractive index, which is low. Basalt glasses have a refractive index ranging from about 1.58 to about 1.67, but their dispersion is apparently unknown. It should be understood that there are all gradations between the various artificial types of glass, and also between obsidians and basalt glasses. Wright and Peddle both worked out diagrams and tables from which the batch composition necessary to give certain physical

[6] F. E. Wright: Optical Glass: *U. S. Ord. Dept. Doc.* 2037, 1921, and *J. Am. Ceram. Soc.* III, p. 783 (1920).

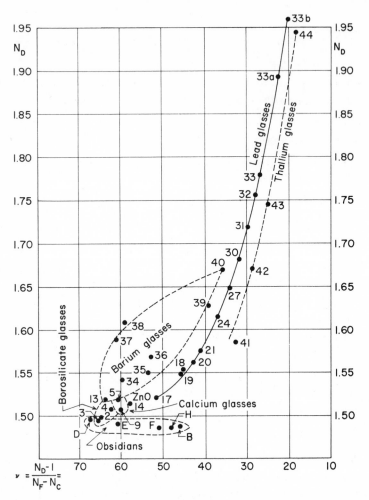

Fig. 11-3. Relations between refractive index and dispersion as measured by
$\nu = \dfrac{N_D - 1}{N_F - N_C}$ in some artificial glasses and obsidians.

properties of glass may be derived. Data of Morey and Merwin[7] are summarized in Fig. 11–4.

Glass has been made from feldspar;[8] such glass is said to be tough; high purity of the crude feldspar is said to be unnecessary. If pure plagioclase

[7] Morey and Merwin: *J. Opt. Soc. Am.* XXII, p. 632 (1932).

[8] Spence: *Min. Met.* XI, p. 103 (1930).

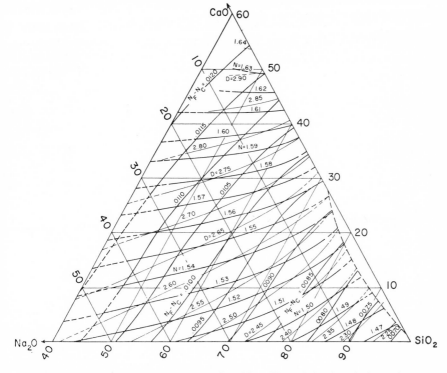

Fig. 11-4. Refractive index, N_D, dispersion, $N_F - N_C$ and density of glasses in part of the ternary system, SiO_2—Na_2O—CaO—(Morey and Merwin, *J. Opt. Soc. Amer.* XXII, p. 632, 1932).

feldspar were used the glass would have the following optical properties:[9]

Per Cent Albite	Per Cent Anorthite	$n(C)$	$n(D)$	$n(F)$	ν	G
100.0	0.0	1.4870	1.4890	1.4957	56.2	2.382
65.37	34.63	1.5141	1.5166	1.5231	57.4	2.483
48.55	51.45	1.5282	1.5307	1.5375	58.3	2.533
32.05	67.95	1.5427	1.5452	1.5520	58.6	2.591
15.87	84.13	1.5571	1.5600	1.5665	59.6	2.648
0.0	100.0	1.5725	1.5755	1.5828	60.6	2.700

Silica is the chief component of nearly all commercial glass, usually being 60 to 80 per cent of the whole. Some glass is pure silica, but its melting point (1710° C.) is so high that it is expensive to make. However, "96%

[9] Larsen: *Am. J. Sci.*, XXVIII, p. 263 (1909). $n(C)$, $n(F)$ (and ν) by graphic solution from indices for Li, Na, and Tl light given by Larsen.

silica" glass (4% is chiefly B_2O_3) introduced by Corning Glass Works in 1939, has some remarkable properties which have made it important. Its low coefficient of expansion makes it extremely resistant to thermal shock. It has very high chemical durability and electrical resistance. One variety of this glass has very high transmission for ultra violet light.

Part Two

Determinative Tables and Charts

Introduction

Separate tables, for isotropic and for anisotropic substances, respectively, are provided. The first table lists substances (other than the glasses covered in Chapter XI, p. 313) arranged by the refractive index n. Each entry shows the formula (or name, or both), the refractive index n, and the page reference in this book.

The tables of anisotropic substances are arranged by birefringence within groups determined by the refractive index n_Y, and each group is keyed by a number in the first column, to a graphical display showing in polar coordinates the values of birefringence $n_Z - n_X$ and optic axial angle $2V$. It will be noted that uniaxial substances fall along the left boundary of each semicircular chart, biaxial ones elsewhere as determined by their properties. Each chart corresponds to one of the groups determined by ranges of n_Y; these ranges are broad enough to cover the uncertainty of an ordinary microscopical measurement of index by the immersion method with white light. Extreme values of n_Y are so rare that two or more such groups have been combined so that no chart will have less than about 15 items.

The use of these tables and charts depends not so much upon knowledge of the exact values of principal refractive indices, which might be considered the fundamental optical constants, as upon values that can be obtained routinely either by examination of grains in immersion oils or by study of thin sections. The value of $2V$ and the optic character ("sign" of $2V$) can be obtained in several well-known ways, including examination of an interference figure of a grain (whether in immersion or in thin section) that shows practically no interference effects between crossed nicols, and therefore is oriented to give an approximately centered optic-axis interference figure. The same grain may also be used to determine n_Y, and by the interference color at the *margin* of the field of the interference figure, it may furthermore be used to estimate the value of the birefringence, $n_Z - n_X$. If a substance is too fine-grained to permit such detailed observations, its mean index, n, may nevertheless be obtained in most cases, and is usually fairly close to n_Y. The birefringence in such a case cannot be estimated accurately, but its order of magnitude may be determined in many instances. At the worst, no more than two or three entire groups from this list may have to be considered. In such instances, other methods will normally be used.

In preparing these tables it was unfortunately necessary in many cases to estimate values of birefringence or of $2V$, or both, from qualitative descriptions such as "birefringence moderate," "2V rather large," etc. This has been done somewhat arbitrarily using the following lists, but modifying the numbers if other evidence was available.

Birefringence scale		Optic axial angle scale	
Description	Assumed value $n_Z - n_X$	Description	Assumed value $2V$
Very weak	0.002	Very small	10° (or 15°)
Low or Weak	0.006	Small	25°
Moderate	0.014	Medium small	40°
Rather strong	0.023	Moderate	50°
Strong	0.032	Medium large	60°
Very strong	0.045	Large	70° (or 75°)
Extreme	>0.05	Very large	85° (or 80°)

Another source of difficulty lies in ambiguous expressions giving ranges to express uncertainty, rather than probable values with standard errors. The center of a range was generally taken as the most probable value unless the ranges of properties were due to varying composition. Thus "$n_Y = 1.698 - 1.721$" would be taken in most cases as "$n_Y = 1.71$," dropping the last figure after the decimal point, but for a known isomorphous series with substantial variation of optical properties, entries are made in several of the n_Y-groups. A similar remark may be made for birefringence and $2V$ as shown on the charts, though for the most part it is assumed that the user of these charts will probably realize the necessity for a sufficient (and variable!) tolerance in his determinations of optical properties.

A very serious source of difficulty in compiling these tables and charts arises from incomplete data. If, for example, two unidentified refractive indices n_1 and n_2, have been published, with or without additional data on birefringence and $2V$, it is always possible to state that $n_1 \leq n_Y \leq n_2$, and that $n_Z - n_X \geq n_2 - n_1$. Such data permit assigning substances to the correct n_Y group in many cases, but the estimation of birefringence and $2V$ is usually very uncertain. If for any reason the birefringence can be assumed to be small, it may be reasonable to show the substance at or near the origin in the semicircular diagram without serious risk of misleading the user.

In some instances it is possible to list a substance in one of the n_Y-groups, but quite impossible to show its position in the diagram. Such limitations of the available data are minimized as much as possible, but must be kept in mind when using the charts. The observed optic angle, $2V$, is too frequently omitted from optical descriptions; if the three principal indices are given, $2V$ can be calculated, and this has been done in preparing the charts, but calculated values of $2V$ seldom agree with observed values, for the calculations are sensitive to very small errors in the refractive indices, especially if the birefringence is small. The equation may be stated in several forms, of which the following is convenient:

$$\tan^2 V_Z = \left(\frac{1}{n_X^2} - \frac{1}{n_Y^2}\right) \Big/ \left(\frac{1}{n_Y^2} - \frac{1}{n_Z^2}\right)$$

A convenient chart giving the solutions to this equation for the most frequently met combinations of optical data was published by J. B. Mertie.[1] Mertie's chart not only indicates the solution quickly, but also furnishes evidence as to the precision thereof. A somewhat more detailed discussion of the use of tables and charts of this type is given in the author's book on "Optical Properties of Minerals."[2]

[1] *Am. Min.* XXVII, p. 538 (1942).
[2] H. Winchell, "Optical Properties of Minerals." Academic Press, New York. In press.

DETERMINATIVE TABLES

I. Isotropic Crystalline Solids
(Glasses described in chapter XI, p. 313f, are excluded)

Arranged in order of increasing refractive index, n.

Substance	n	Page
NaF	1.3258	16
K_2SiF_6, Hieratite	1.339	46
$Li_3Na_3Al_2F_{12}$, Cryolithionite	1.3395	42
K_2SiF_6, Hieratite	1.347	46
KF	1.352	17
KF	1.3629	17
$(NH_4)_2SiF_6$, Cryptohalite	1.3696	46
K_2NaAlF_6, Elpasolite	1.376	43
LiF	1.3921	17
RbF	1.396	17
K_3HfF_7	1.403	47
K_3ZrF_7	1.408	47
KCN	1.410	22
$K_2Zn(CN)_4$ — $K_2Cd(CN)_4$ - Series	1.413	38
Li_3FeF_6	1.42	42
$(NH_4)_3HfF_7$	1.426	47
$Co(ClO_4)_2 \cdot 6NH_3$	1.430	112
$(NH_4)_3ZrF_7$	1.433	47
CaF_2, Fluorite	1.4338	23
$K_2(Cd,Hg)(CN)_4$	1.435	38
$61K_2Cd(CN)_4 \cdot 39K_2Hg(CN)_4$	1.435	38
$Ni(ClO_4)_2 \cdot 6NH_3$	1.437	112
SrF_2	1.438	23
$NaAl(SO_4)_2 \cdot 12H_2O$, Soda Alum	1.4388	158
$Sr(BF_4)_2$	1.44	48
$K_2Cd(CN)_4$ — $K_2Hg(CN)_4$ - Series	1.441	38
$K_2Zn(CN)_4$ — $K_2Hg(CN)_4$ - Series	1.443	38
$Na_7(PO_4)_2F \cdot 19H_2O$	1.4519	205
$Na(CN)$	1.452	22
$NH_2(CH_3)_2Al(SO_4)_2 \cdot 12H_2O$	1.4525	159
KH	1.453	22
$NH_3CH_3Al(SO_4)_2 \cdot 12H_2O$,	1.4531	159
$KAl(SO_4)_2 \cdot 12H_2O$, Potash Alum	1.4565	158
$RbAl(SO_4)_2 \cdot 12H_2O$	1.4566	159

Substance	n	Page
B_2O_3	1.458	59
$K_2Hg(CN)_4$	1.458	38
$CsAl(SO_4)_2 \cdot 12H_2O$	1.4586	159
SiO_2, Lechatelierite	1.4588	65
$NH_3C_2H_5Al(SO_4)_2 \cdot 12H_2O$	1.459	159
$NH_4(NO_3)$	1.459	101
$N(CH_3)_4Al(SO_4)_2 \cdot 12H_2O$	1.4592	159
$NH_2(C_2H_5)_2Al(SO_4)_2 \cdot 12H_2O$	1.4592	159
$NH_4Al(SO_4)_2 \cdot 12H_2O$, Ammonia Alum	1.4594	158
$NH(C_2H_5)_3AlSO_4 \cdot 12H_2O$	1.4594	159
$N(C_2H_5)_4Al(SO_4)_2 \cdot 12H_2O$	1.4595	159
$NH_3C_4H_9Al(SO_4)_2 \cdot 12H_2O$	1.4598	159
$NH_3C_3H_7Al(SO_4)_2 \cdot 12H_2O$	1.4602	159
$NH_3C_5H_{11}Al(SO_4)_2 \cdot 12H_2O$	1.4602	159
$RbIn(SO_4)_2 \cdot 12H_2O$	1.4638	159
B_2O_3	1.464	59
$NH_2(OH)HAl(SO_4)_2 \cdot 12H_2O$	1.4642	159
$NaK(CN)_2$	1.465	22
$RbTi(SO_4)_2 \cdot 12H_2O$	1.465	159
$CsGa(SO_4)_2 \cdot 12H_2O$	1.4650	159
$CsIn(SO_4)_2 \cdot 12H_2O$	1.4652	159
$KGa(SO_4)_2 \cdot 12H_2O$	1.4653	159
$RbGa(SO_4)_2 \cdot 12H_2O$	1.4658	159
$NH_4In(SO_4)_2 \cdot 12H_2O$	1.4664	159
$NH_4Ga(SO_4)_2 \cdot 12H_2O$	1.4684	159
$RbV(SO_4)_2 \cdot 12H_2O$	1.469	159
$Na_7(AsO_4)_2F \cdot 19H_2O$	1.4693	205
$Al(OH)_2SiAlO_4$	1.47	251
NaH	1.470	21
$CsTi(SO_4)_2 \cdot 12H_2O$	1.4736	159
BaF_2	1.4741	25
$NH_3CH_3Cr(SO_4)_2 \cdot 12H_2O$	1.4745	160
$NH_4V(SO_4)_2 \cdot 12H_2O$	1.475	159
$CsV(SO_4)_2 \cdot 12H_2O$	1.478	159
CsF	1.478	18
$NH_3CH_3Al(SeO_4)_2 \cdot 12H_2O$	1.4780	160
$Na_2CaSi_{10}Al_4O_{28} \cdot 20H_2O$, Faujasite	1.48	239
$Li_2Si_8Al_2O_{20} \cdot 5H_2O$	1.480	240
$KAl(SeO_4)_2 \cdot 12H_2O$	1.4801	160
$CsCr(SO_4)_2 \cdot 12H_2O$	1.4810	159
$RbAl(SeO_4)_2 \cdot 12H_2O$	1.4810	160

Substance	n	Page
$KCr(SO_4)_2 \cdot 12H_2O$	1.4814	159
$RbCr(SO_4)_2 \cdot 12H_2O$	1.4815	159
$KFe(SO_4)_2 \cdot 12H_2O$	1.4817	159
$RbFe(SO_4)_2 \cdot 12H_2O$	1.4825	159
$CsMn(SO_4)_2 \cdot 12H_2O$	1.483	159
$Na_4ClSi_3Al_3O_{12}$, Sodalite	1.4837	251
$CsFe(SO_4)_2 \cdot 12H_2O$	1.4838	159
CsF	1.484	18
$NH_4Cr(SO_4)_2 \cdot 12H_2O$	1.4842	159
$NaPO_3$	1.4847	212
$NH_4Fe(SO_4)_2 \cdot 12H_2O$	1.4848	159
$NH_4Al(SeO_4)_2 \cdot 12H_2O$	1.4856	160
$NaSi_2AlO_6 \cdot H_2O$, Analcite	1.486	239
$Na_8SO_4Si_6Al_6O_{24}$, Noselite	1.486	252
SiO_2, Cristobalite	1.486	63
$NH_3(OH)Cr(SO_4)_2 \cdot 12H_2O$	1.4863	160
$CsAl(SeO_4)_2 \cdot 12H_2O$	1.4864	160
$NaSi_3AlO_8$	1.4891	235
$Na_8(WO)_4Si_6Al_6O_{24}$, Noselite WO_4	1.490	252
$KSi_2AlO_6 \cdot H_2O$	1.490	239
KCl, Sylvite	1.4904	15
$RbCl$	1.4936	17
$Na_8SO_4Si_6Al_6O_{24}$	1.494	252
KSi_2AlO_6, Leucite	1.495	226
$Na_4OHSi_3Al_3O_{12}$, Sodalite, OH	1.495	252
$LiSi_4AlO_{10}$	1.495	228
$K_2Mg(CO_3)_2$	1.496	96
$Na_3CaSO_4Si_3Al_3O_{12}$, Hauynite	1.4961	252
$TlAl(SO_4)_2 \cdot 12H_2O$	1.4975	159
$K_2MgSi_5O_{12}$	1.498	254
$Na_4SSi_3Al_3O_{12}$, Lazurite	1.500	252
$2NaCl \cdot 7KCl$	1.500	16
$K_2MgSi_5O_{12}$	1.501	254
$RbRh(SO_4)_2 \cdot 12H_2O$	1.501	159
$2NaCl \cdot 5KCl$	1.503	16
$Na_2Si_2O_5$	1.504	255
$TlGa(SO_4)_2 \cdot 12H_2O$	1.5067	159
$RbFe(SeO_4)_2 \cdot 12H_2O$	1.5070	160
$CsRh(SO_4)_2 \cdot 12H_2O$	1.5077	159
$KSiAlO_4$	1.508	226
$2NaCl \cdot 3KCl$	1.5085	16

Substance	n	Page
$NaSiAlO_4$	1.51	224
$Na_6Mg_2SO_4(CO_3)_4$, Tychite	1.510	100
$NaSiAlO_4$	1.510	224
$NH_4Rh(SO_4)_2 \cdot 12H_2O$	1.5103	159
$CsFe(SeO_4)_2 \cdot 12H_2O$	1.5116	160
$Mg(BrO_3)_2 \cdot 6H_2O$	1.5139	109
$1NaCl \cdot 1KCl$	1.514	16
$TlV(SO_4)_2 \cdot 12H_2O$	1.514	159
$Na_3MgCl(CO_3)_2$, Northupite	1.5144	98
$Na_2B_4O_7$, Borax Glass	1.5147	116
$Na_3MgBr(CO_3)_2$,	1.515	99
$NaClO_3$	1.5151	108
$4NaCl \cdot 3KCl$	1.518	16
$3NaCl \cdot 2KCl$	1.519	16
$NaSi_3GaO_8$	1.519	232
KSi_3GaO_8	1.519	232
$TlAl(SeO_4)_2 \cdot 12H_2O$	1.522	160
$TlCr(SO_4)_2 \cdot 12H_2O$	1.5228	159
$CsSi_2AlO_6$	1.523	226
$K_4Be_3Si_4O_{12}$	1.523	267
$2NaCl \cdot 1KCl$	1.523	16
Na_2MgSiO_4	1.523	299
$Na_7(VO_4)_2F \cdot 19H_2O$	1.5230	205
$TlFe(SO_4)_2 \cdot 12H_2O$	1.5237	159
$Be_3Al_2Si_6O_{18}$	1.526	288
$3NaCl \cdot 1KCl$	1.528	16
$NH_4(NO_3)$	1.530	101
$RbSiAlO_4$	1.531	227
$(NH_4)_2Ca_2(SO_4)_3$	1.532	132
$K_2Mg_2(SO_4)_3$	1.539	132
$5NaCl \cdot 1KCl$	1.533	16
$CsCl$	1.534	18
$K_2Mg_2(SO_4)_3$, Langbeinite	1.5347	132
$7NaCl \cdot 1KCl$	1.536	16
$Li_4K \cdot 10Si_7O_{21}$	1.540	267
$Na_6Zn_8(CO_3)_{11} \cdot 8H_2O$	1.540	96
$K_2SiAl_2O_6$	1.540	226
$LiSiAlO_4$	1.541	227
CaP_2O_6	1.542	211
$NaCl$, Halite	1.5443	15
$Zn(BrO_3)_2 \cdot 6H_2O$	1.5452	109

Substance	n	Page
$TlRh(SO_4)_2 \cdot 12H_2O$	1.548	159
$RbBr$	1.5528	17
$Na_6Mg_2(CrO_4)(CO_3)_4$	1.555	100
KBr	1.5595	17
$AgSi_2AlO_6 \cdot H_2O$	1.56	239
CdF_2	1.56	24
$Cr_2(SO_4)_3 \cdot 18H_2O$	1.564	171
$AlO(OH)$	1.565	70
$Co(ClO_4)_36NH_3$	1.570	112
$Na_4CaSi_3O_9$	1.571	267
$Ba(NO_3)_2$, Nitrobarite	1.5711	103
$K_2Mn_2(SO_4)_3$, Manganolangbeinite	1.572	132
$K_4CaSi_3O_9$	1.572	267
$NaSiBO_4$	1.572	226
$CsSiAlO_4$	1.574	228
$NaSiAlO_4 \cdot CaAl_2O_4$	1.577	225
CsF	1.578	18
KGe_3AlO_8	1.578	232
$Ni_3(OH)_4CO_3 \cdot 4H_2O$, Zaratite	1.58	98
$CsBr$	1.582	18
$Na_{10}Fe_2Si_8O_{24}$	1.583	267
KSi_3FeO_8	1.586	232
$Sr(NO_3)_2$	1.5878	103
$Sr(NO_2)_2 \cdot H_2O$	1.589	106
$Ca_2Si_4Al_3GaO_{16}$	1.591	232
$NaGe_3AlO_8$	1.592	232
$Ca_5Al_6O_{14}$	1.593	77
$Sb_3O_6(OH)$ or $Sb_2O_4 \cdot nH_2O$, Stibiconite	1.6	66
Na_2CaSiO_4	1.60	299
$Ni_3(OH)_4CO_3 \cdot 4H_2O$	1.60	98
$KAlO_2$	1.603	72
$Ca_3Al_2(OH)_{12}$, Hydrogrossularite	1.604	72
$Ca_3Al_2O_6 \cdot 6H_2O$	1.604	83
$Ca_3Al_2O_6 \cdot 6H_2O$	1.605	299
$CaMgSi_2O_6$	1.6071	274
$KFe''Fe'''(SO_4)_3 \cdot 4H_2O$, Voltaite	1.608	157
$Ca_5Al_6O_{14}$	1.608	77
$CaSi_2AlGaO_8$	1.608	232
$BaSi_2O_5$	1.6085	258
$LiNH_2$	1.610	22

Substance	n	Page
$CaSiGeAl_2O_8$	1.611	232
$NaBrO_3$	1.617	108
KGe_3GaO_8	1.617	232
$BO(OH)$	1.619	69
K_2ZnSiO_4	1.622	299
$GeBr_4$	1.6269	35
$Ca_3Si_3O_9$	1.628	292
$Sr_3Si_3O_9$	1.632	288
$CaSi_2Ga_2O_8$	1.633	232
$NaGe_3GaO_8$	1.636	232
$TlSi_2AlO_6$	1.637	226
$Ca_2AlSiAlO_7$	1.638	295
$5(Ca_2MgSi_2O_7) \cdot 5(Ca_2AlSiAlO_7)$	1.638	294
$Ca_2MgSi_2O_7$	1.641	294
$NaBr$	1.6412	17
$CsCl$	1.6418	17
NH_4Cl, Salammoniac	1.6426	21
$(NH_4)_2FeCl_4$	1.6439	36
Li_2O	1.644	56
$BaAl_2O_4 \cdot H_2O$	1.644	83
RbI	1.6474	17
$SrCl_2$	1.6499	26
$Mn_3Al_2Si_3O_{12}$	1.655	298
K_2SnCl_6	1.6574	47
$CaGe_2Al_2O_8$	1.658	232
CsI	1.661	18
$LiCl$	1.662	17
KI	1.6670	17
$Fe_9''Fe_2'''(OH)_{16}Si_{18}O_{20}$, Greenalite	1.674	260
Cs_2GeCl_6	1.68	47
$BaAl_2O_4$	1.683	77
$(NH_4)_2SnCl_6$	1.690	47
Al_2O_3	1.696	60
$CsBr$	1.6984	18
$Sb_3O_6(OH)$ or $Sb_2O_4 \cdot nH_2O$, Stibiconite	1.7	66
$CaMn_4Si_5O_{15}$	1.700	292
NH_4I	1.7031	17
$Mg_3Al_2Si_3O_{12}$, Pyrope	1.705	297
$CaGe_2Ga_2O_8$	1.705	232
$AlVO_4 \cdot 3H_2O$, Steigerite	1.710	201

Substance	n	Page
$Ca_3Al_2O_6$	1.710	77
$Ca_3Fe_2O_6 \cdot 6H_2O$	1.710	83
NH_4Br	1.7108	21
NH_4Br	1.7124	21
$MgAl_2O_4$, Spinel	1.7190	74
$Sr_3Al_2O_6$	1.728	77
Fe	1.73	3
$LiAl_5O_8$	1.735	74
$Ca_3Al_2Si_3O_{12}$, Grossularite	1.735	298
MgO, Periclase	1.7366	57
$NH_4CH_3PtCl_6$	1.74	47
$ZnGa_2O_4$	1.74	76
As_2O_3, Arsenolite	1.755	61
NaI	1.7745	17
$K_2Pb_2Si_2O_7$	1.775	295
$CsHgCl_3$	1.779	37
$CoAl_2O_4$	1.78	76
$Pb(NO_3)_2$	1.7815	103
$ZnAl_2O_4$	1.782	76
LiBr	1.784	17
CsI	1.7876	18
$(NH_4)_2PtCl_6$	1.8	47
$Sb_3O_6(OH)$, or $Sb_2O_4 \cdot nH_2O$, Stibiconite	1.8	66
$Mn_3Al_2Si_3O_{12}$, Spessartite	1.80	298
$K_2PbCu(NO_2)_6$	1.80	105
$ZnAl_2O_4$, Gahnite	1.805	76
$SeCl_4$	1.807	35
$Y_3Al_2Al_3O_{12}$, Yttrogarnet	1.823	298
K_2PtCl_6	1.827	47
$FeAl_2O_4$, Hercynite	1.83	75
$Fe_3Al_2Si_3O_{12}$, Almandite	1.830	298
CaO, Lime	1.837	57
$Na_2U_2O_7 \cdot nH_2O$	1.84	84
$MnAl_2O_4$, Galaxite	1.848	76
$Ca_3Cr_2Si_3O_{12}$, Uvarovite	1.86	298
SrO	1.870	58
$Ca_3Fe_2Si_3O_{12}$, Andradite	1.895	299
$Sb_3O_6(OH)$ or $Sb_2O_4 \cdot nH_2O$, Stibiconite	1.9	66
$MgCr_2O_4$, Magnesiochromite	1.90	75
Y_2O_3	1.910	59

Substance	n	Page
$MnAl_2O_4$	1.923	76
$Pb_2SO_4(OH)_2$	1.93	173
$CuCl$	1.930	19
Mg_2FeO_3	1.95	57
LiI	1.955	17
Mg_2TiO_4	1.959	77
$NaCaCb_2O_6F$, Pyrochlore	1.96	85
$CuCl$, Nantokite	1.973	19
BaO	1.980	58
S (Liquid)	1.998	4
$Sb_3O_6(OH)$ or $Sb_2O_4 \cdot nH_2O$, Stibiconite	2.0	66
Hg_3OCl_4	2.001	51
S_9Se (Liquid)	2.025	4
$MgCr_2O_4$	2.035	75
$PbCu(OH)_2Cl_2$, Percylite	2.05	31
$(Na,Ca)_2Ta_2O_6(O,OH,F)$, Microlite	2.055	85
S_8Se_2 (Liquid)	2.06	4
$AgCl$, Chlorargyrite	2.071	17
Li_2TiO_3	2.087	72
Sb_2O_3, Senarmonite	2.087	61
S_7Se_3 (Liquid)	2.10	4
SnI_4	2.106	35
SrS	2.107	9
$CuBr$	2.116	19
P	2.117	5
$MgFe_2O_3$	2.12	57
$FeCr_2O_4$, Chromite	2.12	76
CaS, Oldhamite	2.137	9
S_6Se_4 (Liquid)	2.15	4
BaS	2.155	9
MnO, Manganosite	2.19	57
ThO_2, Thorianite	2.2	62
AgI, Miersite	2.20	20
Se_5S_5 (Liquid)	2.20	4
$SrSe$	2.220	11
MnO	2.23	57
$TlCl$	2.247	18
$AgBr$, Bromargyrite	2.252	17
$BaSe$	2.268	11
NiO, Bunsenite	2.27	58

Substance	n	Page
Se_6S_4 (Liquid)	2.27	4
MgS	2.271	9
CaSe	2.274	11
$2AgBr \cdot 1AgI$	2.299	17
FeO, Wustitie	2.32	57
CuI, Marshite	2.345	19
Fe	2.36	3
$ZnFe_2O_4$, Franklinite	2.36	76
$1AgBr \cdot 2AgI$	2.36	17
ZnS	2.368	10
Se_7S_3 (Liquid)	2.37	4
$CaTiO_3$, Perovskite	2.38	81
$MgFe_2O_4$, Magnesioferrite	2.39	76
$CdFe_2O_4$	2.39	76
$BaTiO_3$	2.40	81
$LiFeO_2$	2.40	72
SrTe	2.408	12
$SrTiO_3$	2.409	79
TlBr	2.418	19
C, Diamond	2.4195	5
$Fe''Fe_2'''O_4$, Magnetite	2.42	76
Bi_2O_3, Sillenite	2.42	61
BaTe	2.440	12
$4TlBr \cdot 1TlI$	2.468	19
ZnS	2.47	10
MgSe	2.48	11
CdO	2.49	58
Se_8S_2 (Liquid)	2.49	4
CdS, Hawleyite	2.5	10
$1TlBr \cdot 1TlI$	2.567	19
Fe_2O_3, Maghemite, Oxymagnite	2.6	76
CaTe	2.605	12
SiC	2.65	6
$1TlBr \cdot 3TlI$	2.662	19
Se_9S (Liquid)	2.67	4
MnS_2, Hauerite	2.69	12
MnS, Alabandite	2.70	11
Cu_2O, Cuprite	2.705	57
TlI	2.78	19
ZnSe	2.89	12

Substance	n	Page
$(Cu,Fe)_{12}As_4S_{13}$, Tennantite	2.914	13
Se (Liquid)	2.92	4
P (Amorphous)	3.0	5
$(Cu,Fe)_{12}Sb_4S_{13}$, Tetrahedrite	3.128	13
PbS, Galena	3.912	11
PbS	4.71	11
FeS_2, Pyrite	6.22	12

Table II

DETERMINATIVE TABLES

II. Anisotropic Crystalline Solids

Arranged by birefringence, n_z-n_x, within groups based on n_y (or n_o)

No. on Chart	Substance	n_x	n_y	n_z	n_z-n_x	2V	Page
1	$LiBeF_3$		1.33				35
1	$LiNaB_2F_6$		1.33				35
1	Li_2BeF_4		1.34				35
1	$CáBeF_4$		1.355			00	25
1	$CsBF_4$		1.36				43
1	KBF_4, Avogadrite	1.3239	1.3245	1.3247	0.0008	-75	43
2	K_2LiAlF_6	1.390	1.391		0.001	-00	43
3	Na_3AlF_6, Cryolite	1.3376	1.3377	1.3387	0.0011	+43	42
4	NH_4F		1.3147	1.3160	0.0013	+00	21
4	H_2O, Ice		1.3091	1.3104	0.0014	+00	57
5	$Ca(BF_4)_2$		1.36		0.002	-15	49
2	K_2MgF_4	1.377	1.379		0.002	-00	36
·2	K_2GeF_6	1.381	1.383		0.002	-00	47
3	NH_4LiSO_4		1.437		0.002	+40	126
6	Na_2GeF_6	1.324	1.327		0.003	-00	46
6	$(NH_4)_2GeF_6$	1.425	1.428		0.003	-00	47
7	Na_3SO_4F, Schairerite		1.436	1.439	0.003	+00	173
6	Na_2SiF_6, Malladrite	1.3089	1.3125		0.0036	-00	46
8	$Li_2SiF_6 \cdot 2H_2O$	1.296	1.298	1.300	0.004	-90	46
8	K_2TaF_7	1.414	1.417	1.418	0.004	-75	48
8	$Na_2HPO_4 \cdot 12H_2O$	1.4321	1.4361	1.4373	0.0052	-57	192
9	$CoSiF_6 \cdot 6H_2O$		1.3817	1.3872	0.0055	+00	50
10	$NaBF_4$, Ferrucite	1.301	1.3012	1.3068	0.0058	+11	43
11	$Na_5Al_3F_{14}$, Chiolite	1.3424	1.3486		0.0062	-00	43
12	Na_2TiF_6	1.412	1.419		0.007	-00	47
13	$NaCaAlF_6 \cdot H_2O$, Thomsenolite	1.4072	1.4136	1.4150	0.0078	-50	48
14	NH_4HF_2	1.385	1.390	1.394	0.009	-10	21
15	$NaPO_3 \cdot 2H_2O$		1.400		0.009	+70	212
15	$NaCaAlF_6 \cdot H_2O$, Pachnolite	1.411	1.413	1.420	0.009	+76	48
16	$NaHF_2$		1.32	1.33	0.01	+00	21
16	$MgZnF_4$		1.40	1.41	0.01	+00	25
	$Zn(BF_4)_2$		1.36		0.011		48
17	KHF_2	1.342	1.354		0.012	-00	21
18	MgF_2, Sellaite		1.378	1.390	0.012	+00	23
	$Mn(BF_4)_2$	1.346	1.35	1.359	0.013	30	49
19	$ZnSiF_6 \cdot 6H_2O$		1.3824	1.3956	0.0132	+00	50
	$Mg(BF_4)_2$		1.36		0.014	00	49
	$Co(BF_4)_2$		1.40		0.014	00	49
20	$CoF_2 \cdot 5HF \cdot 6H_2O$		1.384	1.399	0.015	+00	54
21	$(NH_4)_2SiF_6$, Bararite	1.391		1.406	0.015	-00	46
20	$NiSiF_6 \cdot 6H_2O$		1.3910	1.4066	0.0156	+00	50
22	$NiF_2 \cdot 5HF \cdot 6H_2O$		1.392	1.408	0.016	+00	54
22	$MgSiF_6 \cdot 6H_2O$		1.3439	1.3602	0.0163	+00	50
23	$MnSiF_6 \cdot 6H_2O$		1.3570	1.3742	0.0172	+00	50
24	$KF \cdot 2H_2O$	1.345	1.352	1.363	0.018	+85	23
25	NH_4HF_2	1.368	1.385	1.387	0.019	-40	21
26	$FeSiF_6 \cdot 6H_2O$		1.3638	1.3848	0.0210	+00	50
27	$Na_2SO_4 \cdot 10H_2O$, Mirabilite	1.396	1.4103	1.419	0.023	-76	136
28	$CaCl_2 \cdot 6H_2O$	1.393	1.417		0.024	-00	28
29	NH_3BF_3	1.335	1.345	1.36	0.025	90	54
30	$(NH_2OH)_2 \cdot H_2GeF_6 \cdot 2H_2O$	1.418	1.438	1.443	0.025	-60	54
31	$2NaH_2PO_3 \cdot 5H_2O$	1.4193	1.4309	1.4493	0.0300	-78	211
32	$Na_2CO_3 \cdot 10H_2O$, Natron	1.405	1.425	1.440	0.035	-71	91
33	$KB_5O_8 \cdot 4H_2O$	1.422	1.436	1.480	0.058	+70	116
34	$NH_4B_5O_8 \cdot 4H_2O$	1.427	1.431	1.486	0.059	+30	117
35	$NaNO_2$	1.340	1.425	1.655	0.315	+15	106

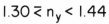

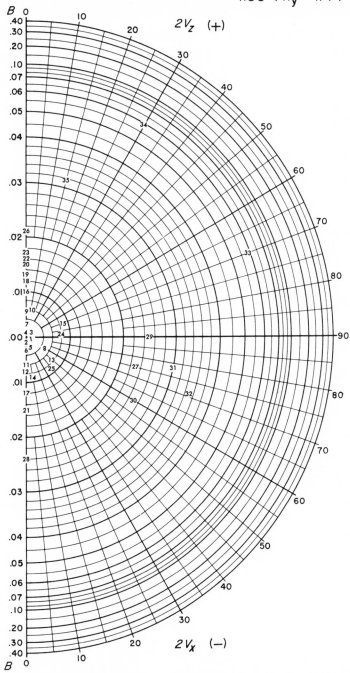

A

343

No. on Chart	Substance	n_x	n_y	n_z	$n_z - n_x$	2V	Page
	CuS, Covellite		1.45			+ 00	11
1	K_2NbF_7	1.437	1.44	1.440	0.003		48
2	$5(Na_3PO_4 \cdot 12H_2O) \cdot Na(OH)$		1.447	1.452	0.005	+ 00	205
2	$4(Na_3PO_4 \cdot 11H_2O) \cdot NaOCl$		1.450	1.455	0.005	+ 00	205
3	$4(Na_3PO_4 \cdot 11H_2O)NaNO_3$		1.444	1.450	0.006	+ 00	215
3	$5(Na_3PO_4 \cdot 11H_2O) \cdot NaCl$		1.447	1.453	0.006	+ 00	205
4	$Na_2HAsO_4 \cdot 12H_2O$	1.4453	1.4496	1.4513	0.0060	- 65	192
3	$Na_3PO_4 \cdot 12H_2O$		1.4458	1.4524	0.0066	+ 00	196
5	$Na_4PO_4BO_2 \cdot 18H_2O$	1.445	1.451	1.453	0.008	- 60	215
6	$Na_3AsO_4 \cdot 12H_2O$		1.4589	1.4669	0.008	+ 00	196
7	$NaPO_3 \cdot 2H_2O$	1.432	1.441		0.009	- 00	212
8	$Na_2SiO_3 \cdot 9H_2O$	1.451	1.455	1.460	0.009	+85	282
7	$SrZnF_4$	1.446	1.455		0.009	- 00	25
9	$Na_2HPO_3 \cdot 5H_2O$	1.443	1.443	1.4434	0.01	+44	211
10	$Na_4P_2O_7 \cdot 10H_2O$	1.4499	1.4525	1.4604	0.0104	+61	214
11	$Na_2HPO_4 \cdot 7H_2O$	1.4412	1.4424	1.4526	0.0114	+39	192
12	$Na(NH_4,K)SO_4 \cdot 2H_2O$, Lecontite	1.440	1.452	1.453	0.013	- 40	136
13	$Na_2SiO_3 \cdot 5H_2O$	1.447	1.454	1.467	0.020	+70	282
14	$KAl(SO_4)_2 \cdot 12H_2O$, Kalinite	1.429	1.456		0.027	- 00	158
15	$KAl(SO_4)_2 \cdot 12H_2O$	1.430	1.452	1.458	0.028	- 52	158
15	$MgSO_4 \cdot 7H_2O$, Epsomite	1.4325	1.4554	1.4608	0.0283	- 51	162
16	$NH_4NaHPO_4 \cdot 4H_2O$, Stercorite	1.439	1.442	1.469	0.030	+36	193
17	$MgSO_4 \cdot 6H_2O$, Hexahydrite	1.426	1.453	1.456	0.030	- 38	166
18	$Na_5P_3O_{10} \cdot 6H_2O$	1.449	1.450	1.482	0.033	+20	214
19	$CuF_2 \cdot 5HF \cdot 6H_2O$	1.395	1.440	1.444	0.049	- 32	55
20	$Rb_2S_2O_6$		1.4565	1.5068	0.0503	+ 00	121
21	$K_2S_2O_6$		1.4550	1.5153	0.0603	+ 00	121
22	$B(OH)_3$	1.340	1.456	1.459	0.119	- 10	71
23	$Co(NO_3)_2 \cdot 6H_2O$	1.38	1.44	1.52	0.14	- 35	103
24	$Na_2CrO_4 \cdot 4H_2O$	1.321	1.447	1.561	0.240	- 80	137

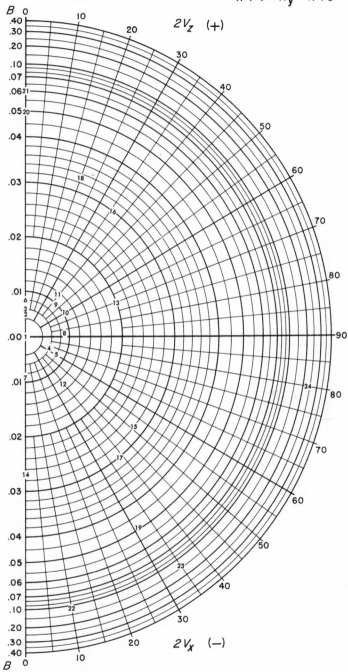

$1.44 \stackrel{=}{<} n_y < 1.46$

B

$2V_z$ (+)

$2V_x$ (−)

B

345

No. on Chart	Substance	n_x	n_y	n_z	$n_z - n_x$	2V	Page
	RbHSO$_4$		1.473			- 56	123
1	LiKSO$_4$	1.4717	1.4723		0.0006	- 00	124
2	P$_2$O$_5$		1.469	1.471	0.002	+00	66
3	Ca$_2$Al$_2$(IO$_6$)$_2$(OH)$_{18}$ · 24H$_2$O	1.471	1.471		0.002	- 00	112
	Ca$_6$Al$_2$O$_9$(IO$_3$)$_2$ · 33H$_2$O		1.471		0.002		86
4	KClO$_4$	1.4731	1.4737	1.4769	0.0038	+50	110
4	RbClO$_4$	1.4692	1.4701	1.4731	0.0039	+55	111
4	SiO$_2$, Tridymite	1.469	1.469	1.473	0.004	+35	64
5	NaSi$_2$AlO$_6$ · 3H$_2$O, Gmelinite	1.46	1.46	1.46	0.005	- 15	240
6	(NH$_4$)$_3$ScF$_6$		1.47		0.005	- 00	44
7	K$_2$Si$_4$O$_9$	1.477	1.479	1.482	0.005	+60	286
8	Na$_2$H$_2$P$_2$O$_7$ · 6H$_2$O	1.4599	1.4645	1.4649	0.0050	- 32	214
9	CsClO$_4$	1.4752	1.4788	1.4804	0.0052	- 62	111
10	Ca$_6$Al$_2$(SO$_4$)$_3$(OH)$_{12}$ · 26H$_2$O, Ettringite	1.458	1.464		0.006	- 00	176
11	Na$_2$CaSi$_{20}$Al$_4$O$_{48}$ · 14H$_2$O, Mordenite	1.474	1.477	1.480	0.006	- 70	245
12	NaPO$_3$	1.474	1.478	1.480	0.006	- 80	212
13	(NH$_4$)$_2$Mg(SO$_4$)$_2$ · 6H$_2$O, Boussingaultite	1.4716	1.4730	1.4786	0.0070	+51	142
14	Na$_2$SiO$_3$ · 8H$_2$O	1.457	1.463	1.465	0.008	- 63	282
15	Mg$_3$(PO$_4$)$_2$ · 22H$_2$O	1.461	1.465	1.469	0.008	- 90	198
16	Al$_2$SO$_4$(OH)$_{10}$ · 10H$_2$O, Parluminite	1.463	1.471	1.471	0.008	- 25	175
17	Ca$_6$Al$_2$O$_9$ · 33H$_2$O	1.466	1:475		0.009	- 00	82
18	ZnF$_2$ · 4H$_2$O	1.46	1.468	1.47	0.01	- 50	30
19	Li$_2$SO$_4$		1.465		0.01	- 72	129
20	Al$_2$(SO$_4$)$_3$ · 15H$_2$O, Alunogen	1.460	1.461	1.470	0.010	+31	172
21	CaZnF$_4$	1.455	1.465		0.010	- 00	25
22	Rb$_2$Mg(SO$_4$)$_2$ · 6H$_2$O	1.4672	1.4689	1.4779	0.0107	+49	142
23	NH$_4$ZnF$_3$		1.47	1.481	0.011	+00	37
	K$_2$HfF$_6$	1.449	1.461		0.012		47
24	(N$_2$H$_4$)$_2$ · H$_2$GeF$_6$	1.452	1.460	1.464	0.012	- 85	54
25	Li(OH)	1.452	1.464		0.012	- 00	68
26	NaClO$_4$	1.4606	1.4617	1.4730	0.0124	+25	110
27	Na$_2$B$_4$O$_7$ · 5H$_2$O, Tincalconite	1.461	1.474		0.013	+00	115
28	Na$_3$PO$_4$ · 8H$_2$O	1.458	1.468	1.471	0.013	- 58	197
29	Na$_2$SO$_4$, Thenardite	1.471	1.477	1.484	0.013	+84	125
30	NaAl(SO$_4$)$_2$ · 12H$_2$O	1.449	1.461	1.463	0.014	- 56	158
31	Na$_2$Si$_3$Al$_2$O$_{10}$ · 2H$_2$O, Natrolite	1.475	1.479	1.489	0.014	+62	245
32	NH$_4$NaHAsO$_4$ · 4H$_2$O	1.4649	1.4663	1.4791	0.0142	+38	192
33	FeSO$_4$ · 7H$_2$O, Melanterite	1.4713	1.4782	1.4856	0.0143	+85	167
34	K$_2$Mg(SO$_4$)$_2$ · 6H$_2$O, Picromerite	1.4607	1.4629	1.4755	0.0148	+48	142
35	Na(OH)	1.457	1.470	1.472	0.015	- 50	68
36	Na$_3$(PO$_4$) · 6H$_2$O	1.462	1.473	1.477	0.015	- 60	197
37	Na$_2$HAsO$_4$ · 7H$_2$O	1.4622	1.4658	1.4782	0.016	+57	192
38	Na$_3$PO$_4$ · 7H$_2$O	1.462	1.470	1.478	0.016	+85	197
39	KPO$_3$		1.465	1.483	0.018	+00	211
40	Na$_3$HP$_2$O$_6$ · 9H$_2$O	1.4653	1.4738	1.4804	0.0182	- 82	213
41	Na$_2$SiO$_3$ · 6H$_2$O	1.465	1.473	1.485	0.020	+70	282
42	Na$_4$P$_2$O$_7$	1.475	1.477	1.496	0.021	+40	214
43	Na$_2$B$_4$O$_7$ · 10H$_2$O, Borax	1.4467	1.4694	1.4724	0.0257	- 39	116
44	Na$_2$HPO$_4$ · 2H$_2$O	1.450	1.461	1.477	0.027	+80	192
45	Na$_5$P$_3$O$_{10}$	1.477	1.478	1.504	0.027	+21	214
46	KMgCl$_3$ · 6H$_2$O, Carnallite	1.4665	1.4753	1.4937	0.0272	+70	39
47	Li$_2$SO$_4$ · H$_2$O	1.459	1.477	1.488	0.029	- 78	136
48	Na$_2$B$_4$O$_7$ · 4H$_2$O, Kernite	1.455	1.472	1.487	0.032	- 80	115
49	BeSO$_4$ · 4H$_2$O	1.4395	1.4720		0.0325	- 00	160
50	Be$_2$(C$_2$H$_5$)$_2$(SO$_4$)$_2$O · 4H$_2$O	1.435	1.473		0.038	- 00	177
51	NaHSO$_4$ · H$_2$O	1.43	1.46	1.47	0.04	- 50	136
52	Na(OH) · 2H$_2$O	1.435	1.470	1.475	0.040	- 45	68
53	NaH$_2$PO$_4$ · 2H$_2$O	1.4401	1.4629	1.4815	0.0414	- 83	193
54	K$_2$ZrF$_6$	1.454	1.465	1.498	0.044	+60	47
55	CaCl$_2$ · 4H$_2$O	1.447	1.477	1.491	0.044	- 68	27
56	NaBO$_2$ · 2H$_2$O	1.439	1.473	1.484	0.045	- 58	115
57	KHSO$_4$, Mercallite	1.445	1.460	1.491	0.046	+56	123
58	NH$_4$HSO$_4$	1.463	1.473	1.510	0.047	+60	123
59	Rb$_2$S$_2$O$_3$		1.46	1.51	0.0504	+00	120
60	MgCO$_3$ · 5H$_2$O, Lansfordite	1.456	1.469	1.508	0.052	- 60	94
61	K$_2$S$_2$O$_8$	1.4609	1.4669	1.5657	0.1048	+30	122
62	B(OH)$_3$, Sassolite	1.337	1.461	1.462	0.125	- 10	71
63	NaNO$_2$	1.354	1.460	1.648	0 294	+75	106

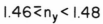

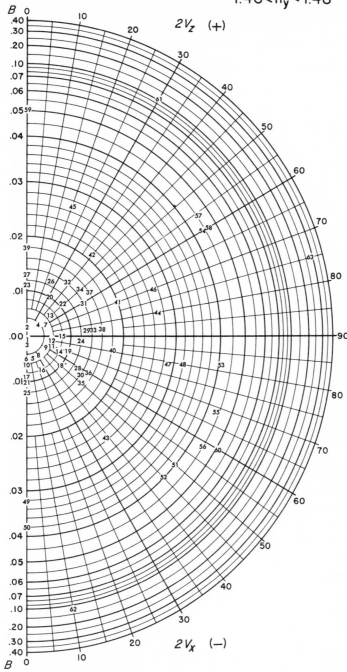

$1.46 \lesssim n_y < 1.48$

$2V_z$ (+)

$2V_x$ (−)

C

347

No. on Chart	Substance	n_x	n_y	n_z	$n_z - n_x$	2V	Page
	$RbSi_2AlO_6 \cdot H_2O$		1.481			00	227
	$CaAl_2O_4 \cdot 10H_2O$		1.48			+00	83
1	SiO_2, Cristobalite	1.484	1.487		0.003	- 00	63
2	$Na_6Mg(SO_4)_4$, Vanthoffite	1.4855	1.4876	1.4893	0.0038	- 84	132
3	$Na_2Mg(SO_4)_2 \cdot 4H_2O$, Bloedite	1.4826	1.4855	1.4869	0.0041	- 71	138
4	$NaSi_2AlO_6 \cdot 3H_2O$	1.48	1.48	1.48	0.005	- 15	240
5	Na_2SO_4	1.480	1.48	1.485	0.005	90	125
6	$K_2Si_6Al_2O_{16} \cdot 7H_2O(?)$, Stilbite, Potassium	1.478	1.481	1.483	0.005	- 70	249
7	$Na_8K_2(SO_4)_5$		1.485	1.490	0.005	+00	124
8	$MgSeO_4 \cdot 6H_2O$	1.4856	1.4892	1.4911	0.0055	- 28	166
9	$Cs_2Mg(SO_4)_2 \cdot 6H_2O$	1.4857	1.4858	1.4916	0.0059	+18	143
	$CaSi_4Al_2O_{12} \cdot 6H_2O$, Chabazite	1.48		1.48	0.006	15	240
10	$Ca_6Fe_2(SO_4)_3(OH)_{12} \cdot 26H_2O$		1.486	1.492	0.006	+00	176
11	NH_4ClO_4	1.4818	1.4833	1.4881	0.0063	+70	110
12	$Ca_5Al_2O_8 \cdot 34H_2O$	1.480	1.487		0.007	- 00	83
13	$MgAl_2(SO_4)_4 \cdot 22H_2O$, Pickeringite	1.476	1.480	1.483	0.008	- 60	170
14	$K_2Mg(SO_4)_2 \cdot 4H_2O$, Leonite	1.479	1.482	1.487	0.008	+70	139
14	$(Fe,Zn,Cu)SO_4 \cdot 7H_2O$	1.479	1.483	1.488	0.009	+70	167
15	$Sr_3Fe_2F_{12} \cdot 2H_2O$	1.473	1.480	1.482	0.009	- 55	49
16	$MgHPO_4 \cdot 7H_2O$, Phosphorroesslerite	1.477	1.485	1.486	0.009	- 38	194
17	$Cd(ClO_4)_2 \cdot 6H_2O$	1.480	1.489		0.009	- 00	112
18	$FeAl_2(SO_4)_4 \cdot 22H_2O$, Halotrichite	1.480	1.486	1.490	0.010	- 35	170
19	$K_2H_2P_2O_6 \cdot 3H_2O$	1.4768	1.4843	1.4870	0.0102	- 62	212
20	$CsSO_3F$	1.4645	1.4755		0.011	- 00	172
21	$(NH_4)_2Mn(SO_4)_2 \cdot 6H_2O$	1.4801	1.4840	1.4913	0.0112	+70	145
21	$(NH_4)_2Cd(SO_4)_2 \cdot 6H_2O$	1.4847	1.4887	1.4959	0.0112	+73	144
22	$K_8H_6(SO_4)_7$, Misenite	1.475	1.480	1.487	0.012	+70	123
22	$Rb_2Zn(SO_4)_2 \cdot 6H_2O$	1.4833	1.4884	1.4975	0.0124	+74	144
22	$(Zn,Fe,Mn)Al_2(SO_4)_4 \cdot 22H_2O$, Dietrichite	1.475	1.480	1.488	0.013	+70	171
23	$Al_2(SO_4)_3 \cdot 12H_2O$	1.483	1.484	1.496	0.013	+30	172
24	Bieberite	1.474	1.4820	1.4885	0.0137	- 88	168
24	$CoSO_4 \cdot 7H_2O$	1.4748	1.4820	1.4885	0.0137	- 88	168
25	$Rb_2Mn(SO_4)_2 \cdot 6H_2O$	1.4767	1.4807	1.4907	0.0140	+67	145
26	$Rb_2Cd(SO_4)_2 \cdot 6H_2O$	1.4798	1.4848	1.4948	0.0150	+72	145
27	$Ca_3Al_2O_6 \cdot 18H_2O$	1.479	1.489	1.495	0.016	- 75	83
28	$Rb_2Fe(SO_4)_2 \cdot 6H_2O$	1.4815	1.4874	1.4977	0.0162	+73	146
29	$CaAl_2O_4 \cdot 6H_2O$		1.489	1.507	0.018	+00	83
30	$K_2Cu(SO_4)_2 \cdot 6H_2O$, Cyanochroite	1.4836	1.4864	1.5020	0.0184	+47	148
31	$Na_2H_2P_2O_6 \cdot 6H_2O$	1.4855	1.4897	1.5041	0.0186	+57	213
32	$K_2Zn(SO_4)_2 \cdot 6H_2O$	1.4775	1.4833	1.4969	0.0194	+68	143
32	$K_2Co(SO_4)_2 \cdot 6H_2O$	1.4807	1.4865	1.5004	0.0197	+69	146
33	$CuSO_4 \cdot 7H_2O$, Boothite	1.47	1.48	1.49	0.02	- 80	167
34	$Na_{22}K(CO_3)_2(SO_4)_9Cl$, Hanksite	1.461	1.481		0.020	- 00	178
35	$K_2Fe(SO_4)_2 \cdot 6H_2O$	1.4759	1.4821	1.4969	0.021	+67	146
36	$NiSO_4 \cdot 7H_2O$, Morenosite	1.4693	1.4893	1.4923	0.023	- 42	163
37	$Mg(ClO_4)_2 \cdot 6H_2O$	1.458	1.482		0.024	- 00	111
38	$Na_4P_2O_7 \cdot 10H_2O$	1.4777	1.4822	1.5036	0.0259	+49	213
39	$ZnSO_4 \cdot 7H_2O$, Goslarite	1.4568	1.4801	1.4836	0.0268	- 46	163
40	$ZnSO_4 \cdot 6H_2O$, Bianchite	1.462	1.4895	1.490	0.028	- 15	166
41	$Ni(BF_4)_2$	1.47	1.46	1.50	0.03	+05	49
42	$MnZnF_4$		1.487	1.517	0.030	+00	25
43	$NaHPO_4 \cdot H_2O$	1.4557	1.4852	1.4873	0.0316	- 29	193
44	$LiClO_4 \cdot 3H_2O$	1.448	1.483		0.035	- 00	110
45	$K_4(CO_3)_2 \cdot 3H_2O$	1.474	1.483	1.510	0.036	+66	91
46	$MgB_4O_7 \cdot 9H_2O$	1.442	1.485		0.043	- 00	116
47	$K_3H(SO_4)_2$	1.4793	1.4899	1.5259	0.0466	- 61	123
48	$K_2Mg(CO_3)_2 \cdot 4H_2O$	1.465	1.485	1.535	0.070	+65	96
	$(NH_4)_2B_{10}O_{16} \cdot 5H_2O$, Ammonioborite	1.470	1.487	1.540	0.070	+60	117
49	$Rb_2S_2O_8$	1.4812	1.4888	1.5719	0.0907	+35	122
50	$Na_3SO_4(NO_3) \cdot H_2O$, Darapskite	1.391	1.481	1.486	0.095	- 27	105
51	$KHCO_3$, Kalicinite	1.380	1.482	1.573	0.193	- 82	89
52	$Ca[N(CN)_2]_2 \cdot 2H_2O$	1.405	1.480	1.82	0.415	+50	32

$1.48 \lesssim n_y < 1.49$

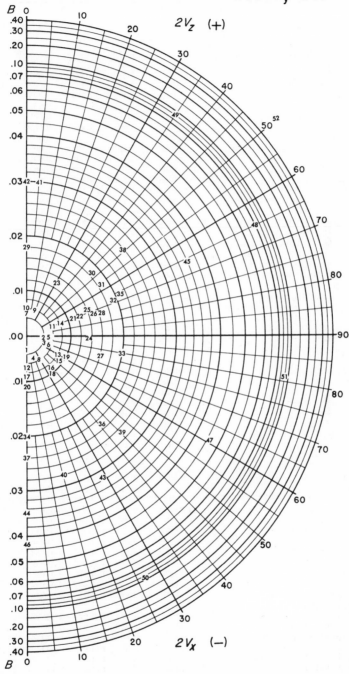

B

$2V_z$ (+)

$2V_x$ (−)

D

349

No. on Chart	Substance	n_x	n_y	n_z	$n_z - n_x$	2V	Page
	$MgSO_4 \cdot 2H_2O$		1.493				164
1	K_2SO_4, Arcanite	1.4935	1.4947	1.4973	0.0038	+67	125
2	$LiNaSO_4$		1.490	1.495	0.005	+00	124
2	$Na_3K_3(SO_4)_3$		1.490	1.495	0.005	+00	124
2	$NaK_3(SO_4)_2$		1.493	1.498	0.005	+00	124
3	$(NH_4)_3UO_2F_5$	1.49	1.495		0.005	-00	37
3	$CaSi_2Al_2O_{10} \cdot 5H_2O$, Levynite	1.491	1.496		0.005	-00	241
2	$Na_2K_4(SO_4)_3$		1.491	1.4965	0.0055	+00	124
	$NaSi_3AlO_8 \cdot H_2O$		1.49		0.006		245
4	$CaSi_6Al_2O_{16} \cdot 5H_2O$, Heulandite	1.497	1.498	1.503	0.006	+32·	249
5	$Na_2K_8(SO_4)_5$		1.4935	1.500	0.0065	+0ŏ	124
	$Na_2SiO_3 \cdot 6H_2O$	1.488		1.495	0.007		282
6	$MgSO_4 \cdot 4H_2O$	1.490	1.491	1.497	0.007	+50	166
7	$K_4P_2O_7$		1.495	1.502	0.007	+00	213
8	$Ca_4Si_8O_{32} \cdot 12H_2O$, Phillipsite	1.493	1.497	1.500	0.007	-70	247
9	$NaNH_2SO_3$	1.494	1.498	1.501	0.007	-83	121
10	$Cs_2Mn(SO_4)_2 \cdot 6H_2O$	1.4946	1.4966	1.5025	0.0079	+60	145
7	$(K,Na)_3Na(SO_4)_2$, Aphthitalite		1.491	1.499	0.008	+00	124
11	$NH_4Mg(PO_4) \cdot 6H_2O$, Struvite	1.495	1.496	1.504	0.009	+37	197
12	$CaSi_6Al_2O_{16} \cdot 7H_2O$, Stilbite	1.49	1.49	1.50	0.01	-40	248
13	$(NH_4)_2Zn(SO_4)_2 \cdot 6H_2O$	1.4888	1.4930	1.4994	0.0106	+79	143
14	$MgSO_4 \cdot 5H_2O$, Pentahydrite	1.482	1.492	1.493	0.011	⁚45	168
15	KOH	1.486	1.492	1.497	0.011	+70	68
16	$(NH_4)_2Fe(SO_4)_2 \cdot 6H_2O$	1.4870	1.4915	1.4989	0.0119	+76	146
17	$NaAl(SO_4)_2 \cdot 6H_2O$, Tamarugite	1.488	1.491	1.500	0.013	+60	160
18	$Ca_4(ClO_4)_2(OH)_6 \cdot 12H_2O$	1.490	1.499	1.503	0.013	-66	113
19	$(NH_4)_2Co(SO_4)_2 \cdot 6H_2O$	1.4902	1.4953	1.5032	0.0130	+82	146
20	NH_4PO_3	1.490		1.505	0.015	+70	211
21	$Fe(ClO_4)_2 \cdot 6H_2O$	1.478	1.493		0.015	-00	111
22	Na_3PO_4	1.493	1.499	1.508	0.015	+76	189
23	$Rb_2Cu(SO_4)_2 \cdot 6H_2O$	1.4886	1.4906	1.5036	0.0150	+45	149
22	$Rb_2Co(SO_4)_2 \cdot 6H_2O$	1.4859	1.4916	1.5014	0.0155	+75	147
24	$Rb_2Ni(SO_4)_2 \cdot 6H_2O$	1.4895	1.4961	1.5052	0.0157	+82	148
25	$Mn(ClO_4)_2 \cdot 6H_2O$	1.475	1.492		0.017	-00	111
26	$AlF_3 \cdot H_2O$	1.489	1.495	1.506	0.017	+76	33
27	$K_2Mg(SeO_4)_2 \cdot 6H_2O$	1.4969	1.4991	1.5139	0.0170	+40	149
28	$Na_4Mg_2(SO_4)_4 \cdot 5H_2O$, Loeweite	1.471	1.490		0.019	-00	137
29	$K_2Ni(SO_4)_2 \cdot 6H_2O$	1.4836	1.4916	1.5051	0.0215	+75	147
	$Na_{56}Si_{42}Al_{38}O_{169} \cdot 24H_2O$		1.498		0.022	00	240
30	$Sr(OH)_2 \cdot 8H_2O$	1.476	1.499		0.023	-00	68
31	$Na_3PO_4 \cdot H_2O$		1.497	1.522	0.025	+00	197
32	$Na_6(PO_4)_2 \cdot H_2O$		1.499	1.525	0.026	+00	197
33	KNH_2SO_3	1.487	1.490	1.515	0.028	+26	121
34	CaP_4O_{11}	1.470	1.497	1.499	0.029	-15	215
35	$H_6(PO_4)_2 \cdot H_2O$	1.485	1.492	1.519	0.034	+56	197
36	$CoSO_4 \cdot 6H_2O$	1.460	1.495		0.035	-00	161
37	$Na_2S_2O_6 \cdot 2H_2O$	1.4820	1.4953	1.5185	0.0365	+75	134
38	$AlF_3 \cdot H_2O$, Fluellite	1.473	1.490	1.511	0.038	+80	33
39	$Ca(NO_3)_2 \cdot 4H_2O$, Nitrocalcite	1.465	1.498	1.504	0.039	-50	103
	$(NH_4)_2MnF_5$	1.46		1.50	0.04		44
40	$Na_6CO_3(SO_4)_2$, Burkeite	1.450	1.490	1.492	0.042	-34	178
41	Na_2HPO_4	1.483	1.499	1.525	0.042	+78	187
42	$Mg_2UO_2(CO_3)_3 \cdot 18H_2O$, Bayleyite	1.455	1.490	1.500	0.045	-30	99
43	$UO_2(NO_3)_2 \cdot 6H_2O$	1.482	1.494	1.572	0.090	-46	105
44	$Na_4(CO_3)_2 \cdot 5H_2O$	1.435	1.492	1.547	0.112	-70	91
45	$Na_3H(CO_3)_2 \cdot 2H_2O$, Trona	1.412	1.492	1.540	0.128	-72	89
46	$NH_4(NO_3)$		1.493	1.623	0.130	+00	101
47	$Li(NO_3) \cdot 3H_2O$	1.365	1.490	1.523	0.158	-55	102

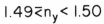

1.49 ≲ n_y < 1.50

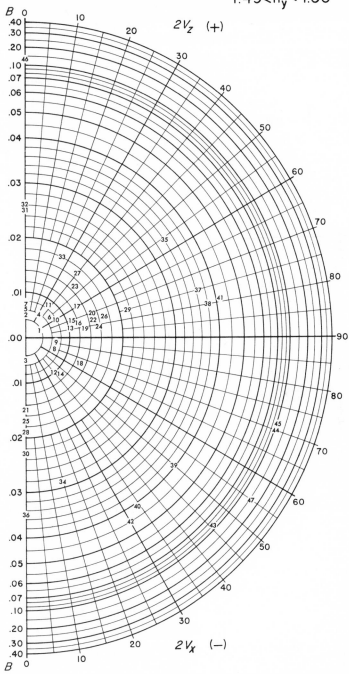

E

351

No. on Chart	Substance	n_x	n_y	n_z	n_z-n_x	2V	Page
	$Cu(BF_4)_2 \cdot 6H_2O$		1.50			- 70	49
	$(NH_4)_2ZnCl_4$		1.5055			+ 54	37
	$Ce_2(S_2O_6)_3 \cdot 15H_2O$		1.507			- 89	135
1	$Na_2Ca_2Si_9Al_6O_{30} \cdot 8H_2O$	1.5073	1.5074	1.5075	0.0002	- 85	246
1	$Na_2Ca_2Si_9Al_6O_{30} \cdot 8H_2O$, Mesolite	1.5048	1.5050	1.5053	0.0005	- 85	246
2	KSi_2AlO_6		1.508	1.509	0.001	+ 00	227
2	$K_2MgSi_5O_{12}$		1.505		0.002		254
3	$Ba_2Si_{11}Al_4O_{38} \cdot 10H_2O$, Harmotome	1.503	1.505	1.508	0.005	+ 79	248
4	$2NaSiAlO_4 \cdot H_2O$	1.503	1.506	1.508	0.005	- 70	242
5	$Na_{26}Si_{22}Al_{18}O_{84} \cdot 12H_2O$	1.495	1.502		0.007	- 00	240
6	$LiNH_2SO_3$		1.507		0.007	- 48	121
7	$Cs_2Zn(SO_4)_2 \cdot 6H_2O$	1.5022	1.5048	1.5093	0.0071	+ 74	144
7	$Cs_2Co(SO_4)_2 \cdot 6H_2O$	1.5057	1.5085	1.5132	0.0075	+ 82	147
8	$Cs_2Cd(SO_4)_2 \cdot 6H_2O$	1.4975	1.5000	1.5062	0.0087	+ 68	145
9	$Cs_2Fe(SO_4)_2 \cdot 6H_2O$	1.5003	1.5035	1.5094	0.0091	+ 75	146
10	$(NH_4)_2Mg(SeO_4)_2 \cdot 6H_2O$	1.5070	1.5093	1.5169	0.0099	+ 55	149
11	$Na_2Fe(SO_4)_2 \cdot 4H_2O$	1.493	1.500	1.503	0.010	- 60	138
12	$K_2Al_6H_{10}(PO_4)_{10} \cdot 15H_2O$	1.495	1.504	1.505	0.010	- 25	196
11	$K_2Si_2O_5$	1.503	1.509	1.513	0.010	- 60	256
10	$Cs_2Cu(SO_4)_2 \cdot 6H_2O$	1.5048	1.5061	1.5153	0.0105	+ 43	149
13	$BaFeF_5 \cdot H_2O$	1.502	1.503	1.513	0.011	+ 20	49
14	$Na_2Si_2O_5$	1.497	1.505	1.508	0.011	- 52	255
15	$Rb_2Mg(SeO_4)_2 \cdot 6H_2O$	1.5011	1.5031	1.5135	0.0124	+ 47	149
16	$(NH_4)_2Ni(SO_4)_2 \cdot 6H_2O$	1.4949	1.5007	1.5081	0.0132	+ 87	148
17	$Na_3(VO_4) \cdot 12H_2O$		1.5095	1.5232	0.0137	+ 00	196
18	$(NH_4)_2Cu(SO_4)_2 \cdot 6H_2O$	1.4910	1.5007	1.5054	0.0144	- 69	148
19	$Ca_4Al_2O_7 \cdot SO_3 \cdot 12H_2O$	1.488	1.504		0.016	- 00	86
19	$Ca_4Al_2SO_4(OH)_{12} \cdot 6H_2O$	1.488	1.504		0.016	- 00	175
20	$MnSO_4 \cdot 5H_2O$	1.495	1.508	1.514	0.019	- 60	170
21	$Na_3K(PO_3)_4$	1.493	1.500	1.514	0.021	- 40	211
22	$Zn(ClO_4)_2 \cdot 6H_2O$	1.487	1.508		0.021	- 00	112
23	$KMgSO_4Cl \cdot 3H_2O$, Kainite	1.494	1.505	1.516	0.022	- 85	176
24	$Al(OH)Si_2O_5 \cdot 2H_2O$, Leverrierite	1.485	1.509	1.510	0.025	- 10	265
25	$NaCaB_5O_9 \cdot 8H_2O$, Ulexite	1.493	1.505	1.519	0.026	+ 73	116
26	$Cu(ClO_4)_2 \cdot 6H_2O$	1.495	1.505	1.522	0.027	+ 54	112
27	$MgB_4O_4(OH)_3 \cdot 15H_2O$, Inderite	1.488	1.508	1.515	0.027	- 63	118
28	$Ca(NH_2SO_3)_2 \cdot 3H_2O$	1.488	1.508	1.512	0.029	- 48	134
29	$K_2Si_2O_5 \cdot H_2O$		1.50		0.03	+ 10	259
30	$K_2SiO_3 \cdot H_2O$		1.50		0.03	+ 25	282
31	$K_4Si_2O_6 \cdot H_2O$		1.50		0.03	+ 85	281
32	$Ca_4Al_2(NO_3)_2(OH)_{12} \cdot 4H_2O$		1.502	1.532	0.030	+ 00	104
32	$Ca_4Al_2O_6(NO_3)_2 \cdot 10H_2O$		1.502	1.532	0.030	+ 00	86
33	$Ba(OH)_2 \cdot 8H_2O$	1.471	1.5017	1.502	0.031	- 09	69
34	$MgCl_2 \cdot 6H_2O$, Bischofite	1.495	1.507	1.528	0.033	+ 79	27
35	NaH_2PO_4	1.481	1.507	1.517	0.036	- 64	187
36	$BeSeO_4 \cdot 4H_2O$	1.4664	1.5007	1.5027	0.0363	- 26	161
37	$KHSi_2O_5$	1.495	1.501	1.535	0.040	+ 40	258
38	KH_2PO_4	1.4684	1.5095		0.0411	- 00	187
39'	$CaSO_4$		1.505	1.548	0.043	+ 00	129
40	$2MgB_6O_{10} \cdot 15H_2O$	1.463	1.5081		0.045	- 00	117
41	$NaH_2AsO_4 \cdot 2H_2O$	1.4794	1.5021	1.5265	0.0471	+ 89	193
42	$Na_2S_2O_3 \cdot 5H_2O$	1.4886	1.5079	1.5360	0.0474	+ 81	135
41	$NaAsO_3$	1.479	1.502	1.5265	0.0475	+ 88	211
43	H_3PO_4	1.455	1.504	1.505	0.050	- 12	189
	$CaSO_4$	1.50		1.56	0.06		129
44	$Na_2Ca(CO_3)_2 \cdot 2H_2O$, Pirssonite	1.5043	1.5095	L.5751	0.0694	+ 31	96
45	$NH_4(NO_3)$		1.509	1.585	0.076	+ 00	101
46	$(NH_4)_2S_2O_8$	1.4981	1.5016	1.5866	0.0885	+ 24	122
47	$Na_2CO_3 \cdot H_2O$	1.420	1.506	1.524	0.104	- 48	90
48	$MgCO_3 \cdot 3H_2O$, Nesquehonite	1.417	1.503	1.527	0.110	- 53	94
49	$Bo(OH)$	1.378	1.503	1.507	0.129	- 23	69
50	$K(NO_3)$, Niter	1.3346	1.5056	1.5064	0.1718	- 07	101
51	$NaHCO_3$, Nahcolite	1.380	1.500	1.586	0.206	- 75	89
52	$Mg(NO_3)_2 \cdot 6H_2O$, Nitromagnesite	1.34	1.506	1.506	0.266	- 05	103

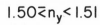

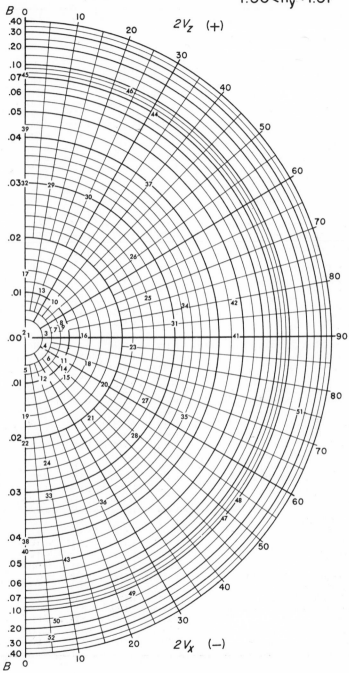

F

No. on Chart	Substance	n_x	n_y	n_z	$n_z - n_x$	2V	Page
	$K_4Cd_2(SO_4)_4 \cdot 3H_2O$		1.51			- 64	138
	$K_4Mn_2(SO_4)_4 \cdot 3H_2O$		1.512			+61	138
1	Rb_2SO_4	1.5131	1.5133	1.5144	0.0013	+ 42	127
2	$Hg(ClO_4)_2 \cdot 6H_2O$	1.509	1.511		0.002	- 00	112
3	$Th(SO_4)_2 \cdot 8H_2O$		1.5168		0.002	+76	172
4	$K_2Al_3H_4(PO_4)_5 \cdot 11H_2O$	1.510	1.51	1.515	0.005	+ 25	195
5	$Li_2K_4Si_6O_{15}$	1.510	1.5125	1.515	0.005	- 87	256
6	$NaSiAlO_4$	1.509	1.514	1.514	0.005	- 12	224
7	$LiAlSi_2O_6$		1.519	1.524	0.005	+00	280
4	$Cs_2Mg(SeO_4)_2 \cdot 6H_2O$	1.5178	1.5179	1.5236	0.0058	+ 19	150
	$Na_2H_2P_2O_7$	1.51		1.517	0.007		214
8	$NaCa_2Si_5Al_5O_{20} \cdot 6H_2O$, Thomsonite	1.511	1.513	1.518	0.007	+75	243
9	$Cs_2Ni(SO_4)_2 \cdot 6H_2O$	1.5087	1.5129	1.5162	0.0075	- 87	148
10	$CaSi_3Al_2O_{10} \cdot 3H_2O$, Scolecite	1.5122	1.5187	1.5194	0.0083	- 36	246
11	$CaB_2O_4 \cdot 6H_2O$	1.505	1.511	1.515	0.010	- 77	116
12	$CaSi_4Al_2O_{12} \cdot 4H_2O$, Leonhardite	1.505	1.514	1.516	0.011	- 27	247
13	$LiSi_4AlO_{10}$, Petalite	1.504	1.510	1.516	0.012	+84	228
14	$CaSi_4Al_2O_{12} \cdot 4H_2O$, Laumontite	1.509	1.518	1.521	0.012	- 40	247
15	$NaBr \cdot 2H_2O$	1.5128	1.5192	1.5252	0.0124	- 85	23
16	$Ca_4Al_2O_7 \cdot 8H_2O$	1.506	1.519		0.013	- 00	82
16	$Ca_4Al_2SO_4(OH)_{12} \cdot 4H_2O$ (?)	1.506	1.519		0.013	- 00	175
16	$Ca_2Al_2O_5 \cdot 8H_2O$	1.506	1.519		0.013	- 00	83
17	$CaSi_5Al_2O_{14} \cdot 4H_2O$, Epistilbite	1.505	1.515	1.519	0.014	+ 44	251
18	$MnSO_4 \cdot 4H_2O$	1.508	1.518	1.522	0.014	- 63	166
19	$Na_2Si_2O_5$	1.500	1.510	1.515	0.015	- 48	255
20	ZnF_2		1.510	1.526	0.016	+00	23
21	$Mg_6Al_2(OH)_{16}CO_3 \cdot 4H_2O$, Hydrotalcite	1.495	1.511		0.016	- 00	85
22	$Rb_2Mn(SeO_4)_2 \cdot 6H_2O$	1.5094	1.5140	1.5258	0.0164	+66	151
23	$Rb_2Cu(SeO_4)_2 \cdot 6H_2O$	1.5153	1.5183	1.5318	0.0165	+53	154
24	$K_2Ca(SO_4)_2 \cdot H_2O$, Syngenite	1.5010	1.5166	1.5176	0.0166	- 28	138
25	$Ca_4Al_2SO_4(OH)_{12} \cdot 6H_2O$	1.499	1.517		0.018	- 00	175
26	$MgHPO_4 \cdot 3H_2O$, Newberyite	1.514	1.517	1.533	0.019	+45	193
27	$Co(ClO_4)_2 \cdot 6H_2O$	1.490	1.510		0.020	- 00	111
28	$Na_6Si_2O_7 \cdot 11H_2O$	1.504	1.510	1.524	0.020	+65	296
29	$Ni(ClO_4)_2 \cdot 6H_2O$	1.498	1.518		0.020	- 00	111
29	$K_2Zn(SeO_4)_2 \cdot 6H_2O$	1.5121	1.5181	1.5335	0.0214	+66	150
30	$NiSO_4 \cdot 6H_2O$, Retgersite	1.4873	1.5109		0.0236	- 00	160
31	$(NH_4)_5H(SO_4)_2$, Letovicite	1.501	1.516	1.526	0.024	- 75	123
32	$CaB_3O_4(OH)_3 \cdot 5H_2O$, Inyoite	1.495	1.51	1.520	0.025	- 70	118
33	$Mg(NH_2SO_3)_2$	1.510	1.517	1.535	0.025	+68	122
34	$K_2Fe(SeO_4)_2 \cdot 6H_2O$	1.5095	1.5182	1.5345	0.0250	+64	152
35	$NaPO_3$	1.498	1.510	1.529	0.031	+78	212
36	$Ca(NH_3)_4(NO_3)_2$	1.475		1.510	0.035	- 45	105
37	$Ca_2P_6O_{17}$	1.477	1.511	1.513	0.036	- 23	215
38	$CaH_4(PO_4)_2 \cdot H_2O$	1.4932	1.5176	1.5292	0.0360	- 70	196
39	PNO_4H_6	1.477	1.515		0.038	- 00	8
40	$MgSO_3 \cdot 6H_2O$	1.464	1.511		0.047	- 00	133
41	$CaMgB_6O_6(OH)_6 \cdot 8H_2O$, Inderborite	1.483	1.512	1.530	0.047	- 77	118
42	$Ca_3(ClO_2)_2(OH)_4$		1.51	1.585	0.075	+00	108
43	$CaMgUO_2(CO_3)_3 \cdot 12H_2O$, Swartzite	1.465	1.51	1.540	0.075	- 40	99
44	$Na_2Ca(CO_3)_2 \cdot 5H_2O$, Gaylussite	1.4435	1.5156	1.5233	0.0798	- 34	96
45	$MgKH(CO_3)_2 \cdot 4H_2O$	1.430	1.51	1.542	0.112	- 65	90
46	$KClO_3$	1.4099	1.5174	1.5241	0.1142	- 27	108
47	$Bo(OH)$	1.376	1.514	1.521	0.145	- 23	69

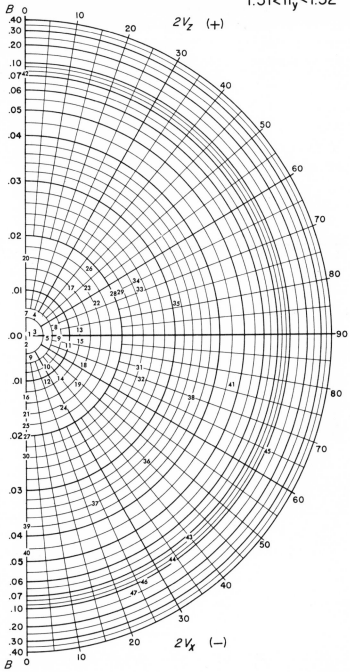

$1.51 \bar{<} n_y < 1.52$

$2V_z$ (+)

$2V_x$ (−)

G

355

No. on Chart	Substance	n_x	n_y	$n_z \cdot$	$n_z - n_x$	2V	Page
	$RbSi_2AlO_6 \cdot H_2O$		1.521			- 00	227
1	$Ca_4Al_2O_6 \cdot (ClO_3)_2 \cdot 10H_2O$	.	1.520	1.521	0.001	+00	86
2	$K_3Cu(CN)_4$	1.519	1.5215		0.002	- 00	22
2	$KSiAlO_4 \cdot nH_2O$	1.523	1.5256		0.002	- 00	239
2	$Ca_4Al_2(ClO_3)_2(OH)_{12} \cdot 4H_2O$	1.521	1.521		0.002	- 00	112
3	$SrS_2O_6 \cdot 4H_2O$	1.5262	1.5297		0.0035	- 00	133
3	$K_5P_3O_{10}$	1.516	1.520		0.004	- 00	213
3	$NaSiAlO_4$	1.522	1.526		0.004	- 00	224
3	$Mg_2Al_3Si_5AlO_{18}$, Indialite	1.524	1.528		0.004	- 00	290
4	$LiSiAlO_4$	1.5195	1.524		0.0045	- 00	227
	$LiK_5Si_2O_7$	1.515		1.520	0.005		296
	Na_6OSiO_4	1.524		1.529	0.005	+	308
	$Na_6Si_2O_7$	1.524		1.529	0.005	+	296
	$RbSi_3AlO_8$	1.524		1.529	0.005		232
5	$AlPO_4$, Berlinite		1.5235	1.529	0.0055	+00	190
6	KSi_3AlO_8, Adularia	1.52	1.525	1.53	0.006	+60	230
7	KSi_3AlO_8, Sanidine	1.520	1.525	1.53	0.006	- 10	229
8	$NaSi_3AlO_8$	1.523	1.528	1.529	0.006	- 42	233
9	KSi_3AlO_8, Microcline	1.518	1.522	1.525	0.007	- 83	231
10	$(NH_4)_2Ca(SO_4)_2 \cdot H_2O$, Koktaite	1.521	1.527	1.529	0.007	- 50	138
11	$Mg_3La_2(NO_3)_{12} \cdot 24H_2O$	1.5150	1.5220		0.0070	- 00	104
11	$Mg_3Ce_2(NO_3)_{12} \cdot 24H_2O$	1.5176	1.5249		0.0073	- 00	104
11	$Mg_3Pr_2(NO_3)_{12} \cdot 24H_2O$	1.5182	1.5255		0.0073	- 00	104
11	$Mg_3Nd_2(NO_3)_{12} \cdot 24H_2O$	1.5192	1.5266		0.0074	- 00	104
12	$NaSi_3AlO_8$	1.5198	1.5242	1.5276	0.0078	- 60	233
13	$CaMg_2Cl_6 \cdot 12H_2O$, Tachyhydrite	1.512	1.520		0.008	- 00	28
14	K_2SiO_3	1.520	1.521	1.528	0.008	+ 35	268
15	$Cs_2Mn(SeO_4)_2 \cdot 6H_2O$	1.5250	1.5279	1.5338	0.0088	+68	151
16	SiO_2, Keatite	1.513	1.522		0.009	- 00	64
16	$Mg_3Si_4O_{11} \cdot nH_2O$, Sepiolite	1.515	1.525	1.525	0.009	- 05	260
17	$CaSO_4 \cdot 2H_2O$, Gypsum	1.5205	1.5226	1.5296	0.0091	+58	164
18	$Mg_2Al_3Si_5AlO_{18}$, Cordierite	1.52	1.525	1.53	0.01	- 60	290
	$KCaCl_3$, Chlorocalcite		1.52		0.010		36
19	$Cs_2Cu(SeO_4)_2 \cdot 6H_2O$	1.5282	1.5298	1.5394	0.0112	+ 48	154
20	$(NH_4)_2Mn(SeO_4)_2 \cdot 6H_2O$	1.5160	1.5202	1.5288	0.0128	+70	151
21	$(NH_4)_2SO_4$, Mascagnite	1.5209	1.5230	1.5330	0.0128	+52	126
22	$(NH_4)_2Cd(SeO_4)_2 \cdot 6H_2O$	1.5206	1.5260	1.5352	0.0146	+77	151
23	Na_2SiO_3	1.513	1.520	1.528	0.015	- 80	268
24	$K_3Cr(CN)_6$	1.5221	1.5244	1.5373	0.0152	+46	44
25	$(NH_4)_2Fe(SeO_4)_2 \cdot 6H_2O$	1.5216	1.5280	1.5381	0.0165	+78	152
25	$Rb_2Zn(SeO_4)_2 \cdot 6H_2O$	1.5162	1.5222	1.5331	0.0169	+75	150
25	$Rb_2Co(SeO_4)_2 \cdot 6H_2O$	1.5199	1.5256	1.5369	0.0170	+74	153
26	$Na_2BO_3Cl \cdot 2H_2O$, Teepleite	1.503	1.521		0.018	- 00	117
26	$ZnSeO_4 \cdot 6H_2O$	1.5039	1.5291		0.0183	- 00	161
27	$CaHAsO_4 \cdot 3H_2O$	1.513	1.524	1.532	0.019	- 70	194
28	$Rb_2Ni(SeO_4)_2 \cdot 6H_2O$	1.5189	1.5291	1.5390	0.0192	+82	153
29	$Rb_2Fe(SeO_4)_2 \cdot 6H_2O$	1.5133	1.5200	1.5328	0.0195	+74	152
30	$Na_2CaUO_2(CO_3)_3 \cdot 6H_2O$, Andersonite		1.520	1.540	0.020	+00	99
31	$Ca_3Al_2O_6 \cdot 8H_2O$	1.502	1.522		0.020	- 00	83
32	$K_2Ca_2Si_9O_{21}$	1.515	1.526	1.535	0.020	- 70	258
30	$Cs_2S_2O_6$		1.5230	1.5438	0.0208	+00	121
33	$Mg_4(OH)_2(CO_3)_3 \cdot 3H_2O$, Hydromagnesite	1.523	1.527	1.545	0.022	+ 50	98
34	$K_2Co(SeO_4)_2 \cdot 6H_2O$	1.5158	1.5218	1.5380	0.0222	+62	152
35	$Na_4Fe(CN)_6 \cdot 10H_2O$	1.5193	1.5295	1.5436	0.0243	+81	40
36	$K_2Ni(SeO_4)_2 \cdot 6H_2O$	1.5181	1.5272	1.5427	0.0246	+73	153
37	$K_2Cu(SeO_4)_2 \cdot 6H_2O$	1.5101	1.5228	1.5349	0.0248	- 88	154
38	$Ca_5Al_2(IO_3)_2(OH)_{15} \cdot 14H_2O$	1.496	1.521		0.025	- 00	112
38	$Ca_5Al_2O_6(IO_3)_2 \cdot 22H_2O$	1.496	1.521		0.025	- 00	86
39	$NaCaB_5O_9 \cdot 5H_2O$, Probertite	1.514	1.524	1.543	0.029	+73	116
40	$Mg_3(PO_4)_2 \cdot 8H_2O$, Bobierrite	1.510	1.520	1.543	0.033	+71	197
41	PNO_2H_2	1.479	1.522		0.043	- 00	8
42	$CaMgB_6O_8(OH)_6 \cdot 8H_2O$, Inderborite	1.496	1.521	1.54	0.044	- 80	118
43	$NH_4H_2(PO_4)$	1.4792	1.5246		0.0454	- 00	187
43	PNO_4H_6	1.4792	1.5246		0.0454	- 00	8
44	$CoSeO_4 \cdot 6H_2O$	1.47	1.5225	1.5227	0.05	- 07	167
45	$K_2(UO_2)(SO_4)_2 \cdot 2H_2O$	1.5144	1.5266	1.5705	0.0561	+60	176
46	$NaNH_2$	1.500	1.527	1.562	0.062	+ 50	22
47	$MgSO_4 \cdot H_2O$, Kieserite	1.523	1.525	L 596	0.063	+57	163
48	$Na_2Fe(SO_4)_2(OH) \cdot 3H_2O$, Sideronatrite	1.508	1.525	1.586	0.078	+ 58	176
49	$NaHSO_3$	1.474	1.526	1.685	0.211	+65	120

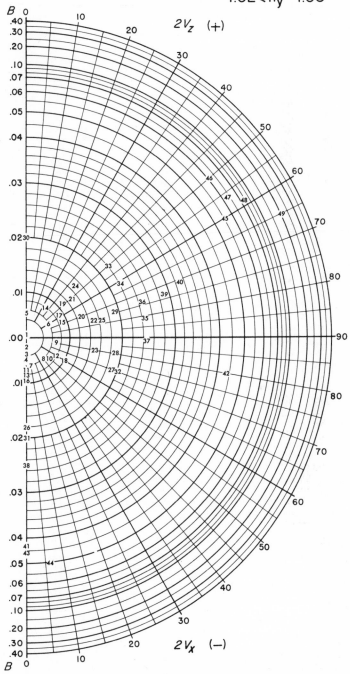
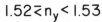

$1.52 \lesssim n_y < 1.53$

357

No. on Chart	Substance	n_x	n_y	n_z	$n_z - n_x$	2V	Page
	$4MgSO_4 \cdot 5H_2O$	1.512	1.530				164
	$(NH_4)_3ZnCl_5$		1.538			+46	37
1	$Ba(ClO_4)_2 \cdot 3H_2O$	1.5323	1.5330		0.0007	-00	112
2	$Na_4ClSi_9Al_3O_{24}$, Marialite		1.532	1.534	0.002	+00	253
2	$KCa_4FSi_8O_{20} \cdot 8H_2O$, Apophyllite		1.535	1.537	0.002	+00	264
	$Ca_2(ClO_4)_2(OH)_2 \cdot 2H_2O$	1.532	1.535		0.003	-	113
3	$RbSiAlO_4$	1.526	1.530		0.004	-00	227
4	$Fe(SO_4) \cdot 4H_2O$	1.533	1.535	1.537	0.004	-85	166
3	$KSiAlO_4$, Kaliophilite	1.533	1.537		0.004	-00	226
3	$NaSiAlO_4$, Nepheline	1.533	1.537		0.004	-00	224
5	$KAl_2(PO_4)_2F \cdot 4H_2O$	1.528	1.530	1.533	0.005	+85	210
5	$BaAl_2O_4 \cdot 6H_2O$	1.535		1.540	0.005	+	83
6	$K_2MgSi_3O_8$	1.524	1.530		0.006	-00	255
	$Mg_3(PO_4)_2 \cdot 3 + H_2O$		1.535		0.006		198
7	$KAl_2(PO_4)_2(OH) \cdot 4H_2O$, Minyulite	1.531	1.534	1.538	0.007	+70	209
8	SiO_2, Chalcedony	1.530	1.537		0.007	-00	65
9	$NaSi_3AlO_8$, Albite	1.533	1.539	1.542	0.007	-50	235
10	$Na_3(VO_4) \cdot 10H_2O$		1.5398	1.5475	0.0077	+00	196
11	$Cs_2Zn(SeO_4)_2 \cdot 6H_2O$	1.5326	1.5362	1.5412	0.0086	+83	150
12	$KSiAlO_4$	1.528	1.536	1.537	0.009	-40	226
13	$Zn(NH_3)_6Cl_2$	1.530	1.539		0.009	-00	53
14	K_2SeO_4	1.5352	1.5390	1.5446	0.0094	+77	128
15	$Cs_2Co(SeO_4)_2 \cdot 6H_2O$	1.5354	1.5399	1.5453	0.0099	+87	153
	Na_4SiO_4		1.536		0.01	-	304
15	$LiSiAlO_4 \cdot 2H_2O$	1.525	1.53	1.535	0.010	90?	242
16	$NaSi_3AlO_8$	1.5274	1.5314	1.5379	0.0105	+65	235
17	$Cs_2Fe(SeO_4)_2 \cdot 6H_2O$	1.5306	1.5352	1.5414	0.0108	+83	152
18	$(NH_4)_2Ca(SO_4)_2 \cdot H_2O$, Koktaite	1.524	1.532	1.536	0.012	-72	138
19	$NH_4NH_2SO_3$	1.526	1.532	1.538	0.012	-84	121
19	Na_4SiO_4	1.524		1.537	0.013	90?	304
20	$Na_6Be_6Si_{14}O_{37}$	1.532	1.533	1.545	0.013	+38	258
21	$Fe(SO_4) \cdot 5H_2O$	1.525		1.539	0.014	90?	167
21	$(NH_4)_2Zn(SeO_4)_2 \cdot 6H_2O$	1.5240	1.5300	1.5385	0.0145	+82	150
22	$(NH_4)_2(NO_3)_2(SO_4)$	1.521	1.531	1.536	0.015	-64	179
23	$NaCa_2Si_5Al_5O_{20} \cdot 6H_2O$	1.530	1.532	1.545	0.015	+50	243
22	$RbNH_2SO_3$		1.537		0.015	-65	122
24	$Ca_4Al_2O_7 \cdot SiO_2 \cdot 12H_2O$	1.523	1.538		0.015	-00	86
21	$(NH_4)_2Co(SeO_4)_2 \cdot 6H_2O$	1.5261	1.5327	1.5417	0.0156	+82	153
25	$Na_2S \cdot 9H_2O$		1.534	1.550	0.016	+00	9
26	$Fe(SO_4) \cdot 5H_2O$, Siderotil	1.526	1.536	1.542	0.016	-50	168
27	$KAlH_2(PO_4)_2 \cdot H_2O$	1.522	1.536	1.539	0.017	-50	195
28	$Ca_4Al_2O_7 \cdot 12H_2O$	1.520	1.537	1.537	0.017	-10	82
29	$(NH_4)_2Ni(SeO_4)_2 \cdot 6H_2O$	1.5285	1.5370	1.5460	0.0185	+86	153
30	$(NH_4)_2Cu(SeO_4)_2 \cdot 6H_2O$	1.5201	1.5344	1.5387	0.0186	-55	154
31	$Mg_2PO_4(OH)$	1.533	1.533	1.552	0.019	+25	201
32	$K_2Ca_2(Si_3O_7)_3$	1.515	1.53	1.535	0.020	-70	267
	$Li_2Si_2O_5$	1.525		1.545	0.020		256
33	$Ca_3Al_2O_6 \cdot 11H_2O$	1.510	1.530		0.020	-00	84
34	$Ca_5O_4Cl_2 \cdot 14H_2O$	1.517	1.532	1.537	0.020	-45	51
35	$Na_2Ca(SO_4)_2$, Glauberite	1.515	1.535	1.536	0.021	-07	132
36	$CaCl_2 \cdot 4H_2O$	1.506	1.530	1.530	0.024	-05	27
37	$MgH(AsO_4) \cdot 7H_2O$, Roesslerite	1.525	1.53	1.550	0.025	+25	194
38	$NiSeO_4 \cdot 6H_2O$	1.5125	1.5393		0.0268	-00	161
39	$(Zn,Cu)SO_4 \cdot 5H_2O$	1.513	1.533	1.540	0.027	-50	170
40	$Ca_4Al_2O_7 \cdot 12H_2O$	1.506	1.533	1.534	0.028	-14	82
41	$Cu(SO_4) \cdot 5H_2O$, Chalcanthite	1.5411	1.5368	1.5435	0.0294	-56	169
42	$BaS_2O_6 \cdot 4H_2O$		1.532		0.03	+88	135
43	$Fe_2(SO_4)_3 \cdot 9H_2O$, Coquimbite		1.536	1.572	0.036	+00	171
44	$CaMgB_6O_8(OH)_6 \cdot 3H_2O$, Hydroboracite	1.522	1.534	1.570	0.048	+63	118
45	$K_2H_2P_2O_6 \cdot 2H_2O$	1.4893	1.5314	1.5363	0.0490	-36	213
46	$SrCl_2 \cdot 6H_2O$	1.4866	1.5364		0.0498	-00	28
46	$SrCl_2 \cdot 6H_2O$	1.4857	1.5356		0.0499	-00	30
46	$K_2Ca(CO_3)_2$, Fairchildite	1.48	1.530		0.05	-00	96
47	$KMgBr_3 \cdot 6H_2O$		1.535		0.05	+87	39
48	$CaB_3O_4(OH)_3 \cdot 2H_2O$, Meyerhofferite	1.500	1.535	1.560	0.060	-78	118
49	$Ca_4O_3Cl_2 \cdot 15H_2O$	1.481	1.536	1.543	0.062	-44	51
50	$MgFe_4(SO_4)_6(OH)_2 \cdot 20H_2O$, Magnesiocopiapite	1.510	1.535	1.575	0.065	+50	178
51	$Cd_2MgCl_6 \cdot 12H_2O$	1.49	1.5331	1.5769	0.08	-85	30
52	$CaCO_3 \cdot 6H_2O$	1.460	1.535	1.545	0.085	-38	95
53	$Na_2Cu(CO_3)_2 \cdot 3H_2O$, Chalconatrite	1.483	1.530	1.576	0.093	+70	97
54	$Ca_2OCl_2 \cdot 3H_2O$		1.535	1.63	0.095	+00	51
54	$Ca(ClO_2)_2 \cdot 2H_2O$		1.53	1.63	0.10	+00	108
55	K_2CO_3	1.426	1.531	1.5411	0.115	-35	90
56	$NaAlCO_3(OH)_2$	1.462	1.537	1.589	0.127	-67	99
57	Na_2CO_3	1.415	1.535	1.546	0.131	-34	90
58	NH_4HCO_3, Teschemacherite	1.4227	1.5358	1.5545	0.1318	-42	87
59	$LiNaCO_3$	1.406	1.538		0.132	-00	90

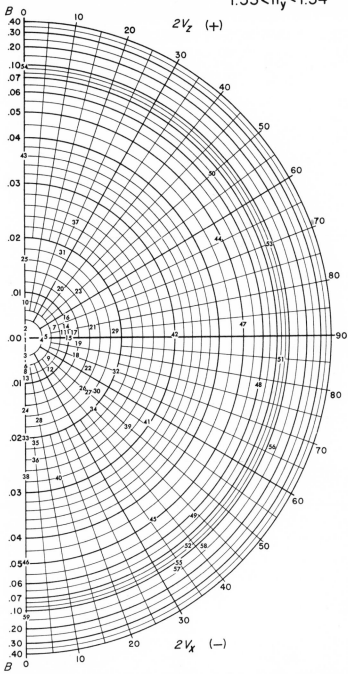

No. on Chart	Substance	n_x	n_y	n_z	$n_z - n_x$	2V	Page
1	$KCa_4FSi_8O_{20} \cdot 8H_2O$, Apophyllite		1.5418	1.5418	0.000	00	264
1	$KCa_4FSi_8O_{20} \cdot 8H_2O$, Apophyllite	1.5429	1.5433		0.0004	- 00	264
2	$NaBe(OH)Si_3O_7$, Epididymite	1.5440	1.5441	1.5464	0.0024	+ 31	266
2	$LiKSi_2O_5$	1.536	1.54	1.540	0.004	53	256
3	$Mg_2Al_3Si_5AlO_{18}$, Indialite	1.537	1.541		0.004	- 00	290
3	$BaZnF_4$		1.544		0.004	- 00	25
4	$KSiAlO_4$, Kalsilite	1.537	1.542		0.005	- 00	226
4	KSi_3GaO_8	1.533		1.539	0.006	- 10?	232
5	$Na_2Mg_2Si_6O_{15}$	1.540	1.5425	1.546	0.006	+70	258
6	$LiSiAlO_4$, Eucryptite	1.54	1.545		0.006	- 00	227
7	$NaBe(OH)Si_3O_7$, Eudidymite	1.545	1.546	1.551	0.006	+ 30	267
8	Oligoclase (High-Temp)	1.540	1.544	1.547	0.007	- 75	235
9	$BaSiO_3 \cdot 6H_2O$	1.542	1.548	1.549	0.007	- 40	281
	$K_2UO_2(NO_3)_4$	1.535		1.542	0.007		105
10	$K_4CaSi_6O_{15}$	1.535	1.541	1.543	0.008	- 60	258
11	$K_2Mg_5Si_{12}O_{30}$		1.543	1.550	0.008	+00	255
12	Oligoclase (Low-Temp)	1.540	1.544	1.548	0.008	- 89	235
13	SiO_2, Quartz		1.5442	1.5533	0.0091	+00	63
14	$Cs_2Ni(SeO_4)_2 \cdot 6H_2O$	1.5395	1.5450	1.5489	0.0094	- 83	154
14	$Mg_2Al_3Si_5AlO_{18}$, Cordierite	1.54	1.545	1.55	0.01	- 85	290
	Reaumurite	1.540		1.55	0.01		257
15	$Ca_4(OH)_2Si_6O_{15} \cdot 3H_2O$, Gyrolite	1.535	1.545		0.010	- 00	265
16	$KAl_2(PO_4)_2OH \cdot 2H_2O$	1.536	1.541	1.547	0.011	+85	210
17	$CaCl_2$	1.531	1.542		0.011	- 00	26
17	$K_8CaSi_{10}O_{25}$	1.537	1.548		0.011	- 00	255
17	$Ca_4Al_2O_7 \cdot (CH_3 \cdot CO_2)_2 \cdot 8H_2O$	1.538	1.549		0.011	- 00	86
18	$CaH(PO_4) \cdot 2H_2O$, Brushite	1.539	1.545	1.551	0.012	+86	194
17	$K_2Al_2(SO_4)_4$	1.533	1.545		0.012	- 00	132
19	$Mg_6(OH)_8Si_4O_{10}$, Chrysotile	1.542	1.543	1.555	0.013	+ 32	260
20	$Na_2Si_3Al_2O_8 \cdot H_2O$	1.534	1.546	1.548	0.014	- 50	242
21	$CaSi_2Al_2O_8 \cdot 4H_2O$, Gismondite	1.5308	1.5402	1.5484	0.0176	- 84	242
22	$Ca_4Al_2O_7 \cdot 12H_2O$	1.53	1.549		0.02	- 00	82
23	$(Mg,Fe)_3(OH)_2Si_3AlO_{10} \cdot 4H_2O$, Vermiculite	1.525	1.545	1.545	0.020	- 04	265
24	$CoSO_4 \cdot 5H_2O$	1.530	1.548	1.550	0.020	- 50	170
25	$Pr_2(SO_4)_3 \cdot 8H_2O$	1.5392	1.5479	1.5592	0.0200	+84	171
25	$Pr_2(SO_4)_3 \cdot 8H_2O$	1.5399	1.5494	1.5607	0.0208	+85	171
26	$Mg_3B_2(OH)_6(PO_4)_2 \cdot 6H_2O$, Lueneburgite	1.520	1.54	1.545	0.025	- 62	215
27	$KMg_3F_2Si_3AlO_{10}$, Phlogopite, Fluorine	1.519	1.545	1.547	0.028	- 10	262
28	$Na_3Fe(CN)_6 \cdot 2H_2O$	1.531	1.549	1.560	0.029	- 77	46
29	$Y_2(SO_4)_3 \cdot 8H_2O$	1.5433	1.549	1.5755	0.0322	+51	171
30	$Na_2Ca(CO_3)_2$	1.504	1.547		0.043	- 00	96
31	$NaCa_3(UO_2)(CO_3)_3(SO_4)F \cdot 10H_2O$, Schroeckingerite	1.495	1.543	1.544	0.049	- 16	179
32	$NaCa_3(UO_2)(CO_3)_3(SO_4)F \cdot 10H_2O$	1.489	1.542	1.542	0.053	- 05	179
33	$(NH_4)_5(NO_3)_3(SO_4)$	1.488	1.540	1.552	0.064	- 50	179
34	$Fe''Fe_4'''(SO_4)_6(OH)_2 \cdot 20H_2O$, Copiapite	1.531	1.546	1.597	0.066	+52	178
35	$NaAlCO_3(OH)_2$, Dawsonite	1.466	1.542	1.596	0.130	- 77	99
36	$NH_4(NO_3)$	1.463	1.543	1.600	0.137	- 80	101
37	CaS_4O_6	1.535	1.540	1.675	0.140	+ 32	123

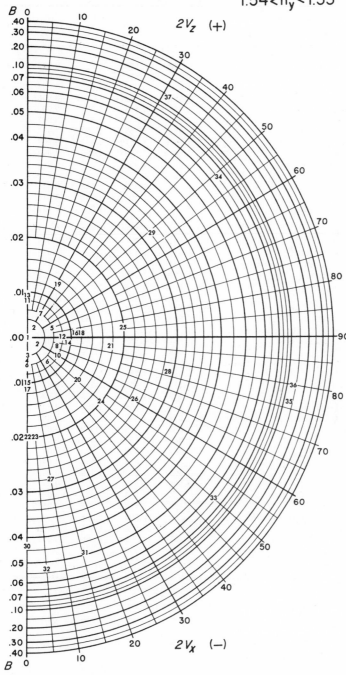

$1.54 \lesssim n_y < 1.55$

No. on Chart	Substance	n_x	n_y	n_z	$n_z - n_x$	2V	Page
	$CaSiO_3 \cdot 2H_2O$, Plombierite		1.550				281
1	$Cs(NO_3)$	1.560	1.558		0.002	- 00	101
1	$Al(OH)_3$, Bayerite		1.55		0.005		71
	$Li_2K_{10}Si_7O_{20}$	1.550		1.555	0.005	13	270
2	Rb_2SeO_4	1.5515	1.5537	1.5582	0.0067	+67	128
3	Andesine (High-Temp)	1.550	1.553	1.557	0.007	- 90	235
3	Andesine (Low-Temp)	1.551	1.554	1.558	0.007	+88	235
2	$Ca_4O_3Br_2 \cdot 15H_2O$	1.552	1.555	1.559	0.007	+70	51
4	$NaBe(PO_4)$, Beryllonite	1.5520	1.5579	1.561	0.009	- 68	191
5	$Nd_2(SO_4)_3 \cdot 8H_2O$	1.5413	1.5505	1.5621	0.0092	+84	172
6	$Ca_4Al_2O_6Br_2 \cdot 10H_2O$	1.546	1.556		0.010	- 00	85
6	$CaS_2O_6 \cdot 4H_2O$	1.5414	1.5516		0.0102	- 00	133
7	$Li_2Si_2O_5$	1.547	1.550	1.558	0.011	+55	256
8	$ZrOCl_2 \cdot 8H_2O$		1.552	1.563	0.011	+00	52
	$Na_2Ca_5(SO_4)_6 \cdot 3H_2O$	1.5557		1.567	0.0113		157
9	$K_8CaSi_{10}O_{25}$	1.539	1.551		0.012	- 00	255
10	$K_3Rh(CN)_6$	1.5498	1.5513	1.5634	0.0136	+ 39	44
11	$HfOCl_2 \cdot 8H_2O$	1.543	1.557		0.014	- 00	52
12	$Ca_4Al_2O_6Cl_2 \cdot 10H_2O$	1.535	1.550		0.015	- 00	85
13	$BaSi_3Al_2O_{10} \cdot 4H_2O$, Edingtonite	1.541	1.553	1.557	0.016	- 54	242
14	$Na_2WO_4 \cdot 2H_2O$	1.5526	1.5533	1.5695	0.0169	+25	183
15	$K_3Mn(CN)_6$	1.5527	1.5547	1.5710	0.0183	+ 43	44
16	$LiNaSiO_3$	1.552	1.557	1.571	0.019	+70	268
17	$Ca_4Al_2O_6 \cdot CO_2 \cdot 11H_2O$	1.532	1.552		0.020	- 00	86
18	$Sm_2(SO_4)_3 \cdot 8H_2O$	1.5427	1.5519	1.5629	0.0202	+70	172
19	$Mn_2Al_3Si_5AlO_{18}$, Cordierite, Mn	1.537	1.558	1.558	0.021	- 25	291
20	$Mg(OH)_2$, Brucite		1.559	1.580	0.021	+00	68
21	$Mg_3F_2SiO_4$	1.548	1.552	1.570	0.022	+33	307
22	$Ca_4Al_2(OH)_{14} \cdot 6H_2O$, Hydrocalumite	1.535	1.553	1.557	0.022	- 24	82
23	$SrBr_2 \cdot 6H_2O$	1.535	1.557		0.022	- 00	29
24	$NaH_2AsO_4 \cdot H_2O$	1.5382	1.5535	1.5607	0.0225	- 68	193
25	$2CaSO_4 \cdot H_2O$	1.559	1.5595	1.5736	0.0246	+ 14	161
26	$2CaSO_4 \cdot H_2O$, Bassanite		1.558	1.586	0.028	+00	161
27	$Na_6CaCO_3(OH)_2Si_3Al_3O_{12}$, Cancrinite	1.519	1.550		0.031	- 00	254
28	$Al(PO_4)$	1.546	1.556	1.578	0.032	+50	190
29	$Mg_5Fe(PO_4)_4 \cdot 16H_2O$	1.5468	1.5533	1.5820	0.0352	+57	198
30	$NiSO_3 \cdot 6H_2O$	1.509	1.552		0.043	- 00	133
	$(NH_4)_2UO_2(SO_4)_2 \cdot 2H_2O$		1.555	1.600	0.045		177
31	$MgCrO_4 \cdot 7H_2O$	1.5211	1.5500	1.5680	0.0469	- 75	163
32	$CoSO_3 \cdot 6H_2O$	1.506	1.553		0.047	- 00	133
33	$Na_3Fe(SO_4)_3 \cdot 3H_2O$, Ferrinatrite		1.558	1.614	0.055	+00	157
34	$CaCl_2 \cdot 6H_2O$	1.4949	1.5504		0.0555	- 00	28
35	$Na_2Co(CNS)_4 \cdot 8H_2O$, Julienite		1.556	1.645	0.089	+00	42
35	$CaCO_3$, Vaterite		1.550	1.645	0.095	+00	93
36	$Rb_2S_3O_6$	1.4874	1.5580	1.5867	0.0993	- 63	121
37	$FeH(SO_4)_2 \cdot 4H_2O$, Rhomboclase	1.533	1.550	1.635	0.102	+ 27	136
38	$KCNO$	1.377	1.552		0.173	- 00	22

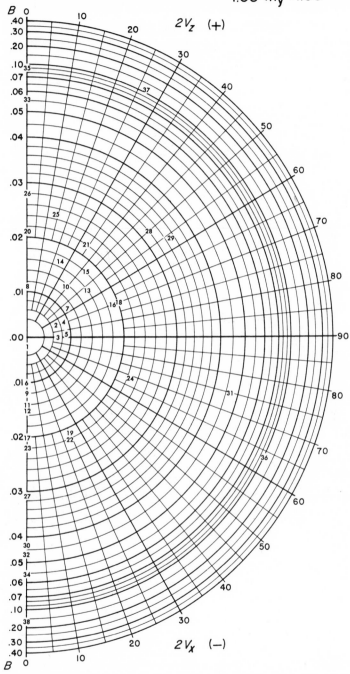

$1.55 \lesssim n_y < 1.56$

$2V_Z$ (+)

$2V_X$ (−)

K

No. on Chart	Substance	n_x	n_y	n_z	$n_z - n_x$	2V	Page
	$3CdSO_4 \cdot 8H_2O$		1.565			- 88	165
1	$Be_3Al_2Si_6O_{18}$, Beryl	1.564	1.568		0.004	- 00	288
2	$La_2(SO_4)_3 \cdot 9H_2O$		1.564	1.569	0.005	+ 00	171
	$CuSeO_4 \cdot 5H_2O$		1.56	1.565			170
3	Rivaite		1.56		0.006	- 25	257
3	$NaSi_3GaO_8$	1.552		1.558	0.006	- ?	232
4	$Al_4(OH)_8Si_4O_{10}$, Dickite	1.560	1.562	1.566	0.006	+75	264
5	$Al_4(OH)_8Si_4O_{10}$, Nacrite	1.557	1.562	1.563	0.006	+90	264
4	$KAl_2(PO_4)_2(OH) \cdot 2H_2O$	1.562	1.564	1.568	0.006	+71	210
3	$Al_4(OH)_8Si_4O_{10}$, Kaolinite	1.561	1.565	1.566	0.006	- 30	263
6	$FeCl_2$, Lawrencite	1.566	1.567		0.006	- 00	26
7	$Cs_2(SO_4)$	1.5598	1.5644	1.5662	0.0064	- 65	127
8	$Mg_3(OH)_4Si_2O_5$, Antigorite	1.55	1.56	1.57	0.007	- 50	261
9	Labradorite	1.559	1.562	1.567	0.008	+82	235
10	$NH_4Al_2(PO_4)_2(OH) \cdot 2.5H_2O$	1.564	1.566	1.572	0.008	+60	210
11	$SmCl_3 \cdot 6H_2O$	1.564	1.569	1.573	0.009	- 70	34
11	$K_2Ca_3Si_6O_{16}$	1.56		1.57	0.01	-	257
12	$MgB_2O_4 \cdot 3H_2O$, Pinnoite		1.565	1.575	0.010	+ 00	115
13	$CaSO_4$	1.562	1.562	1.595	0.013	+ 30	129
14	$Na_2Sn(OH)_6$		1.568	1.582	0.014	+ 00	72
15	$Be(NH_2SO_3)_2$	1.552	1.563	1.567	0.015	- 60	122
16	HNH_2SO_3	1.553	1.563	1.568	0.015	- 63	121
17	$K_3Fe(CN)_6$	1.5660	1.5689	1.5831	0.0171	+49	44
18	$Mg(OH)_2$		1.5662	1.5853	0.0191	+ 00	68
19	$K_2Ca_2Mg(SO_4)_4 \cdot 2H_2O$, Polyhalite	1.547	1.560	1.567	0.020	- 62	157
20	$Al(PO_4) \cdot 2H_2O$,	1.550	1.565	1.570	0.020	- 55	200
21	$Al(OH)_3$, Gibbsite	1.566	1.566	1.587	0.021	+05	71
22	$Al(OH)Si_2O_5 \cdot 2H_2O$	1.543	1.565	1.565	0.022	- 20	265
23	$Ca(UO_2)_2(AsO_4)_2 \cdot 8H_2O$	1.55	1.567	1.572	0.022	- 62	207
24	$Fe_2Al_3Si_5AlO_{18}$, Cordierite, Fe	1.551	1.564	1.574	0.023	- 70	290
25	$(NH_4)_2SeO_4$	1.5607	1.5630	1.5846	0.0239	+ 38	128
26	$Li_2S_2O_6 \cdot 2H_2O$	1.5487	1.5602	1.5788	0.0301	+78	134
27	$K_2Ca_5(SO_4)_6 \cdot H_2O$, Görgeyite	1.550	1.565	1.583	0.033	+85	157
28	$CaCl_2 \cdot 4H_2O$	1.532	1.560	1.571	0.039	- 63	27
	HfF_4		1.56		0.04		35
29	KH_2AsO_4	1.5179	1.5674		0.0495	- 00	187
29	Na_2SO_3	1.515	1.565		0.050	- 00	120
30	$K_2Cd(NO_2)_4$	1.556	1.565	1.608	0.052	+ 48	106
31	$AlCl_3 \cdot 6H_2O$, Chloraluminite	1.507	1.560		0.053	- 00	34
32	$CaS_2O_3 \cdot 6H_2O$	1.545	1.560	1.605	0.060	+60	135
33	$Na_4Ca(PO_4)_6$	1.518	1.564	1.581	0.063	- 80	212
34	$K_2S_3O_6$	1.4934	1.5641	1.602	0.1086	- 72	121
35	$Ca(OH)VO_3 \cdot H_2O$	1.447	1.564	1.583	0.136	- 44	104
36	$KAuCl_4 \cdot 2H_2O$	1.55	1.56	1.69	0.14	+25	45
37	Li_2CO_3	1.428	1.567	1.572	0.144	- 15	90
38	$MgPt(CN)_4 \cdot 7H_2O$		1.5608	1.91	0.35	+ 00	31

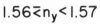

$1.56 \lesssim n_y < 1.57$

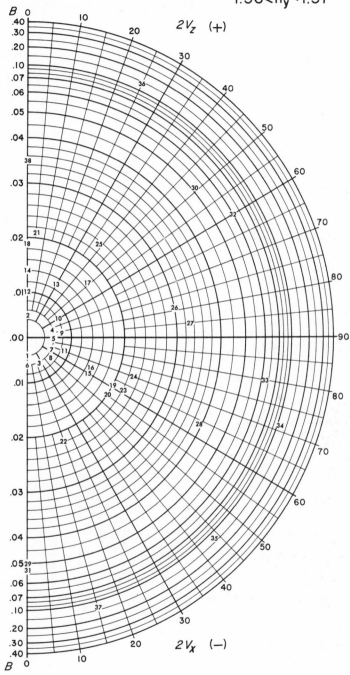

L

No. on Chart	Substance	n_x	n_y	n_z	$n_z - n_x$	2V	Page
	$K_4Fe(CN)_6 \cdot 3H_2O$		1.5772			- 78	41
1	$Ca_4Al_2O_6I_2 \cdot 8H_2O$	1.572	1.575		0.003	- 00	86
2	$BaSi_2Al_2O_8$		1.57	1.5712	0.004	+00	237
3	$Na_2Al_2Si_2O_8 \cdot H_2O$, Lembergite	1.569	1.570	1.573	0.004	+67	259
4	$Ca_2Si_2O_6 \cdot H_2O$, Tobermorite	1.570	1.571	1.575	0.005	+ 25	281
5	$Be_3Al_2Si_6O_{18}$, Emerald	1.573	1.578		0.005	- 00	288
6	$Mg_5 Al(OH)_8Si_3AlO_{10}$, Clinochlore	1.57	1.57	1.58	0.006	+ 20	260
	$Ca_5 H_2(AsO_4)_4 \cdot 9H_2O$	1.568	1.57	1.577	0.009		195
7	$KAl_2(PO_4)_2(OH) \cdot 0.5H_2O$	1.565	1.571	1.574	0.009	- 71	210
8	$Zn(OH)_2$	1.5705	1.5777	1.5796	0.0091	- 51	69
9	$K_2Ca_3Si_6O_{16}$	1.56		1.57	0.01	-	266
9	$GdCl_3 \cdot 6H_2O$	1.565	1.570	1.575	0.010	- 75	34
10	Bytownite	1.567	1.571	1.577	0.010	- 84	236
11	$LiSiAlO_4$		1.573	1.583	0.010	+00	227
12	$LiSi AlO_4$	1.575	1.578	1.586	0.011	+70	227
13	$H_2(UO_2)_2(PO_4)_2 \cdot 8H_2O$, Hydrogen-Autunite	1.568	1.579		0.011	- 00	205
14	$Ca_4Al_2O_6Br_2 \cdot 8H_2O$	1.558	1.570		0.012	- 00	85
15	$NaAlO_2$	1.566	1.575	1.580	0.014	- 30	73
16	Mg_2PO_4F, Wagnerite	1.5678	1.5719	1.5824	0.0146	+ 28	202
17	$Na_2Ca_3Si_6O_{16}$, Devitrite	1.564	1.570	1.579	0.015	+75	256
18	$Mg(UO_2)_2(PO_4)_2 \cdot 8H_2O$, Mg-Autunite	1.559	1.574		0.016	- 00	208
19	Thomsonite, thallian	1.568	1.574	1.585	0.017	∓50	244
20	$Al(OH)_3$	1.577	1.577	1.595	0.018	+05	71
	$Ca_4O_3I_2 \cdot 15H_2O$		1.575	1.595	0.02	+	51
21	$KAl_3(SO_4)_2(OH)_6$, Alunite		1.572	1.592	0.020	+00	173
22	$Na_3Ca_4ClCO_3Si_{15}Al_9O_{48}$	1.550	1.571		0.021	- 00	253
23	$K_2(UO_2)_2(PO_4)_2 \cdot nH_2O$	1.553	1.575	1.575	0.022	- 05	206
24	$Ca(UO_2)_2(PO_4)_2 \cdot 12H_2O$	1.555	1.575	1.578	0.023	- 20	207
25	$Na_3Ir(SO_3)_3(NH_3)_3 \cdot 6H_2O$	1.546	1.570		0.024	- 00	133
26	$1Mg(F,OH)_2 \cdot 1Mg_2SiO_4$, Norbergite	1.563	1.570	1.590	0.027	+ 45	307
27	$Ca(OH)_2$, Portlandite	1.545	1.574		0.029	- 00	69
28	$NH_4Mg_3F_2Si_3AlO_4$, Phlogopite, NH_4	1.54	1.57	1.57	0.03	- 10	262
28	$KFe_3^{II}(Fe^{III},Mg,Al)_5Si_8O_{20} \cdot 4H_2O$, Stilpnomelane	1.546	1.576	1.576	0.030	- 10	265
29	$(Mg,Fe)_3(OH)_2Si_3AlO_{10} \cdot 4H_2O$	1.542	1.573	1.573	0.031	- 04	265
30	$Mg_3(AsO_4)_2 \cdot 8H_2O$, Hoernesite	1.563	1.571	1.596	0.033	+60	198
31	$Mg_3(OH)_2Si_4O_{10}$, Talc	1.540	1.575	1.575	0.035	- 15	259
32	$K_2Mg_5 Al(OH)_4Si_5 Al_3O_{20}$, Eastonite	1.542	1.577	1.578	0.036	- 10	262
33	$Ca(SO_4)$, Anhydrite	1.5698	1.5754	1.6136	0.0438	+ 43	129
34	$KPtCl_3 \cdot NH_3 \cdot H_2O$	1.5438	1.5754	1.588	0.044	- 64	53
34	P_2O_5	1.545	1.578	1.589	0.044	- 65	66
35	$MnCl_2 \cdot 4H_2O$	1.555	1.575	1.607	0.052	+78	29
36	$CaH_4(PO_4)_2$	1.548	1.572	1.602	0.054	+85	188
37	$NH_4H_2(AsO_4)$	1.5217	1.5766		0.0549	- 00	187
38	$Na_2Cu(SO_4)_2 \cdot 2H_2O$, Kroehnkite	1.544	1.578	1.601	0.057	- 79	138
39	$CaH_2P_2O_7$	1.518	1.578		0.060	- 00	214
40	$CuFe_4(SO_4)_6(OH)_2 \cdot 20H_2O$, Cuprocopiapite	1.558	1.575	1.620	0.062	+63	178
41	$CuSO_4 \cdot 3H_2O$	1.554	1.577	1.618	0.064	+75	166
42	$Ba(ClO_3)_2 \cdot H_2O$	1.562	1.577	1.635	0.073	+ 56	109
43	$NiCl_2 \cdot 6H_2O$	1.535	1.57	1.61	0.075	+85	29
44	$Na_4Fe_2(SO_4)_4(OH)_2 \cdot 3H_2O$, Metasideronatrite	1.543	1.575	1.634	0.091	+60	176
45	$(NH_4)_2H(PO_4)$	1.468	1.570	1.582	0.114	- 28	187
46	$Bo(OH)$	1.450	1.574	1.579	0.129	- 22	69
47	$Bo(OH)$	1.434	1.570	1.588	0.154	- 35	69

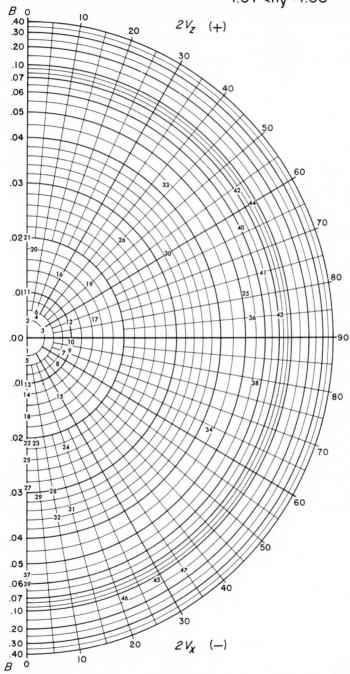

$1.57 \lesssim n_y < 1.58$

M

No. on Chart	Substance	n_x	n_y	n_z	$n_z - n_x$	2V	Page
	$K_4Ru(CN)_6 \cdot 3H_2O$		1.5837			- 54	42
	$MgPt(CN)_4 \cdot C_3H_8O_3 \cdot 5H_2O$		1.584			- 18	31
1	NaK_3FeCl_6, Rinneite		1.5886	1.5894	0.0008	+00	35
2	$Ca_3(PO_4)_2$	1.588	1.5891	1.591	0.003	+75	189
3	$NaCaAlSi_2O_7$	1.575	1.580		0.005	- 00	295
	$Al(OH)_3$, Bayerite		1.583		0.005		71
4	$CaSi_2Al_2O_8$		1.585	1.590	0.005	+00	236
5	$NaSiAlO_4 \cdot CaAl_2O_4$	1.588	1.582		0.006	- 00	225
5	$K_2NaFe(CN)_6$	1.581	1.585	1.590	0.0075	+80	45
6	$Zn_3(PO_4)_2 \cdot 4H_2O$	1.574	1.582	1.582	0.008	- 20	197
7	$MgSnCl_6 \cdot 6H_2O$		1.5885	1.597	0.0085	+00	50
8	$NaH(UO_2)_2(PO_4)_2 \cdot 7H_2O$	1.57	1.580		0.01	- 00	206
9	$Ca_3Si_3O_9 \cdot H_2O$, Xonotlite	1.583	1.583	1.593	0.010	+ 10	291
10	$NH_4Fe_3H_8(PO_4)_6 \cdot 6H_2O$		1.580	1.591	0.011	+00	195
11	$K_2NaFe(CN)_6$	1.580	1.581	1.591	0.011	+31	45
12	$CaH(AsO_4) \cdot 2H_2O$, Pharmacolite	1.583	1.589	1.594	0.011	- 79	194
13	$CaSi_2Al_2O_8$, Anorthite	1.574	1.581	1.586	0.012	- 77	236
14	$SrSi_2Al_2O_8$	1.574	1.582	1.586	0.012	- 70	237
15	Li_2SiO_3		1.587	1.599	0.012	+00	267
16	$Cu_4(OH)_2Si_2O_7$, Custerite	1.586	1.589	1.598	0.012	+60	297
17	$CaSi_2Al_2O_8$	1.5755	1.5832	1.5885	0.0130	- 77	236
17	$CaSi_2Al_2O_8$	1.5768	1.5846	1.5903	0.0135	- 72	236
18	$(NH_4)_2NaFe(CN)_6$	1.584	1.587	1.598	0.014	+ 10	45
19	$K_2Ca_3Si_6O_{16}$	1.575	1.582	1.590	0.015	+70	266
19	$K_2Ca_2Si_6O_{15}$	1.575	1.58	1.59	0.015	+70	257
20	$LiAlO_2$	1.570	1.586		0.016	- 00	73
21	$BaSi_2Al_2O_8$, Paracelsian	1.5702	1.5824	1.5869	0.0167	- 52	237
22	Thomsonite, argentian	1.582	1.588	1.600	0.018	+60	244
23	$UO_2SO_4 \cdot 3H_2O$	1.574	1.589	1.593	0.019	- 54	177
24	$Na_2(UO_2)_2(PO_4)_2 \cdot 6H_2O$	1.562	1.582		0.020	- 00	206
25	CaP_2O_6	1.573	1.587	1.596	0.023	- 80	211
26	$Tl_2Mg(SO_4)_2 \cdot 6H_2O$	1.5705	1.5884	1.5949	0.0244	- 75	143
27	$Ca(UO_2)_2(AsO_4)_2 \cdot 8H_2O$, Uranospinite	1.56	1.586		0.026	- 00	207
28	$Ca_2Fe(CN)_6 \cdot 12H_2O$	1.5700	1.5818	1.5961	0.0261	+85	32
29	$Ca(UO_2)_2(AsO_4)_2 \cdot 8H_2O$	1.560	1.582	1.587	0.027	- 46	207
30	$Ca(UO_2)_2(AsO_4)_2 + H_2O$	1.562	1.589		0.027	- 00	207
31	$(NH_4)_2Ca_5(SO_4)_6 \cdot H_2O$	1.567	1.580	1.595	0.028	+86	157
32	$Al(PO_4) \cdot 2H_2O$, Variscite	1.565	1.588	1.593	0.028	- 50	200
33	$Al(OH)Si_2O_5 \cdot 2H_2O$	1.559	1.588	1.588	0.029	- 30	265
34	$KLiFeAl(OH)_2Si_3AlO_{10}$, Zinnwaldite	1.55	1.58	1.58	0.03	- 30	263
35	$H_2UO_2(SO_4)_2 \cdot 5H_2O$	1.555	1.586	1.586	0.031	- 10	177
36	$(UO_2)_2H_2(SO_4)_3 \cdot 5H_2O$	1.555	1.586	1.586	0.031	- 05	136
37	$(NH_4)_2Al_2H_4(PO_4)_4 \cdot H_2O$	1.565	1.586	1.597	0.032	- 72	195
38	$KAl_2(OH)_2Si_3AlO_{10}$, Muscovite	1.552	1.582	1.588	0.036	- 45	263
39	$2Ca_4O_3(CNS) \cdot 25H_2O$	1.586	1.587	1.622	0.036	+ 12	51
40	$KMg_3(OH)_2Si_3AlO_{10}$, Phlogopite	1.548	1.588	1.588	0.040	- 10	261
41	$AlOHSi_2O_5$, Pyrophyllite	1.552	1.588	1.600	0.048	- 57	261
42	$NaCa_3(UO_2)(CO_3)_3SO_4F \cdot 4H_2O$	1.532	1.581		0.049	- 00	179
43	$Fe_2(SO_4)_3 \cdot 7H_2O$, Kornelite	1.572	1.586	1.640	0.068	+55	171
44	$(La,Ce)_2(CO_3)_3 \cdot 8H_2O$, Lanthanite	1.53	1.587	1.613	0.083	- 63	95
45	$4Co(NH_2)_2 \cdot CaSO_4$	1.523	1.583	1.615	0.092	- 70	179
46	$Na(NO_3)$, Soda-Niter	1.3361	1.5874		0.2513	- 00	101

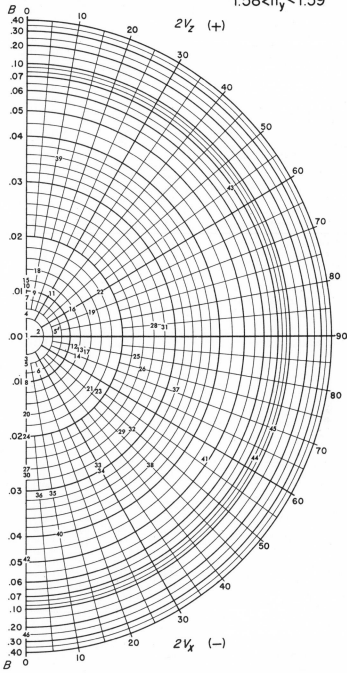

$1.58 \lesssim n_y < 1.59$

$2V_Z$ (+)

$2V_X$ (−)

N

369

No. on Chart	Substance	n_X	n_Y	n_Z	$n_Z - n_X$	2V	Page
	$K_2Cr_2O_7 \cdot Hg(CN)_2 \cdot 2H_2O$		1.591			+57	134
1	K_4CdCl_6		1.5906	1.5907	0.0001	+00	36
1	Cs_2SeO_4	1.5989	1.5999	1.6003	0.0014	-72	128
1	$Na_2Ca_2(SiO_3)_3$	1.596	1.596	1.599	0.003	+	288
2	K_4MnCl_6, Chlormanganokalite		1.59	1.59	0.005	+00	36
2'	$Ca_2Si_4Al_3GaO_{16}$	1.591	1.59	1.596	0.005		232
2'	KGe_3AlO_8	1.590	1.59	1.595	0.005		232
2'	$Na_4Ca_3Al_{10}O_{20}$		1.592		0.005	+	73
2'	$Ca_2SiO_4 \cdot 1 + H_2O$		1.597		0.005		305
3	$KFe_3H_8(PO_4)_6 \cdot 6H_2O$		1.595	1.601	0.006	+00	196
3	$B(PO_4)$		1.5947	1.6013	0.0066	+00	190
4	CaP_2O_6	1.588	1.595		0.007	-00	211
5	$Ca_3(OH)_2SiO_4 \cdot H_2O$	1.589		1.597	0.008		306
5	CaP_2O_6	1.587	1.591	1.595	0.008	-85	211
6	$Cu(UO_2)_2(PO_4)_2 \cdot 12H_2O$, Torbernite	1.582	1.592		0.010	-00	208
7	$Zn_3(PO_4)_2 \cdot 4H_2O$, Hopeite	1.589	1.598	1.599	0.010	-37	197
8	$Mg_7Si_8O_{22}(OH)_2$, Anthophyllite	1.584	1.590	1.597	0.013	+70	283
9	$BaSi_2Al_2O_8$, Celsian	1.587	1.593	1.600	0.013	+80	237
10	$Cu_4Si_2O_7F_2$, Cuspidine	1.592	1.595	1.606	0.014	+63	296
11	$Mg_7Si_8O_{22}F_2$	1.583	1.590	1.598	0.015	-89	284
12	$(NH_4)_2ZnCl_4$	1.585	1.590	1.600	0.015	+33	37
13	$(K,Na)_5 Fe_3(SO_4)_6(OH) \cdot 9H_2O$, Metavoltine	1.573	1.590		0.017	-00	177
14	$NaCa_2Mg_5 Si_7BO_{22}F_2$	1.588	1.598	1.605	0.017	-75	286
15	Li_2SiO_3		1.591	1.611	0.020	+00	267
16	$Ca_2Mg_5 Si_8O_{22}F_2$	1.581	1.593	1.602	0.021	-86	285
17	$Ca_2P_2O_7$	1.584	1.599	1.605	0.021	-50	213
18	$BaS_2O_6 \cdot 2H_2O$	1.5860	1.5951	1.6072	0.0212	+84	135
19	$Ba(NH_2SO_3)_2$		1.599		0.022	-48	122
20	$Tl_2Mn(SO_4)_2 \cdot 6H_2O$	1.5861	1.5996	1.6084	0.0223	-71	145
21	$Fe(OH)Si_2O_5 \cdot 2H_2O$	1.585	1.593	1.608	0.023	-26	266
22	$SrCl_2 \cdot 2H_2O$	1.5942	1.5948	1.6172	0.0230	+25	29
23	P_2O_5		1.599	1.624	0.025	+00	66
24	$NaCaBeSi_2O_6F$, Leucophanite	1.571	1.595	1.598	0.027	-39	295
25	$CaB_3O_4(OH)_3 \cdot H_2O$, Colemanite	1.5863	1.5920	1.6140	0.0277	+55	118
26	ZrF_4	1.57	1.59	1.60	0.03	-70	35
27	$Mg_5 F_2Si_2O_8$	1.582	1.594	1.612	0.030	+50	307
28	$Cr(PO_4) \cdot 6H_2O$	1.568	1.591	1.599	0.031	-13	201
29	$K_3Rh(SO_3)_3(NH_3)_3 \cdot 6H_2O$	1.563	1.597		0.034	-00	133
30	$NaAl_2(OH)_2Si_3AlO_{10}$, Paragonite	1.564	1.599	1.600	0.036	-40	263
31	$Sr_3Si_3O_9$		1.599	1.637	0.038	+00	288
32	$K(Fe,Mg)_3F_2Si_3AlO_{10}$, Biotite	1.551	1.596	1.596	0.045	-02	262
33	$Na_2Mg(CO_3)_2$	1.54	1.594		0.054	-00	96
34	$Mn(SO_4) \cdot H_2O$, Szmikite	1.562	1.595	1.632	0.070	+85	163
35	C_2Cl_6	1.590	1.598	1.668	0.078	-38	33
36	$Fe(SO_4)(OH) \cdot 3H_2O$, Amarantite	1.516	1.598	1.621	0.105	-30	177
37	$K_2Mg(CO_3)_2$	1.47	1.597		0.127	-00	96
38	$Na_2Ru(NO_2)_5 \cdot 2H_2O$	1.5889	1.5943	1.7163	0.1274	+25	106
39	$K_2Ni(CN)_4 \cdot 3H_2O$	1.4657	1.5915	1.5955	0.1298	-21	41
37	$K_6Ca_2(CO_3)_5 \cdot 6H_2O$, Buetschliite	1.455	1.595		0.140	-00	96
	$Li_2Pt(CN)_6$		1.59	1.95	0.36		48

370

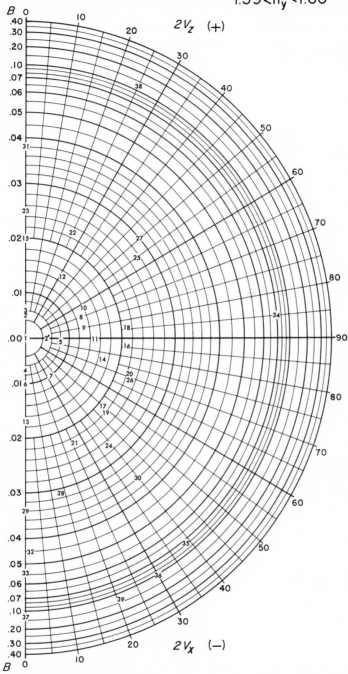

$1.59\lesssim n_y<1.60$

$2V_z\ (+)$

$2V_x\ (-)$

O

371

No. on Chart	Substance	n_x	n_y	n_z	$n_z - n_x$	2V	Page
	$Cu(UO_2)_2(AsO_4)_2 \cdot 16H_2O$, Zeunerite		1.602			- 00	209
	$K_4Os(CN)_6 \cdot 3H_2O$		1.6071			- 47	42
	$Cu_2(UO_2)_2 \cdot (AsO_4)_2 \cdot 10H_2O$		1.610			- 00	209
	$Zn(NH_3)_2Cl_2$		1.618			- 75	53
1	$Ca_5H_2(AsO_4)_4 \cdot 5H_2O$	1.613	.	1.615	0.002		195
1	$Cu(UO_2)_2(PO_4)_2 \cdot 8H_2O$		1.61	1.61	0.002	+00	208
2	$Ca_3(PO_4)_2$		1.607	1.604	0.003	- 00	189
1	$BaAl_2O_4 \cdot 2H_2O$	1.610	1.611	1.613	0.003	+	83
3	K_2CaSiO_4		1.600	1.605	0.005	+00	300
4	$Ca_2Si_2O_6 \cdot H_2O$, Riversideite	1.600	1.601	1.605	0.005	+ 50	281
5	$Ca_{10}(PO_4)_6CO_3 \cdot H_2O$	1.598	1.603		0.005	- 00	204
6	$Ca_2SiO_4 \cdot H_2O$, Hillebrandite	1.605	1.61	1.612	0.007	- 42	305
6'	$CaSi_2AlGaO_8$	1.604		1.611	0.007	90?	232
6'	$CaSiGeAl_2O_8$	1.608		1.615	0.007	90?	232
6''	$CaSi_2AlGaO_8$	1.604		1.611	0.007	90?	232
6'	KSi_3FeO_8	1.601		1.609	0.008	90?	232
7	$Ba(UO_2)_2(PO_4)_2 \cdot 6H_2O$, Uranocircite	1.604	1.613		0.009	- 00	209
8	$Ca(UO_2)_2(PO_4)_2 \cdot 10H_2O$, Autunite	1.59	1.60		0.01	- 00	207
8	$Mn(UO_2)_2(PO_4)_2 \cdot 8 - H_2O$, Mn-Autunite	1.59	1.60		0.01	- 00	208
8'	$Al_4OSi_2Al_2O_{12}$, Mullite	1.600		1.610	0.010		268
8	$Ca(UO_2)_2(PO_4)_2 \cdot 8 - H_2O$, Meta-Autunite - I	1.590	1.600		0.010	- 00	208
8	$CoCl(ClO_4)_2\, 6NH_3$	1.600	1.610		0.010	- 00	112
8	$(NH_4)_2(UO_2)_2(AsO_4)_2 \cdot 8H_2O$	1.601	1.611		0.010	- 00	206
9	$Al_2F_2SiO_4$, Topaz	1.6072	1.6104	1.6176	0.0104	+67	306
10	$Mg_2P_2O_7$	1.602	1.604	1.615	0.013	+21	214
11	$CaCl_2$, Hydrophilite	1.600	1.605	1.613	0.013	+ 50	26
	$NaGe_3AlO_8$	1.606	1.61	1.619	0.013		232
12	SiO_2	1.599	1.60	1.604	0.014	+ 54	64
13	$Ca_2Si_2O_6 \cdot 3H_2O$, Crestmoreite	1.593	1.603	1.607	0.014	- 70	282
14	$Na_{10}Fe_2Si_8O_{24}$		1.609	1.625	0.016	+00	267
	$SrH(PO_4)$	1.608		1.625	0.017		187
15	$Mg_5 Fe_2Si_8O_{22}F_2$	1.604	1.613	1.623	0.019	+88	284
16	$Na_2CaMg_5 Si_8O_{22}F_2$	1.603	1.614	1.622	0.019	- 72	285
17	$NaCa_2Mg_5 Si_7AlO_{22}F_2$	1.605	1.61	1.624	0.019	- 69	286
18	$Tl_2Cu(SO_4)_2 \cdot 6H_2O$	1.5996	1.6096	1.6190	0.0194	- 85	149
19	$NaCa_2Mg_5 Si_7AlO_{22}(OH)_2$, Edenite	1.61	1.613	1.63	0.02	+ 50	286
20	Li_4SiO_4	1.594	1.60	1.614	0.020	+25	304
21	$Tl_2Ni(SO_4)_2 \cdot 6H_2O$	1.6024	1.6183	1.6224	0.0200	- 62	148
18	$Fe(OH)_2Si_2O_5 \cdot 2H_2O$	1.589	1.600	1.610	0.021	- 86?	266
22	$Zn_4(OH)_2Si_2O_7 \cdot H_2O$, Hemimorphite	1.614	1.617	1.636	0.022	+46	296
23	$Tl_2Co(SO_4)_2 \cdot 6H_2O$	1.6009	1.6176	1.6238	0.0229	- 67	147
23	$Tl_2Fe(SO_4)_2 \cdot 6H_2O$	1.5929	1.6093	1.6162	0.0233	- 69	146
23	$Tl_2Zn(SO_4)_2 \cdot 6H_2O$	1.5931	1.6093	1.6168	0.0237	- 69	144
24	$BaSi_2O_5$, Sanbornite	1.597	1.612	1.621	0.024	- 75	258
	$(NH_4)_4(UO_2)(CO_3)_3$	1.60	1.6	1.625	0.025	-	99
25	$Ca_2Mg_5 Si_8O_{22}(OH)_2$, Tremolite	1.599	1.613	1.625	0.026	- 88	285
26	$NH_4Fe(CN)_6 \cdot 2NH_4Cl \cdot 3H_2O$	1.5922	1.6198		0.0276	- 00	42
26	Hydrogen - Uranospinite	1.584	1.612		0.028	- 00	205
26	$H_2(UO_2)_2(AsO_4)_4 \cdot 8H_2O$	1.584	1.612		0.028	- 00	205
27	$Mg_9F_2Si_4O_6$	1.608	1.618	1.636	0.028	+76	308
28	$Ca(UO_2)_2(AsO_4)_2 \cdot nH_2O$, Air dried	1.591	1.619	1.621	0.030	- 30	207
29	$Na_2(UO_2)_2(AsO_4)_2 \cdot 8H_2O$	1.586	1.617		0.031	- 00	206
30	$Mg_7F_2Si_3O_{12}$	1.598	1.606	1.630	0.032	+59	307
31	$Fe_3(OH)_2Si_4O_{10}$, Minnesotaite	1.586	1.618	1.618	0.032	- 04	259
32	$CaAl_4O_7$	1.617	1.617	1.651	0.035	+05	79
33	Al_3BO_6	1.586	1.603	1.623	0.037	+87	114
34	$HNaCa_2Si_3O_9$, Pectolite	1.595	1.604	1.632	0.037	+60	293
35	$KFeH_2(PO_4)_2 \cdot H_2O$	1.592	1.614	1.630	0.038	- 79	195
36	$Li_2K_2Fe(CN)_6 \cdot 3H_2O$	1.5883	1.6007	1.6316	0.0433	+66	40
37	$Ca_3Si_3O_9$, Pseudowollastonite	1.610	1.611	1.654	0.044	+10	291
38	$Y(PO_4) \cdot 2H_2O$, Weinschenkite	1.600	1.608	1.645	0.045	+30	200
39	$Ca_4(CO_3)Si_6Al_6O_{24}$, Meionite	1.565	1.610		0.045	- 00	253
40	$CaH(AsO_4) \cdot H_2O$, Haidingerite	1.590	1.602	1.638	0.048	+58	194
41	$AlBr_3 \cdot 6H_2O$	1.555	1.605		0.050	- 00	34
42	$Fe_3(PO_4)_2 \cdot 8H_2O$, Vivianite	1.5788	1.6024	1.6294	0.0506	+84	198
43	$CaH(PO_4)$, Monetite	1.587	1.615	1.640	0.053	- 70	188
44	$K_2S_4O_6$	1.5896	1.6057	1.6435	0.0539	+67	122
45	$Gd(BrO_3)_3 \cdot 9H_2O$	1.551	1.605		0.054	- 00	110
45	$Sm(BrO_3)_3 \cdot 9H_2O$	1.551	1.605		0.054	- 00	110
46	$Sr(ClO_3)_2$	1.5670	1.6047	1.6257	0.0587	- 72	109
47	$K_2PbSi_4O_{10}$	1.590	1.612	1.650	0.060	+75	257
48	$Na_2Pt(CN)_4 \cdot 3H_2O$	1.541	1.608	1.611	0.070	- 24	41
49	$MnCl_2 \cdot 2H_2O$	1.584	1.611	1.666	0.082	+7-	28
50	$SrPt(CN)_4 \cdot 5H_2O$	1.547	1.613	1.637	0.090	- 52	33
51	$CaNi(CN)_4 \cdot 5H_2O$	1.5405	1.617	1.638	0.0975	- 40	32
52	$CaPd(CN)_4 \cdot 5H_2O$	1.539	1.602	1.639	0.100	- 68	32
51	$SrPd(CN)_4 \cdot 5H_2O$	1.495	1.6025	1.612	0.117	- 40	32
53	$Ca(N_3)_2 \cdot 2(N_2H_4)$	1.583	1.610	1.70	0.117	+80	8
54	$(NH_4)_2(UO_2)(NO_3)_4 \cdot 2H_2O$	1.508	1.619	1.639	0.131	- 45	105
55	$SrNi(CN)_4 \cdot 5H_2O$	1.492	1.612	1.6235	0.1315	- 30	32
56	$NH_4(NO_3)$, Ammonia-Niter	1.413	1.611	1.637	0.224	- 35	101
57	$NaKPt(CN)_6 \cdot 3H_2O$	1.6088	1.61	1.90	0.29	+ 10	40
58	$Ca(CN)_2$		1.60		0.35	+00	8

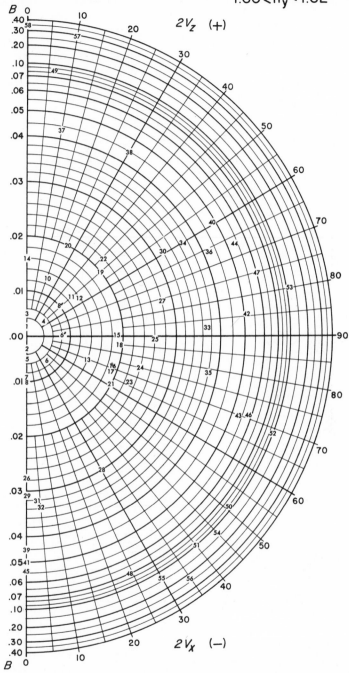
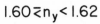

No. on Chart	Substance	n_x	n_y	n_z	$n_z - n_x$	2V	Page
	$Pb(UO_2)_2(PO_4)_2 \cdot 8H_2O$		1.626			- 00	209
1	$Cu(UO_2)_2(PO_4)_2 \cdot 8H_2O$, Metatorbernite	1.62	1.62		0.002	+00	208
1	$Na_4Ca_3Si_5O_{17}$		1.620		0.002		270
2	$FeBaSi_4O_{10}$, Gillespite	1.619	1.621		0.002	- 00	254
2	$Sr_5(PO_4)_3F$	1.619	1.621		0.002	- 00	204
2	$Ca_5(PO_4)_3F$, Fluorapatite	1.630	1.6325		0.0025	- 00	203
3	$Ca_3(PO_4)_2$, Whitlockite	1.626	1.629		0.003	- 00	189
4	$Ca_2P_2O_7$		1.624	1.628	0.004	+00	213
4'	$CaSi_2Ga_2O_8$	1.625		1.631	0.004	- 75?	232
3	$Ca_2OCl_2 \cdot 2H_2O$	1.634	1.638		0.004	- 00	51
5	$KAg(CN)_2$		1.625	1.623	0.005	+00	22
6	$Ca_2OCl_2 \cdot H_2O$	1.623	1.628		0.005	- 00	51
7	$K_2Pt(CN)_4 \cdot 3H_2O$	1.615	1.62	1.62	0.005	+40	42
7	$CaAs_2O_6$	1.629		1.635	0.006	+?	212
8	$Ca_8Si_3O_{14} \cdot 3H_2O$	1.630		1.636	0.006	+10	281
7	$ZnSiO_3$	1.616		1.623	0.007	+?	268
9	$(Ca,Sr)SiO_3$		1.623	1.630	0.007	+00	280
9	$Ca_2MgSi_2O_7$, Akermanite		1.632	1.639	0.007	+00	294
10	$(Ni, Mg)_6(OH)_6Si_4O_{11} \cdot H_2O$, Garnierite	1.622	1.62	1.630	0.008	+05	260
11	$Ca_5(PO_4)_2SiO_4$, Silicocarnotite	1.632	1.636	1.640	0.008	- 70	215
12	$Ca_{10}(PO_4)_6(CO_3) \cdot H_2O$, Carbonate-Apatite	1.619	1.628		0.009	- 00	204
13	$Ca_2P_2O_7$		1.630	1.639	0.009	+00	213
14	$Al_2(F,OH)_2SiO_4$	1.629	1.631	1.638	0.009	+48	306
14	$Sr(SO_4)$, Celestite	1.6215	1.6232	1.6305	0.0092	+50	131
15	$(UO_2)_6(OH)_{10}(SO_4) \cdot 12H_2O$, Uranopilite	1.620	1.624	1.630	0.010	+50	177
16	Al_2OSiO_4, Andalusite	1.634	1.639	1.645	0.011	- 86	309
17	$(Ca,Sr)SiO_3$		1.639	1.650	0.011	+00	280
18	$BaSO_4$, Barite	1.6363	1.6373	1.6484	0.0121	+37	130
19	KGe_3GaO_8	1.615		1.628	0.013		232
19	$Ca_5Mg_2Si_6O_{19}$	1.621	1.627	1.635	0.014	+80	291
19'	$Ba(UO_2)_2(PO_4)_2 \cdot 6H_2O$	1.607	1.621		0.014	- 00	209
20	$Ca_3Si_3O_9$, Wollasionite	1.620	1.632	1.634	0.014	- 39	291
21	$Tl_2Mg(SeO_4)_2 \cdot 6H_2O$	1.6250	1.6337	1.6404	0.0154	- 78	150
22	$Ca_3Si_2O_7 \cdot 3H_2O$, Afwillite	1.6169	1.6204	1.6336	0.0167	+55	297
23	$(NH_4)_2Mg(CrO_4)_2 \cdot 6H_2O$	1.6363	1.6371	1.6531	0.0168	+27	155
24	$Ca_3Si_3O_9$, Parawollastonite	1.614	1.629	1.631	0.017	- 35	291
25	$Ca_{10}Si_5O_{20} \cdot 6H_2O$	1.614	1.620	1.623	0.019	+50	306
26	$Ca_2SiO_4 \cdot H_2O$	1.614	1.620	1.633	0.019	+68	305
27	$PbS_2O_6 \cdot 4H_2O$		1.6366	1.6557	0.0191	+00	133
28	$Mg(F,OH)_2 \cdot 2Mg_2SiO_4$, Chondrodite	1.613	1.623	1.643	0.02	+71	307
29	$NaCa_2Mg_4AlSi_6Al_2O_{22}(OH)_2$, Hastingsite	1.62	1.63	1.64	0.02	+85	286
	$Ca_2OBr_2 \cdot 3H_2O$		1.623	1.645	0.02	+	51
30	$Al(AsO_4) \cdot 2 H_2O$, Mansfieldite	1.622	1.624	1.642	0.020	+ 30	200
29	$Mg_3Fe_4Si_8O_{22}F_2$	1.625	1.634	1.645	0.020	+86	284
31	$Zn_2PO_4(OH)$	1.608	1.624	1.629	0.021	- 70	201
32	$K_2CuCl_4 \cdot 2H_2O$	1.6148	1.6365		0.0217	- 00	39
33	$Rb_2Mg(CrO_4)_2 \cdot 6H_2O$	1.6217	1.6330	1.6435	0.0218	- 87	156
32	$Ca(UO_2)_2(AsO_4)_2 \cdot H_2O$ Heated 110°	1.615	1.637		0.022	- 00	207
34	$Zn_3(PO_4)_2 \cdot 4H_2O$, Parahopeite	1.614	1.625	1.637	0.023	+85	199
35	$Fe(OH)Si_2O_5 \cdot 2H_2O$, Nontronite	1.617	1.637	1.640	0.023	- 40	266
36	$Ba_2Si_3O_8$	1.620	1.625	1.645	0.025	+54	256
37	$Ba_2Si_3O_8$	1.620	1.625	1.645	0.025	+58	268
38	$BaAl_2O_4 \cdot 4H_2O$	1.625	1.628	1.650	0.025	+40	83
39	$SrAl_4O_7$	1.614	1.623	1.640	0.026	+75	79
40	KIO_4		1.6205	1.6479	0.0274	+00	110
41	$HNa(Ca,Mn)_2Si_3O_9$, Schizolite	1.631	1.636	1.660	0.029	+48	293
42	$H_8Na_6(MoO_4)_7 \cdot 18H_2O$		1.627		0.03	- 84	183
43	$CaCuSi_4O_{10}$	1.6053	1.6354		0.0301	- 00	254
44	$1Mg(F,OH)_2 \cdot 3Mg_2SiO_4$, Humite	1.623	1.634	1.655	0.032	+69	307
45	$Ce(PO_4) \cdot 2H_2O$, Churchite	1.620	1.620	1.654	0.034	+10	200
46	$CoCO_3SO_4 \cdot 4NH_3 \cdot 3H_2O$	1.595	1.631	1.632	0.037	- 24	179
47	$CuAl_6(PO_4)_4(OH)_8 \cdot 4H_2O$, Turquois	1.61	1.62	1.65	0.04	+40	207
48	$Zn_3(AsO_4)_2 \cdot 8H_2O$, Koettigite	1.622	1.638	1.671	0.049	- 74	199
49	$Fe_2(SO_4)_3 \cdot 6H_2O$, Lausenite	1.605	1.635	1.657	0.052	- 70	171
50	$H_2(UO_2)_2(AsO_4)_2 \cdot 8H_2O$, Troegerite	1.585	1.630		0.055	- 00	206
51	$Pd(NH_3)_4Cl_2 \cdot H_2O$	1.557	1.620		0.063	- 00	53
52	$(NH_4)_2(UO_2)Cl_4 \cdot 2H_2O$	1.566	1.633	1.637	0.071	- 25	40
53	$FeSO_4 \cdot H_2O$, Szomolnokite	1.591	1.623	1.663	0.072	+80	163
54	$CoSO_4 \cdot H_2O$	1.603	1.639	1.683	0.080	- 85	164
55	$Rb_2Pt(CN)_4 \cdot 3H_2O$	1.6111	1.62	1.696	0.085	+60	42
56	$3K_2S_5O_6 \cdot 2H_2O$	1.570	1.63	1.658	0.088	- 65	134
57	$NaCNS$	1.545	1.625	1.695	0.150	- 82	22
58	$LiRbPt(CN)_4 \cdot 3H_2O$	1.6204	1.6233	1.9310	0.3106	+13	40
59	$CsICl_2$		1.637	2.15	0.513	+00	21
60	$LiKPt(CN)_4 \cdot 3H_2O$	1.6237	1.6278	2.2916	0.6679	+19	40

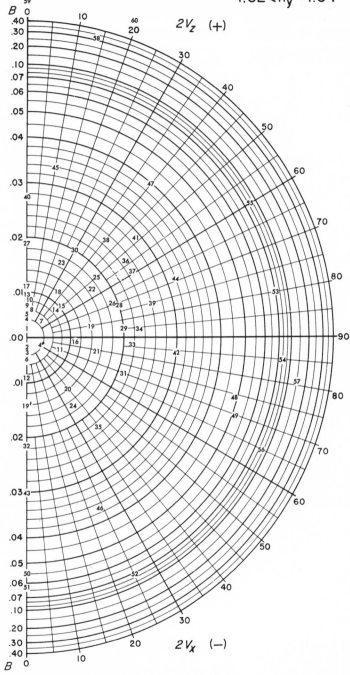

Q

No. on Chart	Substance	n_x	n_y	n_z	$n_z - n_x$	2V	Page
	$FeCl_2 \cdot 2H_2O$		1.6435				28
	$2CdCl_2 \cdot 5H_2O$		1.6513			+57	29
1	$Ca_2MgSi_2O_7 \cdot Ca_2AlSiAlO_7$	1.652	1.653		0.001	- 00	294
2	$Ca_4(PO_4)_2O$, Hilgenstockite	1.643	1.645	1.647	0.004	+80	202
3	$Ca_9Si_6O_{21} \cdot H_2O$	1.649	1.65	1.654	0.005	90	281
4	$Sr_5(PO_4)_3Cl$		1.650	1.655	0.005	+00	204
5	$Sr_{10}(PO_4)_6CO_3$	1.638	1.644		0.006	- 00	204
6	$CaGe_3Al_2O_8$	1.641	1.645	1.647	0.006	- 70	232
	$AlO(OH)$		1.65		0.006		70
7	$Ca_4(PO_4)_2O$	1.650	1.651	1.656	0.006	+30	202
8	$Sr_5(PO_4)_3Cl$		1.658	1.664	0.006	+00	204
9	$BaClF$	1.633	1.640		0.007	- 00	25
9	$Ca_5(PO_4)_3OH$, Hydroxylapatite	1.644	1.651		0.007	- 00	203
9	$Na_4(OH)_3Si_3Al_3O_{12}$	1.64	1.647		0.007	- 00	254
10	$MgSiO_3$, Enstatite	1.650	1.653	1.658	0.008	+55	271
11	$Ca_3Si_2O_7$, Rankinite	1.641	1.645	1.650	0.009	+64	296
12	$Ca_7(PO_4)_2Si_2O_8$, Nagelschmidtite	1.652	1.652	1.661	0.009	+20	215
10	$MgSiO_3$, Clinoenstatite	1.651	1.654	1.660	0.009	+53	271
13	$IrCl_3(NH_3)_4 \cdot H_2O$		1.6576	1.6666	0.009	+00	53
14	$Cs_2MnCl_4 \cdot 2H_2O$	1.64		1.65	0.01		39
14	$Ca_3(PO_4)_2 \cdot 2Ca_2SiO_4$, Nagelschmidtite	1.64	1.642	1.65	0.01	+20	215
15	MgO	1.634	1.644		0.010	- 00	68
16	$TlClO_4$	1.6427	1.6445	1.6541	0.0114	+25	111
17	$Al_6OSi_2Al_2O_{12}$, Mullite	1.642	1.644	1.654	0.012	+48	268
18	$NaAlSi_2O_6$, Jadeite	1.655	1.659	1.667	0.012	+70	279
19	$MgMgSi_2O_6$	1.6484	1.6503	1.6605	0.0121	+20	273
18	$Na_2Mg_2Si_2O_7$	1.641	1.646	1.654	0.013	+70	296
20	$AlBO_3$, Jeremejevite	1.640	1.653		0.013	- 00	114
21	$Mn_5H_2(PO_4)_4 \cdot 4H_2O$, Hureaulite	1.647	1.654	1.660	0.013	- 75	195
	$SrAl_2O_4$	1.649		1.663	0.014		78
22	$CaMgSiO_4$, Monticellite	1.639	1.646	1.653	0.014	+85	304
23	$LiAlSi_2O_6$	1.648	1.655	1.662	0.014	+90	280
24	$Tl_2Co(SeO_4)_2 \cdot 6H_2O$	1.6442	1.6535	1.6590	0.0148	- 67	153
25	Ca_2SiO_4, Shannonite	1.642	1.645	1.654	0.015	+52	301
26	$AlO(OH)$, Boehmite	1.646	1.652	1.661	0.015	+80	70
26	$NaGe_3GaO_8$	1.638		1.654	0.016		232
27	$7(Ca_2AlSiAlO_7) \cdot 3(NaCaAlSi_2O_7)$	1.628	1.644		0.016	- 00	295
28	$AlO(OH)$	1.649	1.649	1.665	0.016	- 25	70
29	Be_2SiO_4, Phenacite		1.654	1.670	0.016	+00	300
30	$Cs_2Mg(CrO_4)_2 \cdot 6H_2O$	1.6369	1.6425	1.6547	0.0178	+67	156
31	$CaH(AsO_4)$	1.635	1.650	1.653	0.018	- 50	188
32	$Tl_2Ni(SeO_4)_2 \cdot 6H_2O$	1.6378	1.6498	1.6560	0.0182	- 59	154
33	$Fe_3Mg_4Si_8O_{22}(OH)_2$	1.641	1.650	1.660	0.019	- 85	283
34	Li_2SiO_3	1.65	1.65	1.67	0.02	+20	267
35	$Cu(UO_2)_2(AsO_4)_2 \cdot 8H_2O$, Metazeunerite	1.623	1.643		0.020	- 00	209
36	$Ca_2Mg_3Al_2Si_6Al_2O_{22}(OH)_2$, Tschermakite	1.637		1.657	0.020	- 80	286
37	$Na_4SnS_4 \cdot 18H_2O$	1.643	1.6485	1.663	0.020	- 68	14
38	$CaAl_2O_4$	1.643	1.655	1.663	0.020	- 56	78
37	$Tl_2Zn(SeO_4)_2 \cdot 6H_2O$	1.6414	1.6539	1.6615	0.0201	- 69	150
39	$Na_2Li_3Al_6(OH)_4B_3O_9Si_6O_{18}$, Elbaite	1.625	1.646		0.021	- 00	289
40	$Mg_3B_2O_6$, Kotoite	1.652	1.653	1.673	0.021	+21	114
41	$NaMg_3Al_6(OH)_4B_3O_9Si_6O_{18}$, Tourmaline	1.628	1.650		0.022	- 00	289
42	$Tl_2Fe(SeO_4)_2 \cdot 6H_2O$	1.6352	1.6514	1.6589	0.0237	- 70	152
43	$SrClF$	1.627	1.651		0.024	- 00	25
43	$Cu(UO_2)_2(AsO_4)_2 \cdot 5H_2O$	1.63	1.654		0.024	- 00	209
44	$Mg_2Fe_5Si_8O_{22}F_2$	1.647	1.657	1.671	0.024	+85	284
45	$BaCl_2 \cdot 2H_2O$	1.635	1.646	1.660	0.025	+84	29
46	$Mg_4Fe_3Si_8O_{22}(OH)_2$, Cummingtonite	1.640	1.647	1.665	0.025	+65	283
47	$Tl_2Mn(SeO_4)_2 \cdot 6H_2O$	1.6276	1.6429	1.6531	0.0255	- 72	151
48	$BaCl_2 \cdot 2H_2O$	1.6291	1.6419	1.6583	0.0292	+84	29
49	$(NH_4)_3PdSO_3Cl_3 \cdot H_2O$		1.643	1.67	0.03	+00	173
49	$KReO_4$		1.643	1.673	0.030	+00	82
	$Ca_6Si_3O_{12} \cdot 2H_2O$	1.642	1.65	1.672	0.030	+	306
50	$LiI \cdot 3H_2O$	1.625	1.655		0.030	- 00	23
51	$Zn_4(PO_4)_2O$	1.63	1.656	1.660	0.030	- 30	202
52	$Tl_2Cu(SeO_4)_2 \cdot 6H_2O$	1.6396	1.6565	1.6720	0.0324	- 85	155
53	B_2O_3	1.615	1.648		0.033	- 00	59
54	$Ba_2Al_2O_5 \cdot 5H_2O$	1.642	1.655	1.676	0.034	+75	83
55	Mg_2SiO_4, Forsterite	1.635	1.651	1.670	0.035	+81	302
56	$K_2CuCl_4 \cdot 2H_2O$, Mitscherlichite	1.6133	1.6485		0.0352	- 00	39
57	$(NH_4)_2MnCl_4 \cdot 2H_2O$	1.607	1.644		0.037	- 00	39
58	$BaCdCl_4 \cdot 4H_2O$	1.610	1.646	1.653	0.043	- 61	30
59	$HNa(Ca,Mn)_2Si_5O_9$	1.633	1.641	1.677	0.044	+51	293
60	$Al(NO_3(IO_3)_2 \cdot 6H_2O$		1.6516	1.6987	0.0471	+00	113
61	$7BaS_3O_6 \cdot 2H_2O$	1.620	1.640	1.670	0.050	+60	134
62	Cs_3CuCl_4	1.625	1.648	1.678	0.053	+84	37
63	$Na_6P_2Mo_5O_{23} \cdot 14H_2O$	1.5962	1.6411	1.6520	0.0558	- 51	184
64	$Ni_3(AsO_4)_2 \cdot 8H_2O$, Annabergite	1.622	1.658	1.687	0.065	+84	199
65	$BaPd(CN)_4 \cdot 4H_2O$	1.583	1.646	1.651	0.068	- 29	33
	$Cs_2(UO_2)Cl_4$	1.614		1.695	0.08		37
66	$Ca(IO_3)_2 \cdot 6H_2O$	1.604	1.644	1.686	0.082	+85	109
67	$Ca(IO_4)_2 \cdot 6H_2O$	1.604	1.644	1.686	0.082	+88	112
68	$BaNi(CN)_4 \cdot 4H_2O$	1.569	1.658	1.658	0.089	- 05	33
69	$Na_2SnS_2 \cdot 8H_2O$	1.605	1.647	1.746	0.141	- 66	14
70	CaB_2O_4	1.540	1.656	1.682	0.142	- 51	115
71	$CaPt(CN)_4 \cdot 5H_2O$	1.623	1.644	1.767	0.144	+48	32
72	$Hg(CN)_2$	1.492	1.645		0.153	+ 00	27
72	$CaCO_3$, Calcite	1.4864	1.6584		0.1720	- 00	91

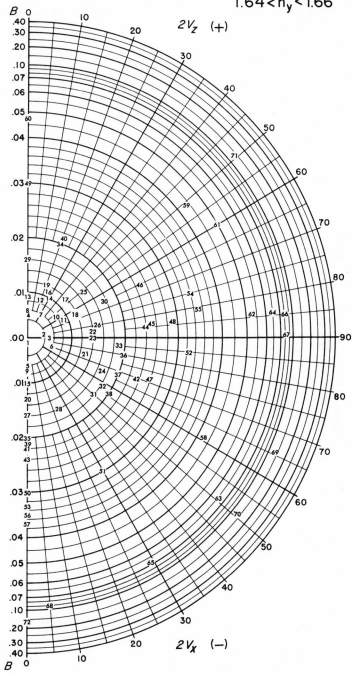

$2V_z$ (+)

$2V_x$ (−)

R

No. on Chart	Substance	n_x	n_y	n_z	$n_z - n_x$	2V	Page
1	$Ca_5(PO_4)_3Cl$, Chlorapatite	1.6675	1.6684		0.0009	- 00	203
2	$Na_2Ca_2Si_2O_7$	1.665	1.665	1.665	0.003	70	296
3	$Ba_5(PO_4)_3F$	1.665	1.669		0.004	- 00	204
4	$Ca_2FeSiAlO_7$, Ferrigehlenite	1.661	1.666		0.005	- 00	295
5	$BaSiO_3$	1.673	1.674	1.678	0.005	+ 29	268
6	$Ca_2ZnSi_2O_7$, Hardystonite	1.6624	1.6718		0.0094	- 00	295
	$NH_4FeH_2(PO_4)_2$		1.66		0.01		189
7	$Ca_3(PO_4)_2 \cdot 2Ca_2SiO_4$, Nagelschmidtite	1.67	1.675	1.68	0.01	+ 20	215
6	$Ca_{12}(PO_4)_6SiO_5$, Steadite		1.66		0.01	- 00	215
8	$Mg_3B_7O_{13}Cl$, Boracite	1.658	1.662	1.668	0.010	+ 82	117
9	$LiMnPO_4$, Lithiophilite	1.663	1.666	1.673	0.010	+ 65	191
10	$Ca_3AlSiAlO_8$	1.675	1.679	1.685	0.010	+ 60	305
11	$Mg_3B_7O_{13}Cl$	1.6622	1.6670	1.6730	0.0108	+ 80	117
12	$Ca_2AlSiAlO_7$, Gehlenite	1.658	1.669		0.011	- 00	295
13	$ZnSO_4$, Zinkosite	1.658	1.669	1.670	0.012	- 25	130
14	$2(Ca_2MgSi_2O_7) \cdot 8(Ca_2FeSi_2O_7)$, Melilite	1.658	1.670		0.012	- 00	294
15	$CaAl_4O_7$	1.662	1.671	1.674	0.012	- 35	79
14	Justite	1.657	1.670		0.013	- 00	295
16	$Ca_6Si_3O_{12} \cdot H_2O$	1.650	1.661	1.664	0.014	- 25	281
17	$CaMnSi_2O_6$, Bustamite	1.662	1.674	1.676	0.014	- 44	293
18	$LiAlSi_2O_6$, Spodumene	1.661	1.666	1.676	0.015	+ 75	280
	$SrH(AsO_4)$	1.65		1.67	0.02		188
19	$Ca_2(PO_4)Cl$, Chlor-spodiosite	1.649	1.665	1.670	0.021	- 70	201
20	$Ag_2CO_3 \cdot 4NH_3 \cdot H_2O$	1.66	1.66	1.68	0.023	+ 10	100
21	Al_2OSiO_4, Sillimanite	1.661	1.670	1.684	0.023	+ 28	309
22	$Ca_2Mg_4FeSi_8O_{22}F_2$, Actinolite	1.655	1.665	1.68	0.025	- 80	285
23	$Fe_7Si_8O_{22}F_2$	1.665	1.676	1.690	0.025	+ 85	284
24	$K_2Al_{12}O_{19}$	1.64	1.668		0.028	00	80
25	$CaMgSi_2O_6$, Diopside	1.6658	1.6720	1.6946	0.0288	+ 58	274
26	$NaFe_3Al_6(OH)_4B_3O_9Si_6O_{18}$, Schorlite	1.639	1.668		0.029	- 00	289
26'	Andalusite	1.662	1.671	1.691	0.029	- 71	309
27	$Ce_2Pt_3(CN)_{12} \cdot 18H_2O$	1.65	1.66	1.68	0.03	+ 70	49
28	$(NH_4)_2CuCl_4 \cdot 2H_2O$	1.641	1.671		0.030	- 00	40
29	$Co(NH_3)_6 \cdot Fe(CN)_6$		1.662	1.695	0.033	+ 00	53
30	$Ag_2S_2O_6 \cdot 2H_2O$	1.631	1.662	1.665	0.034	- 30	134
31	$Mg_7Fe_2Si_4O_{16}F_2$, Clinohumite	1.664	1.673	1.698	0.034	+ 62	308
32	$Na_2Al_{12}O_{19}$	1.633	1.670		0.037	- 00	80
33	$Y(OH)_3$		1.676	1.714	0.038	+ 00	72
34	$Ca_5CO_3(SiO_4)_2$, Spurrite	1.640	1.674	1.679	0.039	- 39	311
35	$(NH_4)_9Ag(S_2O_3)_4Br$	1.6294	1.6769		0.0475	- 00	121
36	$KFeH_2(PO_4)_2$	1.631	1.665	1.680	0.049	- 66	188
37	$NaAlAsO_4F$, Durangite	1.634	1.673	1.685	0.051	- 45	202
38	$K_2HgCl_4 \cdot H_2O$	1.648	1.678	1.699	0.051	- 78	39
39	$Fe_3(AsO_4)_2 \cdot 8H_2O$, Symplesite	1.635	1.668	1.702	0.067	- 86	199
40	$Co_3(AsO_4)_2 \cdot 8H_2O$, Erythrite	1.626	1.661	1.699	0.073	+ 90	198
41	$Cu(SO_4) \cdot H_2O$	1.626	1.671	1.699	0.073	- 75	164
42	$Ca_2B_2O_5$	1.585	1.662	1.667	0.082	- 25	114
43	$MgCl_2$, Chloromagnesite	1.59	1.675		0.085	- 00	26
44	$CoCl_2 \cdot 2H_2O$	1.626	1.662	1.721	0.095	+ 78	28
45	$K_2Pt(NO_2)_4$	1.590	1.670	1.685	0.095	55	106
46	$Na_6Te(MoO_4)_6 \cdot 22H_2O$	1.577	1.662	1.683	0.106	- 51	184
47	$K_2PtBr_2(NO_2)_2 \cdot H_2O$	1.626	1.6684	1.757	0.131	+ 72	106
48	$CaBa(CO_3)_2$, Alstonite	1.525	1.673	1.673	0.148	- 07	95
49	$BaCO_3$, Witherite	1.529	1.676	1.677	0.148	- 16	94
48	$SrCO_3$, Strontianite	1.5199	1.6666	1.6685	0.1486	- 07	93
50	$FeSO_4(OH) \cdot 2H_2O$, Butlerite	1.588	1.678	1.749	0.161	- 70	177
51	$CaMg(CO_3)_2$, Dolomite	1.502	1.679		0.177	- 00	95
52	KCNS	1.532	1.660	1.730	0.198	- 68	22
53	$BaPt(CN)_4 \cdot 4H_2O$	1.666	1.6745	1.919	0.253	+ 25	33

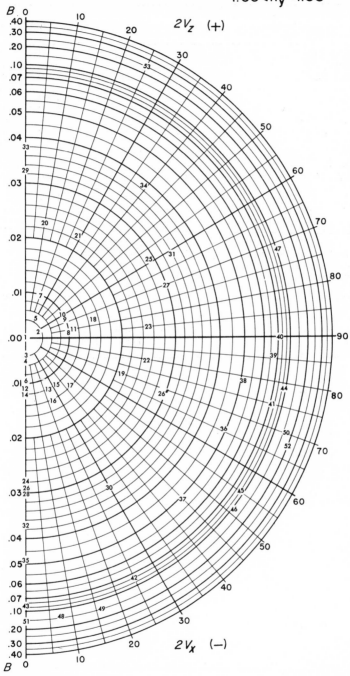

No. on Chart	Substance	n_x	n_y	n_z	$n_z - n_x$	2V	Page
1	$Na_3AsS_4 \cdot 8H_2O$		1.6802		0.006	- 88	14
2	$Ba_{10}(PO_4)_6(CO_3)$	1.683	1.691		0.008	- 00	204
3	$K_2Ca_{23}Si_{12}O_{48}$		1.695	1.703	0.008	+ 00	300
4	$BAsO_4$		1.681	1.690	0.009	+ 00	190
5	$Ca_2BaSi_3O_9$	1.668	1.681		0.013	- 00	288
6	$Ca_2FeSi_2O_7$, Ferroakermanite	1.673	1.690		0.017	- 00	295
7	Zn_2SiO_4, Willemite		1.695	1.715	0.020	+ 00	300
8	$Ca_5(BO_3)_2SiO_4$	1.666	1.682	1.690	0.024	- 50	119
9	$ZnCl_2$		1.687	1.713	0.026	+ 00	26
10	Augite	1.687	1.694	1.713	0.026	+ 59	278
11	$Na_2Al_{12}O_{19}$	1.650	1.686		0.036	- 00	80
11	$K_2Al_{12}O_{19}$, Alumina, Gamma	1.660	1.696		0.036	- 00	80
11'	$Mg_{16}Fe_4(SiO_4)_{10}$, Olivine	1.674	1.692	1.712	0.038	- 87	303
12	GeO_2		1.695	1.735	0.040	+ 00	63
13	$Ca(UO_2)_4(PO_4)_2(OH)_4 \cdot 6H_2O$	1.658	1.699	1.699	0.041	- 25	210
13'	$(UO_2)_2SiO_4 \cdot 2H_2O$, Soddyite	1.65	1.68	1.71	0.06	- 85?	308
14	$(NH_4)_2Fe_2H_4(PO_4)_4 \cdot H_2O$	1.655	1.680	1.715	0.060	+ 57	195
15	$Na_2Cr_2O_7 \cdot 2H_2O$	1.6610	1.6994	1.7510	0.090	+ 84	135
16	$CuCl_2 \cdot 2H_2O$, Eriochalcite	1.644	1.684	1.742	0.098	+ 81	29
17	$K_2Rh_2(NH_3)_4(NO_2)_8 \cdot H_2O$	1.612	1.690	1.716	0.104	- 62	107
18	K_2PtCl_4	1.553	1.683		0.130	- 00	36
18	K_2PtCl_4	1.557	1.690		0.133	- 00	36
18	$KBrO_3$	1.54	1.68		0.14	- 00	108
18	K_2PtCl_4	1.548	1.693		0.145	- 00	36
19	NH_4CNS	1.546	1.685	1.692	0.146	- 23	22
20	$CaCO_3$, Aragonite	1.5300	1.6810	1.6854	0.1554	- 18	93
21	$AgCN$		1.685	1.94	0.255	+ 00	22

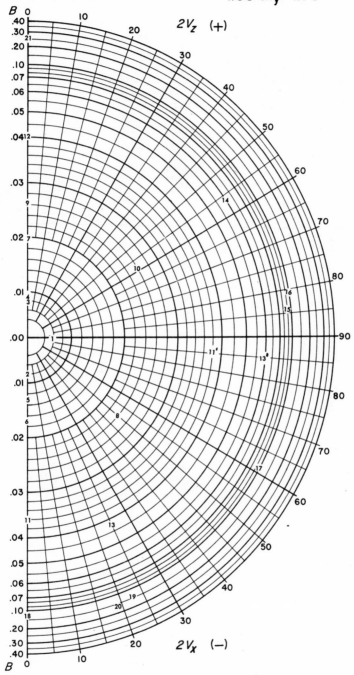

$1.68 \lesssim n_y < 1.70$

$2V_Z$ (+)

$2V_X$ (−)

S

No. on Chart	Substance	n_x	n_y	n_z	$n_z - n_x$	2V	Page
	$BaN_6 \cdot H_2O$		1.7				8
	$BaCdBr_4 \cdot 4H_2O$		1.702			- 70	30
1	$Ba_5(PO_4)_3Cl$	1.699	1.701		0.002	- 00	204
2	$K_2Pb(SO_4)_2$, Palmierite	1.68	1.712		0.03	- 00	132
3	$Pt(NH_3)_5Cl_4 \cdot H_2O$		1.718	1.722	0.004	+00	53
4	$Mg_4Al_{10}Si_2O_{23}$, Sapphirine	1.7055	1.7088	1.7112	0.0057	- 69	86
4	$LiFePO_4$, Triphylite	1.696	1.700	1.702	0.006	- 65	191
	$Co(NH_3)_6Cl_3$		1.706		0.006		54
5	$Mg_4Al_{10}Si_2O_{23}$	1.714	1.719	1.720	0.006	- 50	86
6	$CaGe_2Ga_2O_8$	1.705	1.71	1.711	0.006	90?	232
6	$Rh(NH_3)_5Cl_2$	1.700	1.703	1.707	0.007	+85	53
7	$SrAl_{12}O_{19}$	1.694	1.702		0.008	- 00	80
7	$BaAl_{12}O_{19}$	1.694	1.702		0.008	- 00	80
8	$NaCa_4Al_3O_9$	1.702	1.708	1.710	0.008	- 50	73
8	Zn_2SiO_4		1.700		0.009	- 49	300
9	$ZnClF$		1.70		0.009	+70	25
10	$(NH_4)_3IrCl_6 \cdot H_2O$	1.706	1.714	1.718	0.012	- 66	46
11	Ca_2SiO_4, Bredigite	1.712	1.716	1.725	0.013	+ 30	301
12	BeO, Bromellite		1.719	1.733	0.014	+00	58
13	$Mn_2P_2O_7$	1.695	1.704	1.710	0.015	+85	214
14	$Ca_2FeMn_3Si_6O_{18}$	1.692	1.705	1.707	0.015	- 35	293
15	Zn_2SiO_4	1.685	1.700	1.703	0.018	- 40	300
16	$Ca(Fe,Mn,Mg)_2Si_3O_9$, Vogtite	1.685	1.701	1.703	0.018	- 66	292
17	$Ca_3Mg(SiO_4)_2$, Merwinite	1.706	1.712	1.724	0.018	+66	305
18	$Cu(OH)_3NO_3$, Gerhardtite	1.703	1.713	1.722	0.019	+85	104
19	Rb_2CrO_4		1.71	1.72	0.02	- 60	128
20	Ca_2SiO_4, Larnite	1.707	1.715	1.730	0.023	+50	301
21	$Na_4Zr_2(SiO_4)_3$	1.692	1.715		0.023	- 00	300
22	$Ca(UO_2)_4(PO_4)_2(OH)_2 \cdot 2H_2O$, Phosphuranylite	1.682	1.706	1.708	0.026	- 30	210
23	$CaMnSi_2O_6$, Johannsenite	1.710	1.719	1.738	0.028	+ 70	279
24	$FeMgSi_2O_6$	1.7079	1.7089	1.7370	0.0291	+20	273
24'	$(NH_4)_3H_6Al(MoO_4)_6 \cdot 7H_2O$	1.700	1.700	1.741	0.041	+10	183
25	$MgFe_6Si_8O_{22}(OH)_2$, Grunertite	1.686	1.709	1.729	0.043	- 86	284
26	$(UO_3)_4 \cdot 9H_2O$, Schoepite	1.690	1.714	1.733	0.045	- 89	67
27	$NaAgS_2O_3 \cdot H_2O$	1.69	1.715	1.74	0.05	+90	134
28	$KCo(NH_3)_2(NO_2)_4$	1.702	1.713	1.760	0.058	+55	107
29	$Cu_4SO_4(OH)_6 \cdot H_2O$, Langite	1.654	1.713	1.722	0.068	- 37	175
30	$Cs_6Te(MoO_4)_6 \cdot 7H_2O$	1.709	1.716	1.797	0.088	+34	184
31	$Li_6Te(MoO_4)_6 \cdot 13H_2O$	1.612	1.703		0.091	- 00	183
32	$SrCr_2O_7 \cdot 3H_2O$	1.7146	1.7174	1.812	0.0954	+ 20	135
33	$K_6Te(MoO_4)_6 \cdot 8H_2O$	1.66	1.70	1.76	0.10	+81	183
34	$(UO_2)_3(SO_4)_2(OH)_2 \cdot 8H_2O$, Zippeite	1.655	1.717	1.765	0.110	- 83	177
35	$(NH_4)_2PtCl_4$	1.574	1.706		0.132	- 00	37
36	K_2PdCl_4	1.537	1.715		0.178	- 00	36
36	Rb_2PdCl_4	1.533	1.715		0.182	- 00	37
36	K_2PdCl_4	1.523	1.710		0.187	- 00	36
37	$MgCO_3$, Magnesite	1.509	1.700		0.191	- 00	91

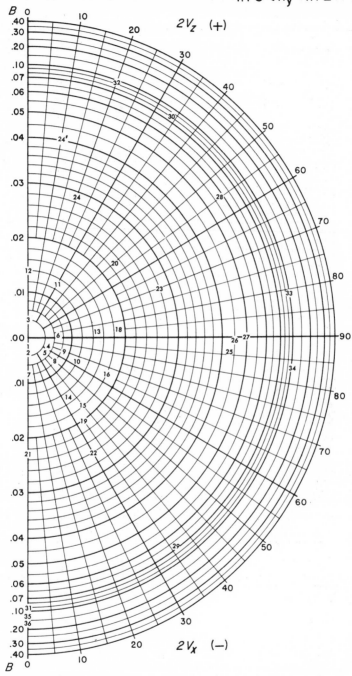

T

383

No. on Chart	Substance	n_x	n_y	n_z	$n_z - n_x$	2V	Page
	$H_6Mg(WO_4)_4 \cdot 5H_2O$		1.74			+78	183
1	$Mg_{84}Al_{10}Si_2O_{23}$	1.729	1.734	1.734	0.005	- 60	86
2	Ca_3OSiO_4	1.716	1.722		0.006	- 00	308
3	$MgBeAl_4O_8$	1.717	1.724		0.007	- 00	78
4	$NaK_3Cr_2O_8$		1.7278	1.7361	0.0083	+00	125
5	$BeAl_2O_4$, Chrysoberyl	1.732	1.734	1.741	0.009	+70	78
	$Ba_3Al_2O_6$		1.735		0.009		77
6	$CaMn_4Si_5O_{15}$, Rhodonite	1.729	1.731	1.739	0.010	+60	292
6	$BeAl_2O_4$	1.746	1.748	1.756	0.010	+60	78
7	$BaCl_2$	1.7302	1.7361	1.7420	0.0117	+85	26
8	Ca_2SiO_4		1.724	1.738	0.014	+00	301
	Cd_2SiO_4		1.74		0.014		304
9	Ca_2SiO_4	1.725	1.728	1.740	0.015	+ 33	301
	Ca_2GeO_4	1.724		1.739	0.015		79
10	$CuSO_4$, Chalcocyanite	1.724	1.733	1.739	0.015	- 70	130
11	$MgFeSi_2O_6$	1.7117	1.724	1.7268	0.0151	- 47	272
12	Al_2OSiO_4, Kyanite	1.7131	1.7219	1.7285	0.0154	- 82	310
13	$Ca_3Fe_2O_6$	1.73			0.017		79
13	$CaFe_2Si_3O_9$	1.716	1.725	1.734	0.018	- 85	292
14	$Pb(UO_2)_4(PO_4)_2(OH)_4 \cdot 7H_2O$, Renardite	1.715	1.736	1.739	0.018	- 41	210
15	$NaCa_2Fe_5Si_7AlO_{22}(OH)_2$, Ferroednite	1.71		1.73	0.02	- 20	286
16	$NaCa_2Fe''_4Fe'''Si_6Al_2O_{22}(OH)_2$, Ferrohastingsite	1.72		1.74	0.02	- 35	286
17	$CuSeO_3 \cdot 2H_2O$, Chalcomenite	1.710	1.731	1.732	0.022	- 34	134
18	$Sr_2SiW_{12}O_{40} \cdot 16H_2O$		1.749		0.023	+87	184
19	$Ca_2Fe_5Si_8O_{22}(OH)_2$, Ferrotremolite	1.710		1.735	0.025	- 75	286
20	Augite	1.726	1.732	1.753	0.027	+49	278
21	$La(OH)_3$		1.740	1.768	0.028	+00	71
21	$Nd(OH)_3$		1.740	1.768	0.028	+00	71
21	$Sm(OH)_3$		1.740	1.768	0.028	+00	72
22	Sr_2SiO_4	1.7275	1.732	1.756	0.0285	+ 32	305
23	$CaFeSi_2O_6$, Hedenbergite	1.7260	1.7318	1.7551	0.0291	+60	274
24	$Ca_2Fe''_3Fe'''_2Si_6Al_2O_{22}(OH)_2$, Ferrotschermakite	1.72		1.75	0.03	- 70	286
25	$NH_4Co(NH_3)_2(NO_2)_4$	1.73	1.73	1.76	0.03	+ 35	107
26	$BaBr_2 \cdot 2H_2O$	1.7129	1.7266	1.7441	0.0312	+84	29
27	$FePO_4 \cdot 2H_2O$, Strengite	1.730	1.732	1.762	0.032	+ 25	200
28	$HCa_2Fe''Fe'''Si_5O_{15}$	1.713	1.726	1.746	0.033	+62	294
29	$HCa_2Fe''Fe'''Si_5O_{15}$, Babingtonite	1.720	1.731	1.753	0.033	+76	294
30	$KFe_2(PO_4)_2(OH) \cdot 2H_2O$	1.706	1.720	1.741	0.035	+81	210
31	$Zn_2AsO_4(OH)$, Adamite	1.722	1.742	1.761	0.039	+88	202
32	$KAuBr_4$	1.74	1.74		0.04	- 10	43
33	$Mg_{12}Fe_8(SiO_4)_{10}$, Olivine	1.712	1.735	1.753	0.041	- 78	303
	$(NH_4)_3H_6Al(MoO_4)_6 \cdot 7H_2O$	1.700	1.741		0.041		183
34	$Mn(OH)_2$, Pyrochroite	1.681	1.723		0.042	- 00	69
35	K_2CrO_4, Tarapacaite	1.687	1.722	1.731	0.044	- 52	127
36	$CaFeSiO_4$	1.696	1.734	1.743	0.047	- 49	303
37	$HAlO_2$, Diaspore	1.702	1.722	1.750	0.048	+84	73
	$SbBr_3$		1.74		0.05		34
38	$Zn_2AsO_4(OH)$	1.708	1.734	1.758	0.050	- 87	202
39	$CaMnSiO_4$, Glaucochroite	1.685	1.723	1.736	0.051	- 61	304
40	$Cu_3SO_4(OH)_4$, Antlerite	1.726	1.738	1.789	0.051	+53	173
41	$(NH_4)_6Te_2(OH)_6(MoO_4)_6 \cdot 7H_2O$	1.684	1.727	1.741	0.057	- 58	184
42	$AgNO_3$	1.729	1.744	1.788	0.059	+62	102
43	$Pt(NH_3)_2O_2(OH)_2Cl_2$	1.690	1.730	1.756	0.066	- 75	53
44	$PtCONH_3Cl_2$	1.722	1.745	1.790	0.068	+74	54
45	$Cs_6Te(MoO_4)_6 \cdot 7H_2O$	1.669	1.734	1.738	0.069	- 30	184
46	$Pt(NH_3)_2(NO_2)_2$	1.711	1.742	1.790	0.079	+80	107
47	$Rh(NH_3)_3(NO_2)_3$	1.700	1.720	1.780	0.080	+69	107
48	UO_2CO_3, Rutherfordine	1.715	1.730	1.795	0.080	+53	98
49	$Cu_2PO_4(OH)$, Libethenite	1.701	1.743	1.787	0.086	- 85	201
50	CaI_2	1.652	1.743		0.091	- 00	27
51	YPO_4, Xenotime		1.7207	1.8155	0.0948	+00	190
52	$K_2Cr_2O_7$, Lopezite	1.7202	1.7380	1.8197	0.0995	+52	122
53	$KFe''_3(Fe''',Mg,Al)_5Si_8O_{20} \cdot 4H_2O$	1.625	1.735	1.735	0.110	- 10	265
54	$Zn_5(OH)_6(CO_3)_2$, Hydrozincite	1.640	1.736	1.750	0.110	- 40	98
55	NH_4SH	1.74	1.74		0.14	- 00	9
56	$MN_3B_4O_9$	1.617	1.738	1.776	0.159	- 56	115
57	Cs_2PdCl_4	1.560	1.720		0.160	- 00	37
58	$NiCl_2 \cdot 2H_2O$	1.620	1.723	1.783	0.163	- 72	28
57	$(NH_4)_2PdCl_4$	1.553	1.723		0.170	- 00	37
59	$(NH_4)_2PdCl_4$	1.544	1.736		0.192	- 00	37
59'	$Fe_2(MoO_4)_3 \cdot 8H_2O$, Ferrimolybdite	1.720	1.733	1.935	0.215	+ 10?	183
60	$Hg_2(OH)_2(NO_3)_2 \cdot H_2O$	1.69	1.72	1.92	0.23	+70	104
61	$LiNO_3$	1.435	1.735		0.300	- 00	100

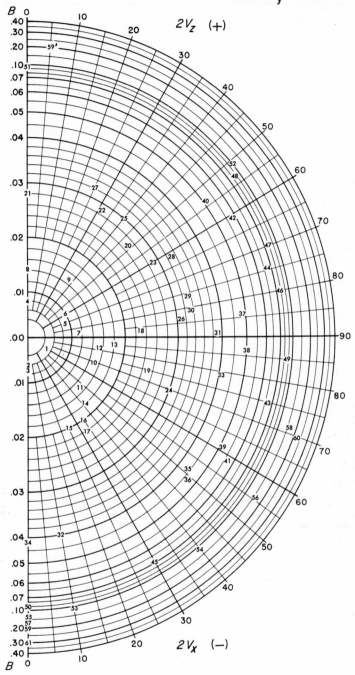

U

No. on Chart	Substance	n_x	n_y	n_z	$n_z - n_x$	2V	Page
	Fe(AsO$_4$)		1.78				190
1	ZrSiO$_4$, Malacon		1.76	1.76	0.00	+00	299
2	Na$_4$Sn$_5$O$_2$S$_{10}$ · 20H$_2$O		1.79		0.0019	-25	14
1	CsHgCl$_3$		1.779		0.002		37
2	Pt(NH$_3$)$_2$BrNO$_2$	1.778	1.78	1.78	0.002		107
	LaO(OH)		1.798		0.006		70
3	CaAl$_{12}$O$_{19}$	1.750	1.757		0.007	-00	80
4	Al$_2$O$_3$, Corundum	1.7604	1.7686		0.0082	-00	60
5	Fe$_2$(SO$_4$)$_3$	1.760	1.770		0.010	-00	131
5	Cs$_3$Tl$_2$Cl$_9$	1.774	1.784		0.010	-00	44
5	CaAl$_{12}$O$_{19}$	1.780	1.790		0.010	•00	80
5	Ca(UO$_2$)$_2$(AsO$_4$)$_2$, Heated 1000°	1.765	1.778		0.013	•00	207
6	CuO · UO$_3$ · 2H$_2$O	1.765	1.792	1.82	0.015	90	84
7	(NH$_4$)$_3$RhCl$_6$ · H$_2$O	1.740	1.750	1.756	0.016	-70	45
8	4Na$_2$O · P$_2$O$_5$ · 24WO$_3$ · nH$_2$O	1.766	1.776	1.789	0.023	+69	185
	Na$_8$Sn$_5$O$_2$S$_{12}$ · 32H$_2$O		1.79		0.024	-	14
9	Pt(NH$_3$)$_2$ClNO$_2$	1.764	1.786	1.790	0.026	-46	107
10	Ag$_2$SO$_4$	1.7583	1.7748	1.7842	0.0269	+73	127
11	Fe"Fe'''Si$_2$O$_6$	1.7677	1.7691	1.7976	0.0299	+25	273
12	CuO · UO$_3$ · 2H$_2$O, Vandenbrandeite	1.77	1.78	1.80	0.03	-70	84
13	SeO$_2$		1.76		0.03	+00	63
14	Fe(AsO$_4$) · 2H$_2$O, Scorodite	1.784	1.795	1.814	0.030	+75	200
15	Zn$_2$(AsO$_4$)(OH)	1.742	1.768	1.773	0.031	-23	202
16	Zn$_2$GeO$_4$		1.769	1.802	0.033	+00	300
17	6Fe$_2$SiO$_4$ · 4Mg$_2$SiO$_4$	1.748	1.778	1.792	0.044	-69	303
18	BaTiSi$_3$O$_9$, Benitoite		1.757	1.804	0.047	+00	288
19	Na$_2$ZrOSiO$_4$	1.741	1.790	1.790	0.049	-20	308
20	CaC$_2$		1.75		0.05	+15	5
21	(Ce,La)(PO$_4$)	1.785	1.787	1.840	0.055	+25	191
22	(NH$_4$)$_2$FeCl$_5$ · H$_2$O, Kremersite	1.750	1.775	1.814	0.064	+78	45
23	Fe"Fe$_2$'''(PO$_4$)$_2$(OH)$_2$, Barbosalite	1.77	1.79	1.835	0.065	+70	203
24	Pt(NH$_3$)$_2$Cl$_2$	1.745	1.790	1.812	0.067	-70	54
25	Cu$_4$SO$_4$(OH)$_6$, Brochantite	1.728	1.771	1.800	0.072	-77	173
	Pt(NH$_3$)$_2$Cl$_2$	1.706	1.778	1.790	0.084		54
26	K$_2$FeCl$_5$ · H$_2$O, Erythrosiderite	1.715	1.75	1.80	0.085	+62	45
27	Cs$_3$Ag$_2$Ba(CNS)$_7$	1.6788	1.7761		0.0973	-00	38
28	Cu$_3$(OH)$_2$(CO$_3$)$_2$, Azurite	1.730	1.754	1.836	0.106	+67	97
29	CaV$_2$O$_6$ · 4H₂O, Rossite	1.710	1.770	1.840	0.130	-70	212
28	Pt(NH$_3$)$_2$Cl(NO$_2$)$_3$	1.755	1.797	1.89	0.135	+66	107
30	K$_2$PtI$_2$(NO$_2$)$_2$ · 2H$_2$O	1.6527	1.7909		0.1382	-00	106
31	K$_2$Cr$_2$O$_7$	1.715	1.762	1.892	0.177	+64	122
32	CaFe(CO$_3$)$_2$, Ferrodolomite	1.555	1.765		0.210	-00	95
33	Fe$_2$(MoO$_4$)$_3$ · 8H$_2$O, Ferrimolybdite	1.78	1.79	2.04	0.26	+25	183
34	Pt(NH$_3$)$_2$(NO$_2$)$_2$	1.531	1.779	1.80	0.269	-32	107

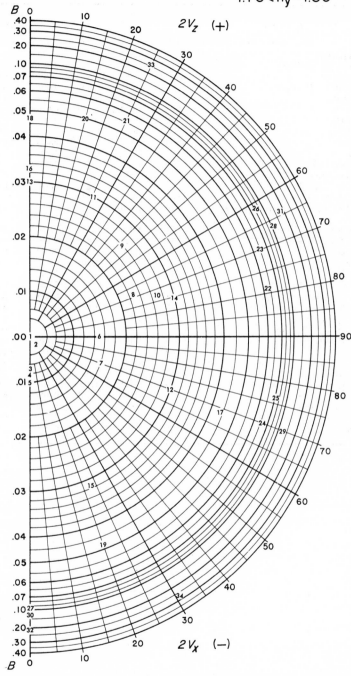

V

No. on Chart	Substance	n_x	n_y	n_z	$n_z - n_x$	2V	Page
	Lipscombite		1.83				203
1	$Na_4Sn_5O_2S_{10} \cdot 18H_2O$		1.80		0.0016	- 60	14
2	Ag_2HPO_4	1.7983	1.8036		0.0053	- 00	187
3	$Cu_2(OH)_3Cl$, Paratacamite		1.842	1.848	0.006	+00	31
	YO(OH)		1.845		0.01		71
4	$Fe_2(SO_4)_3$	1.802	1.814	1.818	0.016	- 60	131
	Ba_2SiO_4	1.810		1.830	0.02		302
5	$Be_2SiW_{12}O_{40} \cdot 16H_2O$		1.816		0.023	- 79	184
6	$NaSiYO_4$	1.804	1.832		0.028	- 00	228
	$KFeSi_2O_6$		1.80		0.03	-	279
	$2CrPO_4 \cdot H_2O$		1.810		0.03		199
7	Mn_2SiO_4, Tephroite	1.78	1.805	1.82	0.04	- 50	303
8	$8Fe_2SiO_4 \cdot 2Mg_2SiO_4$	1.786	1.821	1.834	0.048	- 62	303
9	$(Ce,La)PO_4$, Monazite	1.800	1.801	1.849	0.049	+ 13	191
10	$NH_4Fe_3(SO_4)_2(OH)_6$, Ammoniojarosite	1.750	1.800		0.05	- 00	174
	$KMnO_4$	1.80		1.85	0.05		82
11	$CuPbSO_4(OH)_2$, Linarite	1.8090	1.8380	1.8593	0.0503	- 80	175
13	$NaFeSi_2O_6$, Acmite	1.7710	1.8103	1.8271	0.0561	- 60	279
14	$AgBrO_3$		1.8466	1.920	0.0734	+00	108
	Na_2ZrO_3	1.720		1.80	0.08	-	73
	$PbH_4(AsO_4)_2$	1.74	1.82		0.08	-	188
15	$RbFe_3(SO_4)_2(OH)_6$	1.720	1.805		0.085	- 00	174
15	$H_2O \cdot Fe_3(SO_4)_4(OH)_5 \cdot H_2O$, Carphosiderite	1.728	1.816		0.088	- 00	174
16	$(UO_3)_7 \cdot 11H_2O$, Becquerelite	1.735	1.820	1.830	0.095	31	67
17	$Ca(IO_3)_2$, Lautarite	1.792	1.840	1.888	0.096	+85	109
18	$KFe_3(SO_4)_2(OH)_6$, Jarosite	1.715	1.820		0.105	- 00	174
18	$Cs_3Cu_2Ba(CNS)_7$	1.6882	1.8013		0.1131	- 00	38
19	KIO_3	1.700	1.828	1.832	0.132	- 25	108
20	$(Mg,Fe)_2FeBO_5$, Ludwigite	1.83	1.83	1.97	0.14	+25	114
21	$KHg(CNS)_3$	1.735	1.82	1.88	0.150	- 65	38
22	$Cu_2(SO_4)O$, Dolerophanite	1.715	1.820	1.880	0.165	+85	175
22	$(NH_4)_2Cr_2O_7$	1.725	1.80	1.905	0.180	+85	122
23	$MnCO_3$, Rhodochrosite	1.597	1.816		0.219	- 00	92
23	$ZnCO_3$, Smithsonite	1.621	1.848		0.227	- 00	93
24	$K_2Hg(CNS)_4$	1.645	1.80	1.9	0.255	- 88	38

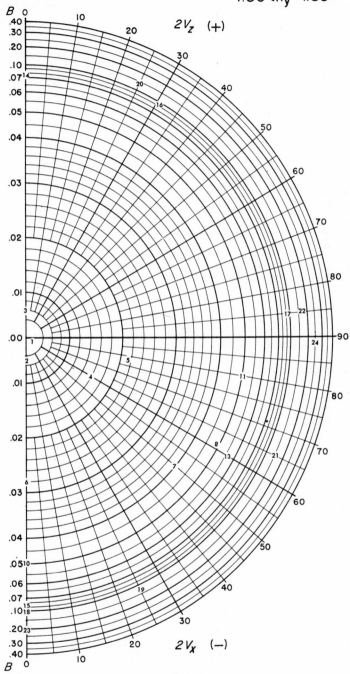

$1.80 \lesssim n_y < 1.85$

$2V_z$ (+)

$2V_x$ (−)

W

No. on Chart	Substance	n_X	n_Y	n_Z	$n_Z - n_X$	2V	Page
1	$CaSi_2La_2O_8$	1.874	1.880		0.006	- 00	228
	NdO(OH)		1.850		0.01		70
2	$CaV_2O_6 \cdot 2H_2O$, Metarossite	1.840	1.85	1.85	0.01	70	212
	SmO(OH)		1.860		0.01		71
	$Pb_2UO_2(PO_4)_2 \cdot H_2O$, Parsonsite	1.85		1.862	0.012		210
3	$PbSO_4$, Anglesite	1.8781	1.8832	1.8947	0.0166	+68	131
4	Tl_2SO_4	1.8600	1.8671	1.8853	0.0253	+68	127
5	$KSiLaO_4$	1.840	1.867		0.027	- 00	228
5	$NaSiLaO_4$	1.840	1.867		0.027	- 00	228
5	$LiSiLaO_4$	1.843	1.870		0.027	- 00	228
6	$NaSiNdO_4$	1.861	1.889		0.028	- 00	228
6	$NaSiPrO_4$	1.861	1.889		0.028	- 00	228
7	$(UO_2)_2 \cdot 7H_2O$, Ianthinite		1.88	1.91	0.03	- 10	66
8	$NaSiSmO_4$	1.867	1.898		0.031	- 00	228
9	$Cu_2(OH)_3Cl$, Atacamite	1.831	1.861	1.880	0.049	- 75	30
10	Fe_2SiO_4, Fayalite	1.824	1.864	1.875	0.051	- 47	303
11	$Tl(NO_3)$	1.817	1.862	1.869	0.052	- 53	102
12	$K_2Pt(CN)_6$	1.820	1.890		0.070	- 00	48
12	$K_2Pt(CNS)_6$	1.820	1.890		0.070	- 00	48
13	$PbFe_6(SO_4)_4(OH)_{12}$, Plumbojarosite	1.783	1.870		0.087	- 00	174
14	$AgFe_3(SO_4)_2(OH)_6$, Argentojarosite	1.785	1.882		0.097	- 00	174
15	$(UO_3)_4 \cdot 5H_2O$	1.79	1.89	1.91	0.12	- 48	67
16	$Cs_3Cu_2Sr(CNS)_7$	1.6982	1.8535		0.1553	- 00	38
17	$(Mg,Fe)_2FeBO_5$	1.85	1.85	2.02	0.17	+25	114
18	$HgCl_2$	1.725	1.859	1.965	0.240	- 85	26
19	$FeCO_3$, Siderite	1.633	1.875		0.242	- 00	93
20	$Cu_2(OH)_2CO_3$, Malachite	1.655	1.875	1.909	0.254	- 43	98
21	$CoCO_3$, Cobaltocalcite	1.60	1.855		0.255	- 00	93

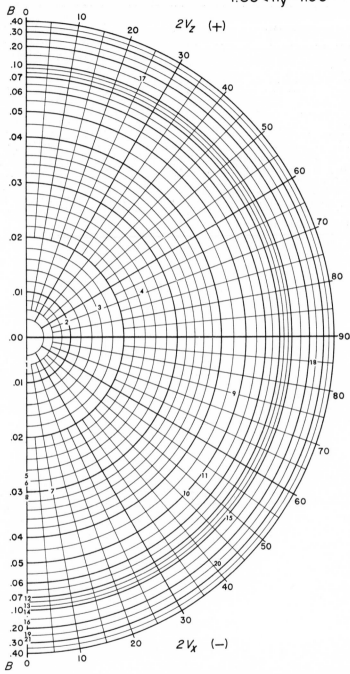

No. on Chart	Substance	n_x	n_y	n_z	$n_z - n_x$	2V	Page
1	$SrMoO_4$		1.9210	1.9258	0.0048	+00	181
2	$CaSi_2Nd_2O_8$	1.898	1.903		0.005	- 00	228
3	$BiO(OH,Cl)$, Daubréeite	1.90	1.91		0.01	- 00	52
4	$Y_3Al_2Al_3O_{12}$, Yttroalumite	1.927	1.942		0.015	- 00	298
5	$CaWO_4$, Scheelite		1.9200	1.9365	0.0165	+00	180
6	$ZrSiO_4$, Hyacinth		1.90	1.92	0.02	+00	299
7	$PbAl_2O_4$	1.85	1.91		0.06	- 00	78
8	$Pb_2UO_2SiO_4 \cdot H_2O$, Kasolite	1.80	1.90	1.967	0.077	+43	311
9	$PbHAsO_4$, Schultenite	1.8903	1.9097	1.9765	0.0862	+66	187
10	$PbO \cdot UO_3 \cdot 5H_2O$, Fourmarierite	1.85	1.92	1.94	0.09	- 70	84
11	$3Cu(IO_3)_2 \cdot 2H_2O$, Bellingerite	1.890	1.90	1.99	0.10	+50	109
12	As_2O_3, Claudetite	1.87	1.92	2.01	0.14	+58	61
13	$Ca(UO_2)_2(VO_4)_2 \cdot nH_2O$, Tyuyamunite	1.76	1.93	1.96	0.17	- 48	209
14	$K_2(UO_2)_2(VO_4)_2 \cdot 3H_2O$, Carnotite	1.750	1.925	1.950	0.200	- 40	206
15	$K_2Pb_2Si_2O_7$	1.72	1.93		0.21	- 00	295
16	$(UO_2)_2 \cdot 7H_2O$, Ianthinite	1.674	1.90	1.92	0.246	- 10	66

1.90 ≲ n_y < 1.95

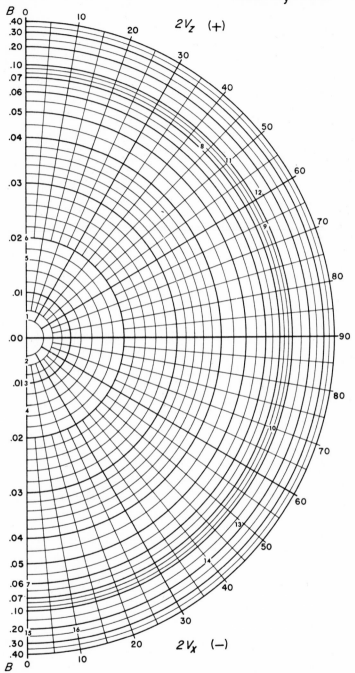

$1.90 \lesssim n_y < 1.95$

$2V_z$ (+)

$2V_x$ (−)

Y

393

No. on Chart	Substance	n_x	n_y	n_z	$n_z - n_x$	2V	Page
1	$SrMoO_4 \cdot 39.7\% \, Ce_2(MoO_4)_3$		1.952	1.956	0.004	+00	181
2	$CaMoO_4 \doteq 4.7\% \, Y_2(MoO_4)_3$		1.993	2.002	0.009	+00	180
	$Na_{12}Fe_8O_8Si_5O_{20}$		1.96		0.01		308
3	$CaMoO_4$, Powellite·		1.974	1.984	0.010	+00	180
4	Tl_2SeO_4	1.9493	1.9592	1.9640	0.0147	-73	128
5	$Pb_3Si_3O_9$, Alamosite	1.947	1.961	1.968	0.023	-65	291
6	$Pb_3(PO_4)_2$		1.9702	1.9364	0.0338	-00	189
7	$Pb_3(PO_4)_2 \cdot Ce(PO_4)$	1.9326	1.9697		0.0371	-00	189
8	Ni_2SiO_4	1.976	1.987	2.019	0.043	+60	304
9	$Ca_6Al_4Fe_2O_{15}$	1.94	1.99	1.99	0.05	-25	79
10	$ZrSiO_4$, Zircon		1.96	2.02	0.06	+00	299
11	$(Ca,Mg,Fe,Fe,Al)_2(Si,Al)_2O_6$, Mellorite	1.92	1.95	2.00	0.08	+75	272
12	GeO_2		1.99	2.08	0.09	+00	63
13	$CaTiOSiO_4$, Sphene, Titanite	1.950	1.970	2.092	0.142	+20	310
14	$WO_3 \cdot 2H_2O$, Hydrotungstite	1.70	1.95	2.04	0.34	-52	67
15	$HgCl$, Calomel		1.9733	2.6559	0.6826	+00	20

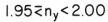

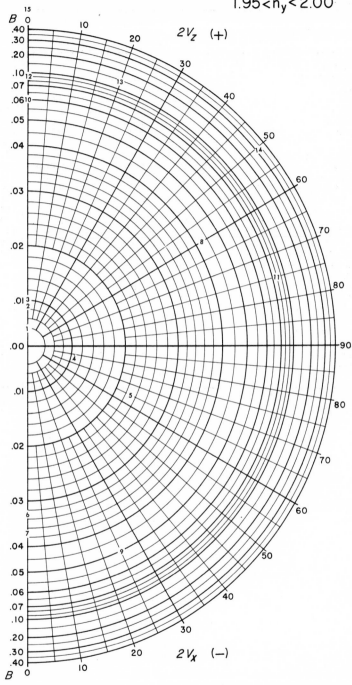

$1.95 \lesssim n_y < 2.00$

$2V_z$ (+)

$2V_x$ (−)

Z

395

No. on Chart	Substance	n_x	n_y	n_z	$n_z - n_x$	2V	Page
	C, Graphite		2.0			- 00	5
	$(Ca,Na_2)U_2O_7 \cdot nH_2O$		2.00			-	84
	$Pb_2As_2O_7$		2.03				214
1	$(Nd,Pr)_2(MoO_4)_3$	2.02	2.026		0.00	- 00	182
1	$Y_2(MoO_4)_3$		2.03	2.031	0.001	+ 00	182
1	$Nd_2(MoO_4)_3$	2.0218	2.0239		0.0021	- 00	182
2	$Pr_2(MoO_4)_3$	2.007	2.01		0.003	- 00	182
3	S		2.058		0.01	- 58	4
4	$Pb_5(PO_4)_3Cl$, Pyromorphite	2.048	2.058		0.011	- 00	204
5	$Ce_2(MoO_4)_3$	2.0277	2.0403		0.0126	- 00	182
6	ZnO, Zincite		2.013	2.029	0.016	+ 00	58
7	$Pb(Cu,Ag)Cl_2(OH)_2 \cdot H_2O$, Boleite	2.03	2.05		0.02	- 00	31
	Rosickyite		2.058		0.03	-	4
8	$Na_2SnS_3 \cdot 3H_2O$		2		0.06	+ 00	14
9	$PbO \cdot 3UO_3 \cdot 2H_2O$	2.05	2.08	2.12	0.07	+ 50	84
10	$Ca_4Al_2Fe_2O_{10}$, Brownmillerite	1.96	2.01	2.04	0.08	- 75	78
11	SnO_2, Cassiterite		2.0006	2.0972	0.0966	+ 00	62
12	$Pb_2(SO_4)O$, Lanarkite	1.928	2.007	2.036	0.108	- 60	174
13	Clarkeite ($\sim CaU_2O_7 \cdot nH_2O$)	1.997	2.098	2.180	0.117	- 40	84
13	$Na_2Ti_2Si_2O_9$, Lorenzenite	1.91	2.01	2.02	0.12	- 39	268
14	$Pb_4SO_4(CO_3)_2(OH)_2$, Leadhillite	1.87	2.00	2.01	0.14	- 10	100
15	$Pb_3(OH)_2(CO_3)_2$, Hydrocerussite	1.94	2.09		0.15	- 00	97
16	$WO_3 \cdot H_2O$, Tungstite	1.82	2.03	2.04	0.22	- 27	67
	AgN_3	1.80	2.05	2.05	0.25	-	7
17	$PbCO_3$, Cerussite	1.8037	2.0763	2.0780	0.2743	- 09	94
18	$Cu(OH)IO_3$	1.775	2.046	2.052	0.277	- 15	109
19	S, Sulfur	1.9579	2.0377	2.2452	0.2875	+ 68	4
20	$Cu(OH)IO_3$, Salesite	1.786	2.070	2.075	0.289	- 05	109
21	NiS	1.908	2.046	3.22	1.212	+ 70	11

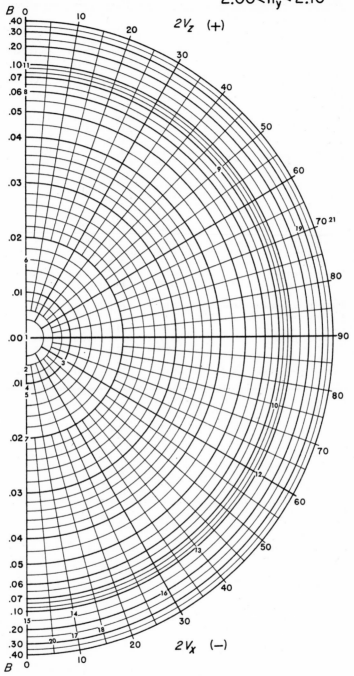

No. on Chart	Substance	n_x	n_y	n_z	$n_z - n_x$	2V	Page
1	AgI, Iodyrite		2.218	2.229	0.011	+00	20
1	$(BiO)_2CO_3$, Bismutite		2.12	2.12	0.014?	+00	97
2	$Pb_5(AsO_4)_3Cl$, Mimetite	2.128	2.147		0.019	- 00	204
3	$Pb_2Cl_2CO_3$, Phosgenite		2.1181	2.1446	0.0265	+00	97
4	$PbWO_4$, Raspite	2.27	2.27	2.30	0.03	+ 10	182
5	BiOCl, Bismoclite		2.15		0.03	- 00	52
6	$PbZrO_3$	2.16	2.18	2.2	0.039	- 85	81
7	$BiAsO_4$, Rooseveltite	2.14	2.15	2.18	0.04	+ 50	191
8	Pb_2SiO_4	2.13	2.15	2.18	0.05	- 80	304
9	$Ca_3Ti_2O_7$	2.16	2.22		0.06	- 00	81
10	$PbCl_2$, Cotunnite	2.199	2.217	2.260	0.061	+66	26
11	AlN		2.13	2.20	0.07	+00	8
12	ZrO_2, Baddeleyite	2.13	2.19	2.20	0.07	- 30	66
13	$Pb_3O_2Cl_2$, Mendipite	2.24	2.27	2.31	0.07	+85	52
14	$PbWO_4$, Stolzite	2.19	2.27		0.08	- 00	181
15	Pb(OH)Cl, Laurionite	2.077	2.116	2.158	0.081	- 70	31
15	$PbO \cdot 3UO_3 \cdot 2H_2O$, Curite	2.06	2.11	2.15	0.09	- 70	84
16	$Ca_2Fe_2O_5$	2.20	2.22	2.29	0.09	+50	78
17	$H_2K_2TeI_2O_{10} \cdot 2H_2O$	2.030	2.142		0.112	- 00	113
18	$MgTi_2O_5$	2.11	2.19	2.23	0.12	- 70	81
19	$MnWO_4$, Huebnerite	2.150	2.195	2.283	0.133	+75	181
17	PbClF, Matlockite	2.006	2.145		0.139	- 00	26
17	$CaBi_2O_2(CO_3)_2$, Beyerite	1.99	2.13		0.14	-00	99
20	$Zn_2Mn_4O_8 \cdot H_2O$, Hydrohetaerolite	2.10	2.26		0.16	- 00	83
21	H_2WO_4, Tungstite	2.09	2.24	2.26	0.17	- 14	67
21	$WO_3 \cdot H_2O$	2.09	2.24	2.26	0.17	- 14	67
22	MnO(OH), Manganite	2.25	2.25	2.53	0.28	+25	70
23	$MgTiO_3$	1.95	2.28		0.33	- 00	80
24	TeO_2, Tellurite	2.00	2.18	2.35	0.35	- 70	65
25	FeO(OH), Lepidocrocite	1.94	2.20	2.51	0.57	- 83	70

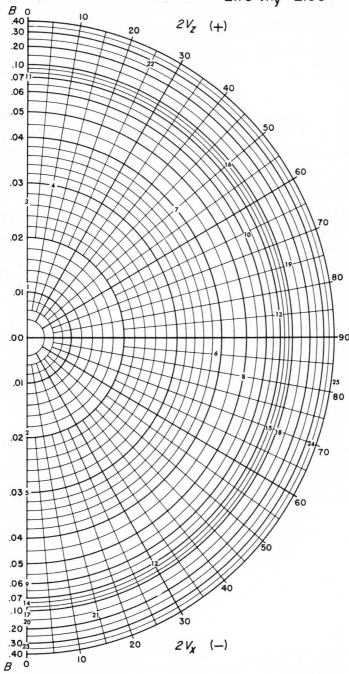

2.10 ≤ n_y < 2.30

No. on Chart	Substance	n_x	n_y	n_z	$n_z - n_x$	2V	Page
	BI_2O_3, Bismite		2.43				61
1	PbO_2, Plattnerite		2.30		0.005	- 00	63
1	Pb_3O_4, Minium	2.41	2.42		0.006	- 00	77
2	$BaTiO_3$	2.395	2.401	2.406	0.011	- 75	81
3	ZnS		2.46	2.48	0.02	+00	9
4	ZnS, Wurtzite		2.365	2.378	0.022	+00	9
5	Fe_2TiO_5, Pseudobrookite	2.38	2.39	2.42	0.04	+50	81
6	$Pb_5(VO_4)_3Cl$, Vanadinite	2.350	2.416		0.066	- 00	205
7	$Pb_4O_2SiO_4$	2.31	2.34	2.38	0.07	+40	308
8	$PbSbO_2Cl$, Nadorite	2.30	2.35	2.40	0.10	+85	53
9	$PbBr_2$	2.434	2.476	2.553	0.119	+70	27
10	$PbMoO_4$, Wulfenite	2.2826	2.4053		0.1227	- 00	181
11	$HFeO_2$, Goethite	2.260	2.393	2.398	0.138	- 10	73
12	$FeWO_4$, Ferberite	2.255	2.305	2.414	0.159	+68	181
13	Sb_2O_3, Valentinite	2.18	2.35	2.35	0.17	- 10	61
14	$ZnMn_2O_4$, Hetaerolite	2.10	2.35		0.25	- 00	77
14	$MnTiO_3$, Pyrophanite	2.210	2.481		0.271	- 00	80
15	$MnMn_2O_4$, Hausmannite	2.15	2.45		0.30	- 00	77
16	$MgTiO_3$, Geikielite	1.95	2.31		0.36	- 00	80
17	$PbCrO_4$, Crocoite	2.29	2.36	2.66	0.37	+57	131
18	$AsI_3 \cdot 3S_8$	1.8636	2.3036		0.440	- 00	54

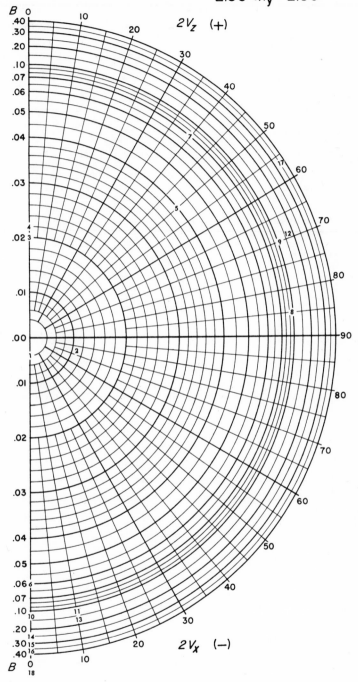

3

No. on Chart	Substance	n_x	n_y	n_z	$n_z - n_x$	2V	Page
	Cr_2O_3		2.5			+00	60
1	$(Ag,Cu)_{16}Sb_2S_{11}$, Polybasite		2.72+		0.04	- 22	12
2	CdS, Greenockite		2.506	2.529	0.023	+00	10
3	CuO		2.84		0.03	- 75	59
4	SiC		2.648	2.691	0.043	+00	6
	$Pb_2As_2S_5$, Dufrenoysite		2.72		0.045		14
5	Al_4C_3		2.7	2.75	0.05	+00	6
6	$AgAsS_2$, Trechmannite		2.60		0.05	- 00	13
7	TiO_2, Anatase - Octahedrite	2.4880	2.5612		0.0732	- 00	62
8	$BiVO_4$, Pucherite	2.41	2.50	2.51	0.10	- 19	190
9	TiO_2, Brookite	2.5895	2.5904	2.7091	0.1196	+10	65
10	$AgAsS_2$	2.48	2.58	2.60	0.12	- 26	13
11	PbO, Litharge	2.535	2.665		0.13	- 00	59
11	$CaFe_2O_4$	2.43	2.58		0.15	- 00	77
12	AsS, Realgar	2.538	2.684	2.704	0.166	- 47	11
	Hydrohematite - Turgite	2.4	2.6		0.2		60
13	PbO, Massicot	2.51	2.61	2.71	0.20	+90	59
14	HgS		2.58	2.82	0.24	+00	10
15	HgO, Montroydite	2.37	2.5	2.65	0.28	+75	58
16	TiO_2, Rutile		2.6211	2.9085	0.2874	+00	62
17	HgI_2	2.455	2.748		0.293	- 00	27
18	Hg_2OCl, Terlinguaite	2.35	2.64	2.66	0.31	- 20	52
19	HgS, Cinnabar		2.81	3.14	0.33	+00	10
20	AsI_3	2.23	2.59		0.36	- 00	34
21	SbI_3	2.36	2.78		0.42	- 00	34
22	P		2.72	3.15	0.43	+00	5
23	$AgSbS_2$, Miargyrite		2.72		0.45	- 50	13
22	P		2.72	3.20	0.48	+00	5
24	As_2S_3, Orpiment	2.4	2.81	3.02	0.62	- 76	12
	$HgSb_4S_7$, Livingstonite		3.		0.06		14
10	P	3.11	3.20	3.21	0.10	- 24	5
25	$(Pb,Tl)_2(Cu,Ag)As_5S_{10}$, Hutchinsonite	3.078	3.176	3.188	0.118	- 38	14
26	Ag_3SbS_3, Pyrargyrite	2.881	3.084		0.203	- 00	13
26	Fe_2O_3, Hematite	2.78	3.01		0.23	- 00	60
17	Ag_3AsS_3, Prousite	2.7924	3.0877		0.2953	- 00	13
27	$AgAsS_2$, Smithite		3.27		0.45	- 65	13
22	Se		3.00	4.04	1.04	+00	3
28	Sb_2S_3, Stibnite	3.194	4.046	4.303	1.109	- 26	12

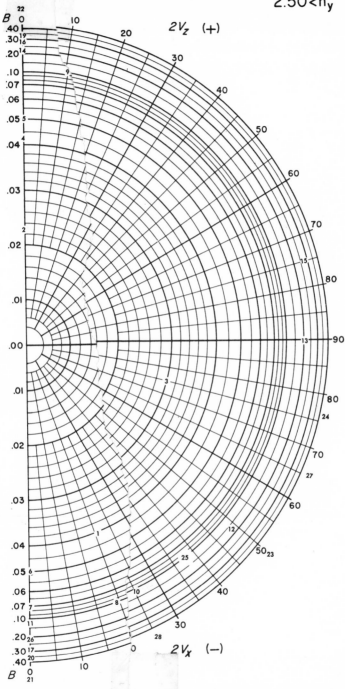

2.50 ≲ n_y

$2V_z$ (+)

$2V_x$ (—)

4

Author Index

Numbers in parentheses are reference numbers and are included when an author's work is referred to and his name is not mentioned in the text.

ALPHABETICAL INDEX TO SUBSTANCES

417

Index of Substance Names